# R. Gupta's®
## Popular Master Guide

# IESO
## INTERNATIONAL EARTH SCIENCE OLYMPIAD

## Entrance Test

Specialised Study & Practice Material
with Solved Previous Years' Papers

by
AJHAR HUSSAIN

# 2020
### EDITION

**Ramesh Publishing House,** New Delhi

*Published by*
O.P. Gupta *for* Ramesh Publishing House

*Admin. Office*
12-H, New Daryaganj Road, Opp. Officers' Mess,
New Delhi-110002 ① 23261567, 23275224, 23275124

E-mail: info@rameshpublishinghouse.com
Website: www.rameshpublishinghouse.com

*Showroom*
● Balaji Market, Nai Sarak, Delhi-6 ① 23253720, 23282525
● 4457, Nai Sarak, Delhi-6, ① 23918938

**Book Code: R-2011**

**ISBN: 978-93-87918-99-3**

**HSN Code: 49011010**

# CONTENTS

## PREVIOUS YEARS' PAPERS (SOLVED)

## STUDY MATERIAL

Minerals; Properties of Minerals; Elements in the Earth's Crust; Rocks and Its Classification; Rock Cycle; Important Terminology related to Rock Cycle; Principal of Stratigraphy; Geological Time Scale; Stratigraphic Classification; Sedimentary Structures; Graded Bedding; Cross-bedding; Ripple marks; Mud Crack; What is Palaeontology?; What is Fossil?; Classification of Organisms; Species; Classification of Homo Sapiens; Plate Tectonics and Its Application; Plate Tectonic Boundaries; Rate of Plate Movement; What is Deformation?; What Is Seismology?; Stage of Deformation; What are Seismic Waves?; P–Waves; S–Waves; Surface Waves; Love Waves; Rayleigh Waves; Seismic Wave Velocities; Types of Earthquakes; Measuring of Earthquakes; Seismograph; Measurement of Earthquakes Waves; What is Volcanoes?; What is Geomorphology?; Geomorphic Processes; Endogenic Processes; Exogenic Processes; What is Soil?; Soil Profile; Weathering; Type of Weathering Processes; Types of Transportation due to Running Water; Meanders and Oxbow Lakes; Braided Channels; Landforms made by Glacier; Landforms Made by Wind; Landforms made by Karst topography; What is Climate?; What Is Climate Change?; Types of Climate Region; Causes of Climate Variation; **Multiple Choice Questions; Answers.**

# International Earth Science Olympiad (IESO)
## Entrance Exam, 2019*

Total Marks : 100

No Negative markings

1. Identify the massive volcanic eruptions of Cretaceous to Eocene times from western India:
   (a) Panjal Traps
   (b) Sylhette Traps
   (c) Deccan Traps
   (d) Nidar volcanic

2. What type of rocks result from volcanic eruptions?
   (a) Granites
   (b) Syenites
   (c) Basalts
   (d) Sandstone

3. Ore deposits of aluminium are known as:
   (a) Bauxite deposits
   (b) Bastite deposits
   (c) Barite deposits
   (d) Emery deposits

4. Which of the following minerals is known as the heavy spar?
   (a) Bauxite
   (b) Barite
   (c) Garnet
   (d) Diamond

5. Boundaries where plates move away from each other are known as:
   (a) Convergent boundaries
   (b) Transcurrent boundaries
   (c) Transform boundaries
   (d) Divergent boundaries

6. Identify the most common igneous rock of the ocean floor:
   (a) Granite
   (b) Basalt
   (c) Limestone
   (d) Peridotite

7. Orthoclase is:
   (a) Softer than quartz and harder than apatite
   (b) Softer than fluorite and harder than apatite
   (c) Softer than quartz and harder than topaz
   (d) Harder than topaz and softer than quartz

8. What type of metamorphism is involved in the formation of rocks at the contact with a high temperature magmatic body?
   (a) Cataclastic metamorphism
   (b) Dynamothermal metamorphism
   (c) Contact/thermal metamorphism
   (d) Metasomatism

9. Ruby is type of:
   (a) Garnet
   (b) Feldspar
   (c) Pyroxene
   (d) Corundum

10. A Mid-Oceanic Ridge present in the Bay of Bengal is known as:
    (a) 90 degree East Ridge
    (b) 45 degree East Ridge
    (c) Bay of Bengal Ridge
    (d) East Indian Ocean Ridge

11. Maximum ozone is found in which region of the Earth's atmosphere?
    (a) Troposphere
    (b) Stratosphere
    (c) Thermosphere
    (d) Mesosphere

12. How does air circulate around a surface high pressure area in southern hemisphere?
    (a) Counter clockwise
    (b) Clockwise spiral
    (c) Linear
    (d) Clockwise linear

13. Which type of aerosols cause heating?
    (a) Sulphate rich aerosols
    (b) Black carbon poor aerosols
    (c) Black carbon rich aerosols
    (d) All of the above

14. How global warming will modulate the Earth's atmospheric thermal structure (full line represents normal thermal structure and dotted line represent modulated thermal structure)?

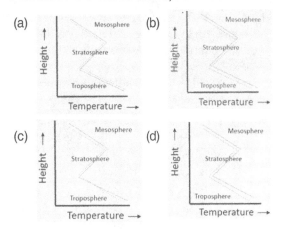

15. Which region of the Earth's atmosphere is having minimum turbulence?

(a) The ionosphere
(b) The troposphere
(c) The stratosphere
(d) The mesosphere

16. Tropical cyclones are formed with what minimum ocean water temperature?
(a) 50 deg C
(b) 26 deg C
(c) 10 deg C
(d) 90 deg C

17. Which type of scattering takes place from clouds?
(a) Rayleigh scattering
(b) Raman scattering
(c) Resonance scattering
(d) Mie scattering

18. At an altitude of 5 km percentage of $N_2$ in the air is about 78% (in the Earth's Atmosphere). What will be the percentage of $N_2$ in the air (in the Earth's Atmosphere) at an altitude of ~50 km?
(a) 90%
(b) 60%
(c) 78%
(d) 70%

19. What form of heat transfer is responsible for creating a thunderstorm?
(a) Conduction
(b) Convection
(c) Advection
(d) Radiation

20. Which region of the atmosphere plays important role in radio communications?
(a) Troposphere
(b) Stratosphere
(c) Ionosphere
(d) Mesosphere

21. During which period the Sun does not rise at the South Pole?
(a) September 21 - March 21
(b) March 21 - September 21
(c) December 21 - June 21
(d) June 21 - December 21

22. A RADAR (Radio Detection and Ranging) is operating at 50 MHz and receives an echo after 2 milli seconds. From which altitude this echo coming?
(a) 150 km
(b) 350 km
(c) 300 km
(d) 200 km

23. What is Tropopause height in the Equatorial regions and in the High Latitude regions, respectively?
(a) ~18 km and ~10 km
(b) ~10 km and ~18 km
(c) ~12 km and ~12 km
(d) ~8 km and ~18 km

24. Meteorological satellites measures which properties?
(a) IR images
(b) Visible images
(c) Water vapour images
(d) All of the above

25. A meteorite of mass 700 gm fell on earth from a height of 1000 km from the earth surface. How much energy is expelled on impact considering that all the energy is transferred to the earth. (g = 9.8 m/s$^2$). (Ignore Air resistance)
(a) 6860 J
(b) 6370 J
(c) 6086 J
(d) 700 J

26. Two ball A and B of diameter 60 cm & 90 cm respectively with A having greater mass than B are dropped from a height of 100 km from the earth. Considering no atmosphere, which ball will reach earlier to the surface?
(a) Ball B
(b) Ball A
(c) Both will reach at same time
(d) Both will escape in deep space

27. Two ball A and B of diameter 50 cm & 100 cm respectively with both having similar mass are dropped from a height of 100 km from the earth. Considering there is atmosphere, which ball will reach earlier to the surface?
(a) Ball B
(b) Ball A
(c) Both will reach at same time
(d) Both will escape in deep space

28. Neil standing on a cliff on moon fired two bullets. Both bullets B$_1$ and B$_2$ were fired with speed of 20 m/s, one directly downwards and other upward from same initial position. What will be their velocity just before touching the surface of the moon? (Acceleration due to gravity of moon = 1.62 m/s$^2$):
(a) B$_1$ will have greater velocity than B$_2$
(b) B$_2$ will have greater velocity than B$_1$
(c) Both B$_1$ & B$_2$ will have same velocity
(d) B$_1$ will have no velocity

29. Which of these planets while seeing from surface of Mars will show phases which look similar to the phases of moon.
(a) Mercury, Earth, Jupiter
(b) Mercury, Venus, Earth
(c) Venus, Jupiter, Saturn
(d) Earth, Uranus, Neptune

30. What is acceleration due to gravity at surface of proxima centauri, the closest star to earth after sun if its mass is around 0.2 × 10$^{20}$ kg and radius of 2000 km?
(G = 6.67 × 10$^{-11}$ Nm$^2$/kg$^2$)

(a) $3.335 \times 10^6$ m/s$^2$
(b) $2.335 \times 10^6$ m/s$^2$
(c) $4.335 \times 10^6$ m/s$^2$
(d) $5.335 \times 10^6$ m/s$^2$

31. If pole star is seen at an altitude of 25 deg. in the sky, then what is the latitude of that place?
(a) 20.0 deg.
(b) 23.3 deg.
(c) 35.3 deg.
(d) 25 deg.

32. Which of these are biggest natural satellite of Jupiter?
(a) Europa, Ganymede, Callisto, Io
(b) Europa, Phobos, Deimos, Titan
(c) Phobos, Deimos, Puck, Mimas
(d) Miranda, Oberon, Callisto, Tethys

33. Choose the incorrect statement:
(a) During total lunar eclipse moon is in earth's umbra
(b) Lunar eclipse usually occurs during New moon
(c) Solar eclipse occurs when moon is between sun and earth
(d) Danjon scale measures moons darkness of lunar eclipse

34. We do not see Lunar/Solar eclipse during every Full/New moon day in a year because :
(a) Moons orbit is tilted by around to orbit of Earth.
(b) Moons orbit is tilted by around to orbit of Earth.
(c) Precession of earth's axis
(d) Earth's spin axis is tilted 5° with respect to its orbit around the sun.

35. The supergiant star Nimo has an absolute temperature of about 3000 K and emits a radiant power of approximately. Assuming that Nimo is a perfect emitter (emissivity $e$ = 1) and spherical, what will happen if absolute temperature doubles?
(a) Radiated power increases by a factor of 4
(b) Radiated power increases by a factor of 8
(c) Radiated power increases by a factor of 12
(d) Radiated power increases by a factor of 16

36. 1 kg of liquid water at 273 Kelvin is placed outside on day when temperature is 250 Kelvin. In which case will it take longer for water to freeze? (A) When surface area is smaller (B) When Surface area is larger:
(a) Case A
(b) Case B
(c) In both cases it will take same time
(d) Water will never freeze in both cases

37. In which zodiacal constellation will the sun be on 26th December, 2018?
(a) Leo
(b) Virgo
(c) Libra
(d) Sagittarius

38. Today Moon rise time is 7 p.m. At what approx. time will moon rise next day?
(a) 7:52 pm
(b) 8:13 pm
(c) 8:47 pm
(d) 6:17 pm

39. 21st June, 2019 is the longest day in Northern Hemisphere which is also called as:
(a) Spring Equinox
(b) Full moon day
(c) Autumnal Equinox
(d) Summer Solstice

40. On 30th April 2019, Sun is in constellation of Aries, Which is the correct order of the constellation sun will travel in next four months?
(a) Taurus, Cancer, Gemini, Leo
(b) Taurus, Leo, Gemini, Cancer
(c) Taurus, Gemini, Cancer, Leo
(d) Gemini, Taurus, Cancer, Leo

41. This year Equinox is on 20th March 2019, when will be the succeeding equinox.
(a) 30th June, 2019
(b) 23rd September, 2019
(c) 20th March, 2020
(d) 22nd December, 2019

42. Where is Asteroid belt situated?
(a) Between Earth and Venus
(b) Between Earth and Mars
(c) Between Mars and Jupiter
(d) Between Jupiter and Saturn

43. Temperature of a star increased from 5000 K to 8000 K, what would happen to its wavelength and frequency.
(a) Wavelength increases frequency decreases
(b) Wavelength decreases frequency increases
(c) Both will increase
(d) Both will decrease

44. Which of the following planet will not show retrograde motion?
(a) Venus
(b) Mars
(c) Jupiter
(d) Saturn

45. Telescope has Focal length of 1200 mm and eyepiece used is 6 mm. What will be the magnification obtained by this combination?
(a) 7200
(b) 720
(c) 200
(d) 400

46. Arrange the following from increasing order of grain size:

(i) Sand      (ii) Boulder
(iii) Pebble      (iv) Silt
(a) (i), (iii), (iv), (ii)    (b) (ii), (iii), (i), (iv)
(c) (iv), (i), (iii), (ii)    (d) (iv), (i), (ii), (iii)

47. A right side up sedimentary sequence will have:
    (a) Coarse grains at the top
    (b) Mixed grain size throughout the sequence
    (c) Finest at the top
    (d) None

48. Which of the following is the largest lithospheric plate by area?
    (a) African plate
    (b) Pacific plate
    (c) North American plate
    (d) Nazca plate

49. Ichno fossils are:
    (a) Casts      (b) Moulds
    (c) Trace fossils      (d) None

50. S30°W may also be represented as:
    (a) 30°      (b) 210°
    (c) 140°      (d) 180°

51. Ganga basin is:
    (a) Back arc basin
    (b) Peripheral foreland basin
    (c) Retro arc basin
    (d) None

52. Bird foot deltas are formed by:
    (a) Tidal processes    (b) Waves
    (c) Rivers      (d) None of the above

53. Which of the following is not associated with glaciers?
    (a) Drumlins      (b) Varves
    (c) Eskers      (d) Braid bars

54. Goethite is an ore for:
    (a) Iron      (b) Copper
    (c) Manganese      (d) Gold

55. Greywacke is a type of:
    (a) Limestone      (b) Shale
    (c) Sandstone      (d) Granite

56. Halite and sylvite are:
    (a) Similar in internal structure and occurrence
    (b) Similar in internal structure but different in composition
    (c) Different in internal structure but similar in composition
    (d) Different in internal structure and composition

57. Radiocarbon dating method is used for material formed:

(a) < 50,000 years
(b) Between 100,000 – 10,00,000 years
(c) Between 10 m.a. – 100 m.a.
(d) >100 m.a.

58. Most commonly used mineral as a weighing agent in rotary well-drilling fluid is:
    (a) Quartz      (b) Mica
    (c) Barite      (d) Halite

59. The first land plants appeared in:
    (a) Ordovician      (b) Silurian
    (c) Devonian      (d) Carboniferous

60. The exoskeleton of sponges is made up of:
    (a) Silica
    (b) Calcite
    (c) Aragonite
    (d) Calcium phosphate

61. A flow, which is a balance of pressure gradient and Coriolis force, is called:
    (a) Gradient flow    (b) Geostrophic flow
    (c) Inertial flow      (d) Coriolis flow

62. Which current is NOT a part of global ocean thermohaline circulation?
    (a) North Atlantic Deep water
    (b) Indonesia Through Flow
    (c) East India Coastal Current
    (d) Gulf stream

63. Ocean western boundary currents are:
    (a) Warm, slow and narrow currents in both hemisphere
    (b) Warm in northern hemisphere but cold in southern hemisphere
    (c) Cold, fast, shallow currents
    (d) Warm, fast and narrow currents in both hemisphere

64. The movement of Inter-tropical convergence zone (ITCZ) occurs in:
    (a) Tropical to polar regions in both hemisphere
    (b) Tropical region
    (c) Arctic region
    (d) Northern Indian Ocean

65. Ocean's mixed layer depth (MLD) refers to:
    (a) Near uniform density region
    (b) Oxygen minimum zone region
    (c) Maximum density region
    (d) Low light region

66. The strong salinity range 37-40 in the central parts of Persian Gulf is due to the:
    (a) Low rainfall
    (b) High evaporation

(c) Strong winds

(d) All of the above

67. Seawater density of $1.02603$ g/cm$^3$ is expressed as density sigma ($\sigma$) =
   (a) 0.2603          (b) 2.603
   (c) 26.03           (d) 1.02603

68. Typical periodicity of MJO (Madden Julian Oscillation) is:
   (a) 90-100 days     (b) 30-60 days
   (c) 2-7 years       (d) ~10 years

69. Ionic abundance of chemical elements in sea water are in the following order:
   (a) Mg > Ca > K > Sr
   (b) K > Ca > S > Mg
   (c) Ca > S > K > Mg
   (d) Mg > S > K > Ca

70. El-Nino is:
   (a) Warm water anomaly in the south eastern Pacific
   (b) Cold water anomaly in the south eastern Pacific
   (c) Warm water anomaly in the south western Pacific
   (d) Cold water anomaly in the south western Pacific

71. In the Indian Ocean, south equatorial currents crosses the equator during:
   (a) Spring
   (b) Southwest monsoon
   (c) Northeast monsoon
   (d) Western disturbance

72. The difference between sea level at high tide and sea level at low tide is called the:
   (a) Tidal range       (b) Tidal Frequency
   (c) Tidal height      (d) Tidal wavelength

73. In the depth range, where salinity changes rapidly is called:
   (a) Thermocline       (b) Pycnocline
   (c) Halocline         (d) Nutricline

74. The major light harvesting pigments in phytoplankton are:
   (a) Chlorophylls
   (b) Carotenoids
   (c) Both of the above
   (d) None of the above

75. What are the major nutrients which limit the phytoplankton growth in the marine environment?
   (a) Nitrate and Phosphate
   (b) Phosphate and Iron

(c) Iron and Molybdenum

(d) Strontium and Sodium

76. What are Nektons?
   (a) Micro-organisms that drift with the ocean currents
   (b) Aquatic organisms which are able to swim and move on their own
   (c) Phytoplankton
   (d) Bacteria

77. In low nutrient environment, growth advantage is shifted towards which type of following phytoplankton cells?
   (a) Diazotrophs
   (b) Big phytoplankton cells
   (c) Elongated phytoplankton cells
   (d) Small phytoplankton cells

78. Which of the followings limit primary production in the Southern Ocean?
   (a) Vanadium          (b) Molybdenum
   (c) Iron              (d) All

79. Solid support structure that forms the hard base upon which corals live is composed of
   (a) Calcium Carbonate
   (b) Silicate
   (c) Both of the above
   (d) None of the above

80. Which colour penetrates the deepest in the open ocean?
   (a) Violet            (b) Blue
   (c) Yellow            (d) Red

81. Which of the following statement is TRUE?
   (a) Nutrient minimum and $O_2$ minimum are in the northern hemisphere
   (b) Nutrient maximum and $O_2$ maximum are about at the same depth
   (c) Nutrient minimum and $O_2$ maximum are in the deepest ocean
   (d) Nutrient maximum and $O_2$ minimum are about at the same depth

82. The major source of iron to the surface layer of the open ocean is:
   (a) Dissolved sediment along continental margins
   (b) Fluids from hydrothermal vents
   (c) Atmospheric deposition of dust from the continents
   (d) Ocean currents

83. Which of the followings is the most energetically expensive process?
   (a) Anammox           (b) Denitrification
   (c) Nitrification     (d) Nitrogen fixation

84. What causes depletion of dissolved oxygen minimum in the deeper depths?
    (a) Rate of photosynthesis is greater than the rate of respiration at these depths
    (b) Rate of photosynthesis is lesser than the rate of respiration at these depths
    (c) Upwelling of deeper waters
    (d) Less primary productivity in surface ocean water

85. Which of the following nitrogen substrates, autotrophs preferably use as a nutrient?
    (a) Nitrogen
    (b) Ammonium
    (c) Nitrite
    (d) Nitrate

86. Following picture is taken during a spring bloom in the eastern Arabian Sea. Which bloom does it represent?

    (a) *Coccolithophore*
    (b) *Trichodesmium*
    (c) *Noctiluca*
    (d) *Dinophysis*

87. Following figure represents zonal mean anthropogenic $CO_2$ inventories in the different oceans across latitudes. In the figure, black, red and blue lines, respectively represent:

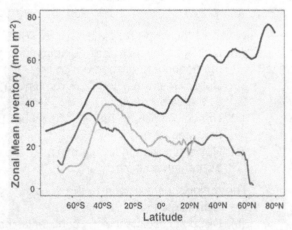

    (a) Pacific, Indian and Atlantic Oceans
    (b) Indian, Pacific and Atlantic Oceans
    (c) Atlantic, Pacific and Indian Oceans
    (d) Atlantic, Indian and Pacific Oceans

88. Following plot shows the variation in solubility of dissolved inorganic carbon (DIC) in water versus pH. In the plot, green, red and blue lines, respectively represent the concentration of:

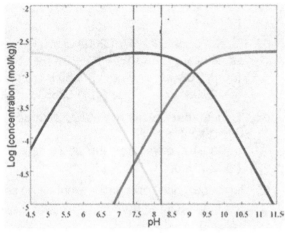

    (a) $CO_2$, $HCO_3^-$, $CO_3^{2-}$
    (b) $CO_3^{2-}$, $CO_2$, $HCO_3^-$
    (c) $HCO_3^-$, $CO_3^{2-}$, $CO_2$
    (d) $CO_2$, $CO_3^{2-}$, $HCO_3^-$

89. Which one of the followings is NOT a thermally driven circulation?
    (a) Hadly Cell
    (b) Ferrel Cell
    (c) Polar Cell in southern hemisphere
    (d) Polar Cell in southern hemisphere

90. Which of the following can be taken as an evidence to suggest that the Moon's surface is tectonically not active?
    (a) Presence of Mars basalt
    (b) Presence of water
    (c) Presence of craters of different ages
    (d) Presence of highlands

91. Pegmatite, generally, contains large size minerals compared to other rocks, because:
    (a) Higher number of crystal nuclei form during crystallization
    (b) The lower viscosity of parental liquid facilitates the crystal growth
    (c) It forms under high-strain zones in the collision belts.
    (d) It cools slowly compared to other plutonic rocks

92. Which of the following minerals is a silicate?
    (a) Halite
    (b) Hematite
    (c) Sphalerite
    (d) Topaz

93. Which one among the given minerals forms the shells of some marine organisms?
    (a) Aragonite
    (b) Barite
    (c) Augite
    (d) Beryl

94. Which one of the following rocks is generally found in the island-arcs?
(a) Granite
(b) Pegmatite
(c) Andesite
(d) Limestone

95. Island arcs are generally convex towards the:
(a) Subducting plate
(b) Overriding plate
(c) South pole
(d) North pole

96. If a lithospheric plate A moves with an absolute velocity of 5 cm/yr towards the north, and another lithospheric plate B which is in contact with the plate A along an E-W trending boundary, moves with an absolute velocity of 3 cm/yr in north, then the boundary between them would be:
(a) A spreading ridge
(b) A subduction zone
(c) A collision zone
(d) A transform fault

97. Explosive volcanoes differ from the non-explosive volcanoes mainly in:
(a) Their temperature
(b) The pressure at the site of their respective magma-chambers
(c) Volatile content in the magma
(d) The colour of their product rocks

98. Transform faults, in terms of the kinematics of faulting, are similar to the
(a) Thrust faults
(b) Normal faults
(c) Strike-slip faults
(d) Oblique faults

99. Traditional Water Harvesting Structures in Rajasthan are known as:
(a) Tube Wells
(b) Percolation Tanks
(c) Tankas
(d) Kattas

100. Two metamorphic rocks having experienced same grade of metamorphism have developed different mineral assemblages. This may be due to:
(a) Their being present at different tectonic setting
(b) Their different bulk chemical composition
(c) Their metamorphism at different depths in the crust
(d) Their different structures

## ANSWERS

| 1 | 2 | 3 | 4 | 5 | 6 | 7 | 8 | 9 | 10 |
|---|---|---|---|---|---|---|---|---|---|
| (c) | (c) | (a) | (b) | (d) | (b) | (a) | (c) | (d) | (a) |
| 11 | 12 | 13 | 14 | 15 | 16 | 17 | 18 | 19 | 20 |
| (b) | (a) | (c) | (a) | (c) | (b) | (d) | (c) | (b) | (c) |
| 21 | 22 | 23 | 24 | 25 | 26 | 27 | 28 | 29 | 30 |
| (b) | (c) | (a) | (d) | (a) | (c) | (b) | (c) | (b) | (a) |
| 31 | 32 | 33 | 34 | 35 | 36 | 37 | 38 | 39 | 40 |
| (d) | (a) | (b) | (b) | (d) | (a) | (d) | (a) | (d) | (c) |
| 41 | 42 | 43 | 44 | 45 | 46 | 47 | 48 | 49 | 50 |
| (b) | (c) | (b) | (a) | (c) | (c) | (c) | (b) | (c) | (b) |
| 51 | 52 | 53 | 54 | 55 | 56 | 57 | 58 | 59 | 60 |
| (b) | (c) | (d) | (a) | (c) | (b) | (a) | (c) | (b) | (a) |
| 61 | 62 | 63 | 64 | 65 | 66 | 67 | 68 | 69 | 70 |
| (b) | (c) | (d) | (b) | (a) | (d) | (c) | (b) | (a) | (a) |
| 71 | 72 | 73 | 74 | 75 | 76 | 77 | 78 | 79 | 80 |
| (b) | (a) | (c) | (c) | (a) | (b) | (d) | (c) | (a) | (b) |
| 81 | 82 | 83 | 84 | 85 | 86 | 87 | 88 | 89 | 90 |
| (d) | (c) | (d) | (b) | (d) | (b) | (d) | (d) | (b) | (c) |
| 91 | 92 | 93 | 94 | 95 | 96 | 97 | 98 | 99 | 100 |
| (b) | (d) | (a) | (c) | (a) | (c) | (c) | (c) | (c) | (b) |

## HINTS AND SOLUTIONS

1. **Panjal traps:** The geological age is late Permian. The Panjal Traps or the Tethyan Plume is a large igneous province (LIP) that erupted during the Early-Middle Permian in what is now north-western India.

   **Deccan Traps:** The age is Cretaceous to Eocene time. The Deccan Traps are a large igneous province located on the Deccan Plateau of west-central India (17°-24°N, 73°-74°E). They are one of the largest volcanic features on Earth. They consist of multiple layers of solidified flood basalt.

2. 

| Plutonic rocks | Volcanic Equivalents |
|---|---|
| Granite | Rhyolite |
| Syenites | Trachyte |
| Gabbro | Basalt |
| Sandstone | Clastic Sedimentary rock |

3. **Bauxite Deposits:** Bauxite ore is the world's primary source of aluminium. The ore must first be chemically processed to produce alumina (aluminium oxide). Alumina is then smelted using an electrolysis process to produce pure aluminium metal. Many people are surprised to learn that bauxite is not a mineral. It is a rock composed mainly of aluminium-bearing minerals. It forms when laterite soils are severely leached of silica and other soluble materials in a wet tropical or subtropical climate.

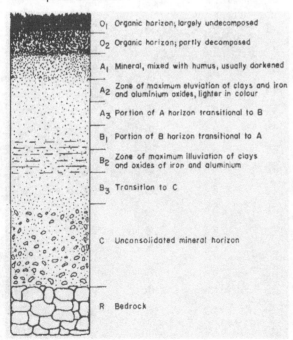

4. Barite($BaSO_4$) is a heavy spar minerals.

| Colour | Colourless, white, light shades of blue, yellow, grey, brown |
|---|---|
| Crystal habit | Tabular parallel to base, fibrous, nodular to massive |
| Cleavage | Perfect cleavage parallel to base and prism faces: {001} Perfect, {210} Perfect, {010} Imperfect |
| Fracture | Irregular/uneven |
| Tenacity | Brittle |
| Mohs scale hardness | 3-3.5 |
| Luster | Vitreous, Pearly |
| Streak | White |
| Diaphaneity | Transparent to opaque |
| Specific gravity | 4.3-5 |
| Density | 4.48 g/cm |
| Optical properties | Biaxial positive |

5. **Plate Boundaries:**

   Types of Plate Boundaries

   Plate boundaries can be categorized in three fundamental types:

   (a) **Divergent boundaries**, where plates separate and move in opposite directions, allowing new lithosphere to form from upwelling magma. This either occurs at mid-ocean ridges (the so-called seafloor spreading) or at rifted continental margins;

   (b) **Convergent boundaries**, where plates move towards each other. One plate either sinks beneath the other along a subduction zone or plates collide because neither can be subducted; and

   (c) **Transform fault boundaries**, where plates move horizontally past each other.

| Type of Margin | Divergent | Convergent | Transform |
|---|---|---|---|
| Motion | Spreading | Subduction | Lateral sliding |
| Effect | Constructive (oceanic lithosphere created) | Destructive (oceanic lithosphere destroyed) | Conservative (lithosphere neither created or destroyed) |
| Topography | Ridge/Rift | Trench | No major effect |
| Volcanic activity? | Yes | Yes | No |

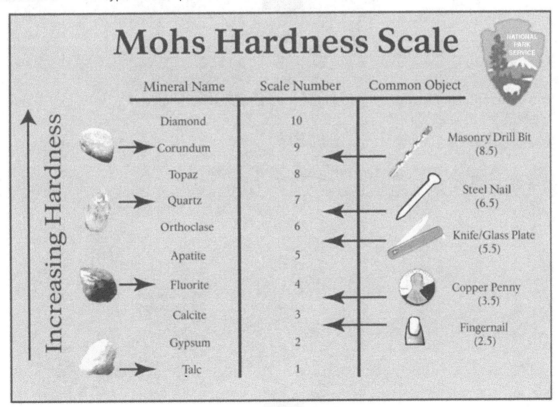

(a)    (b)    (c)

6. **Composition of the ocean floor:** The composition of the Ocean floor is basaltic which geological age less than 200 Ma.

7. **Orthoclase:** It is a type of feldspar which is tectosilicate mineral.

## Mohs Hardness Scale

Increasing Hardness

| Mineral Name | Scale Number | Common Object |
|---|---|---|
| Diamond | 10 | |
| Corundum | 9 | Masonry Drill Bit (8.5) |
| Topaz | 8 | |
| Quartz | 7 | Steel Nail (6.5) |
| Orthoclase | 6 | |
| Apatite | 5 | Knife/Glass Plate (5.5) |
| Fluorite | 4 | |
| Calcite | 3 | Copper Penny (3.5) |
| Gypsum | 2 | Fingernail (2.5) |
| Talc | 1 | |

8. **Types of Metamorphism:** Type of metamorphism is involved in the formation of rocks at the contact with a high temperature magmatic body, contact/thermal metamorphism.

9. **Ruby:** A ruby is a pink to blood-red coloured gemstone, a variety of the mineral corundum (aluminium oxide). Other varieties of gem-quality corundum are called sapphires.

10. A Mid-Oceanic Ridge present in the Bay of Bengal is known as 90 degree East Ridge.

11. **Different layers in Atmosphere:**

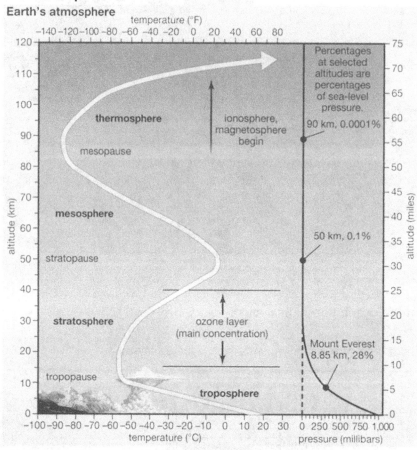

12. **Air circulation in hemisphere:** Air circulate around a surface high pressure area in southern hemisphere is counter clockwise direction.

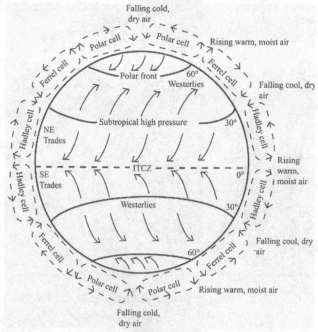

13. **Aerosols:** Aerosols are minute particles suspended in the atmosphere. When these particles are sufficiently large, we notice their presence as they scatter and absorb sunlight. Their scattering of sunlight can reduce visibility (haze) and redden sunrises and sunsets.

Aerosols interact both directly and indirectly with the Earth's radiation budget and climate. As a direct effect, the aerosols scatter sunlight directly back into space. As an indirect effect, aerosols in the lower atmosphere can modify the size of cloud particles, changing how the clouds reflect and absorb sunlight, thereby affecting the Earth's energy budget.

The dispersal of volcanic aerosols has a drastic effect on Earth's atmosphere. Follow an eruption, large amounts of sulphur dioxide ($SO_2$), hydrochloric acid (HCl) and ash are spewed into Earth's stratosphere. HCl, in most cases, condenses with water vapour and is rained out of the volcanic cloud formation. $SO_2$ from the cloud is transformed into sulphuric acid, $H_2SO_4$. The sulphuric acid quickly condenses, producing aersol particles which linger in the atmosphere for long periods of time. The interaction of chemicals on the surface of aerosols, known as heterogeneous chemistry, and the tendency of aerosols to increase levels of chlorine gas react with nitrogen in the stratopsher, is a prime contributor to stratospheric ozone destruction.

14. Thermal Structure of the atmosphere:

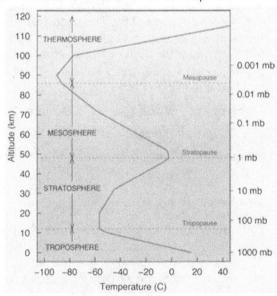

15. Stratosphere region of the Earth's atmosphere is having minimum turbulence.

16. **Tropical cyclones:** Tropical Cyclones are low pressure systems that form over warm tropical waters and have gale force winds (sustained winds of 63 km/h or greater and gusts in excess of 90 km/h) near the centre. Technically they are defined as a non-frontal low pressure system of synoptic scale developing over warm waters having organised convection and a maximum mean wind

speed of 34 knots or greater extending more than half-way around near the centre and persisting for at least six hours.

The gale force winds can extend hundreds of kilometres from the cyclone centre. If the sustained winds around the centre reach 118 km/h (gusts in excess 165 km/h), then the system is called a severe tropical cyclone. These are referred to as hurricanes or typhoons in other countries.

**The circular eye** or centre of a tropical cyclone is an area characterised by light winds and often by clear skies. Eye diameters are typically 40 km but can range from under 10 km to over 100 km. The eye is surrounded by a dense ring of cloud about 16 km high known as the eye wall which marks the belt of strongest winds and heaviest rainfall.

**Tropical cyclones** derive their energy from the warm tropical oceans and do not form unless the sea-surface temperature is above 26.5°C, although once formed, they can persist over lower sea-surface temperatures. Tropical cyclones can persist for many days and may follow quite erratic paths. They usually dissipate over land or colder oceans.

17. **Type of Scattering:** Mie scattering takes place from clouds.

19. **Thunderstorm:** A thunderstorm, also known as an electrical storm or a lightning storm, is a storm characterized by the presence of lightning and its acoustic effect on the Earth's atmosphere, known as thunder. Relatively weak thunderstorms are sometimes called thundershowers. Thunderstorms occur in a type of cloud known as a cumulonimbus. They are usually accompanied by strong winds, and often produce heavy rain and sometimes snow, sleet, or hail, but some thunderstorms produce little precipitation or no precipitation at all.

20. **Ionosphere:** This layer play important role for the radio communications.

The ionosphere is a shell of electrons and electrically charged atoms and molecules that surrounds the Earth, stretching from a height of about 50 km (31 mi) to more than 1,000 km (620 mi). It exists primarily due to ultraviolet radiation from the Sun.

The lowest part of the Earth's atmosphere, the troposphere extends from the surface to about 10 km (6.2 mi). Above that is the stratosphere, followed by the mesosphere. In the stratosphere incoming solar radiation creates the ozone layer. At heights of above 80 km (50 mi), in the thermosphere, the atmosphere is so thin that free electrons can exist for short periods of time before they are captured by a nearby positive ion. The number of these free electrons is sufficient to affect radio propagation. This portion of the atmosphere is partially *ionized* and contains a plasma which is referred to as the ionosphere.

21. **March 21 - September 21 period the Sun does not rise at the South pole.**

23. **Tropopause:** The tropopause is the upper limit of the troposphere and therefore constitutes the boundary between it and the Stratosphere.

    According to the World Meteorological Organisation, the "first tropopause" is conventionally defined as the lowest level at which the lapse rate decreases to 2°C/km or less, provided also that the average lapse rate between this level and all higher levels within 2 km does not exceed 2°C/km. If the average lapse rate above this "first tropopause" between any level and all higher levels within 1 km exceeds 3°C/km, then a "second tropopause" is defined by the same criterion as the first. This second tropopause may be either within or above the 1 km layer.

    Near the mid-latitudes there may be two layers of tropopauses: polar and tropical. For aviation purposes, however, significant weather charts generally show one tropopause, using the average heights of the two tropopauses to denote its height in flight level.

    Due to the changes in tropopause heights, especially in mid-latitude polar frontal systems, in certain cases stratospheric air may be brought into the warm air troposphere as a result of the lower tropopause height over the cold air and the jetstream associated with polar frontal system. The airflow effect may "draw" stratospheric air from above and enter the warm air troposphere by way of the jet stream.

24. Meteorological satellites carry sensors that are pointing towards the ground, enabling them to have bird eye view of the globe from the space. There are two types of meteorological satellites characterized by their orbits. They are geo-stationary satellites and polar-orbiting satellites. The measure properties are IR images, visible images, water vapour images.

29. The seeing from the surface of Mars will in sequence from the Mercury, Venus, Earth.

32. **Satellites of the Jupiter:** Phobos, Deimos, Puck and Mimas.

Phobos and Deimos, the two natural satellites of Mars, are small, irregularly shaped rocky objects. With maximum dimensions of 27 km (Phobos) and 15 km (Deimos), they are more similar in size and shape to asteroids than to the other much larger planetary satellites.

34. We do not see Lunar/Solar eclipse during every Full/New moon day in a year because, Moons orbit is tilted by around to orbit of Earth.

35. The supergiant star Nimo has an absolute temperature of about 3000 K and emits a radiant power of approximately. Assuming that Nimo is a perfect emitter (emissivity $e = 1$) and spherical, Radiated power increases by a factor of 16 absolute temperature doubles?

36. 1 kg of liquid water at 273 Kelvin is placed outside on day when temperature is 250 Kelvin. In case A will it take longer for water to freeze. (A) When surface area is smaller (B) When surface area is larger.

38. **Moonrise system:**

    The time of day that the Moon rises or sets depends on its phase. This should be obvious when you remember that the phase of the Moon depends on the relative positions of the Sun, Moon and Earth. For example when the Moon is full it is opposite the Earth from the Sun, so when the Sun sets, the Moon must rise and vice versa. Here is a table summarizing that:

    | Moon phase | Moon rise | Moon set |
    | --- | --- | --- |
    | New | Sunrise | Sun set |
    | 1st quarter | Local noon | Local midnight |
    | Full | Sun set | Sunrise |
    | 3rd quarter | Local midnight | Local noon |

    By local noon and local midnight I mean the points when the Sun crosses the meridian, and exactly 12 hours later. This can be different from the time on your watch because we define time zones which all use the local time at the centre of the zone.

    So when the Moon is new, it rises and sets with the Sun, and the position of Moon rise/set varies just like that of Sun rise/set. When the Moon is full however the pattern is inverted.

39. **Summer Solstice:** Summer solstice, the two moments during the year when the path of the Sun in the sky is farthest north in the Northern Hemisphere (June 20 or 21) or farthest south in the Southern Hemisphere (December 21 or 22).

The summer solstice (or estival solstice), also known as midsummer, occurs when one of the Earth's poles has its maximum tilt toward the Sun. It happens twice yearly, once in each hemisphere (Northern and Southern). For that hemisphere, the summer solstice is when the Sun reaches its highest position in the sky and is the day with the longest period of daylight. Within the Arctic circle (for the northern hemisphere) or Antarctic circle (for the southern hemisphere), there is continuous daylight around the summer solstice. On the summer solstice, Earth's maximum axial tilt toward the Sun is 23.44°. Likewise, the Sun's declination from the celestial equator is 23.44°.

## Equinoxes and solstices on Earth

| Event | Equinox | | Solstice | | Equinox | | Solstice | |
|---|---|---|---|---|---|---|---|---|
| Month | March | | June | | Sept. | | Dec. | |
| Year | Day | Time | Day | Time | Day | Time | Day | Time |
| 2014 | 20 | 16:57 | 21 | 10:51 | 23 | 02:29 | 21 | 23:03 |
| 2015 | 20 | 22:45 | 21 | 16:38 | 23 | 08:21 | 22 | 04:48 |
| 2016 | 20 | 04:30 | 20 | 22:34 | 22 | 14:21 | 21 | 10:44 |
| 2017 | 20 | 10:28 | 21 | 04:24 | 22 | 20:02 | 21 | 16:28 |
| 2018 | 20 | 16:15 | 21 | 10:07 | 23 | 01:54 | 21 | 22:23 |
| 2019 | 20 | 21:58 | 21 | 15:54 | 23 | 07:50 | 22 | 04:19 |
| 2020 | 20 | 03:50 | 20 | 21:44 | 22 | 13:31 | 21 | 10:02 |
| 2021 | 20 | 09:37 | 21 | 03:32 | 22 | 19:21 | 21 | 15:59 |
| 2022 | 20 | 15:33 | 21 | 09:14 | 23 | 01:04 | 21 | 21:48 |
| 2023 | 20 | 21:24 | 21 | 14:58 | 23 | 06:50 | 22 | 03:27 |
| 2024 | 20 | 03:07 | 20 | 20:51 | 22 | 12:44 | 21 | 09:20 |

42. **Asteroid Belt:** The asteroid belt is the circumstellar disc in the Solar System located roughly between the orbits of the planets Mars and Jupiter. It is occupied by numerous irregularly shaped bodies called asteroids or minor planets.

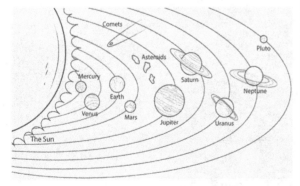

43. Temperature of a star increased from 5000 K to 8000 K, Wavelength Decreases Frequency Increases.

44. **Retrograde motion of the planets:** The most commonly discussed "retrograde" motion is the apparent backward motion of a planet caused by its being lapped by another planet, or vice-versa. Both planets move in a direct (eastward) motion around the Sun, but the planet with the inside (smaller) orbit moves faster than the planet on the outside (larger) orbit, and when it passes the slower-moving planet, each sees the other one as apparently moving backwards relative to its usual motion around the sky. *In this "retrograde" motion, neither planet is actually moving backwards; it only appears that way during the time that one laps the other.*

45. Telescope has Focal length of 1200 mm.

    and eyepiece used is 6 mm.

    magnification will be = 1200/6 = 200

46. Sediments size:

| Millimeters (mm) | Micrometers (μm) | Phi (φ) | Wentworth size class | |
|---|---|---|---|---|
| 4096 | | -12.0 | Boulder | Gravel |
| 256 | | -8.0 | Cobble | Gravel |
| 64 | | -6.0 | Pebble | Gravel |
| 4 | | -2.0 | Granule | Gravel |
| 2.00 | | -1.0 | | |
| 1.00 | | 0.0 | Very coarse sand | Sand |
| 1/2  0.50 | 500 | 1.0 | Coarse sand | Sand |
| 1/4  0.25 | 250 | 2.0 | Medium sand | Sand |
| 1/8  0.125 | 125 | 3.0 | Fine sand | Sand |
| 1/16  0.0625 | 63 | 4.0 | Very fine sand | Sand |
| 1/32  0.031 | 31 | 5.0 | Coarse silt | Silt |
| 1/64  0.0156 | 15.6 | 6.0 | Medium silt | Silt |
| 1/128  0.0078 | 7.8 | 7.0 | Fine silt | Silt |
| 1/256  0.0039 | 3.9 | 8.0 | Very fine silt | Silt |
| 0.00006 | 0.06 | 14.0 | Clay | Mud |

47. A right side up sedimentary sequence will have finest at the top.

48. A tectonic plate (also called lithospheric plate) is a massive, irregularly shaped slab of solid rock, generally composed of both continental and oceanic lithosphere. Plate size can vary greatly, from a few hundred to thousands of kilometers across; the Pacific and Antarctic Plates are among the largest. Plate thickness also varies greatly, ranging from less than 15 km for young oceanic lithosphere to about 200 km or more for ancient continental lithosphere (for example, the interior parts of North and South America).

49. Ichnofossils are an expression of the alteration of the depositional fabric of in sedimentary rocks by living organisms. Often the organism that produced these structures has left no skeletal remains and

it is for this reason the products of their activities are known as "trace" fossils. Common among these structures are burrows, borings, trails and tracks.

Sometimes these biogenic sedimentary structures have long temporal ranges and are preserved intact. Should these trace fossils be common in un-fossiliferous rocks they can extend the geologists capability to interpret the depositional setting of those rocks. Assemblages of trace fossils used to determine ancient depositional settings and sedimentary facies are known as "ichnofacies", as for instance those of "glossifungites".

52. **Bird foot delta:** A bird's foot delta forms at a river where waves, tides and currents are very weak. Deposition of large amounts of fine sediments occurs at the river mouth. The deposits block the channel of the river, which then divides into few distributaries. Each distributary continues to deposit its load maintaining levees as it extends into the sea. Some distributaries extended further than others creating the shape of a bird's foot.

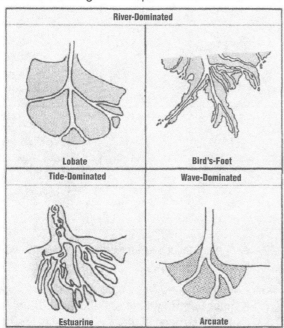

53. Braid bar is associated with river deposit. Braid bar/ Braid bars, or mid-channel bars, are landforms in a river that begin to form when the discharge is low and the river is forced to take the route of less resistance by means of flowing in locations of lowest elevation.

54. **Goethite:** Goethite (FeO(OH); is an iron-bearing hydroxide mineral of the diaspore group. It is found in soil and other low-temperature environments such as sediment. Goethite has been well-known since ancient times for its use as a pigment (brown ochre).

55. **Classification of the Greywacke:** Greywacke is a variety of argillaceous sandstone that is highly indurated and poorly sorted.

**Texture :** Clastic.

**Grain size :** < 0.06 - 2 mm, clasts typically angular, visible to the naked eye.

**Hardness :** Hard.

**Colour :** Grey to black; often with white quartz veins.

**Clasts :** Quartz, lithics, minor feldspar (orthoclase, plagioclase), pyroxene (augite), mica (biotite, chlorite, muscovite); often quartz veins visible.

**Other features :** Gritty to touch (like sandpaper), often veined, non-vesicular.

**Uses :** Widely used as aggregate, fill etc. in the construction and roading industries; as armour rock for sea walls etc.

59. Evaluation of plants with geological age:

| ERA | PERIOD | AGE (millions of years) |
|---|---|---|
| CENOZOIC | Quaternary | 2.5 — Incision of Great Falls (30,000 ya) |
| | Neogene | First humans |
| | | 23 |
| | Paleogene | |
| | | 65 — Dinosaurs go extinct |
| MESOZOIC | Cretaceous | |
| | | 145 — First flowering plants |
| | Jurassic | First birds / Atlantic Ocean begins to form |
| | | 200 |
| | Triassic | First dinosaurs, first mammals |
| | | 251 — Major extinction event |
| PALEOZOIC | Permian | |
| | | 300 — Appalachian Mountains form |
| | Pennsylvanian | 318 |
| | Mississippian | 359 |
| | Devonian | First amphibians |
| | | 416 |
| | Silurian | 443 |
| | Ordovician | First land plants |
| | | 488 |
| | Cambrian | First vertebrates |
| | | 542 — First animals |
| PRECAMBRIAN | | 4600 |

Geologic time scale with major geologic and evolutionary events.

60. The exoskeleton of sponges is made up of silica.

61. A flow, which is a balance of pressure gradient and Coriolis force, is called Geostrophic flow.

63. Ocean western boundary currents are warm, fast and narrow currents in both hemisphere.

64. ITCZ:

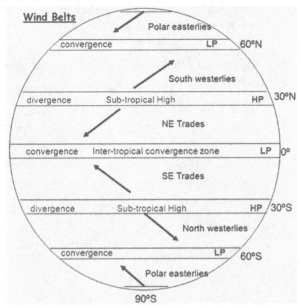

**Wind Belts**

65. **MLD depth in Ocean:** The mixed layer is also important as its depth determines the average level of light seen by marine organisms. In very deep mixed layers, the tiny marine plants known as phytoplankton are unable to get enough light to maintain their metabolism. The deepening of the mixed layer in the wintertime in the North Atlantic is therefore associated with a strong decrease in surface chlorophyll. However, this deep mixing also replenishes near-surface nutrient stocks. Thus when the mixed layer becomes shallow in the spring, and light levels increase, there is often a concomitant increase of phytoplankton biomass, known as the "spring bloom".

The mixed layer is characterized by being nearly uniform in properties such as temperature and salinity throughout the layer. Velocities, however, may exhibit significant shears within the mixed layer. The bottom of the mixed layer is characterized by a gradient, where the water properties change.

67. **Density sigma to seawater density:**

| Ion | Sea salt (ppm) | Seawater[a] (ppm) |
|---|---|---|
| Salinity: around 35 ppt | | |
| $Cl^-$ | 19,290 | 19,353 |
| $Na^+$ | 10,780 | 10,781 |
| $SO_4^{2-}$ | 2,660 | 2,712 |
| $Mg$ | 1,320 | 1,284 |
| $K^+$ | 420 | 399 |
| $Ca^{2+}$ | 400 | 412 |
| $CO_3^{2-}/HCO_3^-$ | 200 | 126 |
| $Br^-$ | 56 | 67 |
| $Sr^{2+}$ | 8.8 | 7.9 |
| $Li^+$ | 0.3 | 0.173 |
| $Ba^{2+}$ | <0.04 | 0.014 |
| $Mn^{2+}$ | <0.025 | <0.001 |
| $Cd^{2+}$ | <0.002 | <0.001 |
| Salinity: around 32 ppt (sea salt) and 35 (seawater) | | |
| Concentration (g $L^{-1}$) | 38 | 35.169 |
| Alkalinity (mEq $L^{-1}$) | 3.0–4.0 | 2.32 |
| Calcium ion (mg $L^{-1}$) | 349–392 | 411.9 |
| Magnesium ion (mg $L^{-1}$) | 1,150–1,310 | 1,284 |

[a] Data for seawater values are from Pilson (1998)

70. **El- Nino:** El Niño is a climate pattern that describes the unusual warming of surface waters in the eastern equatorial Pacific Ocean. Trade winds and atmosphere are also impacted by El Niño.

71. In the Indian ocean, south equatorial currents crosses the equator during Southwest monsoon.

72. The difference between sea level at high tide and sea level at low tide is called the Tidal range.

73. In the depth range, where salinity changes rapidly is called Halocline.

74. The major light harvesting pigments in phytoplankton are Chlorophylls and Carotenoids.

75. Nitrate and Phosphate are the major nutrients which limit the phytoplankton growth in the marine environment.

76. Aquatic organisms which are able to swim and move on their own are Nektons.

77. In low nutrient environment, growth advantage is shifted towards Small phytoplankton cells type of phytoplankton cells.

79. Solid support structure that forms the hard base upon Calcium Carbonate corals live is composed.

80. Blue colour penetrates the deepest in the open ocean.

81. The following statement is TRUE.
Nutrient maximum and $O_2$ minimum are about at the same depth.

82. The major source of iron to the surface layer of the open ocean is Atmospheric deposition of dust from the continents.

83. Nitrogen fixation of the followings is the most energetically expensive process.

84. Rate of photosynthesis is lesser than the rate of respiration at these depthscauses depletion of dissolved oxygen minimum in the deeper depths.

85. Nitrate of the following nitrogen substrates, autotrophs preferably use as a nutrient.

86. Following picture is taken during a spring bloom in the eastern Arabian Sea. *Trichodesmium* bloom does it represent.

87. Following figure represents zonal mean anthropogenic $CO_2$ inventories in the different oceans across latitudes. In the figure, black, red and blue lines, respectively represent: Atlantic, Indian and Pacific oceans.

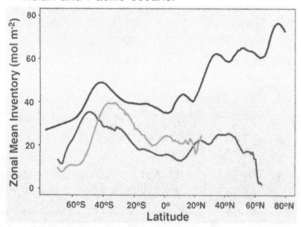

88. Following plot shows the variation in solubility of dissolved inorganic carbon (DIC) in water versus pH. In the plot, green, red and blue lines, respectively represent the concentration of: $CO_2$, $CO_3^{2-}$, $HCO_3^-$.

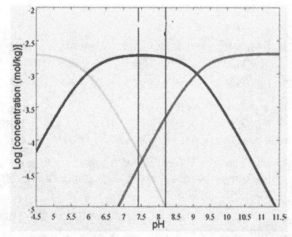

89. Ferrel Cellone of the followings is NOT a thermally driven circulation.

90. Presence of craters of different ages of the following can be taken as an evidence to suggest that the Moon's surface is tectonically not active.

91. Pegmatite, generally, contains large size minerals compared to other rocks, because the lower viscosity of parental liquid facilitates the crystal growth.

92. Topaz of the following minerals is a silicate.

93. Aragonite one among the given minerals forms the shells of some marine organisms.

94. Andesite one of the following rocks is generally found in the island-arcs.

95. Island arcs are generally convex towards the Subducting plate.

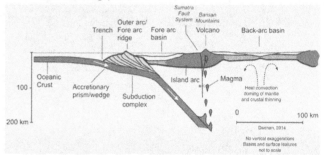

96. If a lithospheric plate A moves with an absolute velocity of 5 cm/yr towards the north, and another lithospheric plate B which is in contact with the plate A along an E-W trending boundary, moves with an absolute velocity of 3 cm/yr in north, then the boundary between them would be A spreading ridge.

97. Explosive volcanoes differ from the non-explosive volcanoes mainly in Volatile content in the magma.

98. Transform faults, in terms of the kinematics of faulting, are similar to the Strike-slip faults.

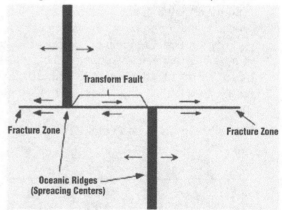

99. Traditional Water Harvesting Structures in Rajasthan are known as Tankas.

100. Two metamorphic rocks having experienced same grade of metamorphism have developed different mineral assemblages. This may be due to their different bulk chemical composition.

# International Earth Science Olympiad (IESO)

# Previous Years' Papers (Solved)

# International Earth Science Olympiad (IESO)
## Entrance Exam, 2018*

**Total Marks : 100**                                      **No Negative markings**

---

1. Echo sounding is used to estimate:
   (a) Atmospheric pressure
   (b) Ocean depth
   (c) Ocean temperature
   (d) Atmospheric temperature

2. El-Nino is related to:
   (a) Unusual warming of Peru-Chile coast during December
   (b) Unusually high rainfall during monsoon
   (c) Earthquake in the Pacific
   (d) Hurricanes in the Atlantic

3. During El-Nino period, thermocline depth deepens over the:
   (a) Western equatorial Pacific
   (b) Eastern equatorial Pacific
   (c) Southern Pacific
   (d) North Pacific

4. Bioavailable nitrogen (such as nitrate) is lost from the ocean through:
   (a) Nitrification        (b) Denitrification
   (c) Initrogen fixation   (d) Ammonification

5. Age of the earth can be determined by the radio-active element that has a half-life of the order of:
   (a) Thousand years       (b) Ten thousand years
   (c) Million years        (d) Billion years

6. In ocean, respiration exceeds over primary production:
   (a) In the euphotic depth
   (b) Below euphotic depth
   (c) In the mixed layer
   (d) Above thermocline

7. Following profile in the ocean belongs to..............

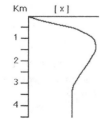

   (a) Conservative        (b) Scavenged
   (c) Nutrient            (d) Mixed type

8. Carbon : Nitrogen : Phosphorus in the deeper ocean is:
   (a) 100:10:1            (b) 10:100:1
   (c) 16:106:1           (d) 106:16:1

9. High Nutrient Low Chlorophyll regions are located in the:
   (a) Equatorial oceans
   (b) Tropical oceans
   (b) Sub-tropical oceans
   (d) Polar oceans

10. To change pH of a solution from 10 to 8, how many times do you expect a change in [H$^+$]:
    (a) 1000               (b) 100
    (c) 10                 (d) 1

11. Green House gases:
    (a) Trap Sun's heat
    (b) Trap the heat released from the earth's surface
    (c) Decrease earth's temperature
    (d) Are not produced by burning of fossil fuels

12. Which of the following reactions is the best representative of photosynthesis?
    (a) $CH_2O + O_2 \rightarrow CO_2 + H_2O$
    (b) $2C + 3H_2 \rightarrow C_2H_6$
    (c) $H_2 + \frac{1}{2} O_2 \rightarrow H_2O$
    (d) $CO_2 + H_2O \rightarrow CH_2O$

13. Atmospheric pressure at sea level is:
    (a) 0.03 kg cm$^{-2}$      (b) 1.03 kg cm$^{-2}$
    (c) 2.3 kg cm$^{-2}$       (d) 10.3 kg cm$^{-2}$

14. Most critical aspect among the essential ones for: the ocean circulation to be constantly functional is
    (a) Formation of horizontal pressure gradients
    (b) Formation of vertical pressure gradients
    (c) Formation of deep water masses
    (d) Formation of density gradients

15. During evaporation, water experiences:
    (a) Specific heat loss
    (b) Latent heat loss

(c) Specific heat gain

(d) Latent heat gain

16. In general, the ocean does not respond to the seasonally changing insolation as strongly as the atmosphere. However, there is a region where the ocean circulation changes dramatically every year between summer and winter. Where and why?
    (a) In the northern Indian Ocean due to changing wind patterns (monsoons) causing a reversal of currents
    (b) In the Pacific, due to the changing wind patterns caused by the so-called El Niño events.
    (c) In the Antarctic, where winds change direction completely which becomes visible through reversal of the circumpolar current.
    (d) In the wind-driven ocean gyres where plastic accumulates every summer when the gyres spin up, and where the plastic is released when the gyres slow down.

17. Which of the following is not a greenhouse gas?
    (a) $N_2$
    (b) $CO_2$
    (c) $N_2O$
    (d) $CH_4$

18. What is the average depth of the Oceans?
    (a) 35 m
    (b) 350 m
    (c) 3500 m
    (d) 35000 m

19. Pure water reaches its maximum density at:
    (a) 50°F
    (b) 0°C
    (c) 32°F
    (d) 4°C

20. Which process increases the salinity of surface sea water?
    (a) Rainfall
    (b) Riverine flux
    (c) Sea-ice formation
    (d) Upwelling

21. A windy day is an example of:
    (a) Weather
    (b) Climate
    (c) Both
    (d) None of these

22. Collectively, the suspended, single-celled, photosynthesizing microorganisms in the world ocean are called:
    (a) Zooplankton
    (b) Virioplankton
    (c) Phytoplankton
    (d) Jellyplankton

23. Which of the following geological processes is not related to the convergent plate boundary?
    (a) Building of new ocean floor
    (b) Explosive volcanism
    (c) Mountain building
    (d) Thrust faulting

24. Which of the following has the longest chain of volcanoes on the Present globe?
    (a) Indonesian islands
    (b) Japanese islands
    (c) Hawaiian Islands
    (d) Mid Oceanic Ridges

25. Fracture zones on the Present globe are generally:
    (a) Transverse to the Mid Oceanic Ridge segments
    (b) Parallel to the Mid Oceanic Ridge segments
    (c) Within the median valley of the Mid Oceanic Ridges
    (d) Along the hot-spot tracks

26. Choose a pair of minerals which represents aluminosilicates
    (a) Muscovite—Biotite
    (b) Kyanite—Sillimanite
    (c) Apatite—Chlorite
    (d) Tremolite—Actinolite

27. Which one of the following is a difference between a transform fault and a transcurrent fault?
    (a) A transcurrent fault is a strike-slip fault but the transform fault is a thrust fault
    (b) Transform fault is a strike-slip fault but the transcurrent fault is a normal fault
    (c) Transform fault is limited between the plate boundaries but the transcurrent fault continues beyond the plate boundary
    (d) Transform fault is limited to ocean floor but the transcurrent fault is limited to continental crust.

28. Which of the following is Not true for the early period of Earth?
    (a) There was no free oxygen in the atmosphere
    (b) There were frequent meteorite impacts
    (c) More heat was being produced from the radioactive elements compared to present
    (d) Continental crust occupied larger surface area than present

29. What are the three components of the stream power equation?
    (a) Stream discharge, river width and river depth
    (b) Hydraulic radius, channel slope and dissolved oxygen levels
    (c) Stream discharge, channel slope and water density
    (d) Channel slope, river width and mean annual precipitation

30. An example of a white mica is:
    (a) Phlogopite
    (b) Biotite
    (c) Muscovite
    (d) Chlorite

31. A lithospheric fragment on being stretched may develop a rift. The rifting would be accompanied by:
    (a) Normal faulting
    (b) Thrust faulting
    (c) Strike-slip faulting
    (d) Thrust and strike slip faulting both

**32.** If a fragment of oceanic lithosphere is found on a continent, that would be called:
(a) Kimberlite    (b) Ophiolite
(c) Mylonite      (d) Hot-spot

**33.** What is the name of the process in which small particles become trapped by larger particles in the bedload so that they cannot be entrained even though flow is great enough?
(a) Floodplain aggradation
(b) Hellicoidal flow
(c) Particle Imbrication
(d) Rock cohesion

**34.** Mean water velocity in an open channel is estimated using which of the following?
(a) Manning's equation
(b) Hjulström curve
(c) Water balance curve
(d) Reynolds number

**35.** A set of parallel planes, defined by alignment of minerals, produced during metamorphism in the regionally metamorphosed rocks are called:
(a) Faults      (b) Joints
(c) Bedding     (d) Foliation

**36.** Surface of the moon has numerous craters that are created due to the heavy bombardment. We don't have so many craters on Earth, because:
(a) Earth did not experience heavy bombardment
(b) Surface of the Earth has been under continuous modification due to geological processes
(c) Craters on Earth are in oceans
(d) Bombardment on Earth was by lighter objects that could not form craters.

**37.** A portion of the mantle undergoes partial melting. The ratio of an incompatible to a compatible element in the resultant melt would be:
(a) Same as that in the residual solid mantle
(b) Higher than the residual solid mantle
(c) Lower than the residual solid mantle
(d) Depends on the isotope of the elements involved

**38.** Zircon grains are generally dated by U-Pb dating method and not by Rb-Sr dating method, because:
(a) The initial U/Pb ratio in the zircon is much lower compared to the initial Rb/Sr ratio, making it easier to measure the increase in U/Pb ratio due to radioactive decay of U.
(b) U is radioactive decaying to Pb but Rb and Sr both are not radioactive
(c) The initial U/Pb ratio in the zircon is very high making it easier to measure the radiogenic Pb

(d) The Rb-Sr system has lower half life than the U-Pb system

**39.** Which of the following is not a Garnet?
(a) Almandine    (b) Pyrope
(c) Grossular    (d) Cordierite

**40.** A gabbroic rock is observed within the layers of shale which overlies a limestone. The limestone is cut by a dolerite dyke which is not found continuing into the shale. Which of the following statement is true?
(a) Limestone is chemically precipitated simultaneous to an underwater volcanic eruption that emplaced dolerite dyke.
(b) Limestone is the oldest rock of the three while the gabbroic rock is a sill within shale.
(c) Dolerite dyke is the youngest while the limestone is the oldest rock.
(d) The shale is the youngest rock while the dolerite dyke, the gabbroic rock and the limestone all formed simultaneously.

**41.** Which of the following marks the eastern boundary of the India plate?
(a) Eastern Ghats
(b) Coromondal coast
(c) Indo-Myanmar Range
(d) Karakoram fault

**42.** Which of the following observations helped understand the continental drift hypothesis?
(a) Regular arrangements of paleomagnetic anomalies on sea-floor
(b) Rugged topography of the sea-floor
(c) Volcanism within the sea-floor
(d) Presence of serpentinites on continents

**43.** Which of the following is NOT a supercontinent?
(a) Purana       (b) Rodinia
(c) Gondwana     (d) Pangea

**44.** The mantle convection takes place because of:
(a) Plate-movements
(b) Rotation of earth
(c) Temperature and density differences
(d) Heterogeneous distribution of mass within the continental crust

**45.** If a radioactive nuclide decays by $\beta$-decay the resultant daughter would have:
(a) Same mass number but different atomic number
(b) Same atomic number but different mass number
(c) Same mass number and same atomic number
(d) Different mass number and different atomic number

**46.** The difference between the temperature variation in crust and mantle is that temperature:
   (a) Increases with a faster rate in the crust but with a slower adiabatic rate in the mantle
   (b) Increases with slower adiabatic rate in the crust but with a faster rate in the mantle
   (c) Remains constant in the crust but decreases in the mantle
   (d) Decreases in the crust but increases in the mantle.

**47.** Magma originated by partial melting inside the Earth would:
   (a) Crystallize completely after some time at the same depth of origin
   (b) Start rising up due to buoyancy
   (c) Assimilate the country rock and become a larger magma chamber at the depth of origin
   (d) Would sink deeper to add to the liquid core.

**48.** A transform fault connecting an overriding plate margin with another overriding plate margin, would:
   (a) Decrease in length with time
   (b) Increase in length with time
   (c) Not change in length with time
   (d) Become a transcurrent fault with time

**49.** According to the plate-tectonic theory:
   (a) Continents drift relative to each other but oceans remain fixed
   (b) Sea floor spreading takes place but no movement occurs in continents
   (c) Plates consisting of oceans and/or continents move relative to each other
   (d) Crust floats over a liquid mantle

**50.** Which of the following is generally not a part of oceanic crust?
   (a) Sedimentary rocks  (b) Basaltic lavas
   (c) Gabbro            (d) Granite

**51.** Quartz crystallises in which system:
   (a) Cubic             (b) Tetragonal
   (c) Hexagonal         (d) Orthorhombic

**52.** Rocks on a rapidly subducting plate are likely to experience which of the following metamorphic facies conditions first, if they are taken to depth away from arc magmatism?
   (a) Amphibolite
   (b) Granulite
   (c) Hornblende hornfels
   (d) Blueschist

**53.** The arcuate shape of Island arcs is a consequence of:
   (a) Wedge shaped mantle below
   (b) Subduction in a spherical surface
   (c) Plate movement over a fixed hot spot
   (d) Zigzag plate margins

**54.** Some folded rock-layers are found cropping out on the surface. It means:
   (a) These rocks were subjected to stresses under high pressure, temperature conditions
   (b) These rocks are made up of foldable material at surface temperature conditions
   (c) These rocks are folded during the thrust faulting that exposed them on the surface
   (d) These are not silicate rocks.

**55.** The velocity of seismic waves increases at the depth of 670 km in the mantle, this is because of:
   (a) Change in crystal structure from spinel to perovskite type
   (b) Presence of heavy Fe-Ni material
   (c) Refraction of waves from the lower-mantle boundary
   (d) Core-mantle boundary

**56.** Olivine is generally the first mineral to crystallize from a basaltic melt. Which of the following elements would get more depleted in the residual melt due to the olivine crystallization?
   (a) Al                (b) K
   (c) Na                (d) Mg

**57.** A 2 billion year old zircon is discovered from a sedimentary rock which was deposited at 550 million year back. This means:
   (a) The zircon was the first mineral to get deposited and the deposition process continued from 2 billion year ago to 550 million year ago
   (b) The primary source rock of the zircon must have formed 2 billion year ago
   (c) The zircon was buried deep inside the Earth from 2 billion year ago to 550 million year ago
   (d) There was no geological activity from 2 billion year ago to the 550 million year ago.

**58.** Sr gets incorporated more easily in plagioclase mineral compared to in the biotite, because:
   (a) Plagioclase has higher melting point than the biotite
   (b) Plagioclase has larger stability range in terms of pressure and temperature compared to the biotite
   (c) Ca in plagioclase is similar in size and charge to the Sr and therefore get replaced by it easily
   (d) Silica tetrahedral makes a framework structure in plagioclase providing larger space for Sr compared to the sheet structure in biotite

**59.** Which of the following is an ore mineral of uranium?
   (a) Zircon            (b) Pitchblende
   (c) Magnetite         (d) Apatite

**60.** Which of the following samples would be most suited for Carbon-dating?
(a) Quartz tool from an archaeological site
(b) A bone sample from an Harappan archaeological site
(c) A sample of lignite from Miocene coal beds
(d) A sample of coal from Gondwana coal beds

**61.** A suture zone is a:
(a) Trace of thrust fault along a convergent plate boundary
(b) Axis of median rift valley along a divergent plate boundary
(c) Line of ocean closure at a convergent plate boundary
(d) Zone of thrusting along a convergent plate boundary

**62.** Which rocks find application in the manufacture of fertilizers?
(a) Sandstone      (b) Phosphorites
(c) Granites       (d) Marbles

**63.** Mercury rises before Sun when:
(a) It is at greatest western elongation
(b) It is at greatest eastern elongation
(c) When it makes an angle of 1800 at earth
(d) None of these

**64.** Indian standard time is different from the Greenwich meantime because of:
(a) Longitude difference
(b) Latitude difference
(c) Rotation of earth
(d) None of the above

**65.** Which of the following is a result of direct interaction between lithosphere atmopsphere-hydrosphere and biosphere?
(a) Movement of plates
(b) Volcanic eruption
(c) Formation of soil
(d) Recharge of underground aquifer

**66.** Acceleration due to Earth's gravity at the center of earth is:
(a) 0.0 km/s$^2$       (b) 9.8 km/s$^2$
(c) 11.2 km/s$^2$      (d) 6400 km/s$^2$

**67.** Pointer in the magnetic compass is directed towards:
(a) Geographic north   (b) Geomagnetic north
(c) Both               (d) None

**68.** The Coriolis force is a force and its direction in the northern hemisphere is:
(a) Pseudo, clockwise
(b) Pseudo, anticlockwise
(c) Real, clockwise
(d) Real, anticlockwise

**69.** At quadrature the elongation of the planet is:
(a) Perpendicular to the sun
(b) 180 degree
(c) 0 degree
(d) None of these

**70.** To facilitate a satellite in an elliptical orbit to move farther from earth, which of the following technique is useful?
(a) Increasing the velocity at perigee
(b) Decreasing the velocity at perigee
(c) Increasing the velocity at apogee
(d) Decreasing the velocity at apogee

**71.** What is the ratio of the angle covered by earth in its orbit around sun in one month at perigee and apogee (15 days on both sides of apogee and perigee point)? Given that the Aphelion to perhelion distance ratio is 1.034.
(a) 0.923       (b) 0.935
(c) 0.911       (d) 0.900

**72.** Calculate the energy of the H $\propto$ (Balmer) photon (Rydberg constant R $\infty$ is 1.0973731568508 × 10$^7$ per metre).
(a) 1.89 eV      (b) 2.56 eV
(c) 3.03 eV      (d) 3.40 eV

**73.** Given a uniform mass distribution of the disc galaxy, which of the following is the correct representation of tangential velocity as a function of radius (assume no dark matter)?

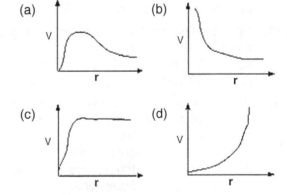

**74.** 1 parsec in centimeters is:
(a) 3.086 × 10$^{18}$      (b) 3.086 × 10$^{15}$
(c) 3.086 × 10$^{17}$      (d) 3.086 × 10$^{14}$

**75.** Given the bolometric magnitude of Deneb = −8.38, find the luminosity of Deneb in terms of solar-luminosity (bolometric magnitude of the sun is 4.24).
(a) 111640 times solar luminosity
(b) 111686 times solar luminosity
(c) 100000 times solar luminosity
(d) 100500 times solar luminosity

**76.** Upper crust is made up of granite. What is the lower crust made up of:
(a) Syenite
(b) Adamellite
(c) Granulite
(d) Quartzite

**77.** Which of the following relation is true in case of circumpolar stars, where δ is declination and φ is latitude of the place?
(a) $\delta + \phi >= 90^0$
(b) $\delta + \phi = 90^0$
(c) $\delta +$ Hour angle $= 90^0$
(d) $\delta +$ Hour angle $> = 90^0$

**78.** Given that the hour angle of vernal equinox is 8 hours and right ascension of a star is 6 hours, find the hour angle of the star.
(a) 2 hours
(b) 14 hours
(c) 1 hour
(d) We need more information to calculate this

**79.** The focal ratio of a 10 inches aperture telescope is 0.4. Calculate the focal length of the telescope in mm.
(a) 1100 mm
(b) 1000 mm
(c) 1200 mm
(d) 1400 mm

**80.** Parabolic mirror is used in a reflecting telescope to get rid of which of the following aberrations?
(a) Coma
(b) Spherical aberration
(c) Astigmatism
(d) Chromatic aberration

**81.** Calculate the apparent recession velocity of a galaxy at redshift of 0.1.
(a) $3 \times 10^7$ m/s
(b) $3 \times 10^6$ m/s
(c) $3 \times 10^5$ m/s
(d) $3 \times 10^4$ m/s

**82.** What is the correct order of the Earth's atmospheric layers from surface of the Earth to the top?
(a) Stratosphere, Mesosphere, Exosphere, Troposphere, Thermosphere
(b) Troposphere, Stratosphere, Mesosphere, Thermosphere, Exosphere
(c) Mesosphere, Stratosphere, Troposphere Thermosphere, Exosphere
(d) Troposphere, Mesosphere, Stratosphere, Thermosphere, Exosphere

**83.** Most of the tropical cyclones originate in which region?
(a) Over the sub-tropical regions
(b) Between 10 and 20 degree North and South of the Equator
(c) To the east of easterly winds
(d) Between 0 and 5 Degree North and South of the Equator

**84.** Albedo is the fraction of which of the following?
(a) Radiation reflected by the Earth
(b) Momentum and energy received by the atmos-phere
(c) Moisture and water content of the atmosphere
(d) Greenhouse gas and oxygen in the atmosphere

**85.** The graph given below depicts the daily temperature cycle at Bhopal for two days. Which of the following statements is correct?

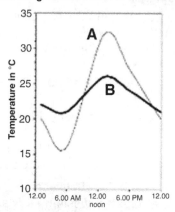

(a) Graphs A and B represent the temperature cycle of a cloudy day
(b) Graph A represents the temperature cycle of a clear day and graph B represents the temperature cycle of a cloudy day
(c) Graphs A and B represent the temperature cycle of a clear day
(d) Graph A represents the temperature cycle of a cloudy day and Graph B represents the temperature cycle of a clear day

**86.** Which region on the surface of the Earth receives more solar energy?
(a) High-Latitudes Regions
(b) Sub-tropical Regions
(c) Equatorial Regions
(d) Mid-Latitudes Regions

**87.** Depletion of ozone in the Earth's atmosphere will cause which of the following process?
(a) Decrease in the UV radiation reaching to the Earth's surface
(b) Decrease in atmospheric temperature
(c) Increase in the UV radiation reaching to the Earth's surface
(d) Decrease in the Earth's UV radiation

**88.** Which of the following is associated with Aeronomy?
(a) Botany
(b) Chemical composition
(c) Oceanography
(d) Radiation from space

89. Different types of solar radiations are causing different types of effects. Which of the following is correct?
    (a) Infrared causes more heating effects
    (b) Infrared causes more chemical effects
    (c) Ultraviolet causes more heating effects
    (d) Infrared causes more visible effects

90. What will be the mean molecular weight of the atmosphere consisting of $N_2$, $O_2$ and Ar only, given that the molecular weights of $N_2$, $O_2$ and Ar are 28.01, 32 and 39.85 respectively?
    (a) 28.00
    (b) 28.97
    (c) 29.00
    (d) 32.12

91. Different types of aerosols are causing different types of effects in the radiation balance of the atmosphere. Which of the following statement is incorrect?
    (a) Black carbon rich aerosols cause cooling
    (b) Black carbon rich aerosols cause heating
    (c) Sulphate rich aerosols cause cooling
    (d) None of the above

92. Remote sensing is very good technique for atmospheric studies. Which of the following is incorrect regarding remote sensing?
    (a) Remote sensing is of two types: Active and Passive
    (b) Signal is transmitted and received in the active remote sensing
    (c) Signal is not transmitted only received in the passive remote sensing
    (d) Signal is transmitted and received in the passive remote sensing

93. Turbulence is one of the processes taking place in the different regions of the Earth's atmosphere. Which of the following statement is correct about turbulence?
    (a) Turbulence is very strong in the troposphere
    (b) Turbulence is very weak in the troposphere
    (c) Turbulence is very strong in the stratosphere
    (d) No turbulence in the mesosphere

94. A mineral popularly known as 'fools' gold belongs to which group?
    (a) Oxides
    (b) Carbonates
    (c) Sulphides
    (d) Arsenides

95. Assume the Sun and the Earth behaving like black bodies at mean temperatures 6000 K and 300 K, respectively. What will be the ratio (Sun : Earth) of the emitted wavelengths from the Sun & Earth?

    (a) 1 : 1
    (b) 1 : 20
    (c) 20 : 1
    (d) 2 : 1

96. Visibly, sometimes, clouds look different in colours, but most of the times clouds look white. Due to which process the clouds look white?
    (a) Rayleigh scattering
    (b) Raman scattering
    (c) Resonance scattering
    (d) Mie scattering

97. Space weather effects are less pronounced in low latitude regions, why?
    (a) Low latitude regions are having shield of geomantic filed lines
    (b) Low latitude regions are getting more solar flux
    (c) Low latitude regions are surrounded by oceans
    (d) Low latitude regions are having open geomantic filed lines

98. A westerly wind means a ..................
    (a) Wind in the Northern hemisphere
    (b) Wind coming from the West
    (c) Wind in Southern hemisphere
    (d) Wind coming from the East

99. The age of the Deccan volcanism is around:
    (a) 55 million yrs
    (b) 66 million yrs
    (c) 5 million yrs
    (d) 4.5 billion yrs

100. From the figure given below find out which two atmospheric layers have temperature profiles that promote convection?

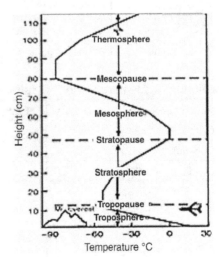

    (a) Mesosphere and Stratosphere
    (b) Mesosphere and Thermosphere
    (c) Mesosphere and Troposphere
    (d) Stratosphere and Thermosphere

# ANSWERS

| 1 | 2 | 3 | 4 | 5 | 6 | 7 | 8 | 9 | 10 |
|---|---|---|---|---|---|---|---|---|---|
| (b) | (a) | (b) | (b) | (d) | (b) | (c) | (d) | (d) | (b) |
| **11** | **12** | **13** | **14** | **15** | **16** | **17** | **18** | **19** | **20** |
| (b) | (d) | (b) | (a) | (b) | (a) | (a) | (c) | (d) | (c) |
| **21** | **22** | **23** | **24** | **25** | **26** | **27** | **28** | **29** | **30** |
| (a) | (c) | (a) | (d) | (a) | (b) | (c) | (d) | (c) | (c) |
| **31** | **32** | **33** | **34** | **35** | **36** | **37** | **38** | **39** | **40** |
| (a) | (b) | (c) | (a) | (d) | (b) | (b) | (c) | (d) | (b) |
| **41** | **42** | **43** | **44** | **45** | **46** | **47** | **48** | **49** | **50** |
| (c) | (a) | (a) | (c) | (a) | (a) | (b) | (a) | (c) | (d) |
| **51** | **52** | **53** | **54** | **55** | **56** | **57** | **58** | **59** | **60** |
| (c) | (d) | (b) | (a) | (a) | (d) | (b) | (c) | (b) | (b) |
| **61** | **62** | **63** | **64** | **65** | **66** | **67** | **68** | **69** | **70** |
| (c) | (b) | (a) | (a) | (c) | (a) | (b) | (b) | (a) | (a) |
| **71** | **72** | **73** | **74** | **75** | **76** | **77** | **78** | **79** | **80** |
| (b) | (a) | (a) | (a) | (b) | (c) | (a) | (a) | (b) | (b) |
| **81** | **82** | **83** | **84** | **85** | **86** | **87** | **88** | **89** | **90** |
| (a) | (b) | (b) | (a) | (b) | (c) | (c) | (d) | (a) | (b) |
| **91** | **92** | **93** | **94** | **95** | **96** | **97** | **98** | **99** | **100** |
| (a) | (d) | (a) | (c) | (b) | (d) | (a) | (b) | (b) | (c) |

# HINTS AND SOLUTIONS

## 1. Instruments and Its Uses

| Name of the instruments | Work of the instruments |
|---|---|
| Barometer | Atmospheric pressure |
| Fathometer | Ocean depth |
| CTD or Sonde | Ocean temperature |
| Thermometer | Atmospheric temperature |

## 2. El-Nino:

El Niño term first time used in 1600s century by fishermen due to the off coast of South America for unusually warm water in Pacific ocean, it means Little Boy/ Christ Child in Spanish. The large scale ocean atmosphere climate interaction linked to a periodic warming in sea surface temperatures. It is very important influence weather patterns, ocean conditions and others marine related information likes fisheries etc. with respect to the globe.

## 5. Radioactive Elements and Its Half-Life:

| Parent Isotope (Radioactive) | Daughter Isotope (Radiogenic) | Half –life ($t_{1/2}$) |
|---|---|---|
| Carbon (C-14) | Nitrogen (N-14) | 5730 years ($5.73 \times 10^3$ years) |
| Beryllium (Be-10) | Boron (B-10) | 1.5 million years ($1.5 \times 10^6$) years |
| Uranium (U-235) | Lead (Pb-207) | 704 million years ($7.04 \times 10^8$) years |
| Uranium (U-238) | Lead (Pb-206) | 4400 million years ($4.4 \times 10^9$) years |
| Potassium (K-40) | Argon (Ar-40) | 11930 million years ($1.193 \times 10^{10}$) years |
| Thorium (Th-232) | Lead (Pb-208) | 14010 million years ($1.401 \times 10^{10}$) years |
| Lutecium (Lu-176) | Halfnium (Hf-176) | 35700 million years ($3.57 \times 10^{10}$) years |
| Rhenium (Re-187) | Osmium (Os-187) | 42300 million years ($4.23 \times 10^{10}$) years |
| Rubidium (Rb-87) | Stronitium (Sr-87) | 48800 million years ($4.88 \times 10^{10}$) years |
| Samarium (Sm-147) | Neodymium (Nd-143) | 106000 million years ($1.06 \times 10^{11}$) years |

6. **Depth of the Ocean:** The different layers of the Ocean with respect to the changes:

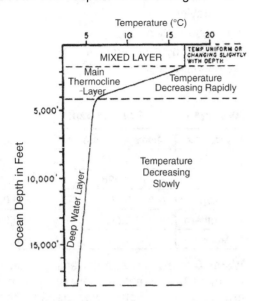

8. **Elements in the ocean:** Seawater composition (by mass) (salinity = 3.5%)

| Elements | Percent (%) (Salinity = 3.5%) |
|----------|-------------------------------|
| Oxygen | 85.84 |
| Hydrogen | 10.82 |
| Chloride | 1.94 |
| Sodium | 1.08 |
| Magnesium | 0.1292 |
| Sulphur | 0.091 |
| Calcium | 0.04 |

9. **Chlorophyll and Sea Surface Temperature of Different part of the Ocean:** The ocean surface is a mixer of the different organism like single celled, phytoplankton, plant like algae due to photosynthesis processes. The micro – organism exits due to availability of the food, temperature, salinity and Sun's light, in the ocean environments the cold water have more nutrients than the warm water. The availability of the chlorophyll low, the phytoplankton is low and high respectively. Finally, we can say the relation between chlorophyll and phytoplankton is directly proportional to each other. This information is measured by two NASA's Terra and Aqua satellites.

- The concentration of chlorophyll is a proxy for the amount of photosynthetic plankton, or phytoplankton, present in the ocean. Phytoplankton populations are influenced by climatic factors such as sea surface temperatures and winds.
- Some of the highest average chlorophyll concentrations are located near continental coasts of the Pacific and Atlantic Oceans.
- Changes in phytoplankton populations may impact fish and other marine life, which can affect economic productivity and food availability. Decision makers can use this indicator to understand the health and productivity of marine ecosystems that depend on phytoplankton.

10. **pH values and its effect on Ocean depth:**

11. **Green Houses Gases:**

| Greenhouse Gases | Chemical Formula | Sources |
|------------------|------------------|---------|
| Carbon Dioxide | $CO_2$ | Fossils fuel combustion |
| Methane | $CH_4$ | Fossils fuels, Waste dumps |
| Nitrous Oxide | $N_2O$ | Fertilizer |
| Tropospheric Ozone | $O_3$ | Industrial emissions, Fossils fuel |
| CFC-12 | $CCl_2F_2$ | Liquid coolants, Foams |
| HCFC-22 | $CCl_2F_2$ | Refrigerants |
| Sulphur Hexafluoride | $SF_6$ | Dielectric fluid |

- **Major Contributors of greenhouse gases:** $CO_2$ (Fossil fuels) > $CO_2$ (Deforestation) > $CH_4$ > $N_2O$
- **Major Sources of greenhouse gases:** Electricity >Transportation > Industry > Commercial & Residential

12. **Photosynthesis and its example:** The word photosynthesis consists of two words—"Photo" which means light and "synthesis" that is a complete process by which the plants make their own food. There are some alternate sources for the complete process as follow:
- Carbon dioxide
- Water
- Sunlight

We already know that plants need carbon dioxide, water and sunlight to make their food. We also know that the food they make is called glucose. In addition to glucose, plants also produce oxygen. This can be understood by following equation:

$$\text{carbon dioxide} + \text{water} \xrightarrow{\text{sunlight}} \text{glucose} + \text{oxygen}$$

The equation below is the same as the one above but it shows the chemical formula for carbon dioxide, water, glucose and oxygen.

$$\underset{\text{carbon dioxide}}{6CO_2} + \underset{\text{water}}{6H_2O} \xrightarrow{\text{light energy}} \underset{\text{glucose}}{C_6H_{12}O_6} + \underset{\text{oxygen}}{6O_2}$$

13. **Atmospheric pressure variation with different layers:**

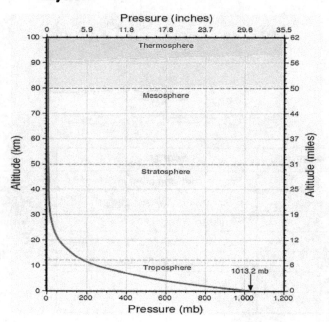

14. **Causes of Ocean Circulation:** The followings are causes of the Ocean Circulation:
- Gravity
- Wind friction
- Water density variation
- Coriolis effect
- Gyres

18. **Average depth of the Ocean:**

| Oceans | Average depth (m) | Area (Sq km) |
|---|---|---|
| Pacific | 4,028 | 165,250,000 |
| Atlantic | 3,926 | 106,400,000 |
| Indian | 3,963 | 73,560,000 |
| Southern | 5,000 | 20,330,000 |
| Arctic | 1,205 | 13,990,000 |

19. **Water Density Variation:** Density is defined as the mass of any material per unit volume. Gases always have much lower density than the condensed phases. Most materials have a lower density of the liquid than the solid but this isn't always true. Water has a higher density in the liquid state than the solid, so ice cubes float.

**Density of Liquid Water**

| Temp (°C) | Density (Kg/m³) |
|---|---|
| +100 | 958.4 |
| +80 | 971.8 |
| +60 | 983.2 |
| +40 | 992.2 |
| +30 | 995.6502 |
| +25 | 997.0479 |
| +22 | 997.7735 |
| +20 | 998.2071 |
| +15 | 999.1028 |
| +10 | 999.7028 |
| +4 | 999.9720 |
| 0 | 999.8395 |
| -10 | 998.117 |
| -20 | 993.547 |
| -30 | 983.854 |

The values below 0 °C refer to super-cooled water.

Temperature is related to the average kinetic energy of the atoms or molecules within the substance. We know that, for gases, the volume is directly proportional to temperature by the equation $PV=nRT$.

**20. Salinity of the Sea Water:** Salt in sea water form due to different chemicals, most derived from the different sources carrying rivers and others transported agencies. The main one is sodium chloride, often just called salt. Most seawater has about 35 g (7 teaspoons) of salt in every 1,000 g (about a litre) of water. Salinity can affect the properties of the seawater; it has more density than freshwater and salty water have to be colder than freshwater before it freezes.

- Variation in salinity in sea water from place to place, there are parts of the ocean where hardly any rain falls but warm dry winds cause lots of evaporation. This evaporation removes water – when water vapour rises into the atmosphere, it leaves the salt behind, so the salinity of the seawater increases. This causes the seawater to become denser.
- The Mediterranean Sea in Europe has very high salinity – 38ppt or more. It is almost closed from the main ocean, and there is more evaporation than there is rain or extra freshwater added from rivers.

- Some parts of the ocean have lots of rain. The freshwater added at the surface dilutes the seawater, reduces the salinity and so makes the seawater less dense. Seawater can also be less saline near land, where rivers add freshwater.
- The ocean around Antarctica has a low salinity of just below 34ppt, and around the Arctic it is down to 30ppt in places. Thawing icebergs add freshwater – icebergs that have broken off ice sheets formed over land do not contain salt, and the freezing of seawater into ice floes removes more salt.
- The difference between 34ppt and 36ppt salinity doesn't sound very much, but it is enough to cause a difference in density. Even slightly denser seawater sinks below less dense water. However, the effect is greater if the salty water gets cold, as temperature has a greater effect on density than salinity does. A combination of high salinity and low temperature makes seawater so dense that it sinks to the bottom of the ocean and flows across ocean basins as deep, slow currents.

**22. Classification of Plankton based on size:** The classification of the Zooplankton given by Schutt 1892.

| Types | Size | Remarks |
|---|---|---|
| Femtoplankton | 0.02 – 0.20 µm | Marine viruses |
| Picoplankton | 0.2 – 2 µm | Small eukaryotic protists, bacteria, chrysophyta |
| Nano-plankton | 2 – 20 µm | Heterotrophic nanoflagellates feeding on bacteria |
| Microplankton | 20 – 200 µm | Protozoans like ciliates |
| Mesoplankton | 0.2 – 20 mm | Metazoans (Copepod, Medusa) |
| | | Members of hydromedusae, mysids, siphonophores, scyphomedusae, ctenophores |
| Megaplankton | >200 mm | Metazoans (Jelly fish) |

**23. Plate setting with geological features:**

| Geological Features | Plate Setting |
|---|---|
| New ocean floor | Divergent plate setting |
| Explosive volcanism | Convergent plate setting |
| Mountain building | Convergent plate setting |
| Thrust faulting | Convergent plate setting |

**26. Mineral with silicate example:**

| Minerals Chains | Remarks |
|---|---|
| Muscovite-Biotite | Orthosilicate |
| Kyanite-Silimanite | Aluminosilicate |
| Chlorite | Phyllosilicate |
| Apatite | Phosphate |
| Tremolite-Actinolite | Ionosilicate |

**27. Transform and Transcurrent faults:**

| Transform fault | Transcurrent fault |
|---|---|
| In this special case of transcurrent faulting in which the transverse fault marks the boundary between two lithospheric plates that are sliding past each other. | A transverse fault in which crustal blocks move horizontally in the direction of the fault; *also known as a strike-slip fault because movement at a transcurrent fault occurs along the strike of a fault.* |

29. **Stream Power equation:** The Stream Power Equation is defined as the rate of energy dissipation (or loss) against the beds or banks of a body of water like lake or stream. It is usually in geophysics and geology concept. The concept of the stream power is solve the model of landscape, water flowing and etc.

30. **Types of mica:**

| Types of mica | Compositions |
|---|---|
| Biotite | Magnesium – iron/black mica |
| Muscovite | White mica/ potash mica |
| Phlogopite | Magnesium mica/amber mica |
| Lepidolite | Lithium mica |

32. **Terms and Its Compositions:**

**Kimberlite:** The kimberlite is a dark coloured and heavy fragmented intrusive igneous rocks which may contain diamonds in its association. The texture is porphyritc with large rounded crystal phenocrysts surrounded by fine grained groundmass. The composition of the Kimberlite is mica peridotite with olivine and also minerals are phlogopite type mica; chromium- and pyrope-rich garnet phenocrysts; chrome-bearing diopside, composition also vary with location of the kimberlite. Kimberlite, along with a similar rock called lamproite, is important for delivering diamonds to the crust through magmatic intrusions that solidify into pipelike structures.

**Ophiolite:** Ophiolite is a stratified sequence of igneous rock complex with composed of upper basalt member, middle gabbro member and lower peridotite member. Some large complexes measure more than 10 km thick, 100 km wide and 500 km long. The term "ophiolite" means "snake stone" in Greek. Basalt and gabbro are commonly altered to patchy green rocks, and peridotite is mostly changed into black, greasy serpentinite. The term comes from such serpentine appearance of these altered, metamorphosed, or sometimes highly fragmented members.

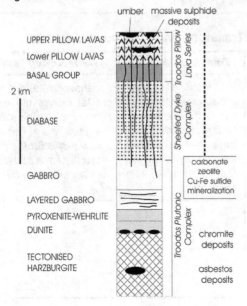

34. **Manning's Equations:** The Manning's equation uses for the open channel flow in pipes, as a hydraulic structures for the better results:
   - The channel must be straight for at least 200 feet.
   - The channel must be homogeneous in cross section, slope and roughness.
   - There should be no rapids, dips, sudden contractions / expansions, or tributary flows.
   - The flow should not backup or be submerged.

The Manning formula uses water surface slope, cross-sectional area, and wetted perimeter of a length of uniform channel to determine the flow rate.

$$Q = \frac{K\,A\,R^{2/3}\,S^{1/2}}{n}$$

Q = flow rate
A = cross-sectional area of flow
R = hydraulic radius (cross-section area divided by wetted perimeter
S = slope of the channel at the point of measurement
n = surface roughness (based upon channel material and condition)
K = constant dependent upon units

**Reynolds Number:** The Reynolds number is defined as the ratio of inertial forces to viscous forces. **It is a dimensionless number** comprised of the physical characteristics of the flow. An increasing Reynolds number indicates an increasing turbulence of flow. It is defined as:

$$\text{Re} = \frac{\rho\,vl}{\mu} = \frac{vl}{\upsilon}$$

Where :
$v$ = Velocity of the fluid
$l$ = The characteristics length, the chord width of and airfoil
$\rho$ = The density of the fluid
$\mu$ = The dynamic viscosity of the fluid
$\upsilon$ = The kinematic viscosity of the fluid

**Laminar flow:**
   - Re < 2000.
   - 'Low' velocity.
   - Fluid particles move in straight lines.
   - Layers of water flow over one another at different speeds with virtually no mixing between layers.
   - The flow velocity profile for laminar flow in circular pipes is parabolic in shape, with a maximum flow in the center of the pipe and a minimum flow at the pipe walls.
   - The average flow velocity is approximately one half of the maximum velocity.
   - Simple mathematical analysis is possible.
   - Rare in practice in water systems.

**Turbulent Flow:**

- Re > 4000.
- 'High' velocity.
- The flow is characterized by the irregular movement of particles of the fluid.
- Average motion is in the direction of the flow.
- The flow velocity profile for turbulent flow is fairly flat across the center section of a pipe and drops rapidly extremely close to the walls.
- The average flow velocity is approximately equal to the velocity at the center of the pipe.
- Mathematical analysis is very difficult.
- Most common type of flow.

**37. Partial melting:** The magma forms by the process of the partial melting of the upper mantle and crust. It means that only fraction of the available material form a melt and remainder stays solid. The partial melting materials rise because of its lower density and ascend through crust. The reason mantle and crust can form partial melts is because they are not homogeneous, with different minerals assemblage.

*Factors that Influence Partial Melting:*

- Temperature
- Composition of the materials
- Water Content (an additional component, lowers melting temperature).
- Pressure (decrease of pressure favours melt, less dense packing is allowed).

**38. Radioactive Dating:** The radioactive dating is a technique for the rocks and minerals using its isotopes. This is the natural processes may be stable or unstable. The radioactivity measure due to its parent and daughter decay elements with constant rate. The rate of decay (given the symbol $\lambda$) is the fraction of the 'parent' atoms that decay in unit time. For geological purposes, this is taken as one year. Another way of expressing this is the half-life period (given the symbol T). The half-life is the time it takes for half of the parent atoms to decay. The relationship between the two is: $T = 0.693 / \lambda$. There are many isotopes techniques used for dating; many different radioactive isotopes and techniques are used for dating. Some methods as follow:

| Methods | Applications/ uses |
|---|---|
| Carbon dating (C-14) | The carbon dating uses for Recent organic materials, usually charcoal, but also bone and antlers, which half-life is very short time. |
| Rubidium-Strontium dating (Rb-Sr) | This technique is used on ferromagnesian (iron/magnesium-containing) minerals such as micas and amphiboles or on limestone which also contain abundant strontium. This technique is less used now. |
| Potassium-Argon dating (K-Ar) | This techniques have great advantage of Mesozoic and Cenozoic rocks but not older than this date, which most rocks contain potassium, usually locked up in feldspars, clays and amphiboles. However, potassium is very mobile during metamorphism and alteration. |
| Argon-Argon dating (39Ar-40Ar) | This technique uses the same minerals and rocks as for K-Ar dating but restricts measurements to the argon isotopic system which is not so affected by metamorphic and alteration events. It is used for very old to very young rocks. |
| Samarium-Neodymium dating (Sm-Nd) | It is useful for dating very old igneous and metamorphic rocks and also meteorites and other cosmic fragments. However, there is a limited range in Sm-Nd isotopes in many igneous rocks, although metamorphic rocks that contain the mineral garnet are useful as this mineral has a large range in Sm-Nd isotopes. This technique also helps in determining the composition and evolution of the Earth's mantle and bodies in the universe. |
| Rhenium-Osmium dating (Re-Os) | The main limitation is that it only works on certain igneous rocks as most rocks have insufficient Re and Os or lack evolution of the isotopes. This technique is good for iron meteorites and the mineral molybdenite. |
| Uranium-Lead dating (U-Pb) | The great advantage is that almost all igneous and metamorphic rocks contain sufficient U and Pb for this dating. It can be used on powdered whole rocks, mineral concentrates (isotope dilution technique) or single grains (SHRIMP technique). |
| The SHRIMP dating (Sensitive High Resolution Ion MicroProbe) | Using the SHRIMP, selected areas of growth on single grains of zircon, baddeleyite, sphene, rutile and monazite can be accurately dated (to less than 100 000 years in some cases). This technique not only dates older mineral cores (what we call inherited cores), but also later magmatic and/or metamorphic overgrowths so that it unravels the entire geological history of a single mineral grain. It can even date nonradioactive minerals when they contain inclusions of zircons and monazite, as in sapphire grains. |
| Fission track dating | Fission track dating is commonly used on apatite, zircon and monazite. It helps to determine the rates of uplift (for geomorphology studies), subsidence rates (for petroleum exploration and sedimentary basin studies), and the age of volcanic eruptions (this is because fission tracks reset after the eruption). However, care is needed as some samples have fission tracks reset during bushfires, giving far too young ages. Fission track dating is mostly used on Cretaceous and Cenozoic rocks. |

### 39. Garnet and its Composition:

| Types of garnet | Compositions |
|---|---|
| Pyrope | $Mg_3Al_2(SiO_4)_3$ |
| Almandite | $Fe_3Al_2(SiO_4)_3$ |
| Spessartite | $Mn_3Al_2(SiO_4)_3$ |
| Uvarovite | $Ca_3Cr_2(SiO_4)_3$ |
| Grossularite | $Ca_3Al_2(SiO_4)_3$ |
| Andradite | $Ca_3Fe_2(SiO_4)_3$ |

### 42. Continental Drift Hypothesis:
The continental drift theory given by Alfred Wegener 1912, the continents were composed into a single proto-continent which is called Pangaea (all lands) and after time they drifted into their current distribution. According to that Pangaea was intact until the late Carboniferous period about 300 million years when it begun to break. This theory also explains the formation of the mountains.

#### *Evidences:*
- Coast line similarities
- Geological fit trends
- Fossils records
- Tectonic setting
- Glacial deposits
- Magnetic evidences

### 43. Continents with Remarks:

| Name of the Supercontinent | Remarks |
|---|---|
| Purana | Geological time scale (Era) |
| Rodinia | Supercontinent |
| Gondwana | Supercontinent |
| Pangea | Supercontinent |

### 44. Mantle Convection:
Convection is the process by heat transport mechanism, it is generally observed in different natural settings. In the mantle convection the earth's interior is heat transported. The mantle is heated due to the core and in the area is hotter and rise upward due to different compositions (silicate minerals).

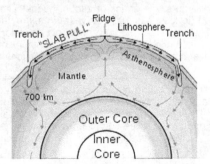

### 45. Alpha and Beta Decay:

| Radioactivity | Emission | Change in Atomic Number | Change in Mass Number | Condition of Unstable Nuclei |
|---|---|---|---|---|
| Alpha decay | $^4_2He$ | +2 | +4 | Atomic number > 83 |
| Beta decay | $^0_{-1}\beta$ | −1 | no change | n/p ratio too high |
| Positron emission | $^0_{+1}e$ | +1 | no change | n/p ratio too low |
| Gamma emission | $\gamma$-rays | no change | no change | Excited nucleus; concurrent with electron and positron emission |

### 46. Temperature variation with in the Earth:
The interior of the earth the temperature varies from earth surface to the core with respect to the depth.

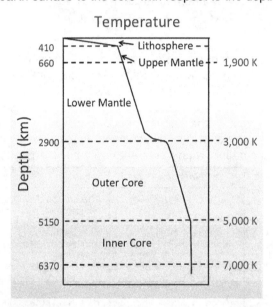

### 47. Causes of Magma Origin:
Magma forms by **partial melting** of upper mantle and crust. Partial melt means that only a fraction of the available material forms a melt, and that the remainder stays solid. The partial melt rises because of its lower density and ascends through the crust. The reason why the mantle and crust can form partial melts is because they are not homogeneous substances.

#### *Factors that Influence Partial Melting:*
- Temperature.
- Composition.
- Water Content (an additional component, lowers melting temperature).
- Pressure (decrease of pressure favors melt, less dense packing is allowed).

**Origin of Basaltic Magma :** The formation of the basaltic magma from the upper mantle due to basaltic volcanoes on oceanic and continental crusts.

**Oceanic Basalts:** The most abundant volcanic rock on Earth are **M**id-**O**cean **R**idge **B**asalts (MORBs), which cover 65% of the Earth's surface. The composition is low concentarion of sodium, potassium and aluminium from the upper mantel sources. This is formed at oceanic spreading centres, where mantle materials melts as it rises under the base of thin crust, generally MORBs flow in thousand of seawater.

**Continental Basalts:** The continental basalts is very low but similar to oceanic basalts. Basalts associated with continental rifting and intraplate volcanics have compositions that indicate a deep mantle. The just like a associated with subduction zone an upper mantle source. All continental basalts, however, must migrate through tens of kilometres of continental crust, and some assimilation of the crust may occur, producing greater variations in their compositions.

**Origin of Rhyolitic Magma:** Rhyolitic volcanoes occur in regions of continental crust or in regions of andesitic volcanism. They do not occur on oceanic crust. This implies that continental crust must be involved in the formation of rhyolitic magma.

**Origin of Andesitic Magma:** The Andesitic volcanoes are also found on both continental and oceanic on specific locations. In the Pacific region, for example, andesitic volcanoes do not occur within the Pacific Ocean basin, but are common just outside the basin. The line separating these two regions is known as the Andesite Line. This line corresponds to regions of subducting plate boundaries. As andesitic magma is close to the composition of average continental crust, it is possible to produce andesitic magma by the complete melting of continental crust. Although some andesitic magma may be produced in this way, the vast majority is produced at subduction zones, either by the wet partial melting of the oceanic (basaltic) crust or from the fractional crystallisation of basaltic melts.

48. **What is Transform Fault:** When we say that **transform faults** are conservative plate boundaries, we don't mean that they vote republican or believe in lower tax rates. A **conservative boundary** occurs when two tectonic plates come together, but neither create nor destroy the earth's crust by pulling apart or smashing together. They simply move past each other. This is what happens at transform faults, which we find at the edges between tectonic plates. Transform faults are a specialized type of **strike-slip fault**, which occur when the earth

on either side of the fault moves side to side, or 'horizontally.' On either side of a transform fault are other faults.

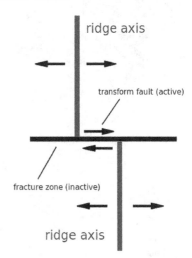

49. **Plate Tectonic Theory:** Plate tectonic theory had its beginnings in 1915 when Alfred Wegener proposed his theory of "continental drift". Wegener proposed that the continents plowed through crust of ocean basins, which would explain why the outlines of many coastlines (like South America and Africa) look like they fit together like a puzzle. Wegener was not the first to notice this puzzle-like fit of the continents (Magellan and other early explorers also noticed this on their maps), but he was one of the first to realize that the Earth's surface has changed through time, and that continents that are separated now may have been joined together at one point in the past. The plate tectonics explain the global distribution of the plate movement with geological processes; mainly it refers to the earth's lithosphere plates. This involve the formation, collision, movement and destruction of the Plates due to different phenomenon such as seismicity, volcanism, continental drift and mountain building.

### *Types of Plate Setting:*

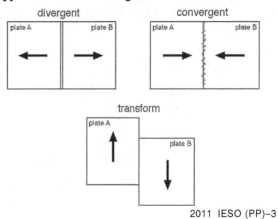

## 50. Interior of the Earth with Composition:

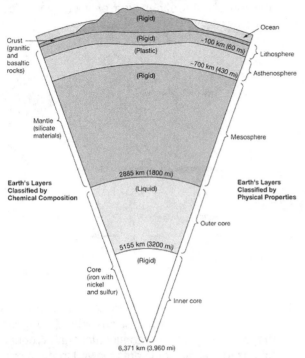

| Property | Crust | Mantle | Core |
|---|---|---|---|
| Fraction of earth | < 1% mass | 70 % | 30% |
| State | Broken | Plastic | Semi–liquid |
| Depth | 0–30 km | 30–3000 km | 3000–6371 km |
| Density | 2.7 g/cubic cm | 3.5–5.5 g/cubic cm | 10–12 g/ cubic cm |
| Chemical composition | $SiO_2$ | $(Fe,Mg)\ SiO_4$ | Fe, Ni |
| Temperature | 300–500 K | 500–3000 K | 3000–5300 K |
| Pressure | 1–1000 (Atmosphere) | $10^3$–$10^6$ (Atmosphere) | $10^6$–$10^7$ (Atmosphere) |

## 51. Polymorph of Quartz and its crystal system:

| Types of quartz | Crystal system |
|---|---|
| Alpha Quartz | Trigonal |
| Beta quartz | Hexagonal |
| Tridymite | Orthorhombic |
| Crystobalite | Tetragonal |
| Coesite | Monoclinic |

## 52. Metamorphic facies with P-T conditions:

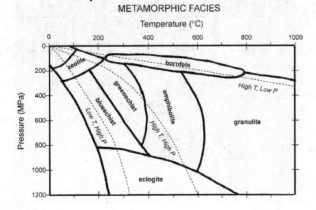

## 55. Seismic waves in earth with velocity:

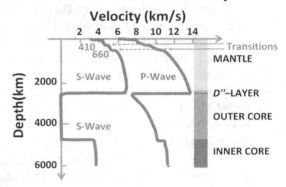

## 57. Zircon Dating : Zircon may be nature's best clock. It is ideal for use in dating, or geochronology, for many reasons.

- It is very hard, which means makes it resistant to weathering.
- It is resistant to mechanical weathering, which is the process of big rocks breaking into smaller ones, and chemical weathering, which is the erosion of rocks caused by chemical reactions.
- It is also resistant to metamorphism, which is when heat or pressure causes a rock to change its composition or structure.
- Zircon is commonly found as the primary mineral in igneous rocks. Since igneous rocks have no fossils, this makes zircon valuable in dating them. Zircon also concentrates Uranium (U) and (although less so) Thorium (Th) and excludes lead (Pb), which means it has a very high U/Pb ratio. This means that any lead found in zircon minerals was made by radioactive decay, after the formation of the mineral. The ratio of lead versus uranium in the zircon is what is used to determine the age of the rock.

## 59. Ores Minerals:

| Minerals | Ores |
|---|---|
| Uranium | Uraninite, Carnotite, Tyuyamunite, Torbernite and Autunite. |
| Iron | Magnetite, Hematite, Goethite, Limonite or Siderite. |
| Phosphate | Apatite or Fluorapatite. |
| Copper | Chalcopyrite, Chalcocite, Covellite, Bornite, Tetrahedrite, Enargite. |

## 60. Carbon dating: The radioactive dating as a method developed by the Willard Libby, C-14 is a weakly radioactive isotope of Carbon; also known as radiocarbon, it is an isotopic chronometer.

**C-14 dating** is only applicable to organic and some inorganic materials (not applicable to metals).Gas proportional counting, liquid scintillation counting, and accelerator mass spectrometry are the three principal radiocarbon dating methods.**C14 dating** labs use Oxalic Acid I and Oxalic Acid II as modern standards. Radiocarbon measurements are reported as Conventional Radiocarbon Age. Some basic principles:

- Radiocarbon, or carbon 14, is an isotope of the element carbon that is unstable and weakly radioactive. The stable isotopes are carbon 12 and carbon 13.
- Carbon 14 is continually being formed in the upper atmosphere by the effect of cosmic ray neutrons on nitrogen 14 atoms. It is rapidly oxidized in air to form carbon dioxide and enters the global carbon cycle.
- Plants and animals assimilate **carbon 14** from carbon dioxide throughout their lifetimes. When they die, they stop exchanging carbon with the biosphere and their carbon 14 content then starts to decrease at a rate determined by the law of radioactive decay.
- Radiocarbon dating is essentially a method designed to measure residual radioactivity. By knowing how much carbon 14 is left in a sample, the age of the organism when it died can be known. It must be noted though that radiocarbon dating results indicate when the organism was alive but not when a material from that organism was used.

61. **Suture Zone:** Suture zone is a collision zone, when two continents collide with each other due to plate tectonic, the sediments/ rocks between them get sheared and folded, and form mountain range. The linear range along which the plates collide and join is known as suture.

62. **Rocks and its uses:**

| Rocks | Application/uses |
|---|---|
| Sandstone | Residential and commercial uses. |
| Phosphorites | Fertilizer industry |
| Granite | Building stone |

64. **Indian Standard Time:** Indian Standard Time (IST) observed in India with UTC+5:30. India does not oberve daylight saving time (DST) or other seasonal adjustments, although DST was used briefly about 1962. The Indian standard time is calculated on the basis of 82.5 $^0$E longitude which is just west of the town of Mirzapur, near Allahabad in the state of Uttar Pradesh.

The longitude difference between Mirzapur and the United Kingdom's Royal Observatory at Greenwich translates to an exact time difference of 5 hours and 30 minutes. Local time is calculated from a clock tower at the Allahabad Observatory (25.15° N 82.5° E) though the official time-keeping devices are entrusted to the National Physical Laboratory, located in New Delhi.

66. **Earth's Gravity:** Gravity is the type of the force by which a planet or other body draws objects toward its center. The force of gravity keeps all of the planets in orbit around the Sun. Earth's gravity comes from all its mass. All its mass makes a combined gravitational pull on all the mass in your body. That's what gives you weight. On Earth, gravity gives weight to physical objects and causes the ocean tides. The force of Earth's gravity is the result of the planets mass and density – $5.97237 \times 10^{24}$ kg ($1.31668 \times 10^{25}$ lbs) and 5.514 g/cm$^3$, res-pectively. This results in Earth having a gra-vitational strength of 9.8 m/s$^2$ close to the surface (also known as 1 g), which naturally decreases the farther away one is from the surface. In addition, the force of gravity on Earth actually changes depending on where you're standing on it. The first reason is because the Earth is rotating. This means that the gravity of Earth at the equator is 9.789 m/s$^2$, while the force of gravity at the poles is 9.832 m/s$^2$. In other words, you weigh more at the poles than you do at the equator because of this centripetal force, but only slightly more.

67. **Magnetic and Geographic north:**The Earth's two geographic north and south pole and two magnetic pole. The geographic and magnetic poles are not similar to each other, not the same location. The magnetic poles are near, but not quite in the same places as, the geographic poles. The needle in a compass points towards a magnetic pole. When you are far away from a pole a compass is very helpful if you want to find your way around. The compass needle points pretty much due North (or South if you live in the Southern Hemisphere!). However, if you are near either pole, a compass becomes useless. It points towards the magnetic pole, not the true geographic pole.

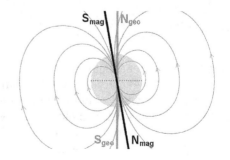

**68. Coriolis Force:** Once air has been set in motion by the pressure gradient force, it undergoes an apparent deflection from its path, as seen by an observer on the earth. This apparent deflection is called the "Coriolis force" and is a result of the earth's rotation. As air moves from high to low pressure in the northern hemisphere, it is deflected to the **right** by the Coriolis force. In the southern hemisphere, air moving from high to low pressure is deflected to the **left** by the Coriolis force.

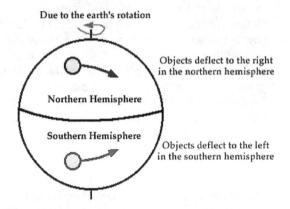

**70. Perigee and Apogee:**

**Perigee:** A satellite when follow a non-circular orbit around the earth, the path is an ellipse with center of the earth at one focus. Each satellite have variables orbital speed and altitude. The point of the lowest altitude is called perigee. The term also applies to the minimum distance in kilometers or miles between the satellite and the center of the earth. (Perigee can be measured between the satellite and the earth's surface, although this is a less precise specification because the earth is not a perfect sphere. The difference is approximately 4,000 miles or 6,400 kilometers.)

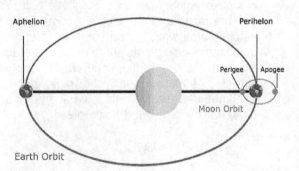

**Apogee:** When a satellite follows a non-circular orbit around the earth, the satellite's path is an ellipse with the center of the earth at one focus. Such a satellite has variable altitude and variable orbital speed. The point of highest altitude is called apogee. The term also applies to the

maximum distance in kilometers or miles between the satellite and the center of the earth. (Apogee can be measured between the satellite and the earth's surface, although this is a less precise specification because the earth is not a perfect sphere. The difference is approximately 4,000 miles or 6,400 kilometers.)

**71. Perihelion and Aphelion:**

| Terms | Remarks |
|---|---|
| Perihelion | The **perihelion** is the point in the orbit of a celestial body where it is nearest to its orbital focus, generally a star. |
| Aphelion | It is the opposite of **aphelion**, which is the point in the orbit where the celestial body is farthest from its focus. |

**74. Parsec:** This is the unit of the distance from the stars to the galaxies. The distance from the Sun and Earth is 1.30 parsec, and one parsec equal to 3.26 light years which is equal to $3.09 \times 10^{13}$ km. Distances to the closest stars can be measured through measurement of their trigonometric parallax. The parsec was defined to be the distance at which 1 AU (perpendicular to the line of sight) subtends an angle of 1 arcsecond:

1 parsec (pc) = distance d when angle is 1 arc second = $3.086 \times 10^{13}$ km = 3.26 light year

Using the Earth's **orbit** as a **baseline**, the distance (in parsecs) to a **star** can be calculated using:

$d = 1/p$

Where $p$ is measured in **arcseconds**.

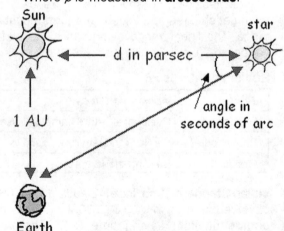

**77. Relation in Circumpolar Star:** Circumpolar is an area which is around the pole, and which circular area where stars exist in circumpolar of earth's North and South Pole.

**79. Parts of the Telescope:** There are the different parts of the telescope for the different model:

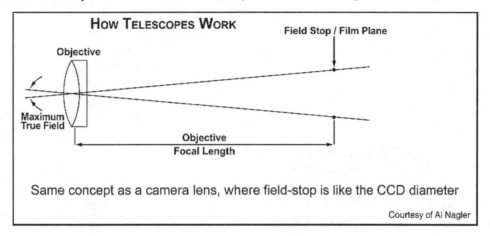

**82. Component of Atmosphere:** The nitrogen, oxygen, argon, carbon dioxide and others gases is components of the atmosphere. Other like water vapour, helium, ozone, methane, hydrogen, neon and carbon monoxide, is a minor quantity.

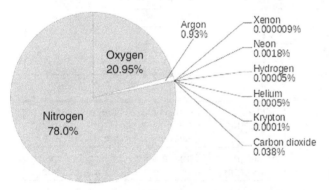

**83. What is a Tropical Cyclone:** A tropical cyclone is the generic term for a low pressure system over tropical or sub-tropical waters, with organised convection (*i.e.*, thunderstorm activity) and winds at low levels circulating either anti-clockwise (in the northern hemisphere) or clockwise (in the southern hemisphere). Although developed in the USA, the Saffir-Simpson Hurricane Wind Scale is used to rank tropical cyclone wind strength in many parts of the world.

- Category 1 : sustained wind speeds of 74 to 95 m.p.h
- Category 2 : sustained wind speeds of 96 to 110 m.p.h
- Category 3 : sustained wind speeds of 111 to 129 m.p.h
- Category 4 : sustained wind speeds of 130 to 156 m.p.h

- Category 5 : sustained wind speeds greater than 156 m.p.h

**84. Albedo:** It is defined as the amount of solar radiation which reflected from any object's surface, measure as a percentage or decimal manner. We can say that the albedo is the reflectivity of the earth's surface, dark objects have low albedo as comparison to the light objects. It is also used for the measurement of the amount of light from surface to the others terrestrial objects, like planets, comet, asteroid etc.

The albedo is the ratio of the reflected light to the incident light **A = reflected light/incident light**

**87. Causes of Ozone depletion:** The main causes of the ozone depletion due to molecules of the chlorofluorocarbon (CFC) and others like halons. They molecules originated from human used objects like refrigerants, anaesthetics, aerosols, fire-fighting equipment and the manufacture of materials such as stryrofoam. When CFCs reach the upper atmosphere they are first degraded by the very high energy of Ultra violet (UV) radiation.

**88. Aeronomy:** The Aeronomy word comes by the International Union of Geology and Geophysics (IUGG) in 1954. This is defined a branch of science which deals about the study of the Atmospherical environmental from the Earth to the Sun. In general, aeronomy is the science that studies all planetary atmospheres in which physical and chemical processes, resulting from the dissociation and ionization phenomena under the influence of the solar radiation, are important. Some example which is study in the atmospheric environmental

conditions:
- Greenhouse effect.
- Ozone depletion.
- Aerosols due to natural and men made activity.
- Propagation of the electromagnetic spectrum in the atmosphere.
- Magnetic storm.

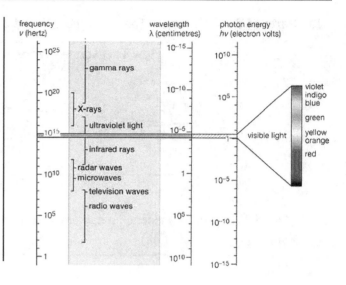

**89. Types of Solar Radiation with Wave Length:** The Solar radiation is the energy which is from the Sun. This energy causes the heat and light on the earth due to photosynthesis. There are different brand due to the ultraviolet, visible and infrared.

**90. Weight of the Atmospheric Consistent:**

| Elements | Atomic weight | Molecular weight | Percentage of mixture | Overall percentage |
|---|---|---|---|---|
| Nitrogen ($N_2$) | 14.01 | 28.02 | 78.02 | 78% |
| Oxygen ($O_2$) | 16.00 | 32.00 | 20.99 | 21% |
| Carbon Dioxide ($CO_2$) | —— | 44.00 | 0.03 | |
| Hydrogen ($H_2$) | 1.008 | 2.02 | 0.01 | |
| Argon (Ar) | 39.95 | 39.95 | 0.94 | 1 % |
| Other gases (excluding water vapour) | ——- | 0.01 | —— | |

**92. Types of remote sensing:**

| Terms | Remarks |
|---|---|
| Active remote sensing | A remote sensing which energy source is its own generation. Example: taking a photograph in night. |
| Passive remote sensing | This type of remote sensing the energy source is natural. Example: taking a photograph in a Sun's light. |

**94. Minerals Characteristics:**

| Terms | Remarks |
|---|---|
| Oxides | Cuprite, hematite, rutile, zincite |
| Carbonate | Calcite, Gaspeite, *Magnesite*, Otavite, *Rhodochrosite*, *Siderite*, *Smithsonite*, *Spherocobaltite*, *Aragonite*, *Cerussite*, *Strontianite*, *Witherite*, Rutherfordine. |
| Sulphides | Iron, copper, nickel, lead, cobalt, silver, and zinc. |

**96. Types of Scattering:**

| Terms | Remarks |
|---|---|
| Non-Scattering selective | In this type the particle size equal to the wavelength of the radiation |
| Mie – scattering | In this type of scattering the particles size larger than the wavelength of the radiation |
| Releigh scattering | The particle size smaller than the wavelength of the radiation |

**99. Deccan volcanoes:** This is one of the largest volcanic provinces in the world. The thickness of the basaltic layers is about 2000 m, and it covers large area about 200,000 square miles. This is a type of the flood basalt.

**100. P-T variation in Atmosphere:** Pressure and temperature variation in different atmospheric layers.

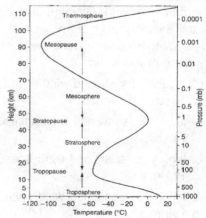

# International Earth Science Olympiad (IESO)
## Entrance Exam, 2017*

**Total Marks : 100**                    **No Negative markings**

1. Rift basin is formed by which of the following crustal processes:
   (a) Compression     (b) Extension
   (c) Both (a) & (b)  (d) Thrust

2. Slicken sides are a type of:
   (a) Foliation    (b) Bedding
   (c) Lineation    (d) Fault plane

3. Repetition of beds on a geological map may be due to:
   (a) Folding        (b) Erosion
   (c) Unconformity   (d) (a) and (b) both

4. Which of the following is associated with fluvial system:
   (a) Mud crack    (b) Ripple marks
   (c) Sand dunes   (d) Hamada

5. Which show highest strain level value among all the Himalayan thrusts:
   (a) Main Boundary Thrust
   (b) Main Central Thrust
   (c) Main Frontal Thrust
   (d) Panjal Thrust

6. Primary foliation forms:
   (a) During crystallisation of magma
   (b) After crystallisation of a magma
   (c) During folding
   (d) During jointing

7. If you are flying a plane and you look down at the landscape, you are seeing a ......... view of the earth:
   (a) Map      (b) Cross-sectional
   (c) Lateral  (d) Horizontal

8. Which of the following tectonic forces tend to push the objects in such a way so that they slide past one another?
   (a) Tensional   (b) Compressive
   (c) Shearing    (d) Extension

9. At convergent plate boundaries one would expect to find:
   (a) Folds
   (b) Faults
   (c) Folds and faults
   (d) Neither folds nor faults

10. Unfolds or arches of layered rocks are called:
    (a) Antiforms    (b) Faults
    (c) Synforms     (d) Unconformities

11. Chemical weathering of rocks will produce:
    (a) Granite    (b) Limestone
    (c) Bauxite    (d) Sandstone

12. Most appropriate example of Geomagnetic reversal is imprinted on the:
    (a) Rift basins   (b) Orogenic belts
    (c) MORs          (d) Trenches

13. In case of a structural basin, dips are:
    (a) Centripetal   (b) Centrifugal
    (c) Vertical      (d) Horizontal

14. The ability of a rock to transmit water is known as:
    (a) Infiltration   (b) Percolation
    (c) Porosity       (d) Permeability

15. Cooling joints are ................. in cross-section.
    (a) Hexagonal    (b) Circular
    (c) Rectangular  (d) Pentagonal

16. Which of the following process is not associated with diagenesis:
    (a) Albitization   (b) Burial
    (c) Cementation    (d) Recrystallization

17. Isoclinal folds have an inter limb angle of:
    (a) 80-90°   (b) 50-60°
    (c) 0-10°    (d) 0-40°

18. Continental drift theory was given by:
    (a) Harry Hess        (b) A. Wagner
    (c) Vine and Mathews  (d) D.W. Condie

19. Meandering of rivers takes place in the:
    (a) Young stage   (b) Mature stage
    (c) Old stage     (d) Both (a) and (b)

20. The planet Mercury is nearest to the sun, its revolution period is:
    (a) 66 days          (b) 77 days
    (c) 88 days          (d) 99 days

21. Arrange the following in increasing order of grain size:
    1. Sand,  2. Boulder,  3. Pebble,  4. Silt
    (a) 1, 3, 4, 2       (b) 2, 3, 1, 4
    (c) 4, 1, 3, 2       (d) 4, 1, 2, 3

22. Which of the following sedimentary structure can be used as Plaeo-current direction indicator?
    (a) Rain prints      (b) Mud cracks
    (c) Flute marks      (d) Symmetric ripples

23. A right side up sedimentary sequence will have:
    (a) Coarse grains at the top
    (b) Mixed grain size throughout the sequence
    (c) Finest at the top
    (d) Fossils at the top

24. Symmetric folds with straight limbs and sharp hinges are called:
    (a) Kink folds       (b) Chevron folds
    (c) Ptygmatic folds  (d) Recumbent folds

25. Lithospheric plates are composed of:
    (a) Crust
    (b) Mantle
    (c) Crust and Mantle both
    (d) Crust, mantle and core

26. During evaporation, ocean:
    (a) gets fresher
    (b) gets saltier
    (c) salt concentration does not change
    (d) salt concentration doubles

27. Deep ocean circulation is driven by:
    (a) Winds
    (b) Temperature and salinity
    (c) Coriolis force
    (d) Gravitational force

28. Density of mean ocean water:
    (a) is maximum at 8° C
    (b) is maximum at 4° C
    (c) is minimum at 4° C
    (d) does not show an anomalous behaviour

29. Which of the following colour penetrate deepest in the open ocean:
    (a) Red              (b) Green
    (c) Blue             (d) Yellow

30. Oxygen concentration at the intermediate ocean (between 200-500 m) is lower in the Pacific than that in the Atlantic, because

    (a) Pacific water is older than Atlantic
    (b) Pacific water is newer than Atlantic
    (c) Pacific is productive than Atlantic
    (d) Deep water of the Pacific is warm

31. Which of the followings is not a stable isotope:
    (a) 12-C             (b) 13-C
    (c) 14-C             (d) 15-N

32. Smaller phytoplankton has advantage over bigger phytoplankton in oligotrophic (less nutrient) waters, because:
    (a) Surface area of smaller phytoplankton is less than the bigger phytoplankton
    (b) Volume of smaller phytoplankton is less than the bigger phytoplankton
    (c) Surface area: volume ratio of smaller phytoplankton is less than the bigger phytoplankton
    (d) Surface area: volume ratio of smaller phytoplankton is more than the bigger phytoplankton

33. Pressure at 750 m ocean depth is:
    (a) 750 bar          (b) 750 mbar
    (c) 76 bar           (d) 75 bar

34. Oceanic Mixed Layer Depth (MLD) increases when
    (a) Rainfall occurs
    (b) Sea surface temperature increases
    (c) Wind speed over the ocean increases
    (d) Primary production increases

35. Approximately how much fraction of the surface organic matter production reaches to the sea floor?
    (a) 50%              (b) 25%
    (c) 10%              (d) 1%

36. Pycnocline refers to:
    (a) Vertical salinity gradient
    (b) Vertical temperature gradient
    (c) Vertical density gradient
    (d) Vertical nutrient gradient

37. Coriolis force:
    (a) Is applied on the objects only at the poles
    (b) Zero at the equator
    (c) Decreases with increasing speed
    (d) Zero at the poles

38. Geostrophic flow conditions occur when:
    (a) Coriolis force is zero
    (b) Pressure gradient force is zero
    (c) Pressure gradient force is balanced by Coriolis force
    (d) Pressure gradient force and Coriolis force are in imbalance

39. The major atmospheric constituents that are homogeneously distributed in the lower atmosphere are:
    (a) $N_2$ $O_2$, $N_2O$        (b) $N_2$, $O_2$, H
    (c) $N_2$, $O_2$, $CO_2$       (d) $N_2$, O, Ar

**40.** Highest mean annual temperatures is observed:
(a) Over the tropics during the summer in respective hemispheres
(b) Near the tropics over the oceans
(c) At the equator over land
(d) At the equator over oceans

**41.** Earth's biosphere is protected from cosmic ray bombardment from outer space because it has:
(a) Ozone layer in the atmosphere
(b) Greenhouse gases
(c) Thick atmosphere
(d) Magnetic field

**42.** During the glacial times, the average salinity of the ocean:
(a) Increased relative to the interglacial stage
(b) Decreased relative to the interglacial stage
(c) Did not change from that in the interglacial stage
(d) Initially decreased then increases

**43.** Inversion layer in the tropical ocean forms during:
(a) Summer when low salinity surface water is warmed.
(b) Summer when high salinity surface water is warmed.
(c) Winter when low salinity surface water is cooled.
(d) Winter when high salinity surface water is cooled.

**44.** Off Spain in the Atlantic, a distinct water mass can be observed around 1000 m depth in a T-S (temperature-salinity) diagram. This water mass belongs to th:
(a) Mediterranean water
(b) Antarctic Intermediate water
(c) Gulf Stream water
(d) Baltic low salinity water

**45.** El Nino Southern Oscillation (ENSO) is an:
(a) Ocean process
(b) Atmospheric process
(c) Ocean-atmosphere process
(d) Ocean-atmosphere-land process

**46.** Earth is a dynamic planet because:
(a) There is water on Earth
(b) There is life on Earth
(c) There is heat energy inside the Earth
(d) The Earth rotates and revolves around the Sun

**47.** Mountain building process generally takes place at
(a) Convergent plate boundary
(b) Divergent plate boundary
(c) Transform faults
(d) Interior of a plate

**48.** Earthquakes do not originate deeper than 700 km because:
(a) Material is liquid at that depth
(b) There are no rocks at that depth
(c) Material is not brittle at that depth
(d) Because those earthquakes cannot be detected at the surface

**49.** Some volcanoes as in Indonesia are explosive in nature while some as in Hawaii are non-explosive, this is because:
(a) The larger content of volatiles in the subduction zone related volcanoes makes them explosive
(b) Tropical region receives larger heat and humidity making the volcanoes present there explosive
(c) Volcanoes in Indonesia are situated within plate while that in Hawaii are at a plate boundary
(d) Hawaiian non-explosive volcanoes are submerged below water while Indonesian volcanoes are above water level.

**50.** The demarcation of crust and mantle and mantle and core inside the Earth is generally done based on:
(a) Change in temperature
(b) Change in pressure
(c) Change in velocities of seismic waves
(d) Presence of exotic minerals

**51.** Consider the following statements about the Earth's magnetic field:
I. It magnetizes the rocks when they are forming and rocks can preserve remnant magnetization for millions of years.
II. It reverses periodically and such polarity reversals of Earth's magnetic field have occurred several times during Earth's history.
III. It is much like a dipole magnetic field.
IV. It is due to dense and permanently magnetised material at the centre.
Which of the above is/are **NOT true**?
(a) III only          (b) I and II
(c) III and IV        (d) IV only

**52.** It is observed in the field that a limestone is intruded by a dolerite dyke. A volcanic flow overlies the limestone. Which of the following statements is more likely to be true?
(a) Limestone is chemically precipitated simultaneous to an underwater volcanic eruption that emplaced dolerite dyke and volcanic flow
(b) Limestone is the oldest rock of the three while the volcanic flow is the youngest

(c) Dolerite dyke and volcanic flow occurred simultaneously prior to the limestone deposition

(d) Dolerite dyke is the youngest rock while the volcanic flow is the oldest

53. Elevation of Earth's crust is bimodal on an average-continents being above sea-level and oceanic crust is below sea level. This is because:
(a) There are mountains on the continents, while there are no such high elevation regions on oceans
(b) Oceanic crust is denser while the continental crust is lighter
(c) Oceanic crust has depressions caused by meteorite impacts during the early history of the Earth
(d) Oceans are formed by melting of continental glacial

54. The mantle convection is caused by:
(a) Plate movements
(b) Rotation of the Earth
(c) Temperature and density difference
(d) Upwelling of pressurized liquid mantle

55. Magmatism takes place at divergent plate boundary because of:
(a) Decompression of mantle below the diverging plates
(b) Percolation of sea-water into the mantle
(c) Frictional heat during divergence of plates
(d) Generation of mantle plume

56. Which of the following layers inside the Earth is dominantly liquid?
(a) Upper mantle       (b) Lower mantle
(c) Outer core         (d) Inner core

57. The density of materials inside the Earth:
(a) Increases with increase in depth
(b) Decreases with increase in depth
(c) Is maximum in mantle
(d) Remains unchanged with depth

58. A given mass weighs slightly different at pole and equator of the Earth. This is because of:
(a) The combined effect of Earth's oblate shape and its rotation, gravity is slightly more at equator than at pole resulting in higher weight at equator
(b) The combined effect of Earth's oblate shape and its rotation, gravity is slightly less at equator than at pole resulting in lower weight at equator
(c) The presence of polar ice of lower density, gravity is less at pole resulting in lower weight at poles

(d) The convergence of magnetic lines at poles, the weight is measured more at pole

59. Which of the following minerals is not a silicate?
(a) Quartz          (b) Corundum
(c) Garnet          (d) Feldspar

60. Cations such as $Mg^{2+}$ and $Fe^{2+}$ replace each other in certain minerals like olivine and pyroxene. It is possible because of:
(a) Change in chemical composition in the surrounding environment of these minerals
(b) Similar charge and size of these cations
(c) These minerals lack a fixed crystal structure
(d) Larger abundance of these elements in these minerals

61. Two different primary igneous rocks undergo metamorphism at same pressure and temperature. Both these rocks, subsequent to metamorphism would have:
(a) Identical mineral assemblage reflecting the metamorphic facies characteristic to that pressure and temperature
(b) Different mineral assemblage because of difference in their bulk chemical composition
(c) No change in their mineral assemblage but their bulk chemical composition would have changed
(d) Identical bulk composition but different mineral assemblage

62. Which of the following minerals is most suited for U-Pb dating?
(a) Quartz          (b) Feldspar
(c) Zircon          (d) Topaz

63. Which of the following minerals is a major constituent of marble?
(a) Serpentine      (b) Quartz
(c) Feldspar        (d) Calcite

64. Which of the following is an aluminium ore?
(a) Bauxite         (b) Hematite
(c) Ilmenite        (d) Rutile

65. Which of the following mineral is a major constituent of china clay?
(a) Leucite         (b) Kaolinite
(c) Anorthite       (d) Olivine

66. Seasons on Earth occur because of:
(a) Disproportionate distribution of land mass in northern and southern hemispheres
(b) Tilt of the Earth's axis of rotation
(c) Changes in the specific heat of water and land mass and the wind circulation that is a consequence of the changes in the temperature

(d) Changes in the circulation and transport of greenhouse gases

67. Which is the third most abundant gas in the atmosphere?
(a) Nitrogen
(b) Water vapour
(c) Argon
(d) Carbon dioxide

68. How many total number of air molecules are there in one cubic meter of air?
(a) $2.6 \times 10^{19}$
(b) $2.6 \times 10^{21}$
(c) $2.6 \times 10^{23}$
(d) $2.6 \times 10^{25}$

69. What is the average scale height of air:
(a) 8 cm
(b) 8 m
(c) 8 km
(d) 80 km

70. Which is the most important natural greenhouse gas in the atmosphere?
(a) Oxygen
(b) Water vapour
(c) Carbon dioxide
(d) Ozone

71. Scale height is:
(a) The height at which the density of the atmosphere decreases by 1/2
(b) The height at which the height of the atmosphere decreases by 1/e
(c) The height at which the pressure of the atmosphere decreases by 1/e
(d) The height at which the density of the atmosphere decreases by 1/e

72. When the scale height of a minor constituent (e.g., ozone, etc.) is equal to the atmospheric scale height then:
(a) The constituent is not well mixed and its mixing ratio is constant with altitude
(b) The constituent is well mixed and its mixing ratio is constant with altitude
(c) The constituent is not well mixed and its mixing ratio varies with altitude
(d) The constituent is well mixed and its mixing ratio varies with altitude

73. The residence time of aerosols increases as a function of altitude. This statement:
(a) Is true for all types of aerosols
(b) Is false for all types of aerosols
(c) Is true for sulphate aerosols only
(d) Is false for carbonaceous aerosols only

74. The heterosphere is so called because of:
(a) Varying chemical composition of atmospheric gases in that region
(b) Constant chemical composition of atmospheric gases in that region
(c) Varying chemical composition of only atmospheric trace gases in that region

(d) Constant chemical composition of only atmospheric trace gases in that region

75. Almost all of the Earth's atmosphere lies in a layer thinner than:
(a) 10 per cent of the radius of the Earth
(b) 5 per cent of the radius of the Earth
(c) 1 per cent of the radius of the Earth
(d) 25 per cent of the radius of the Earth

76. Ozone in the troposphere is called as:
(a) Good ozone as it absorbs harmful ultraviolet radiation
(b) Bad ozone as it causes harmful effects in the atmosphere
(c) Good ozone as it reduces pollution
(d) Good ozone as it reduces global warming

77. Geopotential height is:
(a) Nearly identical to height in the heterosphere
(b) Nearly identical to height in the homosphere
(c) Nearly identical to height in homosphere and heterosphere
(d) Nearly identical to height in the tropics

78. The peak wavelength at which Sun radiates emission is:
(a) 0.48 μm
(b) 0.68 μm
(c) 10.0 μm
(d) 1.0 μm

79. Mercury in a barometer should raise to what height to balance an atmospheric pressure of 1000 mbar (density of mercury is 13558 km m⁻³)?
(a) 0.71 m
(b) 0.95 m
(c) 8 km
(d) 10 m

80. 50% of the atmosphere lies below an altitude of:
(a) 100 km
(b) 48 km
(c) 18 km
(d) 5.5 km

81. The density of dry air at 300K and 1010 mbar is: (R', the gas constant, is 2.8704 m³ kg⁻¹ K⁻¹)
(a) 1.5 kg m⁻³
(b) 1.0 kg m⁻³
(c) 1.2 kg m⁻³
(d) 100 kg m⁻³

82. The partial pressure of water vapour is 10 mbar and the temperature is 20 °C (saturated vapour pressure of water is 25 mbar), what is the relative humidity?
(a) 100%
(b) 50%
(c) 40%
(d) 20%

83. If the observed temperature cools 15K between the ground and 3 km above the ground, the environmental lapse rate will be:
(a) less than the dry adiabatic lapse rate
(b) higher than dry adiabatic lapse rate
(c) same as the dry adiabatic lapse rate
(d) negative of the dry adiabatic lapse rate

**84.** The energy contained in the violet spectrum is ........ the energy contained in the green spectrum.
(a) smaller than (b) larger than
(c) equal to (d) 100 times more

**85.** Temperature in the stratosphere is higher:
(a) air at stratospheric altitudes is more dense
(b) because of ozone absorption
(c) because of water vapour absorption
(d) because of more solar radiation

**86.** The energy for sun comes from:
(a) Nuclear fission
(b) Nuclear fusion
(c) chemical reactions
(d) Burning

**87.** Age of the solar system is about:
(a) 4.5 million years
(b) 4.5 billion years
(c) 450 million years
(d) 450 thousand years

**88.** Stars have different colours because:
(a) They have different temperature
(b) They are at different distances
(c) The interstellar medium changes their colour
(d) They belong to different regions of the galaxy

**89.** Our galaxy is called:
(a) Andromeda Galaxy
(b) M31 Galaxy
(c) W25 Galaxy
(d) Milky Way galaxy

**90.** How many times bigger than the Earth is the Sun?
(a) 100,000 times (b) 10,000 times
(c) 300,000 times (d) 500,000 times

**91.** The nearest star to earth is:
(a) Series (b) Polaris
(c) Proxima Centauri (d) Orion

**92.** The biggest planet in the solar system is:
(a) Jupiter (b) Uranus
(c) Saturn (d) Earth

**93.** One light year is about:
(a) $10^{16}$ km (b) $10^{13}$ km
(c) $10^{10}$ km (d) $10^7$ km

**94.** At its closest, which is the planet closest to Earth?
(a) Venus (b) Mercury
(c) Mars (d) Jupiter

**95.** In size, which planet is most similar to Earth?
(a) Mars (b) Pluto
(c) Venus (d) Mercury

**96.** Amongst the planets, which planet has the strongest magnetic field?
(a) Earth (b) Mercury
(c) Mars (d) Jupiter

**97.** The planet with lowest density in the solar system is:
(a) Jupiter (b) Saturn
(c) Uranus (d) Pluto

**98.** The Main sequence on HR diagram classifies stars by:
(a) Their distance from us
(b) Their surface temperature
(c) Their mass
(d) Their location within Milky Way galaxy

**99.** The colour of a giant star away from the main sequence will typically be:
(a) Red (b) Blue
(c) White (d) Violet

**100.** At the top of Earth's atmosphere, Sunlight is most intense in terms of photons/m² in:
(a) Infrared range
(b) X-ray range
(c) Ultraviolet range
(d) Optical range

## ANSWERS

| 1 | 2 | 3 | 4 | 5 | 6 | 7 | 8 | 9 | 10 |
|---|---|---|---|---|---|---|---|---|---|
| (b) | (c) | (d) | (b) | (b) | (a) | (a) | (c) | (c) | (a) |
| **11** | **12** | **13** | **14** | **15** | **16** | **17** | **18** | **19** | **20** |
| (c) | (c) | (a) | (d) | (a) | (b) | (c) | (b) | (b) | (c) |
| **21** | **22** | **23** | **24** | **25** | **26** | **27** | **28** | **29** | **30** |
| (c) | (c) | (c) | (b) | (c) | (b) | (b) | (d) | (c) | (c) |
| **31** | **32** | **33** | **34** | **35** | **36** | **37** | **38** | **39** | **40** |
| (c) | (d) | (c) | (c) | (d) | (c) | (b) | (c) | (d) | (a) |
| **41** | **42** | **43** | **44** | **45** | **46** | **47** | **48** | **49** | **50** |
| (d) | (a) | (c) | (a) | (c) | (c) | (a) | (c) | (a) | (c) |

| 51 | 52 | 53 | 54 | 55 | 56 | 57 | 58 | 59 | 60 |
|---|---|---|---|---|---|---|---|---|---|
| (d) | (b) | (b) | (c) | (a) | (c) | (a) | (b) | (b) | (b) |
| 61 | 62 | 63 | 64 | 65 | 66 | 67 | 68 | 69 | 70 |
| (b) | (c) | (d) | (a) | (b) | (b) | (c) | (d) | (c) | (b) |
| 71 | 72 | 73 | 74 | 75 | 76 | 77 | 78 | 79 | 80 |
| (b) | (b) | (a) | (a) | (c) | (b) | (b) | (a) | (a) | (d) |
| 81 | 82 | 83 | 84 | 85 | 86 | 87 | 88 | 89 | 90 |
| (c) | (c) | (a) | (a) | (b) | (b) | (b) | (a) | (d) | (c) |
| 91 | 92 | 93 | 94 | 95 | 96 | 97 | 98 | 99 | 100 |
| (c) | (a) | (b) | (a) | (c) | (d) | (b) | (b) | (a) | (d) |

# HINTS AND SOLUTIONS

1. **Plate setting with features:**

| Processes | Features develop |
|---|---|
| Compression/convergent plate setting | Foreland basin |
| Extension / divergent plate setting | Rift basin |
| Transform plate setting | Pull – apart basin |

2. **Features with example:**

| Features | Example |
|---|---|
| Foliation | Flaky and platy minerals |
| Bedding | Layering of the rock strata |
| Lineation | Slicken sides |
| Fault plane | Gouge |

3. **Structural Terminology:**

| Structures | Remarks on the geological map |
|---|---|
| Folding | Repetition of the beds on the geological map |
| Erosion | Beds are not in correct sequence in normal condition on the geological map |
| Unconformity | The sequence of the bed is not a homogeneous |

4. **Sedimentary structures:**

| Features | Characteristics |
|---|---|
| Mud cracks | Naturally occurring mud cracks form in sediment that was once saturated with water. |
| Ripple marks | Formed by the action of the current in shallow water, and this structure also formed by the wind. |
| Sand dunes | The mounds deposited by the wind is called the sand dunes. |
| Hammada | The hard material left and the loose particles moved by the action of the wind deflation is called hammada. |

5. **Stress and Strain:** In respect of the plate tectonics rocks must be stress and due to stress it may be deformed some or more portions, it may due to weight of the overlaying rocks. This may be as follow:

- In regions close to where plates are converging stress is typically compressive—the rocks are being squeezed.
- Where plates are diverging the stress is extensive, rocks are being pulled apart.
- At transform plate boundaries, where plates are moving side by side there is sideways or **shear stress**—meaning that there are forces in opposite directions parallel to a plane.
- Rocks have highly varying strain responses to stress because of their different compositions and physical properties, and because temperature is a big factor and rock temperatures within the crust can vary greatly.

*Classification of the Himalayan Mountain*

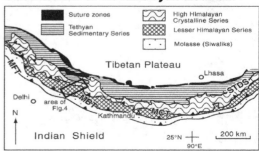

## 6. Processes of magma:

| Process | Features develop |
|---|---|
| During crystallization of the magma | Primary foliation |
| After crystallization of the magma | Secondary foliation |
| During folding | Secondary foliation |
| During jointing | Secondary foliation |

## 7. Maps and its Cross section:

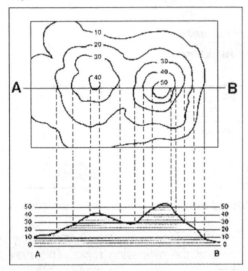

**Geological Cross Section:** A geological cross-section is a graphic representation of the intersection of the geological bodies in the subsurface with a vertical plane of a certain orientation. It is a section of the terrain where the different types of rocks, their constitution and internal structure and the geometric relationship between them are represented.

## 8. Processes of Plate Movements:

| Processes | Movements direction | Example plate setting |
|---|---|---|
| Tensional | Plate movement away from each other | Divergent plate setting |
| Compressive | Plate movement towards each other | Convergent plate setting |
| Shearing | Plate slide past one another | Strike–slip plate setting |

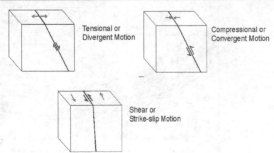

## 9. Types of plate movements:

| Processes | Features develop |
|---|---|
| Convergent plate movement | Island Arc, Benioff zone |
| Divergent plate movement | Mid Oceanic Ridge, Sea mount |
| Transform plate movement | Strike – slip faults |

**Plate setting:** It may be divergent, convergent or transform type.

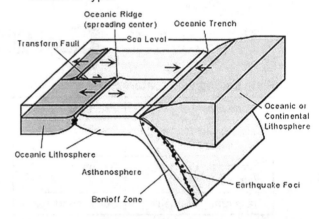

## 10. Structural features and its characteristics:

| Features | Character |
|---|---|
| Antiforms | Upfolds or arches of layered rocks is called antiforms. |
| Faults | The fractures of the rocks masses is observable is called fault. |
| Synforms | A strata show upwardly concave called synforms. |
| Unconformities | The plane of disconformity with time, surface, strata is called unconformities. |

**Types of Unconformities:** The mainly unconformity are the angular, paraconformity, disconformity and nonconformity.

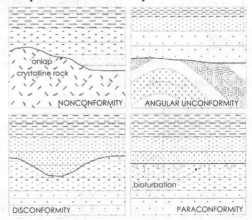

**11. Types of chemical weathering:** The weathering due to chemical reaction as follow :

| Processes | Reactions |
|-----------|-----------|
| Hydration | $2Fe_2O_3 + 3H_2O = 2Fe_2O_2.H_2O$ |
| Dissolution | $NaCl + H_2O = NaCl \ H_2O$ |
| Oxidation | $2Fe_2SiO_4 + 4H_2O + O_2 = 2Fe_2O_3 + 2H_4SiO_4$ |
| Reduction | $2Fe_2O_3 + O_2 = 4FeO$ |

**12. Geomagnetic Reversal:**

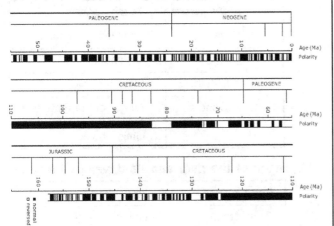

**Oceanic Ridge:** This feature developed due to the upwelling of the mantle to form new oceanic lithosphere, resulting in basaltic magmas which intrude and erupt at the oceanic ridge to create new oceanic lithosphere and crust. As new oceanic lithosphere is created, it is pushed aside in opposite directions. Thus, the age of the oceanic crust becomes progressively older in both directions away from the ridge.

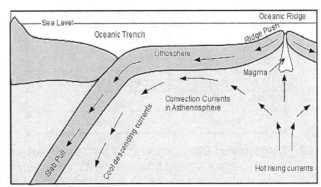

**13. Dip direction with example:**

| Dips Direction | Structural Example |
|----------------|-------------------|
| Centripetal | Basin |
| Centrifugal | Dome |
| Vertical | Vertical isoclinal folds |
| Horizontal | Recumbent fold |

**14. Hydrological Processes:**

| Processes | Characteristics |
|-----------|-----------------|
| Infiltration | Infiltration is the process by which water on the ground surface enters the soil. |
| Percolation | It is the process by which a liquid slowly passing through a filter. |
| Porosity | The volume of the void space to the total volume of the rocks. |
| Permeability | The ability of a rock to transmit water is called permeability. |

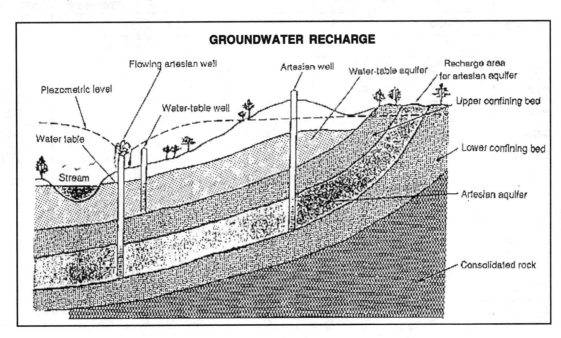

**GROUNDWATER RECHARGE**

## 15. Type of joints with example:

| Types of joints | Example |
|---|---|
| Columnar joints | Basalts |
| Release joints | Sedimentary bedding |
| Extension joints | Gneiss |
| Cross joints | Sandstone |

## 16. Diagenesis:

Diagenesis is the process by which sediments are lithified into sedimentary rocks and represents the sum of physical and chemical changes that occur during burial. Diagenesis involves physical compaction of components due to pressure increase on burial, the precipitation of mineral cements from pore fluids and phase transformations of mineral components.

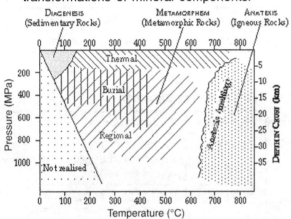

## 17. Types of fold and its limb angle:

| Interlimb angle | Types of folds |
|---|---|
| 0 – 10 | Isoclinal fold |
| 10 – 30 | Tight fold |
| 30 – 70 | Closed fold |
| 70 – 120 | Open fold |

## 18. Theory's with Its Concept:

| Name of the person | Theory explain |
|---|---|
| Harry Hess | Sea floor spreading |
| A. Wagner | Continental drift |
| Vine and Mathew | Plate tectonics |
| Kent C. Condie | Author of the Plate tectonic and crustal evaluation book |

## 19. Stage of the river and its developed feature:

| River stages | Features develop |
|---|---|
| Young stage | V – shaped valley |
| Mature stage | Meanders, ox-bow lakes, alluvial fans |
| Old stage | Flood plain, delta |

## 20. Planets and Its Characteristics:

| Planets | Diameter (Km) | Mass (Earth = 1) | Density (gm/cm³) (Water = 1) | Length of the day (Earth hours) | Period of one revolution around Sun (Earth years) | Average distance from Sun (millions of km) |
|---|---|---|---|---|---|---|
| Mercury | 4880 | 0.0558 | 5.44 | 1416 | 0.24 | 58 |
| Venus | 12104 | 0.815 | 5.20 | 5832 | 0.62 | 108 |
| Earth | 12756 | 1.0 | 5.52 | 24 | 1.00 | 150 |
| Mars | 6787 | 0.108 | 3.93 | 24.6 | 1.88 | 228 |
| Jupiter | 142800 | 317.8 | 1.30 | 9.8 | 11.86 | 778 |
| Saturn | 120000 | 95.2 | 0.69 | 10.2 | 29.50 | 1427 |
| Uranus | 51800 | 14.4 | 1.28 | 17.2 | 84.00 | 2870 |
| Neptune | 49500 | 17.2 | 1.64 | 16.1 | 164.90 | 4497 |

## 21. Grain Size Classification:

| Grain size (mm) | Name |
|---|---|
| > 256 | Boulder |
| 64 – 256 | Cobble |
| 4 – 64 | Pebble |
| 2 – 4 | Granule |
| 2 – 1/16 | Sand |
| 1/16 – 1/256 | Silt |
| < 1/256 | Clay |

## 22. Application of the sedimentary structures:

| Sedimentary structures | Application |
|---|---|
| Rain prints | Top and bottom |
| Mud cracks | Top and bottom |
| Flute marks | Paleocurrent direction |
| Symmetric ripple | Also called wave ripple formed to and fro motion of the waves and have symmetrical profile. |

### Mud Cracks:

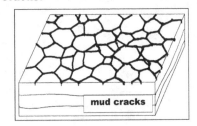

## 23. Grain size with stratigraphic column:

| Grain sequence | Remarks |
|---|---|
| Coarse grains at the top | Regressive sequence of stratigraphic column |
| Finest at the top | Transgressive sequence of stratigraphic column |

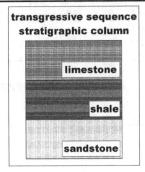

## 25. Interior of the Earth:

| Interior of the earth | Thickness (Km) |
|---|---|
| Sial | 10 |
| Sima | 20 |
| Mantle | 2900 |
| Core | 6371 |

## 24. Types of the Fold:

| Types of folds | Characteristics |
|---|---|
| Kink folds | Narrow folds of chevron fold. |
| Chevron folds | Angular fold which have straight limbs and sharp hinge. |
| Ptygmatic folds | Large amplitude to wavelength ratio. Ptygmatic folds generally represent conditions where the folded material is of a much greater viscosity than the surrounding medium. |
| Recumbent folds | Axial plane is about horizontal. |

### Kink Band and Kink Axis:

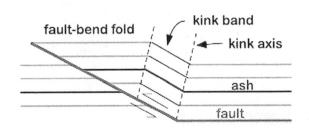

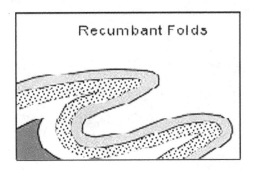

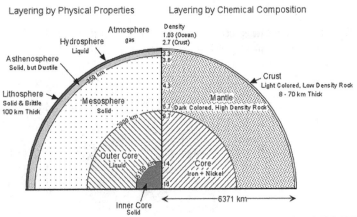

## 26. Ocean Evaporation and Precipitation:

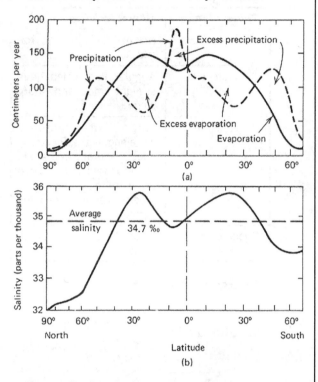

(a)

(b)

**Water Cycle:** Different component of the water cycle. It is the transformation of the evaporation, infiltration and etc.

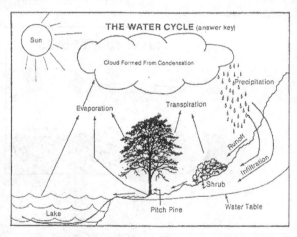

## 27. Ocean Circulation: The oceanic circulation is the phenomena which flow one direction to another.

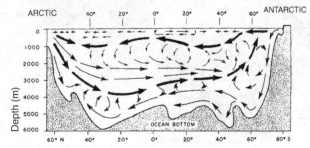

## 28. Temperature, Salinity and Pressure of the Ocean:

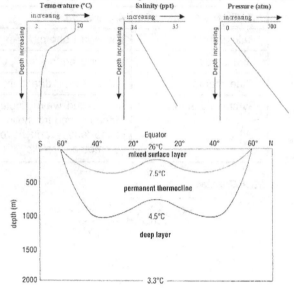

A generalized and schematic cross-section, showing the main thermal layers of the oceans and their average temperatures at the Equator.

## 29. Colour and Its wavelength and frequencies:

| Colours | Wavelength (Nanometres) | Frequency (Tera – Hertz) |
|---------|------------------------|--------------------------|
| Red | 685 – 605 | 435 – 495 |
| Orange | 605 – 585 | 495 – 515 |
| Yellow | 585 – 560 | 515 – 535 |
| Green | 560 – 475 | 535 – 630 |
| Blue | 475 – 455 | 630 – 660 |
| Indigo | 455 – 440 | 660 – 680 |
| Violet | 440 – 405 | 680 – 740 |

## 30. Oxygen concentration in Pacific Ocean:

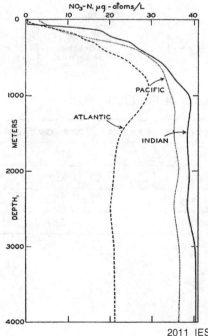

## 31. Different isotopes and its status:

| Isotopes | Remarks |
|----------|---------|
| C-12 | Stable |
| C-13 | Stable |
| C-14 | Unstable |
| N-15 | Stable |

## Isotopes of Carbon:

| Isotopes | Number of Protons | Number of Electrons | Number of Neutrons |
|----------|-------------------|---------------------|--------------------|
| C-11 | 6 | 6 | 5 |
| C-12 | 6 | 6 | 6 |
| C-13 | 6 | 6 | 7 |
| C-14 | 6 | 6 | 8 |

## 32. Organism Distribution in Ocean:

| Species | Earth | | | Ocean | | |
|---------|-----------|-----------|-----------|-----------|-----------|-----------|
| | Catalogued | Predicted | ±SE | Catalogued | Predicted | ±SE |
| **Eukaryotes** | | | | | | |
| Animalia | 953,434 | 7,770,000 | 958,000 | 171,082 | 2,150,000 | 145,000 |
| Chromista | 13,033 | 27,500 | 30,500 | 4,859 | 7,400 | 9,640 |
| Fungi | 43,271 | 611,000 | 297,000 | 1,097 | 5,320 | 11,100 |
| Plantae | 215,644 | 298,000 | 8,200 | 8,600 | 16,600 | 9,130 |
| Protozoa | 8,118 | 36,400 | 6,690 | 8,118 | 36,400 | 6,690 |
| Total | 1,233,500 | 8,740,000 | 1,300,000 | 193,756 | 2,210,000 | 182,000 |
| **Prokaryotes** | | | | | | |
| Archaea | 502 | 455 | 160 | 1 | 1 | 0 |
| Bacteria | 10,358 | 9,680 | 3,470 | 652 | 1,320 | 436 |
| Total | 10,860 | 10,100 | 3,630 | 653 | 1,320 | 436 |
| **Grand Total** | **1,244,360** | **8,750,000** | **1,300,000** | **194,409** | **2,210,000** | **182,000** |

Predictions for prokaryotes represent a lower bound because they do not consider undescribed higher taxa. For protozoa, the ocean database was substantially more complete than the database for the entire Earth so we only used the former to estimate the total number of species in this taxon. All predictions were rounded to three significant digits.

## 34. Oceanic Mixed Layer Depth (MLD):

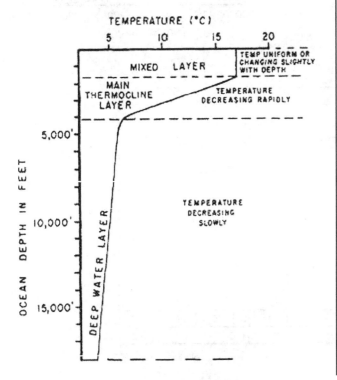

## 35. Distribution of dissolved matter:

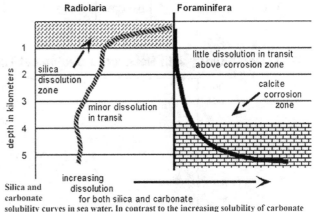

Silica and carbonate solubility curves in sea water. In contrast to the increasing solubility of carbonate with temperature decrease and pressure increase (increasing depth) silica solubility decreases with depth.

## 36. Terminology:

| Statements | Terms |
|------------|-------|
| Vertical salinity gradient | Halocline |
| Vertical temperature gradient | Thermocline |
| Vertical density gradient | Pycnocline |

### 37. Coriolis Force Location:

| Coriolis force | Location |
|---|---|
| Maximum | Pole |
| Minimum | Equator |

### 38. Geostrophic flow:
When isobars are straight, parallel lines, and the only two forces acting on a parcel are the Pressure Gradient Force (PGF) and the Coriolis Force (CF), then the wind is called the geostrophic wind.

- PGF and CF are equal in strength (magnitude) and opposite in direction.

- The geostrophic wind is always parallel to the isobars (height lines on an isobaric chart).

### 39. Constituents in atmosphere

| Constituents in atmosphere | Percentage by volume | Concentration in Parts Per Million (PPM) |
|---|---|---|
| Nitrogen ($N_2$) | 78.084 | 780840.0 |
| Oxygen ($O_2$) | 20.946 | 209460.0 |
| Argon (Ar) | 0.934 | 9340.0 |
| Carbon dioxide ($CO_2$) | 0.036 | 360.0 |
| Neon (Ne) | 0.00182 | 18.2 |
| Helium (He) | 0.000524 | 5.24 |
| Methane ($CH_4$) | 0.00015 | 1.5 |
| Krypton (Kr) | 0.000114 | 1.14 |
| Hydrogen ($H_2$) | 0.00005 | 0.5 |

### 40. Average Global Temperature : (1880–2013)

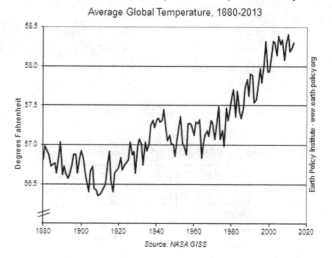

### 41. Ozone Layer:

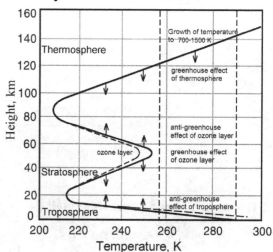

### 42. Ocean Salinity with Respect to Geological Time:

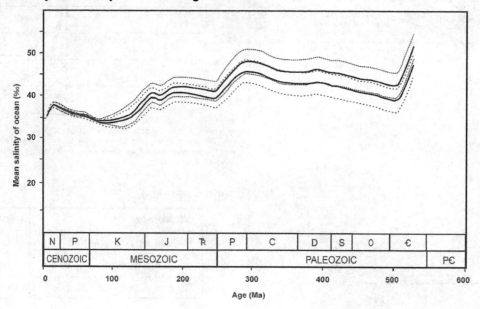

**45. El Nino Southern Osci-llation (ENSO):** The El Niño-Southern Oscillation (ENSO) is a naturally occurring phenomenon that involves fluctuating ocean temperatures in the equatorial Pacific. The warmer waters essentially slosh, or oscillate, back and forth across the Pacific, much like water in a bath tub. For North America and much of the globe, the phenomenon is known as a dominant force causing variations in regional climate patterns.

**46. Interior of Earth with composition:**

| Layer | Thickness (Km) | Density (g/cm³) | | Composition |
|---|---|---|---|---|
| | | **Top** | **Bottom** | |
| **Crust** | 30 | 2.2 | — | Silicic rocks |
| | | — | 2.9 | Andesite, basalt |
| **Upper mantle** | 720 | 3.4 | — | Peridotite, eclogite, olivine |
| | | — | 4.4 | Perovskite, oxides |
| **Lower mantle** | 2171 | 4.4 | — | Magnesium |
| | | — | 5.6 | Oxides |
| **Outer core** | 2259 | 9.9 | — | Iron + oxygen, sulphur |
| | | — | 12.2 | Nickel alloy |
| **Inner core** | 1221 | 12.8 | — | Iron + oxygen, sulphur |
| | | — | 13.1 | Nickel alloy |
| **Total thickness** | **6401** | | | |

**47. Plate boundary and related features:**

| Plate boundary | Features |
|---|---|
| Convergent plate boundary | Trench, Back – arc basin, Mountain building |
| Divergent plate boundary | MOR, Volcanic island |
| Transform fault | San Andreas fault |

**48. Depth classification of the earthquake:**

| Earthquakes types | Depth (miles) |
|---|---|
| Shallow focus | 30 |
| Intermediate focus | 30 – 150 |
| Deep focus | 150 – 450 |

**49. Classification of the volcanoes:**

| Types of volcanoes | Characteristics |
|---|---|
| Hawaiian type | Silent effusion |
| Strombolian type | Little explosion |
| Vulcanian type | Long-time interval of viscous lava |
| Vesuvian | Highly explosive volcanic activity |
| Plinian type | Most violent activity |

**50. Pressure, Temperature and density variation in earth's interior:**

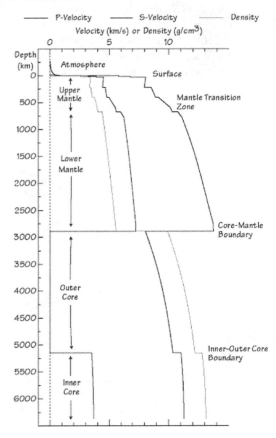

**Temperature variation in earth's interior:**

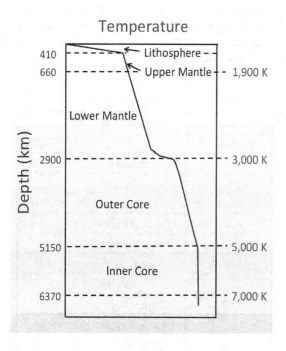

**51. Earth's Magnetic Field Direction:** Earth's magnetic field, also known as the geomagnetic field, is the magnetic field that extends from the Earth's interior out into space, where it meets the solar wind, a stream of charged particles emanating from the Sun.

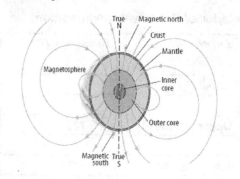

| Types of Magnetization | Example |
|---|---|
| Magnetic | Hematite |
| Ferromagnetic | Magnetite |
| Di – magnetic | Quartz |

**54. Mantle Convection and Its Causes:** The heat- transport the planet earth core and surface is accomplished analogous to our hot water convection. The mantle is heated from below (the core), and in areas that are hotter it rises upwards (due to buoyant), whereas in areas that are cooler it sink down. This results in convection cells in the mantle, and produces horizontal motion of mantle rock (a mixture of silicate minerals) that at any given time would appear solid to us. Yet, when the forces of buoyancy are applied over millions of years, this seemingly solid material does move after all. It behaves like an extremely viscous fluid and creeps along slowly. Also, in the uppermost portions of the mantle, the pressure – temperature conditions are such that a small fraction (a few per cent) of the material is probably in the molten state. Thus, we may have crystals mixed with melt (a very hot slurpee), and that kind of material will flow more easily.

## Convection Currents in the Mantle

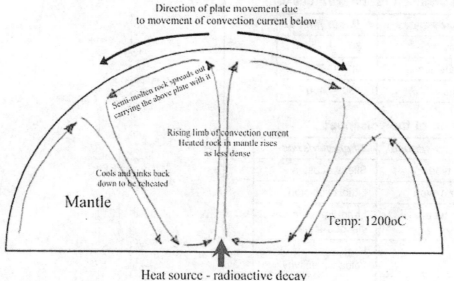

**55. Divergent Plate Boundary:** A divergent boundary occurs when two tectonic plates move away from each other. Along these boundaries, lava spews from long fissures and geysers spurt superheated water. Frequent earthquakes strike along the rift. Beneath the rift, magma—molten rock—rises from the mantle. It oozes up into the gap and hardens into solid rock, forming new crust on the torn edges of the plates. Magma from the mantle solidifies into basalt, a dark, dense rock that underlies the ocean floor. Thus at divergent boundaries, oceanic crust, made of basalt, is created.

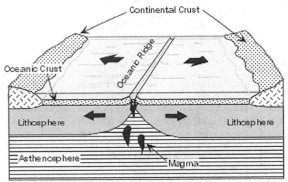

Diverging Plate Boundary
Oceanic Ridge - Spreading Center

**56. Interior of the Earth:**

| Earth's layer | Remarks |
|---|---|
| Crust | Solid |
| Upper mantle | Solid to viscous |
| Lower mantle | Semi solid |
| Outer core | Liquid |
| Inner core | Solid |

**58. Weight and Mass Difference on Equator and Pole:**

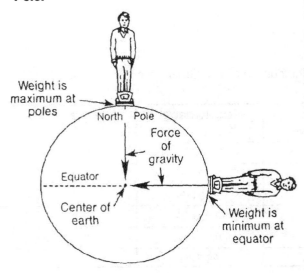

Weight is maximum at poles

North Pole

Force of gravity

Equator

Center of earth

Weight is minimum at equator

**59. Mineral with group:**

| Minerals | Groups |
|---|---|
| Quartz | Tekto-Silicate |
| Corundum | Oxide |
| Garnet | Neso-Silicate |
| Feldspar | Tekto-silicate |

**60. General Formula for Silicates**: The silicate basic structural units, we can construct a general structural chemical formula for the silicates. But on substitution in particular tends to mess things up a bit. This is $Al^{+3}$, the third most abundant element in the Earth's crust. $Al^{+3}$ has an ionic radius that varies between 0.54 and 0.39 depending on the coordination number. Thus, it could either fit in 6-fold coordination with oxygen or 4-fold coordination with oxygen. Because $Al^{+3}$ will go into 4-fold coordination with oxygen, it sometimes substitutes for $Si^{+4}$. If such a substitution takes place, it creates a charge imbalance that must be made up elsewhere in the silicate structure.

**62. Radioactive methods and Its Products:**

| Minerals | Dating technique |
|---|---|
| Quartz | K – Ar |
| Feldspar | Rb – Sr |
| Zircon | U – Pb |

The parent isotopes and corresponding daughter products most commonly used to determine the ages of ancient rocks are listed below:

| Parent Isotope | Stable Daughter Product | Currently Accepted Half – Life Values |
|---|---|---|
| Uranium-238 | Lead-206 | 4.5 billion years |
| Uranium-235 | Lead-207 | 704 million years |
| Thorium-232 | Lead-208 | 14.0 billion years |
| Rubidium-87 | Strontium-87 | 48.8 billion years |
| Potassium-40 | Argon-40 | 1.25 billion years |
| Samarium-147 | Neodymium-143 | 106 billion years |

The mathematical expression that relates radioactive decay to geologic time is called the age equation and is:

$$t = \frac{1}{\lambda} \ln\left(1 + \frac{D}{P}\right)$$

where $t$ is the age of the rock or mineral specimen,
$D$ is the number of atoms of a daughter product today,
$P$ is the number of atoms of the parent isotope today,
ln is the natural logarithm (logarithm to base e), and
$\lambda$ is the appropriate decay constant.

(The decay constant for each parent isotope is related to its half-life,

$t_{1/2}$ by the following expression: $t_{1/2} = \frac{\ln 2}{\lambda}$

## 63. Constituents of the Marble:

| Constituents of the Marble Powder | Percentage |
|---|---|
| $Fe_2O_3 + Al_2O_3 + SiO_2$ | 76.9 |
| MgO | 1.7 |
| $SO_3$ | 1.2 |
| $Na_2O$ | 1.4 |
| CaO | 0.32 |
| $K_2O$ | 0.05 |
| LOI | 2.9 |
| **Specific Gravity** | 2.5 |
| **Water absorption** | 0.8 |

## 64. Ores of the Minerals:

| Ores | Minerals |
|---|---|
| Bauxite | Aluminium |
| Hematite | Iron |
| Ilmenite | Titanium iron oxide |
| Rutile | Titanium dioxide |

## 65. Constituents of the different types of clay:

| Types of clay | Specification (%) |
|---|---|
| Red Earthenware | Red clay |
| White Earthenware | Feldspar 15, Ball clay 25, Kaolin 25, Silica 35 |
| Stoneware | Feldspar 15, Ball clay 40, Kaolin 40, Silica 5 |
| Porcelain | Feldspar 27, Kaolin 55, Silica 17, Bentonite 5 |
| Bone china | Bone Ash 50, Feldspar 25, Kaolin 25 |

## 66. Seasons of the Earth: 
The Earth's axis is tilted from perpendicular to the plane of the ecliptic by 23.45°. This tilting is what gives us the four seasons of the year-*spring*, *summer*, *autumn* (*fall*) and *winter*. Since the axis is tilted, different parts of the globe are oriented towards the Sun at different times of the year.

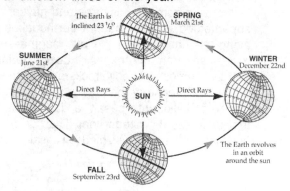

## 67. Atmosphere's Gases:

| Constituents in atmosphere | Percentage by volume | Concentration in Parts Per Million (PPM) |
|---|---|---|
| Nitrogen ($N_2$) | 78.084 | 780840.0 |
| Oxygen ($O_2$) | 20.946 | 209460.0 |
| Argon (Ar) | 0.934 | 9340.0 |
| Carbon dioxide ($CO_2$) | 0.036 | 360.0 |
| Neon (Ne) | 0.00182 | 18.2 |
| Helium (He) | 0.000524 | 5.24 |
| Methane ($CH_4$) | 0.00015 | 1.5 |
| Krypton (Kr) | 0.000114 | 1.14 |
| Hydrogen ($H_2$) | 0.00005 | 0.5 |

## 68. Number of air molecule in one cubic meter:

$$N = \left( 3 \times 10^{16} \frac{molecules}{cm^3} \times \frac{10^9 \frac{molecules}{m^3}}{1 \frac{molecules}{cm^3}} \right)$$

$$= 3 \times 10^{25} \frac{molecules}{m^3}$$

## 70. Green House Gases: 
Anthropogenic (man–made) contribution of the "Greenhouse Effect" expressed as % of total (water vapour included).

| Based on concentrations (ppb) adjusted for heat retention characteristics | Percentage of all Greenhouse gases | Percentage natural | Percentage Man–made |
|---|---|---|---|
| Water vapour | 95.000 % | 94.999 % | 0.001 % |
| Carbon Dioxide ($CO_2$) | 3.618 % | 3.502 % | 0.117 % |
| Methane | 0.360 % | 0.294 % | 0.66% |
| Nitrous Oxide ($N_2O$) | 0.950 % | 0.903 % | 0.047% |
| Misc. gases (CFCs, etc.) | 0.072 % | 0.025 % | 0.047 % |
| Total | 100.00 % | 99.72% | 0.28 % |

71. **Scale height of atmosphere:** A rough measurement of the height of the atmosphere known as the scale height.

72. **Ozone Height:**

Temperature Profile and Vertical Distribution of Ozone in the Atmosphere.

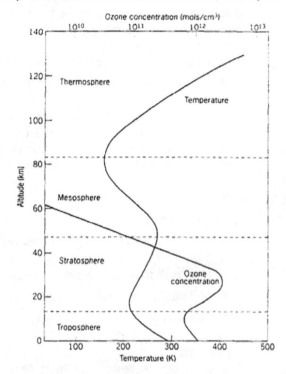

73. **Residence Time of the Aerosols:** Size and density of the aerosol will determine where the aerosol will deposit. Each of the major mechanism are dependent on particle size and mass. Retention rate of aerosol is depended on the type of aerosol (wet/dry) and on the chemical composition of aerosol. Particle interaction is important because it can lead to changes in size and concentration via condensation and nucleation.

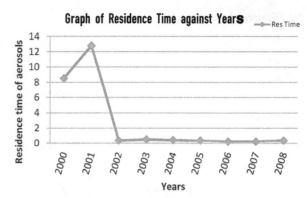

Graph of Residence Time against Years

74. **Homosphere and Heterosphere of the Atmosphere:** There are two layers of the atmosphere.

**Homosphere**: In homosphere there are three regions. Although the composition of the air is the same throughout three regions, the concentration of air decreases significantly with increasing altitude.

1. Troposphere  2. Stratosphere  3. Mesosphere

**Hetrosphere:** There are two regions. These two regions are considered outer space. The ionosphere overlaps the Mesosphere and the Thermosphere.

1. Thermosphere          2. Exosphere

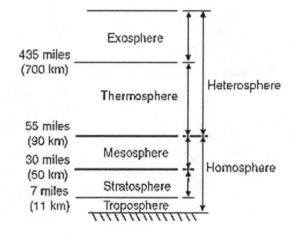

75. **Earth and Its Layers:**

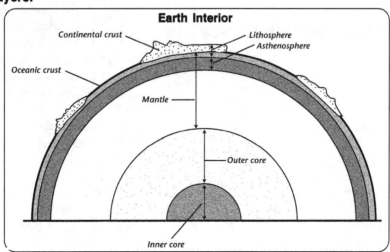

### 76. Ozone Layer and its height:

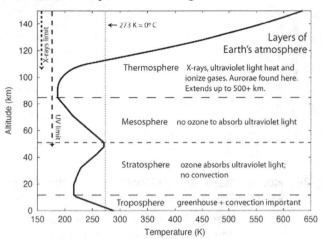

### 77. Geopotential height:

The geopotential height is defined as the height of the pressure surface above mean sea level. Therefore, a geopotential height observation represents the height of the pressure surface on which the observation was taken. Since cold air more dense than warm air, it causes pressure surfaces to be lower in colder air masses, while less dense, warmer air allows the pressure surfaces to be higher. Thus, heights are *lower* in cold air masses, and *higher* in warm air masses.

### 78. Sun's energy processes:

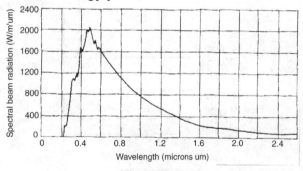

### 80. The attitude of the atmosphere with percentage:

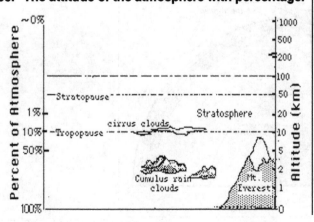

### 82. Relative Humidity

The relative humidity measure in per cent, the amount of water vapour that air is holding compared the amount it can be hold at a specific temperature. The warm air can possess more water vapour than cold air, so with the same amount of absolute/specific humidity, air will have a higher relative humidity. The relative humidity means the 50% means the air holds on that day (specific temperature) holds 50% of water needed for the air to be saturated. Saturated air has a relative humidity of 100%.

The relative humidity of an air-water mixture is also defined as the ratio of the partial pressure of water vapour in the mixture to the saturated vapour pressure of water at a given temperature. Thus the relative humidity of air is a function of both water content and temperature.

**From the question:**

Given, partial pressure of the water vapour is = 10 mbar

Temperature of the water vapour is = 20 °C

Saturated vapour pressure of water is = 25 mbar

Relative Humidity = $\dfrac{10}{25} \times 100$ = 40%

### 83. Lapse Rate

The lapse rate is defined as the rate at which temperature of the atmosphere decreases as the altitude increases. It means the lapse rate show how much the temperature is decreasing the higher in the air. The higher you are in the atmosphere, the colder the temperature will be:

Lapse rate = – dT/ dA

This equation represents the decreasing change in temperature over the change in altitude.

**Environmental Lapse Rate**

The rate at which air temperature decreases with elevation.This refers to the rate of temperature decreasing when it is not being affected by the saturation of water vapour in the atmosphere. However it can be affected by the stability of the air.If the rising air parcel is colder than environment than its heavier and does not rise. Therefor it is stable. Air is unstable when the air parcel is warmer and rises because it is lighter than its environment. Environmental Lapse Rate decreases faster when air is unstable than stable. Different from adiabatic lapse rate because adiabatic is the rate at which temperatures decreases with altitude when the air is either moist of cold. Measured by a balloon device called a radisonde.

## 84. Energy contained in spectrum:

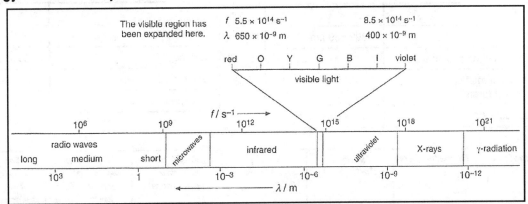

## 85. Temperature variation with respect to height in atmosphere:

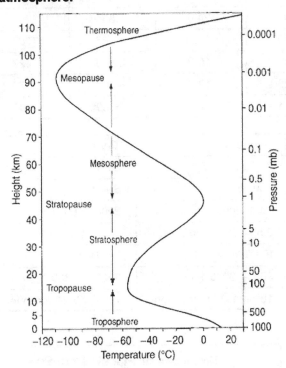

## 86. The energy of the Sun:
Things came together finally in the early twentieth century with the discovery of the atomic nucleus (1911), the exploration of nuclear reactions (the 1920s), and Einstein's theory of relativity (1905). In a typical nuclear reaction, several sub-atomic particles come together, interact, and several (possibly different) particles emerge. There are a series of reactions going on in the Sun, but the net result is the following combination of particles:

$$4_1H^1 + 4e - {}_2He^4 + 2e$$

The left side of this reaction shows four protons and four electrons, basically four hydrogen atoms.

Hydrogen is the natural starting point, since most of the matter in the Sun (and also the stars) is hydrogen gas. Hydrogen is the simplest element, so it's reasonable to expect that in a primitive state much of the universe would be hydrogen. The endpoint is helium, known to be the second most abundant element in the sun. It is often referred to as "hydrogen burning" to helium, and hydrogen is often called "fuel", but one must understand that the reaction is not burning in the sense of a chemical reaction between a fuel, such as coal or wood, and oxygen. It is a nuclear reaction.

## 87. General age of the different earth history:

| Different objects | Geological age |
|---|---|
| Solar system | 4.5 billion years |
| Earth | 4500 million years |
| Atmosphere | 4000 million years |
| Ocean | 200 million years |

## 88. Causes of Stars' colours:
The colour of the star is not easy to identify, due to its surface temperature. As we know the Sun's surface temperature about 5500 K, yellow colour star. In our solar system red stars are cooler than the sun, with surface temperatures of 3,500 K for a bright red star and 2,500 K for a dark red star. The hottest stars are blue, with their surface temperatures falling anywhere between 10,000 K and 50,000 K. Stars are fuelled by the nuclear fusion reactions at their core. There is a dynamic equilibrium maintained throughout the star's life between the expanding heat of the reactive core and gravitational forces holding the star together. Fusion produces extremely high energy. Fusion releases some of the energy that binds the particles of the nucleus together, unleashing remarkable power.

### 90. Size of the Sun and Earth:

| Terms | Sun |
|---|---|
| Diameter | 1,392,539 km |
| Inclination of equator to ecliptic | 7°, 25 |
| Mean axial rotation period (Sidereal) | 25.38 d |
| Mean density | 1.41 g/cm³ |

| Terms | Sun |
|---|---|
| Mass | $1.989 \times 10^{30}$ kg |
| Luminosity | $3.85 \times 10^{26}$ W |
| Volume (Earth = 1) | $1.3 \times 10^{6}$ |
| Escape velocity | 617.3 km/s |

| Planets | Diameter (Km) | Mass (Earth = 1) | Density (gm/cm³) (Water = 1) | Length of the day (Earth hours) | Period of one revolution around Sun (Earth years) | Average distance from Sun (millions of km) |
|---|---|---|---|---|---|---|
| Mercury | 4880 | 0.0558 | 5.44 | 1416 | 0.24 | 58 |
| Venus | 12104 | 0.815 | 5.20 | 5832 | 0.62 | 108 |
| Earth | 12756 | 1.0 | 5.52 | 24 | 1.00 | 150 |
| Mars | 6787 | 0.108 | 3.93 | 24.6 | 1.88 | 228 |
| Jupiter | 142800 | 317.8 | 1.30 | 9.8 | 11.86 | 778 |
| Saturn | 120000 | 95.2 | 0.69 | 10.2 | 29.50 | 1427 |
| Uranus | 51800 | 14.4 | 1.28 | 17.2 | 84.00 | 2870 |
| Neptune | 49500 | 17.2 | 1.64 | 16.1 | 164.90 | 4497 |

| Property | Crust | Mantle | Core |
|---|---|---|---|
| Fraction of earth | < 1% mass | 70 % | 30% |
| State | Broken | Plastic | Semi-liquid |
| Depth | 0 – 30 km | 30 – 3000 km | 3000 – 6371 km |
| Density | 2.7 g/cubic cm | 3.5 – 5.5 g/cubic cm | 10 – 12 g/ cubic cm |
| Chemical composition | $SiO_2$ | $(Fe, Mg) SiO_4$ | Fe, Ni |
| Temperature | 300 – 500 K | 500 – 3000 K | 3000 – 5300 K |
| Pressure | 1 – 1000 (Atmosphere) | $10^3 – 10^6$ (Atmosphere) | $10^6 – 10^7$ (Atmosphere) |

### 91. The distance of the different planets in solar system:

| Celestial object | Diameter (km) | Distance from Sun (km) |
|---|---|---|
| Sun | 1392530 | ——— |
| Mercury | 4879 | 57909711 |
| Venus | 12104 | 108209570 |
| Earth | 12756 | 149600000 |
| Mars | 6792 | 227039534 |
| Jupiter | 142980 | 778294598 |
| Saturn | 120540 | 1423872155 |
| Uranus | 51120 | 2876160232 |
| Neptune | 49530 | 4515865992 |

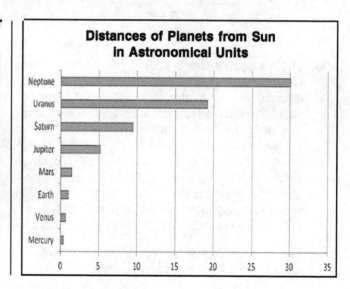

**Distances of Planets from Sun in Astronomical Units**

## 92. Planets and its Characteristics: The following table lists statistical information for the Sun and planets:

| | Distance (AU) | Radius (Earth's) | Mass (Earth's) | Rotation (Earth's) | # Moons | Orbital Inclination | Orbital Eccentricity | Obliquity | Density(g/cm³) |
|---|---|---|---|---|---|---|---|---|---|
| Sun | 0 | 109 | 332,800 | 25-36* | 9 | --- | --- | --- | 1.410 |
| Mercury | 0.39 | 0.38 | 0.05 | 58.8 | 0 | 7 | 0.2056 | 0.1° | 5.43 |
| Venus | 0.72 | 0.95 | 0.89 | 244 | 0 | 3.394 | 0.0068 | 177.4° | 5.25 |
| Earth | 1.0 | 1.00 | 1.00 | 1.00 | 1 | 0.000 | 0.0167 | 23.45° | 5.52 |
| Mars | 1.5 | 0.53 | 0.11 | 1.029 | 2 | 1.850 | 0.0934 | 25.19° | 3.95 |
| Jupiter | 5.2 | 11 | 318 | 0.411 | 16 | 1.308 | 0.0483 | 3.12° | 1.33 |
| Saturn | 9.5 | 9 | 95 | 0.428 | 18 | 2.488 | 0.0560 | 26.73° | 0.69 |
| Uranus | 19.2 | 4 | 17 | 0.748 | 15 | 0.774 | 0.0461 | 97.86° | 1.29 |
| Neptune | 30.1 | 4 | 17 | 0.802 | 8 | 1.774 | 0.0097 | 29.56° | 1.64 |
| Pluto | 39.5 | 0.18 | 0.002 | 0.267 | 1 | 17.15 | 0.2482 | 119.6° | 2.03 |

## 93. Light year:
Light year is a unit of length to astronomical distances not time. It is defined as "a light-year is the distance that light travels in vacuum in one Julian year (365.25 days)". Because it includes the word "year", the term light-year is sometimes misinterpreted as a unit of time, by the International Astronomical Union (IAU). It is about 9.5 quadrillion metres or 5.9 trillion miles. To calculate an idea of the size of a light-year, take the circumference of the earth (24,900 miles), lay it out in a straight line, multiply the length of the line by 7.5 (the corresponding distance is one light-second), then place 31.6 million similar lines end to end. The resulting distance is almost 6 trillion (6,000,000,000,000) miles.

## 96. Magnetic fields of the planets:

| Planet | g (* $g_e$) | $v_{esc}$ (km/s) | Distance (A.U.) | Albedo (%) | Temperature (K) | Atm. press. (* Earth's) | Atm. comp. | Rotation | Mag. field (* Earth's) |
|---|---|---|---|---|---|---|---|---|---|
| Mercury | 0.378 | 4.3 | 0.387 | 5.6 | 100 night, 590—725 day | $10^{-15}$ | 98% He, 2% $H_2$ | 58.81 d | 0.006 |
| Venus | 0.907 | 10.36 | 0.723 | 72 | 737 | 92 | 96.5% $CO_2$, 3.5% $N_2$, 0.015% $SO_2$ | 243.69 d | 0.00 |
| Earth | 1.000 | 11.186 | 1.000 | 38.5 | 283—293 day | 1.000 | 78.084% $N_2$, 20.946% $O_2$, 0.934% Ar, 0.035% $CO_2$, $H_2O$ highly variable (< 1%) | 23.9345 h | 1.000 |
| Mars | 0.377 | 5.03 | 1.524 | 16 | 184—242 day | 0.007—0.009 | 95.32% $CO_2$, 2.7% $N_2$ 1.6% Ar, 0.13% $O_2$, 0.08% CO, 0.021% $H_2O$, 0.01% NO | 24.623 h | 0.00 |
| Jupiter | 2.364 | 59.5 | 5.203 | 70 | 165 | >> 100 | 89% $H_2$, 11% He, 0.2% $CH_4$, 0.02% $NH_3$ | 9.925 h | 19,519 |
| Saturn | 0.916 | 35.5 | 9.539 | 75 | 134 | >> 100 | 89% $H_2$, 11% He, 0.3% $CH_4$, 0.02% $NH_3$ | 10.50 h | 578 |
| Uranus | 0.889 | 21.3 | 19.182 | 90 | 76 | >> 100 | 89% $H_2$, 11% He | 17.24 h | 47.9 |
| Neptune | 1.125 | 23.5 | 30.06 | 82 | 72 | >> 100 | 89% $H_2$, 11% He | 16.11 h | 27.0 |
| Pluto | 0.0675 | 1.1 | 39.53 | 14.5 | 50 | 0.003 | $CH_4$, $N_2$ | 6.405 d | 0.00 |

### 97. Density of the planets:

| Planets | Mass (Earth Masses) | Radius (earth Radii) | Density gm / cm³ |
|---------|---------------------|----------------------|-------------------|
| Mercury | 0.055 | 0.38 | 5.5 |
| Venus | 0.815 | 0.95 | 5.2 |
| Earth | 1.000 | 1.00 | 5.5 |
| Mars | 0.107 | 0.53 | 3.9 |
| Jupiter | 318 | 10.8 | 1.4 |
| Saturn | 95 | 9.0 | 0.7 |
| Uranus | 14.5 | 3.93 | 1.3 |
| Neptune | 17.2 | 3.87 | 1.6 |
| Pluto | 0.002 | 0.178 | 2.1 |

### 99. Colours of the Stars in the Solar system:

| Spectral Type | Colour | Surface Temperature |
|---------------|--------|---------------------|
| O | Blue | $\geq 30{,}000$ K |
| B | Blue – white | $10{,}000 - 30{,}000$ K |
| A | White | $7500 - 10{,}000$ K |
| F | Yellow – white | $6000 - 7500$ K |
| G | Yellow | $5200 - 6000$ K |
| K | Orange | $3700 - 5200$ K |
| M | Red | $< 3700$ K |

### 100. Photons:

A photon is the quantum of electromagnetic radiation. The term quantum is the smallest elemental unit of a quantity, or the smallest discrete amount of something. Thus, one quantum of electromagnetic energy is called a photon. The plural of quantum is quanta. The concept of photons and quanta comes from quantum mechanics and quantum theory. Quantum mechanics is a mathematical model that describes the behaviour of particles on an atomic and subatomic scale. It demonstrates that matter and energy are quantized, or come in small discrete bundles, on the smallest scales imaginable. A photon propagates at the speed of light.

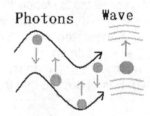

A photon describes the particle properties of an electromagnetic wave instead of the overall wave itself. In other words, we can picture an electromagnetic wave as being made up of individual particles called photons. Both representations are correct and reciprocal views of electromagnetic waves. For example, light exhibits wave properties under conditions of refraction or interference. Particle properties are exhibited under conditions of emission or absorption of light.

# International Earth Science Olympiad (IESO)
## Entrance Exam, 2016*

**Total Marks : 100**                                                    **Time : 90 minutes**

1. What is the thickness of the Earth's atmosphere?
   (a) 100 km          (b) 50 km
   (c) 10 km           (d) 1000 km

2. What is the third largest constituent of Earth's atmosphere?
   (a) Oxygen          (b) Nitrogen
   (c) Argon           (d) Krypton

3. What is the largest constituent of the atmosphere of Venus and Mars?
   (a) Oxygen          (b) Nitrogen
   (c) Argon           (d) Carbon-dioxide

4. What is the maximum water vapour content of Earth's atmosphere?
   (a) 100%            (b) 50%
   (c) 25%             (d) 3%

5. What is the typical monsoon rainfall over India?
   (a) 100cm           (b) 50cm
   (c) 100mm           (d) 50mm

6. Which of the following states receives the maximum monsoon rainfall?
   (a) Meghalaya       (b) Kerala
   (c) Tamil Nadu      (d) Karnataka

7. Western disturbance occurs during...
   (a) March           (b) June
   (c) August          (d) September

8. Most depression that causes rain over the Indo-Gangetic belt form in the
   (a) Southern Bay of Bengal
   (b) Northern Bay of Bengal
   (c) Southern Arabian Sea
   (d) Northern Arabian Sea

9. An anemometer measures:
   (a) rainfall        (b) humidity
   (c) wind speed      (d) wind direction

10. Sun emits maximum power at the wavelength of:
    (a) green           (b) blue
    (c) red             (d) ultraviolet

11. The average value of the Solar Constant is:
    (a) 1400 W/m$^2$    (b) 1300 W/m$^2$
    (c) 1360 W/m$^2$    (d) 1460 W/m$^2$

12. Wien's displacement law is useful in calculating the:
    (a) Surface temperature of stars
    (b) Total power radiated by stars
    (c) Core temperature of stars
    (d) Planck's constant

13. Power radiated by a star is proportional to the _____ power of its surface temperature.
    (a) First           (b) Second
    (c) Third           (d) Fourth

14. Typical glaciated forms are:
    (a) Cuestas and hogbacks
    (b) Horns and Arêtes
    (c) Alluvial fans and cones
    (d) Strath and fill terraces

15. A small flat-topped hill bounded by cliffs is known as
    (a) Plateau         (b) Terrace
    (c) Mesa            (d) Abrasion platform

16. Given the same climatic conditions, drainage density values will be lowest on:
    (a) Shale           (b) Phyllite
    (c) Granite         (d) Gabbro

17. Sea cliffs are not associated with:
    (a) Shore platform  (b) Caves
    (c) Natural Arches  (d) Pediments

18. A broad, flat area of desert covered with wind-swept sand with little or no vegetative cover is:
    (a) Hamada          (b) Bajada
    (c) Erg             (d) Playa

19. The Dead Sea, Lake Tanganyika and Lake Nyasa (Malawi) are examples of:
    (a) Volcanic lakes
    (b) Lakes formed by landslides
    (c) Lakes of tectonic origin
    (d) Artificial lakes

**20.** Frost action is a type of:
(a) Physical weathering
(b) Chemical weathering
(c) Biological weathering
(d) Bio-chemical weathering

**21.** One of the following rivers does not flow into the Atlantic Ocean:
(a) Zambezi          (b) Congo or Zaire
(c) Orinoco          (d) Orange

**22.** The best example of bird's foot or digitate delta is provided by_____ river.
(a) Nile             (b) Rhine
(c) Mississippi      (d) Niger

**23.** One of the following drainage patterns provides an evidence of river capture:
(a) Annual pattern
(b) Barbed pattern
(c) Trellis pattern
(d) Radial pattern

**24.** One of the following is not associated with accelerated soil erosion.
(a) Development of rills
(b) Development of gullies
(c) Thickening of soils horizons
(d) Increase in sediment yield

**25.** The marine influence upon climate acts to:
(a) Increase the annual temperature range.
(b) Increase the annual precipitation total.
(c) Suppress the annual temperature range.
(d) Cause extreme aridity.

**26.** Which type of trees is commonly found in the monsoon region?
(a) Evergreen
(b) Conifers
(c) Broad leaved deciduous
(d) Thorny bushes

**27.** Which one of the following coastal features is formed by wave erosion?
(a) Beach            (b) Dune
(c) Spit             (d) Stack

**28.** What is the term that is used for the layer of loose, assorted weathered material over rocky slopes?
(a) Soil             (b) Laterite
(c) Regolith         (d) Alluvium

**29.** When you look at Dinosaurs & birds, do you think birds are evolved from Dinosaurs?
(a) Yes              (b) No
(c) Not at all       (d) No comparison

**30.** Identify the following Gastropod shell:

(a) Conus            (b) Fuses
(c) Physa            (d) Nautical

**31.** Name the type of structure encountered during your travel along ancient rocky terrain, which shows stratiform, columnar and nodular structures in carbonate rocks resulting from the combination of life activity and sediment trapping and binding ability of algal assemblages and preying bacteria.
(a) Solitary corals  (b) Stromatolites
(c) Schist rock      (d) Slate

**32.** Match the List-I & List-II and chose your answer using given codes

| List-I | List-II |
| --- | --- |
| **1.** Ostracod | **R.** Plate |
| **2.** Foraminifera | **S.** Gastropod |
| **3.** Echinoderm | **T.** Carapace |
| **4.** Turbo | **U.** Test |

*Options:*

|     | (1) | (2) | (3) | (4) |
| --- | --- | --- | --- | --- |
| (a) | T | U | R | S |
| (b) | U | T | S | R |
| (c) | S | T | U | R |
| (d) | R | S | T | U |

**33.** The bedding showing gradation in grain size is _____ .
(a) Planar bedding
(b) Growth bedding
(c) Concordant bedding
(d) Graded bedding

**34.** In which of the following environment would you expect to find Oscillation Ripple marks?
(a) Alluvial         (b) Beach
(c) Deep sea         (d) Estuary

**35.** Which of the following will not make a fossil?
(a) Decomposed organic material
(b) Plant impressions
(c) Animal footprints
(d) Loose animal bones

**36.** What scientific avenue of investigation gave scientists the best estimate of the age of the Earth?
(a) Dating of fossils
(b) Archeological dating
(c) Radiometric dating
(d) Carbon dating

**37.** In which Phylum Trilobite belongs to _____ .
(a) Arthropod  (b) Protozoa
(c) Bryozoans  (d) Chordates

**38.** Petrified fossil is formed:
(a) When minerals replace all or part of a plant
(b) Solid copy of the shape of an organism
(c) An extremely thin coating of carbon on rock
(d) An extremely thick coating of carbon on rock

**39.** Which phylum this fossil belongs to?

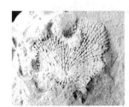

(a) Phylum : Brachiopod
(b) Phylum : Bryozoa
(c) Phylum : Mollusca
(d) Phylum : Chordata

**40.** Is this fossil planktic, benthic, neritic, terrestrial foraminifera?

(a) Planktic  (b) Benthic
(c) Neritic  (d) Terrestrial

**41.** What is Coprolite?
(a) Fossilized Dung  (b) Vertebrate fossil
(c) Microfossil  (d) Fossilized animal

**42.** Ventral valve is larger than dorsal valve with pedicle opening. Identify the fossil from the given options:
(a) Turbo  (b) Turetella
(c) Terebratula  (d) Trinucleus

**43.** Choose the sediment texture from order of largest to smallest:
(a) Boulder-Cobble-Gravel-Sand-Silt-Clay
(b) Boulder-Sand-Gravel-Cobble-Clay
(c) Sand-Boulder-Gravel-Clay
(d) Clay-Sand-Boulder-Gravel

**44.** What is the depth range of the oceans?
(a) 0 to 400 m  (b) 0 to 11000 m
(c) 0 to 40,000 m  (d) 0 to 4000 cm

**45.** What is the average salt content (salinity) of the ocean?
(a) 35%  (b) 3.5%
(c) 0.35%  (d) 0.035%

**46.** What is the major dissolved cation in the ocean?
(a) Potassium  (b) Sodium
(c) Magnesium  (d) Calcium

**47.** What is the major dissolved anion in the ocean?
(a) Chloride  (b) Sulphide
(c) Nitrate  (d) Phosphate

**48.** Which one of the following gases is not dissolved in the ocean?
(a) Oxygen  (b) Carbon dioxide
(c) Nitrogen  (d) Hydrogen

**49.** What is the typical temperature of the oceans in the equatorial region?
(a) 30 °C  (b) 15 °C
(c) 10 °C  (d) 50 °C

**50.** Which zonal belt of the oceans has the highest salinity?
(a) Equator
(b) 30 °N and 30 °S
(c) 10 °N & 10 °S
(d) Poles

**51.** During upwelling deeper waters come to the surface. This **does not** cause one of the following.
(a) Cooling of the surface ocean
(b) Supplying nutrients to the surface ocean
(c) Reducing the pH of the surface ocean
(d) Reducing chlorophyll content of the surface ocean

**52.** If a tsunami has a speed of 100 m/s, what is the water depth where it travels?
(a) 100 m  (b) 10 m
(c) 1000 m  (d) 1 m

**53.** Which of the following oceanic regions **does not** exhibit a thermocline?
(a) Polar  (b) Tropical
(c) Mid-latitude  (d) Equatorial

**54.** Which of the following is a marine plant?
(a) Coccoliths  (b) Foraminifera
(c) Radiolarian  (d) Copepods

**55.** Which of the following organisms make a siliceous test?
(a) Foraminifera  (b) Diatoms
(c) Coccoliths  (d) Pteropods

**56.** How the age of marine microfossils determined?
(a) Counting rings
(b) Counting x-ray boards
(c) Radio carbon dating
(d) Amino acid racemization

**57.** Which of the following features are associated with volcanically derived rocks:

1. Vesicles
2. Amygdules
3. Ropy lava
4. Glass
(a) (1 and 2)
(b) (2 and 3)
(c) (3 and 4)
(d) (1, 2, 3 and 4)

58. Identify the most abundant rock of the crust of the earth:
(a) Slate
(b) Marble
(c) Phyllite
(d) None of the above

59. Identify the type of boundaries associated with the Indian plate:
1. Convergent
2. Divergent
3. Island-arc
4. Passive
(a) 1
(b) 1 and 2
(c) 1, 2 and 3
(d) 1, 3 and 4

60. Two tectonic plates moving towards each other give rise to the formation of:
1. Subduction zone
2. Island-arc
3. Trench
4. Mid-oceanic ridge
(a) 1
(b) 1 and 2
(c) 1, 3 and 4
(d) 1, 2 and 3

61. Fragments of the erstwhile ocean floor found to occur on land present in orogenic belts are:
1. Obducted oceanic crust
2. Ophiolites
3. Sheared serpentines and pillow lavas
4. Mélange
(a) 1, 4
(b) 2 and 3
(c) 1 and 3
(d) 1, 2, 3 and 4

62. Average composition of the Upper Continental Crust of the Earth is:
(a) Granitic
(b) Basaltic
(c) Granodioritic
(d) Ultramafic

63. Lherzolites are the most abundant rocks in the Earth's:
(a) Crust
(b) Mantle
(c) Outer core
(d) Inner core

64. A rock which is composed of quartz and feldspar as essential minerals is called:
(a) Granite
(b) Syenite
(c) Gabbro
(d) Norite

65. A rock composed of pyroxene and plagioclase is known as:
1. Granite
2. Gabbro
3. Basalt
4. Syenite
(a) 1
(b) 2
(c) 2 and 3
(d) 3 and 4

66. A homogeneous crystalline solid of variable composition is said to form:

(a) Isomorphism
(b) Solid solution
(c) Polymorphism
(d) Pseudomorphism

67. Of the following minerals which one occurs in the mantle transition zone:
(a) Tridymite
(b) Cristobalite
(c) Coesite
(d) Stishovite

68. Match the following and chose the correct option:
V. Lithium
1. Syenites
W. Platinum
2. Peridotites
X. Titanomagnetite
3. Gabbros
Y. Diamonds
4. Pegmatites
5. Kimberlites
(a) V-3 W-5 X-4 Y-1
(b) V-4 W-2 X-3 Y-5
(c) V-5 W-2 X-4 Y-1
(d) V-2 W-3 X-5 Y-4

69. Select in order of decreasing stability in the weathering cycle the following minerals:
1. Quartz
2. Felspars
3. Muscovite
(a) (2, 1, 3)
(b) (1, 2, 3)
(c) (3, 1, 2)
(d) (3, 2, 1)

70. Conrad discontinuity is a seismic interface between:
(a) Crust and Mantle
(b) Upper Crust and Lower Crust
(c) Upper Mantle and Lower Mantle
(d) Lower Mantle and Outer Core

71. Andesites are predominant rocks of the Island-arc volcanism because:
(a) It is formed by collision of two oceanic plates
(b) It is formed by partial melts from oceanic and continental crust
(c) It is formed from an acidic magma
(d) It is formed from melting of anorthosite

72. The biggest asteroid known is:
(a) Vesta
(b) Icarus
(c) Ceres
(d) Eros

73. One Jupiter day is equal to which of the following?
(a) 30 hrs 40 min
(b) 9 hrs 50 min
(c) 3 hrs 20 min
(d) 52 hrs 10 min

74. The sunspot cycle is:
(a) 3 years
(b) 11 years
(c) 26 years
(d) 50 years

75. The greatest distance between Earth and the Sun is called what:
(a) Apihelion
(b) Perihelion
(c) Perigee
(d) Apogee

76. The orbital plane of the moon is how many degrees inclined from the ecliptic?
 (a) 5 degrees        (b) 10 degrees
 (c) 15 degrees       (d) 20 degrees

77. A pulsar is actually a:
 (a) Black hole       (b) White dwarf
 (c) Red giant        (d) Neutron star

78. Which of the following is formed during the weathering of rocks on the surface of Earth?
 (a) Quartz           (b) Feldspar
 (c) Muscovite        (d) Bauxite

79. Pycnocline indicates the vertical distribution of:
 (a) Temperature      (b) Salinity
 (c) Density          (d) Oxygen

80. Which of the following has the highest Albedo:
 (a) Clouds           (b) Fresh Snow
 (c) Water            (d) Vegetation

81. Hydraulic conductivity is high in an Aquifer composed of:
 (a) Mudstone         (b) Sandstone
 (c) Granite          (d) Schist

82. Which of the following is present day remnant of Tethys Sea:
 (a) Sargossa Sea
 (b) South China Sea
 (c) Mediterranean Sea
 (d) Bering Sea

83. Among the minerals listed which has the least hardness:
 (a) Quartz           (b) Gypsum
 (c) Corundum         (d) Orthoclase

84. Coral reefs are composed of:
 (a) Sandstone        (b) Phosphorite
 (c) Limestone        (d) Siltstone

85. Gondwana Coals of India are richer in:
 (a) Carbon           (b) Iron
 (c) Sulphur          (d) Aluminium

86. Which of the following will have poorest sorting of sediments:
 (a) Eolian           (b) Fluvial
 (c) Coastal          (d) Glacial

87. Which of the following has least residence time in sea water:
 (a) Sodium           (b) Iron
 (c) Chlorine         (d) Manganese

88. How many minerals in the Mohs scale of hardness are silicates:
 (a) 1                (b) 2
 (c) 3                (d) 4

89. Which of the following is NOT true:
 (a) Rayleigh waves are surface waves
 (b) Love waves are body waves
 (c) P waves travel faster than S waves
 (d) S waves are body waves

90. The Oceanic crust is not older than:
 (a) Permian          (b) Triassic
 (c) Jurassic         (d) Cretaceous

91. The oldest of the Geomagnetic Scale is:
 (a) Brunhes          (b) Gilbert
 (c) Matuyama         (d) Gauss

92. The Flysch formations are:
 (a) Syn-tectonic     (b) Pre-tectonic
 (c) Post-tectonic    (d) All of the above

93. Natural Leeve is an example of:
 (a) Point bar deposit
 (b) Channel fill deposit
 (c) Flood plain deposit
 (d) Glacial deposit

94. A Sinter is:
 (a) Dissolved Silica
 (b) Dissolved Calcium carbonate
 (c) Dissolved Phosphorus
 (d) None of the above

95. Cirques are mainly associated with:
 (a) Streams          (b) Glaciers
 (c) Oceans           (d) All of the above

96. Aragonite crystallises in which crystal system?
 (a) Cubic            (b) Monoclinic
 (c) Triclinic        (d) Orthorhombic

97. Quartz is:
 (a) Non magnetic
 (b) Strongly magnetic
 (c) Weakly magnetic
 (d) None of the above

98. The average value of Poisson's value of rocks is:
 (a) 0.25             (b) 0.50
 (c) 1.0              (d) 1.50

99. Joints are encountered in:
 (a) Sedimentary rocks
 (b) Igneous rocks
 (c) Metamorphic rocks
 (d) All of the above

100. Marine organisms which are confined to normal saline water are called:
 (a) Euryhaline
 (b) Stenohaline
 (c) Polyhaline
 (d) None of the above

# ANSWERS

| 1 | 2 | 3 | 4 | 5 | 6 | 7 | 8 | 9 | 10 |
|---|---|---|---|---|---|---|---|---|----|
| (a) | (c) | (d) | (d) | (a) | (a) | (a) | (b) | (c) | (a) |
| **11** | **12** | **13** | **14** | **15** | **16** | **17** | **18** | **19** | **20** |
| (c) | (a) | (d) | (b) | (c) | (d) | (d) | (c) | (c) | (a) |
| **21** | **22** | **23** | **24** | **25** | **26** | **27** | **28** | **29** | **30** |
| (a) | (c) | (b) | (c) | (c) | (c) | (d) | (c) | (a) | (c) |
| **31** | **32** | **33** | **34** | **35** | **36** | **37** | **38** | **39** | **40** |
| (b) | (a) | (d) | (b) | (a) | (c) | (a) | (a) | (b) | (a) |
| **41** | **42** | **43** | **44** | **45** | **46** | **47** | **48** | **49** | **50** |
| (a) | (c) | (a) | (b) | (b) | (b) | (a) | (d) | (a) | (b) |
| **51** | **52** | **53** | **54** | **55** | **56** | **57** | **58** | **59** | **60** |
| (d) | (c) | (a) | (a) | (b) | (c) | (d) | (d) | (b) | (d) |
| **61** | **62** | **63** | **64** | **65** | **66** | **67** | **68** | **69** | **70** |
| (d) | (c) | (b) | (a) | (c) | (b) | (c) | (b) | (b) | (b) |
| **71** | **72** | **73** | **74** | **75** | **76** | **77** | **78** | **79** | **80** |
| (b) | (c) | (b) | (b) | (a) | (a) | (d) | (d) | (c) | (b) |
| **81** | **82** | **83** | **84** | **85** | **86** | **87** | **88** | **89** | **90** |
| (b) | (c) | (b) | (c) | (a) | (d) | (b) | (d) | (b) | (c) |
| **91** | **92** | **93** | **94** | **95** | **96** | **97** | **98** | **99** | **100** |
| (b) | (a) | (c) | (d) | (b) | (d) | (a) | (a) | (d) | (b) |

# HINTS AND SOLUTIONS

## 1. Thickness of the Atmosphere:

| Different Layers | Thickness (Km) |
|---|---|
| Troposphere | 0 – 12 |
| Stratosphere | 12 – 50 |
| Mesosphere | 50 – 80 |
| Thermosphere | 80 – 150 |
| Exosphere | 150 – 450 |

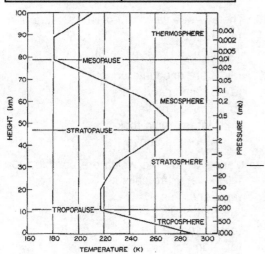

## 2. Different parts of the Solar system:

| Different Layers | Constituents |
|---|---|
| Atmosphere | $N>O>Ar>CO_2$ |
| Lithosphere | O > Si > Al > Fe > Ca > Mg > Na > K |
| Earth | Fe>O>Si |
| Crust | O > Si > Al > Fe > Ca > Mg > Na > K |
| Solar system | H>He>O |

## 3. Planets and its constituents:

| Constituents | Venus | Earth | Mars |
|---|---|---|---|
| Carbon Dioxide $(CO_2)$ | 96.5 % | 0.03 % | 95 % |
| Nitrogen $(N_2)$ | 3.5 % | 78 % | 2.7 % |
| Oxygen $(O_2)$ | Trace | 21 % | 0.13 % |
| Argon (Ar) | 0.007 % | 0.9 % | 1.6 % |
| Methane $(CH_4)$ | 0 % | 0.002 % | 0 % |

| Planets | Diameter (Km) | Mass (Earth = 1) | Density (gm/cm³) (Water = 1) | Length of the day (Earth hours) | Period of one revolution around Sun (Earth years) | Average distance from Sun (millions of km) |
|---|---|---|---|---|---|---|
| Mercury | 4880 | 0.0558 | 5.44 | 1416 | 0.24 | 58 |
| Venus | 12104 | 0.815 | 5.20 | 5832 | 0.62 | 108 |
| Earth | 12756 | 1.0 | 5.52 | 24 | 1.00 | 150 |
| Mars | 6787 | 0.108 | 3.93 | 24.6 | 1.88 | 228 |
| Jupiter | 142800 | 317.8 | 1.30 | 9.8 | 11.86 | 778 |
| Saturn | 120000 | 95.2 | 0.69 | 10.2 | 29.50 | 1427 |
| Uranus | 51800 | 14.4 | 1.28 | 17.2 | 84.00 | 2870 |
| Neptune | 49500 | 17.2 | 1.64 | 16.1 | 164.90 | 4497 |

## 4. Water vapour percent in Atmosphere:

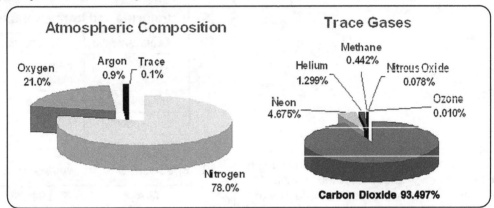

| Permanent Gases | | | Variable gases | | |
|---|---|---|---|---|---|
| Gas | Symbol | %age | Gas | Symbol | %age by volume |
| Nitrogen | $N_2$ | 78 % | Water vapour | $H_2O$ | 0 – 4 |
| Oxygen | $O_2$ | 21 % | Carbon dioxide | $CO_2$ | 0.038 |
| Argon | Ar | 0.9 % | Ozone | $O_3$ | 0.000004 |
| Neon | Ne | 0.0018 % | Carbon monoxide | CO | 0.00002 |
| Helium | He | 0.0005 % | Sulphur dioxide | $SO_2$ | 0.000001 |
| Methane | $CH_4$ | 0.0001 % | Nitrogen dioxide | $NO_2$ | 0.000001 |
| Hydrogen | $H_2$ | 0.00005 % | Particles (dust, pollen) | — | 0.00001 |

## 5. Rainfall in India:

In India, climate a wide range of weather condition across a vast geographic with varied due to topography, making generalisation. Based on the Koppen classi-fication system, India follow six major climatic condition, *i.e.*, arid desert in the west, alpine tundra and glaciers in the north, and humid tropical regions supporting rainforests in the southwest and the island territories. Many regions have starkly different microclimates.

The nation has four seasons:

- Winter (December to February).
- Summer (March to May).
- A monsoon rainy season (June to September).
- A post-monsoon period (October to November).

India's geography and geology are climatically pivotal. The Thar Desert in the northwest and the Himalayas in the north work in tandem to effect culturally and economically important monsoonal regime. As Earth's highest and most massive mountain range, the Himalayas bar the influx of frigid katabatic winds from the icy Tibetan Plateau and northerly Central Asia. Most of North

India is thus kept warm or is only mildly chilly or cold during winter; the same thermal dam keeps most regions in India hot in summer.

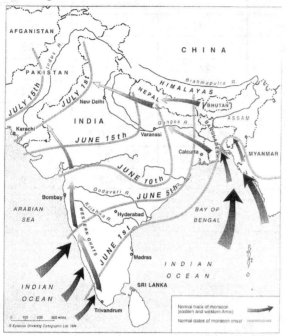

### 6. Maximum rainfall in India:

The highest annual precipitation in India in the village of Mawsynram, in the hilly north-eastern state of Meghalaya. It is about 11,872 mm, highest recorded in Asia. The village, which sits at an elevation of 1,401 metres (4,596 ft), benefits from its proximity to both the Himalayas and the Bay of Bengal. However, since the town of Cherrapunji, 5 kilometres to the east, is the nearest town to host a meteorological office—none has ever existed in Mawsynram. It is officially credited as being the world's wettest place. In recent years the Cherrapunji - Mawsynram region has averaged between 9,296 and 10,820 millimetres of rain annually, though Cherrapunji has had at least one period of daily rainfall that lasted almost two years.

**South Asia's Rainy Monsoon Season (May–October)**

### 7. Western disturbance:

This is a extra-tropical storm originate from the Mediterranean region, which show sudden winter rain to the north – western parts of the Indian subcontinent, with non-monsoonal precipitation pattern driven by the westerlies. The moisture in these storms usually originates over the Mediterranean Sea and the Atlantic Ocean. Extratropical storms are a global phenomenon with moisture usually carried in the upper atmosphere, unlike their tropical counterparts where the moisture is carried in the lower atmosphere. In the case of the subcontinent, moisture is sometimes shed as rain when the storm system encounters the Himalayas. Western Disturbances are important for the development of the Rabi crop, which includes the locally important staple wheat.

### 9. Instruments and its measurements:

| Measurements | Instruments |
|---|---|
| Rainfall | Rain gauge or udometer/ pluviometer or ombrometer. |
| Humidity | Hygrometer |
| Wind speed | Anemometer |
| Wind direction | Anemometer |

### 10. Spectrum and its wavelength:

| Colour | Wavelength |
|---|---|
| Blue | 4500 – 4900 Å |
| Green | 4900 – 5600 Å |
| Yellow | 5600 – 5900 Å |
| Orange | 5900 – 6300 Å |
| Red | 6300 – 7600 Å |

| Region | Wavelength (Angstroms) | Wavelength (centimetres) | Frequency (Hz) | Energy (eV) |
|---|---|---|---|---|
| Radio | $>10^9$ | $>10$ | $<3 \times 10^9$ | $<10^{-5}$ |
| Microwave | $10^9 - 10^6$ | $10 - 0.01$ | $3 \times 10^9 - 3 \times 10^{12}$ | $10^{-5} - 0.01$ |
| Infrared | $10^6 - 7000$ | $0.01 - 7 \times 10^{-5}$ | $3 \times 10^{12} - 4.3 \times 10^{14}$ | $0.01 - 2$ |
| Visible | $7000 - 4000$ | $7 \times 10^{-5} - 4 \times 10^{-5}$ | $4.3 \times 10^{14} - 7.5 \times 10^{14}$ | $2 - 3$ |
| Ultraviolet | $4000 - 10$ | $4 \times 10^{-5} - 10^{-7}$ | $7.5 \times 10^{14} - 3 \times 10^{17}$ | $3 - 10^3$ |
| X-Rays | $10 - 0.1$ | $10^{-7} - 10^{-9}$ | $3 \times 10^{17} - 3 \times 10^{19}$ | $10^3 - 10^5$ |
| Gamma Rays | $<0.1$ | $<10^{-9}$ | $>3 \times 10^{19}$ | $>10^5$ |

### 11. Solar Constant:

The solar constant is a fundamental quantity in atmospheric physics since it represents the amount of solar energy arriving at the top of the atmosphere. This is defined as the total irradiance of the Sun at the mean orbital distance of the Earth. The term remains in use even though the total solar irradiance is not constant.

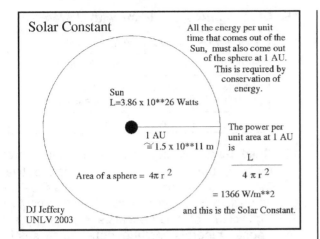

**12. Wien's displacement law:** The temperature of a blackbody radiator increases, the overall radiated energy increases and the peak of the radiation curve moves to shorter wavelength. When the maximum is evaluated from the Planck radiation formula, the product of the peak wavelength and the temperature is found to be a constant.

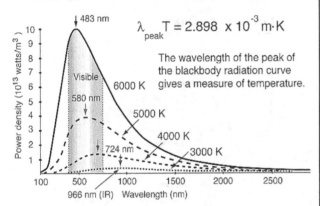

$$\lambda_{peak} T = 2.898 \times 10^{-3} \, m \cdot K$$

The wavelength of the peak of the blackbody radiation curve gives a measure of temperature.

- This relation is called Wien's displacement law and is useful for the determining the temperature of hot radiant objects such as stars, and indeed for a determination of the temperature of any radiant object whose temperature is far above that of its surroundings.
- It should be noted that the peak of the radiation curve in the Wien relationship is peak only because the intensity is plotted as a function of wavelength. If frequency or some other variable is used on the horizontal axis, the peak will be at a different wavelength.
- Stars approximate blackbody radiators and their visible colour depends upon the temperature of the radiator. The curves show blue, white, and red stars. The white star is adjusted to 5270K so that the peak of its blackbody curve is at the peak wavelength of

the sun, 550 nm. From the wavelength at the peak, the temperature can be deduced from the Wien displacement law.

**13. Radiation Curves:**

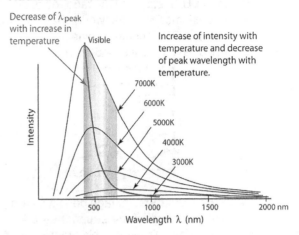

The wavelength of the peak of the blackbody radiation curve decreases in a linear fashion as the temperature is increased (Wien's displacement law). This linear variation is not evident in this kind of plot since the intensity increases with the fourth power of the temperature (Stefan-Boltzmann law). The nature of the peak wavelength change is made more evident by plotting the fourth root of the intensity.

**14. Landforms and its significance:**

| Landforms | Remarks |
|---|---|
| Cuestas | It is a fluvial landform which develops with gentle slop. |
| Hogbacks | It is a type of cuestas where both beds are equal dip. |
| Horns | Glacial erosional feature. |
| Aretes | Glacial erosional feature. |
| Alluvial fans | Conical shape deposition due to load of the old stage of the river. |
| Strath | Fluvial geomorphological feature. |
| Terrace | Fluvial geomorphological feature. |

**15. Mesa:** A mesa is a flat-topped mountain or hill. It is a wide, flat, elevated land form with steep sides.
- *Mesa* is a Spanish word that means table. Spanish explorers of the American southwest, where many mesas are found, used the word because the tops of mesas look like the tops of tables.
- Mesas are formed by erosion, when water washes smaller and softer types of rocks away from the top of a hill. The strong, durable

rock that remains on top of a mesa is called caprock. A mesa is usually wider than it is tall.

- Mesas are usually found in dry regions where rock layers are horizontal. The Grand Mesa in the U.S. state of Colorado, considered the largest mesa in the world, has an area of about 1,300 square kilometres (500 square miles) and stretches for 64 kilometres (40 miles).

16. **Drainage Density:** Drainage density of a basin is the total line length of the stream network divided by basin area. 2D length (planimetric length) or 3D length (slope length) may be used.

**Length of Overland flow:** $L_o = 1/2D_d$

Where $D_d$ = Drainage density

**Form Factor:** $F = A/L^2$

Where  A = Area of the basin

L = Length of the basin

**Compactness Coefficient:** $C_c = P/\sqrt{4\delta A}$

Where  A = Area of the basin

P = Perimeter of the basin

It is the land area or catchment area drained by a single river and its tributaries.

A imaginary line called the watershed separates one drainage basin from another. The watershed usually follows a ridge of high land. Any water falling on the other side of the ridge will flow through the adjacent drainage basin.

17. **Sea cliffs: Cliffs** are formed due to erosion landforms by the processes of weathering and erosion. **Cliffs** are common on coasts, in mountainous areas, escarpments and along rivers. **Cliffs** are usually formed by rock that is resistant to weathering and erosion.

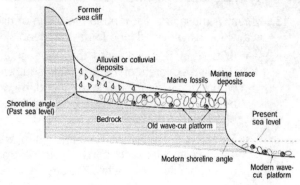

18. **Geomorphological terms with characters:**

| Landforms | Characteristics |
|---|---|
| Hamada | Aeolian landform due to deflation. |
| Bajada | More than one fan joins laterally due to fluvial processes. |
| Playa | Water eroded landform |

19. **Dead Sea:** This sea is a second saltest water body in the earth surface, located between Israel and Jordan, about 15 miles east of Jerusalem. The waters of the Dead Sea contain a high volume of minerals that benefit human health. These minerals include potassium, sulphur, calcium, bromine, collagen, and many more. For centuries, people have flocked to the Dead Sea to enjoy the benefits of soaking in its mineral-rich, salt filled waters. Cleopatra recognized the cosmetic benefits of the Dead Sea and had retreats and factories built along its shores. The Egyptians used elements present in the area for embalming and mummification processes.

**Location of Dead Sea:**

20. **Types of weathering with example:**

| Types of weathering | Example |
|---|---|
| Physical weathering | Frost action, exfoliation |
| Chemical weathering | Hydration, hydrolysis, oxidation |
| Biological weathering | Plants root, snail and due to organisms activity. |
| Bio-chemical weathering | After death of the organism they converted into secondary materials due to bio-chemical processes. |

### 23. Drainage Pattern and Its Signifinace:

| Drainage Pattern | Evidences |
|---|---|
| Annual pattern | Impact structure |
| Barbed pattern | In this pattern the tributaries flow in opposite direction to their master streams. |
| Trellis pattern | Network of the main and tributaries streams |
| Radial pattern | In this pattern the streams diverge from a central higher point in all directions. |

### 24. Formation of Soil:
Soil is a mixture of the parent materials which comes from the different sources. The process of the soil formation is known as the pedogenesis. The climatic and products of the weathering processes is the main role of the formation of soils.

#### Factors that influence the soil formation:
- Climatic condition
- Living organism
- Nature of the parent materials
- Chemical and mineralogical composition of the soil
- Topography of the area
- Time

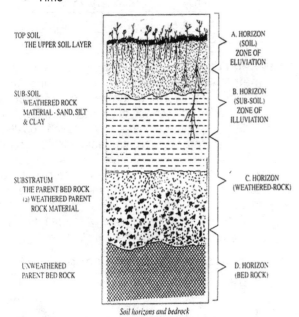

TOP SOIL
THE UPPER SOIL LAYER

A. HORIZON (SOIL) ZONE OF ELUVIATION

SUB-SOIL
WEATHERED ROCK MATERIAL - SAND, SILT & CLAY

B. HORIZON (SUB-SOIL) ZONE OF ILLUVIATION

SUBSTRATUM
THE PARENT BED ROCK
(1) WEATHERED PARENT ROCK MATERIAL

C. HORIZON (WEATHERED-ROCK)

UNWEATHERED PARENT BED ROCK

D. HORIZON (BED ROCK)

*Soil horizons and bedrock*

### 27. Landforms and Its developments agencies:

| Features | Actions |
|---|---|
| Beach | Sea |
| Dune | Wind |
| Spit | Sea |
| Stack | Sea |

### 28. Soil and Its remark:

| Terms | Remarks |
|---|---|
| Soil | It is a mixture of organic matter, minerals...etc. |
| Laterite | Type of the soils which is reddish colour and formed in tropical climate. |
| Alluvium | River deposit materials, layer of the clay, sand and silt. |
| Regolith | First stage of the formation of soils. |

### 29. Evolution of Life through Geological Records:

**GEOLOGIC TIME SCALE**

| EON | ERA | PERIOD | EPOCH | Age in millions of years before present |
|---|---|---|---|---|
| Phanerozoic | Cenozoic | Quaternary | Holocene | Present |
| | | | Pleistocene | 0.01 |
| | | Tertiary (Neogene) | Pliocene | 1.6 |
| | | | Miocene | 5.3 |
| | | | Oligocene | 23.7 |
| | | Tertiary (Paleogene) | Eocene | 36.6 |
| | | | Paleocene | 57.8 |
| | Mesozoic | Cretaceous | | 66.4 |
| | | Jurassic | | 144 |
| | | Triassic | | 208 |
| | Paleozoic | Permian | | 245 |
| | | Pennsylvanian (Carboniferous) | | 286 |
| | | Mississippian | | 320 |
| | | Devonian | | 360 |
| | | Silurian | | 408 |
| | | Ordovician | | 438 |
| | | Cambrian | | 505 |
| Precambrian | Proterozoic | | | 570 |
| | | | | 2500 |
| | Archean | | | 3800 |
| | Hadean | | | 4550 |

| Geological Age | Evolution |
|---|---|
| Quaternary | Man |
| Tertiary | Horses, primitive mammals |
| Cretaceous | Dinosaurs, first flowering plants |
| Jurassic | First birds |
| Triassic | Ammonoids |
| Permian | Reptiles |
| Carboniferous | Coals, amphibians |
| Devonian | Brachiopods, fish |
| Silurian | ——- |
| Ordovician | Nautoloids |
| Cambrian | Trilobites |
| Precambrian | Algae |

### 30. Different Shells and Its Characters:

| Shells | Remarks | Geological age |
|--------|---------|----------------|
| Conus | Gastropods | Upper cretaceous to present |
| Physa | Gastropods | Upper cretaceous to Holocene |
| Nautical | Nautiloidea | Triassic to present |

### 31. Stromatolites:
This is a sedimentary rock which shows layered mounds and sheet like structures. They formed by the different layers of the single celled organism, cyanobacteria, microbial from shallow water, shelf, rivers, lakes or soils.

### 32. Different fossils and its geological records:

| Shells | Remarks | Geological age |
|--------|---------|----------------|
| Ostrocoda | Today found in all aquatic environments | Late Cambrian to present |
| Foraminifera | Calcareous in composition | Cambrian to recent |
| Echinoderm | Echinodermata | Cambrian to Holocene |

### 33. Graded bedding:
The gradation of the grain in the fining upward in normal conditions. The courser materials deposited first and then after fining materials.

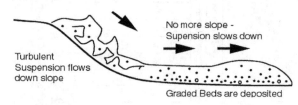

Turbulent Suspension flows down slope

No more slope - Suspension slows down

Graded Beds are deposited

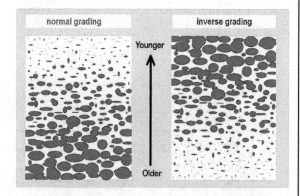

normal grading

inverse grading

Younger

Older

### 34. Geological environments and its ripple:

| Environments | Types of ripple marks |
|--------------|----------------------|
| Alluvial | Current ripple |
| Beach | Oscillation ripple |
| Deep sea | Oscillation ripple |

### 35. Condition of fossilization:
- Hard parts
- Immediate burial

### 37. Classification of Phylum with foraminifer's example:

| Terms | Example |
|-------|---------|
| Phylum | Protozoa |
| Class | Sarcodina |
| Order | Foraminifera |
| Family | Globigeninidae |
| Genus | Globigerina |
| Species | Globigerina bulloides |

### 38. Petrified Fossils:
Petrified fossils form due to petrification processes, which living organic materials convert into the hard part *i.e.*, Stone. In this process molecules of the organism are replaced within the mineral. This is not such fossils it is totally different such as resin fossils or permineralized. Permineralization is often confused with petrification because it is the first step in the petrification process. The difference is with permineralized fossils, the pores of the organism are filled with minerals but the tissue of the plant or animal are still intact and are not replaced with minerals.

### 40. Microfossil and Its Significance:

| Environments | Name | Figure |
|--------------|------|--------|
| Planktic | Globigerina bulloides | |
| Benthic | Nonionella opima | |
| Neritic | Well oxygenated zone | Coastal fishes |
| Terrestrial | Earth surfaces | Earth atmosphere |

41. **Coprolite:** Coprolite derived from Greek words, means "Dung stone". They are the pieces of the poop which fossilized over long time their original structures have replaced by minerals like calcium carbonates and others silicates. They are found in different shape and size with different part of the earth. The main application is that the reconstruction of the evolution and development of the sharks, fish, termites, crocodilians and humans.

42. **Fossils and their characters:**

| Fossils | Characteristics |
|---------|-----------------|
| Turbo | Gastropods |
| Turetella | Gastropods |
| Terebratula | Brachiopods |
| Trinucleus | Trilobites |

43. **Sedimentary Texture:**

| Sedimentary texture | Size (mm) | Equivalent rocks |
|---------------------|-----------|------------------|
| Boulder | >256 | |
| Cobble | 64 – 256 | Rudaceous rocks |
| Pebble | 4 – 64 | |
| Granule | 2 – 4 | |
| Sand | 2 – 1/16 | Arenaceous rocks |
| Silt | 1/16 – 1/256 | |
| Clay | <1/256 | Argillaceous rocks |

44. **Depth range of the Ocean:**

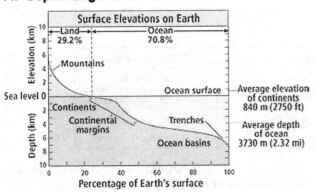

45. **Average salinity of the Ocean:**

| Chemical constituents | Content (Parts per thousand) |
|-----------------------|------------------------------|
| Calcium (Ca) | 0.419 |
| Magnesium (Mg) | 1.304 |
| Sodium (Na) | 10.710 |
| Potassium (K) | 0.390 |
| Bicarbonate (HCO$_3$) | 0.146 |
| Sulphate (SO$_4$) | 2.690 |
| Chloride (Cl) | 19.350 |
| Bromide (Br) | 0.070 |
| **Total dissolved solids (Salinity)** | **35.079** |

46. **Major dissolved anion and cation in the Ocean:**

| Chemical constitution of Water | | |
|---|---|---|
| Non ionic | Ionic | |
| SiO$_2$ | **Anion** | **Cations** |
| Dissolved gases | **Major Anions** | **Major Cations** |
| Oily substance | Bicarbonate | Sodium |
| Synthetic detergent | Chloride | Potassium |
| | Sulphate | Calcium |
| | | Magnesium |

49. **Temperature range in the different ocean region:**

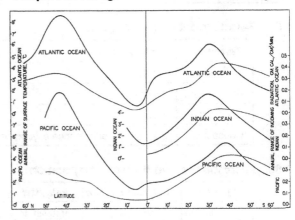

50. **Salinity difference in the Ocean:**

| Salinity Variations | |
|---------------------|--|
| *Location* | *Salinity* |
| Normal open Ocean | 33 – 38 % |
| Baltic Sea | 10 % (brackish) |
| Red Sea | 42 % (Hypersaline) |
| Great Salt Lake | 280 % |
| Dead Sea | 330 % |
| Tap water | 0.8 % |
| Premium bottled water | 0.3 % |

51. **Causes of the upwelling:** It is the processes by which the **current** go down and up due to winds and rotation of the Earth. The earth rotates west to east and winds tends to right in the northern hemisphere and left in the southern hemisphere, this is known as the Coriolis effect. The upwelling influences the cyclone.

53. **Thermocline of the region:** The thermocline region is defined as the temperature decreases with increasing depth, the upper layer of hot water and lower layer of the cold water due to Sun's energy.

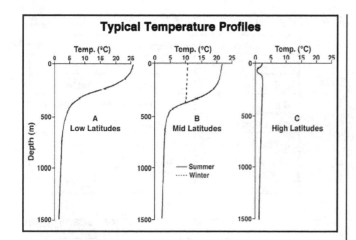

**Typical Temperature Profiles**

A — Low Latitudes
B — Mid Latitudes
C — High Latitudes

— Summer
····· Winter

### 54. Terms and its environments:

| Terms | Environments |
|---|---|
| Coccoliths | Marine |
| Foraminifera | Marine |
| Radiolarian | Marine |
| Copepods | Fresh water and marine environments |

### 55. Microfossils and its test composition:

| Organism | Test composition | Geological age |
|---|---|---|
| Foraminifera | Calcareouos | Cambrian to recent |
| Diatoms | Siliceous | Jurassic to Eocene |
| Coccoliths | Calcium carbonate | Triassic |

### 57. Features of the different derived rocks:

| Features | Derived rock types |
|---|---|
| Vesicles | Volcanic rocks |
| Amygdules | Volcanic rocks |
| Ropy lava | Volcanic rocks |
| Glass | Volcanic rocks |

### 58. Different constituents of the earth:

| Different parts/ Location of the Earth | Remarks |
|---|---|
| Most abundant rock on crust | Felsic |
| Most abundant minerals on crust | Plagioclase feldspar |
| Most abundant elements on crust | Oxygen |
| Most abundant elements in atmosphere | Nitrogen |
| Most abundant elements in universe | Hydrogen |

### 59. Types of plate setting and its Developed Features:

| Types of boundaries | Features |
|---|---|
| Convergent plate boundaries | Island Arc |
| Divergent plate boundaries | Mid-Oceanic ridge |
| Transform plate boundaries | Strike slip fault |

### 60. Plate setting and its Movement Direction:

| Features | Plate setting | Plate movements |
|---|---|---|
| Subduction zone | Convergent plate setting | Same direction |
| Island – arc | Convergent plate setting | Same direction |
| Trench | Convergent plate setting | Same direction |
| Mid – Oceanic ridge | Divergent plate setting | Opposite direction |

### 61. Sequence of Ophiolites:
The Ophiolite means "Snake stone" in Greek. **Ophiolites** is a sequence of the igneous rocks which composed upper basalt member, middle gabbro and lower peridotite.

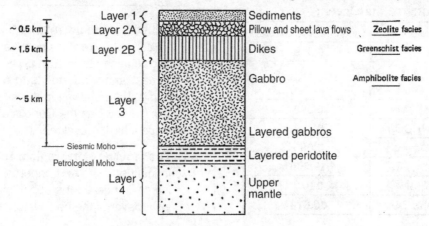

**62. Interior of the earth and its composition:**

| Interior of the Earth | Average compositions |
|---|---|
| Continental crust | Granitic |
| Oceanic crust | Basaltic |
| Mantle | Peridotite |
| Core | It is mostly metallic iron with small amounts of nickel and other elements. |

**66. Different Terms with Example:**

| Terms | Characteristics | Example |
|---|---|---|
| Isomorphism | Crystal structure may same with different compositions. | Albite ($NaAlSi_3O_8$ and orthoclase ($KAlSi_3O_8$) feldspars. |
| Solid solution | A series formed when there are intermediary minerals between two isomorphous minerals. | Albite and Anorthite solid solution series. |
| Polymorphism | Crystalline structures of the two forms are different with same composition. | Quartz |

**67. Mantle Transition zone:** The mantle transition zone lies between in depth about 410 km – 650 km in discontinues seismic depths. This is the depth of the phase changes.

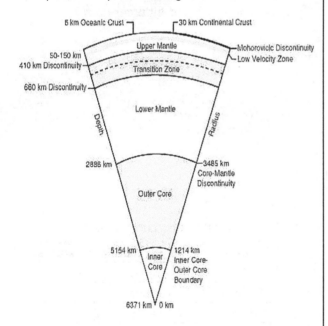

**69. Stability of the minerals:** In general, minerals are most stable at the temperature and pressure at which they form. In the case of the igneous rock minerals described in Bowen's Reaction Series, the higher temperature minerals such as olivine, pyroxene, quartz, etc.

**Bowens Reaction Series**

CONTINUOUS REACTION SERIES

DISCONTINUOUS REACTION SERIES

Declining temperature

Olivine
↘
Mg pyroxene  *(Spinels)*
↘
Mg Ca pyroxene
↘
Amphiboles

Calcic plagioclase
↙ (Bytownite)
Calc-alkalic plagioclase
↙ (Labradorite)
Alkali-calcic plagioclase
(Andesine)
↙
Alkalic plagioclase
(Oligoclase)

Biotites
↘  ↙
Potash feldspar
Muscovite
Quartz

**70. Different layer and discontinuities:**

| Layers | Discontinuity |
|---|---|
| Crust and Mantle | Mohorovicic |
| Upper Crust and Lower Crust | Conrad |
| Upper Mantle and Lower Mantle | Repetti |
| Lower Mantle and Outer Core | Guttenberg |

**71. Island–arc :** The island arc formation is due to sunduction zone of volcanic islands. A volcanoes form above hot spots like the Hawaiian Islands are not volcanic arcs. The Pacific Ring of Fire is home to many of like groups of islands. Islands form an arc when two oceanic plates converge creating a row of islands above the overriding plate. The older plate, which is heavier and denser, is forced beneath the lighter plate. The subducting plate begins to heat up as it descends into the lithosphere.

*Volcanic island eruption, USGS*

**Formation of island arc:** The leading edge of the oceanic plate begins to melt as it is forced deep into the crust and upper mantle. The melting plate feeds magma chambers that supply volcanic islands that form an arc when the molten rock erupts onto the ocean floor of the overriding plate.

**Mariana Islands:** The plates converging then deep oceanic trenches form to the ocean trenches on the overriding plate. The Marianas trench, where the Challenger deep is located, forms the boundary between two converging oceanic plates. The Mariana Islands are parallel to the trench and formed beside the trench.

72. **Asteroid belt:** The *Asteroid Belt* is an area of space between the orbits of Mars and Jupiter. That places it between 2.2 and 3.2 astronomical units (AU) from the Sun.

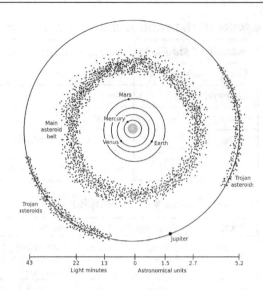

73. **Planets and its days:**

|  | Mercury | Venus | Earth | Moon | Mars | Jupiter | Saturn | Uranus | Neptune |
|---|---|---|---|---|---|---|---|---|---|
| Diameter (miles) | 3032 | 7521 | 7926 | 209 | 246 | 83 | 43 | 7999 | 102 |
| Rotation period (Hours) | 1407.6 | 5832.5 | 23.9 | 655.7 | 24.6 | 9.9 | 10.7 | 17.2 | 16.1 |
| Length of the day (Hours) | 4222.6 | 2802.0 | 24.0 | 708.7 | 24.7 | 9.9 | 10.7 | 17.2 | 16.1 |
| Orbital periods (days) | 88.0 | 224.7 | 365.2 | 27.3 | 687.0 | 4331 | 10.747 | 30.589 | 59.800 |

74. **Sunspot cycle:** The solar magnetic field is very high on the Sunspots region. The amount of magnetic flux that rises up to the Sun's surface varies with time in a cycle called the solar cycle. The one cycle complete about 11 years on average, this cycle also called sunspot cycle. Near the minimum of the solar cycle, it is rare to see sunspots on the Sun, and the spots that do appear are very small and short-lived. During this "solar maximum", there will be sunspots visible on the Sun almost all the time.

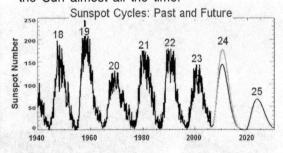

75. **Aphelion and Perihelion in Earth's orbit:**

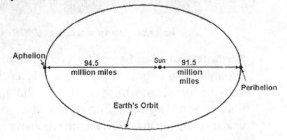

76. **Orbital plane of the moon inclined:** The Moon complete one revolution in earth orbit about 27.323 days, this is called **sidereal month.**

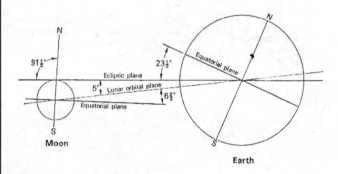

78. **Minerals with hardness scale:**

| Minerals | Formed process | Hardness |
|---|---|---|
| Quartz | Igneous | 7 |
| Feldspar | Igneous | 6 |
| Muscovite | Igneous | 2 – 2.5 |
| Bauxite | Sedimentary | 1 – 3 |

80. **Albedo:** It is the Latin means Whiteness, scale of the reflectance on the body. Surface albedo is the ratio of radiation reflected to the radiation incident on the surface. The proportion reflected is not only determined by properties of the surface itself,

but also by the spectral and angular distribution of solar radiation reaching the Earth's surface.

| Surface | Details | Albedo |
|---|---|---|
| Soil | Dark and wet | 0.05 |
| Dry and light | 0.40 | |
| Sand | | 0.15 – 0.45 |
| Grass | Long | 0.16 |
| | Short | 0.26 |
| Snow | Old | 0.45 |
| | Fresh | 0.95 |
| Agricultural Crops | | 0.18 – 0.25 |
| Tundra | | 0.18 – 0.25 |
| Forest | Deciduous | 0.15 – 0.20 |
| | Coniferous | 0.05 – 0.15 |
| Water | Small Zenith angle | 0.03 – 0.10 |
| | Large Zenith Angle | 0.10 – 1.00 |
| Ice | Sea | 0.30 – 0.45 |
| | Glacier | 0.20 – 0.40 |
| Clouds | Thick | 0.60 – 0.90 |
| | Thin | 0.30 – 0.50 |

81. **Hydraulic Conductivity:** Use an equation based on Darcy's Law to derive hydraulic conductivity experimentally. In the lab, a soil sample is placed in a small cylindrical container creating a one-dimensional soil cross-section through which the liquid, usually water, flows. This method is classified as either a constant-head test or a falling-head test depending on the flow state of the liquid. Constant-head tests are usually used on coarse-grained soils such as clean sands and gravels. Falling-head tests are used on finer grain samples. The basis for these calculations is Darcy's Law:

$$U = -K(dh/dz)$$

Where **U** = average velocity of fluid through a geometric cross-sectional area within the soil; h = hydraulic head; z = vertical distance in the soil; K = hydraulic conductivity. The dimension of K is length per unit of time (l/T).

Use a permeameter to conduct a Constant-Head Test. It is the most commonly used test for determining the saturated hydraulic conductivity of coarse-grained soils in the laboratory. A cylindrical soil sample of cross-sectional area A and length L is subjected to a constant head, H2 - H1, flow. The volume V of the test fluid that flows through the system during time t, determines the saturated hydraulic conductivity K of the soil:

$$K = VL/[At(H2 - H1)]$$

For best results, test several times using different head differences, H2 – H1.

| Materials | Permeability K (m/day) |
|---|---|
| Deep clay beds | $10^{-8} - 10^{-2}$ |
| Clay, sand, gravel mixture (till) | 0.001 – 0.1 |
| Clay soils (surface) | 0.01 – 0.2 |
| Loamy soils (surface) | 0.1 – 1.0 |
| Fine grained sand | 1 – 5 |
| Medium grained sand | 5 – 20 |
| Sand and gravel mixture | 5 – 100 |
| Coarse grained sand | 20 – 100 |
| Gravel | 100 – 1000 |

82. **Tethys Sea:** This name come from the Austrian Geologist Eduard Suess in 1893, there were two Tethys sea, one is show Permian geological age which developed C shape landmass is known as the Pangea and other is Paleo-Tethys which is the body of the water three side surrounded by the Pangea in the age of the Early Triassic developed by the sea floor spreading ridge. This extended all the way from Australia, at the extreme southeast end of Pangaea, northwest to the point where the plates of Europe, North America and Africa met roughly at the center of the 'C'. As the sea floor spread, it created a basin bordered on the south and west by the Gondwana continental plates of the Pangean landmass.

83. **Mineral's Hardness:**

| Minerals | Hardness |
|---|---|
| Quartz | 7 |
| Gypsum | 2 |
| Corundum | 9 |
| Orthoclase | 6 |

## Moh's Scale of Hardness:

| Hardness | Minerals |
|---|---|
| 1 | Talc |
| 2 | Gypsum |
| 3 | Calcite |
| 4 | Fluorite |
| 5 | Apatite |
| 6 | Feldspar |
| 7 | Quartz |
| 8 | Topaz |
| 9 | Corundum |
| 10 | Diamond |

### 84. Coral reef and its composition:

The coral is hard form by the calcium carbonate skeletons, sponges, worms, bivalves, parrotfish. The reef structures form due to coralline algae, bryozoans, mineral's cement, dead organic matter. Naturalist Charles Darwin's theory of coral formation is widely accepted. This theory recognizes three types of reefs: the fringing reef, the barrier reef, and the atoll.

**Fringing reef:** This reefs border shorelines of the continents and islands in tropical seas. This type reefs mainly develop in the South Pacific Hawaiian Islands. **Barrier reef:** This type reef develop due to land masses sink, when a Fringing reefs separated from the shorelines by the wide channels, land masses sink as erosion and sifting the plates. The Great Barrier Reef off northern Australia in the Indo-Pacific is the largest barrier reef in the world. **Atoll:** This type of the reef form due to the land mass as a small island, surrounded by the lagoon. Atolls commonly occur in the Indo-Pacific.

### 85. Constituents of the coal:

| Properties | Gondwana coal | Tertiary coal |
|---|---|---|
| Ash | Moderate to high | —— |
| Sulphur | Low | High |
| Rank | Bituminous to sub-bituminous | Lignite |
| Area | Central and eastern part of the peninsular India | North-eastern india |
| Example | Raniganj, Barakar | Tikak parbat, jaintia Hills |

### 87. Elements and its residence time in Sea water:

| Elements | Residence time (Years) |
|---|---|
| Chloride | 100,000,000 |
| Sodium | 68,000,000 |
| Magnesium | 13,000,000 |
| Potassium | 12,000,000 |
| Sulphate | 11,000,000 |
| Calcium | 1,000,000 |
| Carbonate | 110,000 |
| Silicon | 20,000 |
| Water | 4,100 |
| Manganese | 1300 |
| Aluminium | 600 |
| Iron | 200 |

### 88. Moh's scale of hardness:

| Hardness | Minerals | Mineral group |
|---|---|---|
| 1 | Talc | Silicate |
| 2 | Gypsum | Sulphate |
| 3 | Calcite | Carbonate |
| 4 | Fluorite | Halides |
| 5 | Apatite | Phosphate |
| 6 | Orthoclase | Silicate |
| 7 | Quartz | Silicate |
| 8 | Topaz | Silicate |
| 9 | Corundum | Oxide |
| 10 | Diamond | Native element |

### 89. Earthquake Waves and its physical behaviour: Seismic and the Earth's Structure:

The study if the interior of the earth and its physical study by the seismic waves, which layers is solids, liquid, and molten etc. the depth of the earthquakes also study by the help of the seismic waves. Mainly two types of waves, body and surface waves. The structure of Earth's deep interior cannot be studied directly. But geologists use seismic (earthquake) waves to determine the depths of layers of molten and semi-molten material within Earth. Because different types of earthquake waves behave differently when they encounter material in different states (for example, molten, semi-molten, solid), seismic stations established around Earth detect and record the strengths of the different types of waves and the directions from which they came.

### 90. Geological time scale:

## 91. Geomagnetic scale:

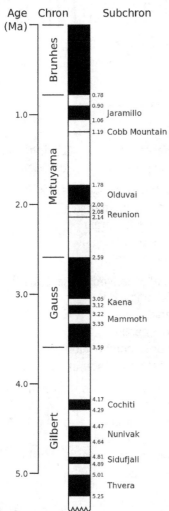

## 93. Types of deposits with example:

| Types of deposits | Example |
|---|---|
| Point bar deposit | Ox-bow lake deposits |
| Channel fill deposit | Crevasse-splay, natural levee |
| Flood plain deposit | Delta |
| Glacial deposit | Drumlin |

## 95. Cirque:
This is the erosional feature formed by the glacier, circular depressions formed due to plucking of the glacier.

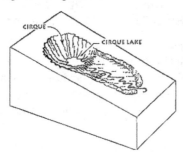

## 96. Crystal system and its example

| Crystal system | Mineral example |
|---|---|
| Cubic /Isometric system | Argentite |
| Monoclinic system | Calaverite |
| Triclinic system | Microcline |
| Orthorhombic system | Nagyagite |
| Tetragonal system | Bornite |
| Hexagonal system | Molybdenite |

## 97. Properties of Quartz:

| Properties | Remarks |
|---|---|
| Crystal system | Hexagonal |
| Chemical composition | $SiO_2$ |
| Colour | White, colourless |
| Streak | White |
| Lustre | Vitreous |
| Hardness | 7 |
| Cleavage | Absent |
| Twining | Common |
| Specific gravity | Low |

## 98. Poisson's ratio:
**Poisson's ratio** is the ratio of transverse contraction strain to longitudinal extension strain in the direction of stretching force. Tensile deformation is considered positive and compressive deformation is considered negative. The definition of Poisson's ratio contains a minus sign so that normal materials have a positive ratio. Poisson's ratio, is also called Poisson ratio or the Poisson coefficient.

| Lithology | Poisson's ratio |
|---|---|
| Shale | 0.28 – 0.43 |
| Coal | 0.35 – 0.45 |
| Limestone | 0.30 – 0.35 |
| Soft sandstone | 0.2 – 0.35 |
| Medium sandstone | 0.15 – 0.25 |
| Hard sandstone | 0.1 – 0.15 |

## 99. Joints with Example:

| Types of Joints | Example |
|---|---|
| Master joint | A joint remark the master structures |
| Conjugate joint | A joint set which many direction |
| Joint set | Individual set of joint |
| Joint system | A joint which more than one set |

# International Earth Science Olympiad (IESO)
## Entrance Exam, 2015

**Total Marks : 100**             **Time : 90 minutes**

---

1. Along the continent continent tectonic boundary there are slices of oceanic crust emplaced on to the continent. These are known as:
   - (a) Oceanites
   - (b) Ophiolites
   - (c) Oncolites
   - (d) Ophicalcites

2. The India Tibet tectonic boundary zone is characterized by peridotites, gabbros, pillow lavas and cherts and is known as:
   - (a) Shilakong nappe
   - (b) Indus Ophiolite Belt
   - (c) Central Crystallines
   - (d) Great Boundary Zone

3. In Ladakh Himalaya an island arc type of assemblage is exposed which contain rocks which are volcanic equivalents of syenite and are known as:
   - (a) Trachyte
   - (b) Pegmatite
   - (c) Rhyolite
   - (d) Basalt

4. Around Cretaceous to Eocene times profuse volcanic eruptions occurred in India and are known as:
   - (a) Panjal Traps
   - (b) Sylhette Traps
   - (c) Deccan Traps
   - (d) Rajamundri Traps

5. The roots of the Himalaya which constitutes the deep crust is made up of metamorphic rocks which are known as:
   - (a) Marble
   - (b) Slate
   - (c) Granulite
   - (d) Phyllite

6. Some of the deep crustal rocks are made up of pyroxene and plagioclase and are known as:
   - (a) Granite
   - (b) Pegmatite
   - (c) Syenite
   - (d) Gabbro

7. In Simla Himalaya metamorphic rock which can be easily cleaved into thin sheets and slabs are exposed. These are known as:
   - (a) Gneiss
   - (b) Marble
   - (c) Slate
   - (d) Quartzite

8. The crust of the Earth has the following mineral group as its predominant constituent:
   - (a) Quartz
   - (b) Pyroxene
   - (c) Feldspars
   - (d) Micas

9. Broadly the Himalayan region is a:
   - (a) Convergent margin
   - (b) Divergent margin
   - (c) Transform margin
   - (d) Transcurrent margin

10. Volcanically derived rocks contain the presence of glass indicating:
    - (a) Rapid cooling
    - (b) Slow cooling
    - (c) Magma composition
    - (d) Constant change in water content

11. Labradorite is common mineral in volcanic rocks belonging to the:
    - (a) Olivine group
    - (b) Pyroxene group
    - (c) Plagioclase group
    - (d) Mica group

12. Ruby is type of:
    - (a) Garnet
    - (b) Corundum
    - (c) Proxene
    - (d) Feldspar

13. Apatite is:
    - (a) Harder than orthoclase and softer than quartz
    - (b) Harder than fluorite and softer than orthoclase
    - (c) Harder than calcite but softer than fluorite
    - (d) Softer than both orthoclase and fluorite

14. Bright green feldspar is known as:
    - (a) Celsian
    - (b) Amazon stone
    - (c) Ruby
    - (d) Oriental sapphire

15. Lahar is a type of:
    - (a) sea wave
    - (b) wind
    - (c) debris flow
    - (d) lava flow

16. Permeability is the:
    - (a) Ability of material to store water.
    - (b) Ability of material to transmit water.
    - (c) Percentage of pore space in material.
    - (d) Percentage of voids in sedimentary rocks.

       2011 IESO (PP)–9-II

17. One of the following type of moraines forms where two lateral moraines merge.
    (a) End moraine
    (b) Medial moraine
    (c) Ground moraine
    (d) Lateral moraine

18. The sand dunes in sandy deserts are commonly asymmetrical in shape. The gentler windward side:
    (a) faces the downwind direction
    (b) faces the upwind direction
    (c) is oriented parallel to the wind direction
    (d) is not oriented any particular direction.

19. Which type of trees are commonly found in the monsoon region?
    (a) Evergreen
    (b) Conifers
    (c) Broad leaved deciduous
    (d) Thorny bushes

20. Which one of the following coastal features is formed by wave erosion and weathering?
    (a) Beach
    (b) Spit
    (c) Coral reef
    (d) Stack

21. Which one of the following is known for the highest tidal range in the world?
    (a) Bay of Fundy
    (b) Gulf of Khambhat
    (c) Severn Estuary
    (d) Gulf of Mexico

22. What is the term that is used for the layer of loose, heterogeneous weathered material lying on top of rocky hillslopes?
    (a) Soil
    (b) Laterite
    (c) Regolith
    (d) Alluvium

23. Which one of the following pairs of surface ocean currents transport warm water from low to higher latitudes?
    (a) Peru and Canary Currents
    (b) Labrador and Benguela Currents
    (c) Gulf Stream and Kuroshio Currents
    (d) Falkland and Brazil Currents

24. Which one of the following is a great circle?
    (a) Tropic of Cancer
    (b) Tropic of Capricorn
    (c) Prime Meridian
    (d) Ring of Fire

25. Relative humidity is "relative" to _____
    (a) Moisture
    (b) Temperature
    (c) Water vapour pressure
    (d) Altitude

26. Temperature inversion commonly occurs:
    (a) during early morning
    (b) during late afternoon
    (c) late evening
    (d) at night

27. The term 'heat island' is used in connection with a
    (a) Volcano
    (b) Hotspot
    (c) City
    (d) Road intersection

28. Contours which close in a circular manner and show decreasing values towards the inner side represent a
    (a) Hill
    (b) Depression
    (c) Valley
    (d) Sand dune

29. Hurricanes are not similar to
    (a) Cyclones
    (b) Typhoons
    (c) Willy-willies
    (d) Thunderstorms

30. Excessive _____ in soil will result in poor drainage.
    (a) Gravel
    (b) Sand
    (c) Silt
    (d) Clay

31. Large streamlined, wind-sculpted ridges that are parallel to the prevailing wind in deserts are known as
    (a) Yardang
    (b) Deflection hollows
    (c) Barchans
    (d) Parabolic dunes

32. Which one of the following will have the lowest value at the centre of the Earth?
    (a) Temperature
    (b) Density
    (c) Pressure
    (d) Gravity

33. The right ascension of the celestial objects which culminate at midnight on December 21 should be
    (a) 0h
    (b) 6h
    (c) 12h
    (d) 18h

34. The critical mass of a star to burn hydrogen in its core is
    (a) 1 solar mass
    (b) 0.5 solar mass
    (c) 0.08 solar mass
    (d) 0.25 solar mass

35. The Kepler's 3rd Laws states that
    (Where $P = $ *orbital period* and $a = $ *semi-major axis* of a planet)
    (a) $P^3/a^2 = 4\pi / G\, m_1 + m_2$
    (b) $P^2/a^3 = 4\pi^2 / G\, m_1 \times m_2$
    (c) $P^3/a^2 = 4\pi^2 / G\, m_1 + m_2$
    (d) none of the above

36. Which nuclear reaction is the energy source of low mass main sequence stars?
    (a) Fission
    (b) pp-chain
    (c) CNO cycle
    (d) Triple alpha

37. The pressure (P) in a white dwarf which is dominated by non-relativistic degenerate electrons. Its equation of state is given by (where $\rho$ denotes density)
    (a) $P \propto T$
    (b) $P \propto \rho 5/3$
    (c) $P \propto \rho 4/3$
    (d) $P \propto \rho$

**38.** In Charge Coupled Device (CCD), to have uniform response and to correct for pixel to pixel variations, one has to take which of the following frame.
(a) Flat field frame      (b) Dark frame
(c) Bias frame            (d) Object frame

**39.** The (B-V) colour index is Zero for stars of spectral type:
(a) A0      (b) B0
(c) F0      (d) G5

**40.** A clear sheet of Polaroid is placed on top of a similar sheet so that their polarizing axes make an angle of 30° with each other. The ratio of the intensity of emerging light to incident unpolarised light is:
(a) 1 : 4      (b) 1 : 3
(c) 1 : 2      (d) 3 : 8

**41.** All the ground-based Telescopes with apertures above 5 meter use which of the following kind of mounts:
(a) Alt-azimuth
(b) Symmetric Equatorial
(c) Asymmetric Equatorial
(d) None

**42.** Atmospheric Cherenkov detector is mostly used in detection of which of the following: wavelength photons.
(a) UV photon
(b) X – ray photon
(c) Both UV & X-ray photons
(d) High energy Gamma –ray photon

**43.** Due to precession, longitude of a star appears to be increasing per year at a rate of:
(a) 50.3 arc seconds
(b) 50.3 arc minutes
(c) 50.3 degrees
(d) 0.53 arc minutes

**44.** Barnard's star has largest proper motion than that of any star, which is about:
(a) 10.3 arc seconds/year
(b) 1.03 arc seconds/year
(c) 1.03 arc minutes/year
(d) 10.3 arc minutes/year

**45.** Which of these places is the coldest in December?
(a) Perth          (b) Santiago
(c) Johannesburg   (d) New Delhi

**46.** Which of the following regions of India gets the maximum precipitation during the northeast monsoon?
(a) Western Ghats   (b) North-east India
(c) Tamil Nadu      (d) Rajasthan

**47.** Western Disturbance occurs:
(a) Over southern India during summer
(b) Over northern India over summer
(c) Over northern India during winter
(d) Over southern India during winter

**48.** The Rainfall distribution in two regions P and Q is shown in the Table Monthly Rainfall (mm):

| Region | Jan | Feb | Mar | Apr | May | Jun | Jul | Aug | Sep | Oct | Nov | Dec |
|--------|-----|-----|-----|-----|-----|-----|-----|-----|-----|-----|-----|-----|
| P | 2 | 0 | 1 | 0 | 0 | 125 | 300 | 450 | 250 | 75 | 10 | 7 |
| Q | 98 | 99 | 102 | 101 | 100 | 115 | 100 | 95 | 105 | 99 | 101 | 105 |

Pick out the correct statement/s.
(a) The inter annual variability of rainfall is more at P than at Q.
(b) The intra-annual variability of rainfall is more at P than Q.
(c) The average monthly rainfall is about 120 mm at Q.
(d) The averages of monthly rainfall at P and Q are very different.

**49.** At present the Earth's surface is 70% oceans and 30 % land. If it were 100% oceans and no land:
(a) There will be no land breeze or sea breeze
(b) There will be sea breeze, but no land breeze
(c) There will no monsoons
(d) Both hemispheres will have the same season (e.g. summer) at the same time

**50.** The most turbulent zone of the Earth's atmosphere is:
(a) Thermosphere   (b) Troposphere
(c) Stratosphere   (d) Mesosphere

**51.** Coriolis force on air parcels is due to:
(a) Pressure gradients
(b) Temperature gradients
(c) Earth's revolution around the Sun
(d) Earth's rotation about its own axis

**52.** When is the relative humidity maximum over India?
(a) January   (b) March
(c) July      (d) December

**53.** During the day when do you expect to get the maximum air temperature?
(a) 6.00 am    (b) 12.00 am
(c) 12.00 pm   (d) 2.00 pm

**54.** A plane, a ship, a car and a bullock cart are moving westwards at 25°N. Which of them will have a bigger acceleration pulling them to the north?
(a) Ship         (b) Plane
(c) Bullock cart  (d) Car

PREVIOUS YEARS' PAPERS # 69

55. Which of the following oceans covers the most surface area of the Earth?
(a) The Pacific Ocean
(b) The Southern Ocean
(c) The Indian Ocean
(d) The Atlantic Ocean

56. What is the average salinity of the Ocean?
(a) 35 g/kg      (b) 35 kg/g
(c) 35 kg/kg     (d) 35 g/g

57. Which of the following seas has the maximum density?
(a) The Arabian Sea   (b) The Bay of Bengal
(c) The Red Sea       (d) The Dead Sea

58. Which is the warmest region in the Oceans?
(a) The Bay of Bengal barrier layer
(b) The Indo-Pacific warm pool
(c) The Arabian Sea seasonal warm pool
(d) The Dead Sea

59. What is the typical density of the oceans?
(a) 1.07 g/cc     (b) 1.27 g/cc
(c) 1.027 g/cc    (d) 1.0027 g/cc

60. Warm ocean currents such as the Gulf Stream are known to mainly cause:
(a) Less rains over the adjoining continent
(b) Desertification in the adjoining continent
(c) Grasslands to form in the adjoining continent
(d) Warming in the adjoining continent

61. The Ocean basin which is mostly isolated from the rest of the Ocean is:
(a) The Southern Ocean
(b) The Bay of Bengal
(c) The South China Sea
(d) The Mediterranean Sea

62. Mixing in the ocean is most rapid:
(a) In the vertical direction
(b) In the horizontal direction
(c) Along the surfaces of equal density
(d) Along the latitude circles

63. Which of the following is responsible for deep ocean circulation?
(a) Winds
(b) Earth tremors
(c) Migration of whales
(d) Temperature and salinity differences

64. How much is a knot, the unit of speed of ships? (choose the nearest correct value)
(a) ~1.8 km/h     (b) ~1.8 km/min
(c) ~1.8 m/h      (d) ~18 m/min

65. Pick the correct statement:
(a) The oceans are heated from below and the atmosphere is heated from above

(b) Both the ocean and the atmosphere are heated from above
(c) Both the ocean and the atmosphere are heated from below
(d) The ocean is heated from above and the atmosphere is heated from below

66. The velocity of sound propagation:
(a) Increases with temperature and is more in seawater than in air
(b) Decreases with temperature and is more in seawater than in air
(c) Increases with temperature and is less in seawater than air
(d) Decreases with temperature and is more in sea water than air

67. Marine algae which do photosynthesis are adversely affected by the presence of:
(a) cadmium        (b) zinc
(c) phosphorus     (d) Heavy metals

68. Biological oxygen demand is maximum at a depth of:
(a) 0-100 m        (b) 100-1000 m
(c) 1000-3000 m    (d) 3000-4000 m

69. Identify the rivers with highest sediment yield:
(a) Indus          (b) Huang Ho
(c) Nile           (d) Amazon

70. About 90 per cent of the atmosphere's total mass lies between the ground surface and a height of about:
(a) 5 km           (b) 10 km
(c) 50 km          (d) 110 km

71. Rocks containing fossils of one of the following would be the oldest:
(a) Dinosaur bones
(b) Trilobites
(c) Bird bones
(d) Woolly mammoth bones

72. Volcanic eruptions in Iceland are not likely to be associated with:
(a) Landslide      (b) Flood
(c) Hurricane      (d) Earthquake

73. Himalia is the name of a:
(a) Peak in Nepal Himalaya
(b) Peak in Grand Canyon
(c) Satellite of Jupiter
(d) Mountain on Mars

74. Hadley cell is a circulation associated with:
(a) Ocean          (b) Atmosphere
(c) Groundwater    (d) River

75. The average depth of the world ocean is close to:
(a) 2 km           (b) 3 km
(c) 4 km           (d) 5 km

**76.** Floating ice of the oceans formed by direct freezing of ocean water is known as:
(a) Sea ice
(b) Ocean ice
(c) Iceberg
(d) Ice Island

**77.** The minimum reading of air temperature typically occurs:
(a) Just after sunset
(b) About mid-night
(c) Around 2:00 am
(d) Close to sunrise

**78.** Which is NOT a correct association of earth components and properties?
(a) Hydrosphere—lakes, oceans
(b) Atmosphere—oxygen—ozone screening layer
(c) Lithosphere—source of mineral elements
(d) Atmosphere—78% oxygen, 21% nitrogen

**79.** The proven phenomenon where visible and U-V radiation is absorbed at the earth's surface and re-emitted as longer infrared wavelengths that are then absorbed by water vapour, carbon dioxide, and methane, is known as:
(a) The ozone layer
(b) The greenhouse effect
(c) Global warming
(d) The Gaia hypothesis

**80.** The present concern over the apparent increase in the temperature of the biosphere is a "greenhouse effect" caused primarily by the:
(a) Decrease in the human population on earth
(b) Increase in carbon dioxide in the atmosphere from the burning of fossil fuels
(c) Increased photosynthesis from increased carbon dioxide
(d) Conversion of grasslands to farmlands

**81.** A terrestrial environment represented by a major biotic unit consisting of a characteristic and easily recognized variety of plant life is called:
(a) A zoogeographical realm
(b) An ecocline
(c) An ecosphere
(d) A biom

**82.** Which is a correct description of the air circulation patterns of the earth?
(a) Warm air rises at the equator and moves all the way to the poles where it cools and sinks
(b) In the Northern Hemisphere the surface air moving north east from 30 to 60 degrees is moist and encounters cold air moving south to form a stormy region
(c) Air evaporating at the equator is dry and therefore causes deserts when it sinks at 30 degrees north
(d) The polar cells are cold and cause rainfall as they descend to the equator

**83.** It is thought that the northern landmass that resulted from the division of Pangaea fragmented and gave rise to:
(a) North America, most of Eurasia, and Greenland
(b) North America and Central and South America
(c) Eurasia, Africa, and Australia
(d) South America, Antarctica, and Australia

**84.** The recent Mangalayan expedition of the ISRO is to explore:
(a) Remote sensing of Pluto
(b) Surface exploration of Jupiter and its moon.
(c) Surface exploration of Saturn
(d) Exploration of the Mars.

**85.** Why does continental drift theory not help explain the distribution of placental mammals?
(a) Placental mammals were agile enough to cross all continental barriers
(b) Placental mammals evolved after the breakup of the major plates
(c) Their fossils were subject to more deformation
(d) We just haven't located enough fossils of them

**86.** When a land bridge was re-established between North and South America at the end of the Pliocene, what happened?
(a) Nothing happened because the major mammal groups had not evolved differently since the previous connection had been broken
(b) Only the porcupine, armadillo, and opossum invaded from the south and survived
(c) Many hoofed animals moved north and displaced North American fauna
(d) There was an enormous exchange of species in both directions

**87.** The mass dinosaur's extinction took place around Myrs in India.
(a) 20-5 Myrs ago
(b) 40-23 Myrs go
(c) 65-63 Myrs ago
(d) 74-70 Myrs ago

**88.** The stromatolites are:
(a) Layered biochemical accretionary structures
(b) Earliest live forms on the earth
(c) Red brown algae
(d) Associated commonly with granite

**89.** Arsenic contamination in the groundwater is widely prevalent in India in the state of:
(a) Goa and Himachal Pradesh
(b) Andhra Pradesh
(c) Tamil Nadu
(d) West Bengal

**90.** Diamonds occur in _____ rocks.
  (a) Sandstone        (b) Granite gneiss
  (c) Kimberlite       (d) Basalt and limestone

**91.** The characteristics that allow a rock to hold fluids and gases is known as:
  (a) Virtuosity       (b) Capacity
  (c) Porosity         (d) Elasticity

**92.** Size, shape and arrangement of component minerals determine the property of a rock known as:
  (a) Structure        (b) Texture
  (c) Composition      (d) Strength

**93.** Sedimentary rocks are characterized by:
  (a) Schistosity      (b) Bedding
  (c) Foliation        (d) Lineation

**94.** Coal and Petroleum are generally encountered in:
  (a) Metamorphic rocks
  (b) Igneous rocks
  (c) Sedimentary rocks
  (d) Cataclastic rocks

**95.** The deepest trench on the ocean floor is known as:
  (a) Owens trench
  (b) Mariana Trench
  (c) San Andreas Trench
  (d) Carlsberg Trench

**96.** The green colour of the ocean and sea waters is due to the presence of:
  (a) Colour of water
  (b) Colour of algae
  (c) Colour of ocean floor
  (d) Colour of sun light

**97.** Which ocean has the largest quantity of poly-metallic nodules?
  (a) Atlantic         (b) Pacific
  (c) Indian           (d) Antarctic

**98.** Weathering of rocks under warm and alternating wet and dry climatic conditions leaves behind a residue known as:
  (a) Latite           (b) Laterite
  (c) Le chatelierite  (d) Levinsonite

**99.** Gypsum deposits are:
  (a) Clastic deposits
  (b) Evaporite deposits
  (c) Supergene deposits
  (d) Bog deposits

**100.** If one travels from Tibet to India that is from North to South across the Himalaya: What type of tectonic boundary does one come across between Tibet and India in modern times:
  (a) Subduction zone   (b) Mid-ocean ridge
  (c) Island arc        (d) Collisional boundary

## ANSWERS

| 1 | 2 | 3 | 4 | 5 | 6 | 7 | 8 | 9 | 10 |
|---|---|---|---|---|---|---|---|---|----|
| (b) | (b) | (a) | (c) | (c) | (d) | (c) | (c) | (a) | (a) |
| **11** | **12** | **13** | **14** | **15** | **16** | **17** | **18** | **19** | **20** |
| (c) | (b) | (b) | (b) | (c) | (b) | (b) | (b) | (c) | (d) |
| **21** | **22** | **23** | **24** | **25** | **26** | **27** | **28** | **29** | **30** |
| (a) | (c) | (c) | (c) | (b) | (d) | (c) | (b) | (d) | (d) |
| **31** | **32** | **33** | **34** | **35** | **36** | **37** | **38** | **39** | **40** |
| (a) | (d) | (b) | (c) | (d) | (b) | (b) | (a) | (a) | (d) |
| **41** | **42** | **43** | **44** | **45** | **46** | **47** | **48** | **49** | **50** |
| (a) | (d) | (a) | (a) | (d) | (c) | (c) | (b) | (a) | (b) |
| **51** | **52** | **53** | **54** | **55** | **56** | **57** | **58** | **59** | **60** |
| (d) | (c) | (d) | (b) | (a) | (a) | (d) | (b) | (c) | (c) |
| **61** | **62** | **63** | **64** | **65** | **66** | **67** | **68** | **69** | **70** |
| (d) | (c) | (d) | (a) | (d) | (a) | (d) | (b) | (b) | (b) |
| **71** | **72** | **73** | **74** | **75** | **76** | **77** | **78** | **79** | **80** |
| (b) | (c) | (c) | (b) | (c) | (a) | (d) | (d) | (b) | (b) |
| **81** | **82** | **83** | **84** | **85** | **86** | **87** | **88** | **89** | **90** |
| (d) | (b) | (a) | (d) | (b) | (d) | (c) | (a) | (d) | (c) |
| **91** | **92** | **93** | **94** | **95** | **96** | **97** | **98** | **99** | **100** |
| (c) | (b) | (b) | (c) | (b) | (b) | (b) | (b) | (b) | (d) |

# HINTS AND SOLUTIONS

1. **Ophiolite Sequence:** Ophiolite is a sequence of the stratified igneous rock complex composed of basalt, gabbro and peridotite members. The term "ophiolite" means "snake stone" in Greek. Basalt and gabbro are commonly altered to patchy green rocks, and peridotite is mostly changed into black, greasy serpentinite.

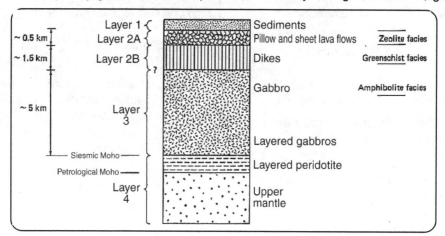

2. **Thrust Belt:**

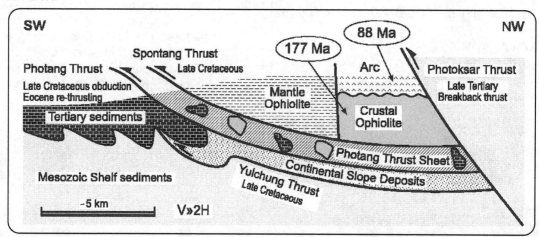

3. **Plutonic and Its Volcanic Rocks:**

| Volcanic Equivalent | Plutonic |
|---|---|
| Basalt | Gabbro |
| Rhyolite | Granite |
| Dacite | Granodiorite |
| Trachyte | Syenite |
| Andesite | Diorite |
| Phonolite | Nepheline syenite |
| Rhyodacite | Adamellite |

4. **Traps and Its Geological Age:**

| Traps | Geological age |
|---|---|
| Panjal Traps | Early – middle Permian |
| Sylhet Traps | Middle Jurassic |
| Deccan Traps | End Cretaceous |
| Rajamundri Traps | K/T boundary |

5. **Different rock units and its Indian Distribution:**

| Rock Types | Distribution in Indian stratigraphy |
|---|---|
| Marble | Makarana Marble of Rajasthan |
| Slate | Metamorphic succession of South India |
| Granulite | Eastern Ghats of the India |
| Phyllite | Archean rocks of the South India |

## 6. Rocks with Associated Minerals:

| Rocks | Remarks |
|---|---|
| Granite | Alkali feldspar predominant |
| Pegmatite | It is a textural terms |
| Syenite | Alkali feldspar dominant |
| Gabbro | Plagioclase of labradorite |
| Nepheline Syenite | Felspar + Felspathoid |

## 8. Zone with Minerals/Elements Constituents:

| Different zone | Minerals/Elements Constituents |
|---|---|
| Quartz | $SiO_2$ (Silicon and oxygen) |
| Pyroxene | $R2SiO_3$ (R = Mg, Ca, Fe, Na, Mn, Li) |
| Feldspar | $RAlSi_3O_8$ (R= K, Na, Ca, Ba) |
| Micas | K, Mg, Fe, Al, silicate with (OH) |

## 9. Plate Margin with Example:

| Types of margin | Example Region |
|---|---|
| Convergent margin | Trench |
| Divergent margin | Mid Oceanic ridge |
| Transform margin | Strike – slip fault |

## 10. Type of Magma Cooling with Grain Size:

| Types of Cooling | Grain Size |
|---|---|
| Rapid cooling | Fine grained glassy |
| Slow cooling | Course grained rock |
| Magma composition | Solid + liquid + gas |
| Lava composition | Liquid + gas |

## 11. Minerals and its Group:

| Minerals groups | Example |
|---|---|
| Olivine group | Forsterite, fayalite |
| Pyroxene group | Enstatite, hypersthene, augite |
| Plagioclase group | Albite, anorthite |
| Mica group | Muscovite, biotite, |

## 12. Minerals with Gem Varieties:

| Minerals | Gem varieties |
|---|---|
| Garnet | Almandine |
| Corundum | Ruby, sapphire |
| Pyroxene | Hiddenite |
| Feldspar | Aventurine |

## 13. Moh's Scale of Hardness:

| Hardness | Minerals | Mineral group |
|---|---|---|
| 1 | Talc | Silicate |
| 2 | Gypsum | Sulphate |
| 3 | Calcite | Carbonate |
| 4 | Fluorite | Halides |
| 5 | Apatite | Phosphate |
| 6 | Orthoclase | Silicate |
| 7 | Quartz | Silicate |
| 8 | Topaz | Silicate |
| 9 | Corundum | Oxide |
| 10 | Diamond | Native element |

## 14. Mineral's Varieties:

| Varieties | Minerals |
|---|---|
| Celsian | Feldspar |
| Amazon stone | Quartz |
| Ruby | Corundum |
| Oriental sapphire | Corundum |

## 16. Hydrological Terms:

| Terms | Remarks |
|---|---|
| Porosity | Pore spaced in a specific volume |
| Permeability | Interconnected pore spaces |
| Aquifer | Porous with permeable |
| Aquifuge | Neither porous nor permeable |

## 17. Moraine and its Types:

| Types of Moraine | Remarks |
|---|---|
| End moraine | Last stage of the moraine |
| Medial moraine | When two lateral moraine join together |
| Ground moraine | Material drag under the glacier |
| Lateral moraine | From the freeze – thaw weathering of valley sides, carried at the side of the glacier |

**Types of Moraine**

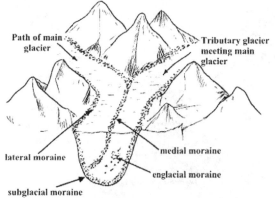

## 18. Dune Direction with Features:

| Sand Dune Direction | Feature |
|---|---|
| Faces in downwind direction | Barchans dune |
| Faces the upwind direction | Parabolic dune |
| Parallel to the wind direction | Longitudinal dune |
| Not oriented any particular direction | Star dune |

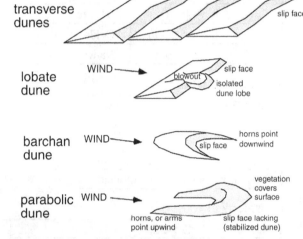

transverse dunes

lobate dune

barchan dune

parabolic dune

## 19. Monsoon with Different Tree:

| Types of Trees | Monsoon Example |
|---|---|
| Evergreen | Tropical evergreen (Coastal area of Tamil Nadu) |
| Conifers | Temperate area |

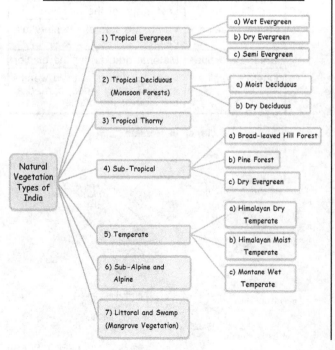

## 20. Features with Development:

| Features | Formed |
|---|---|
| Beach | Sea/ocean |
| Spit | Sea |
| Coral reef | Sea |
| Stack | Sea |

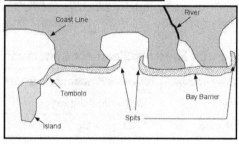

**22. Regolith:** Regolith is a loose, heterogeneous layer on the solid rocks which contain soils, minerals matter, and supports the tree. It is distributed on the Earth, moon, and also some planets.

## 23. Currents and its properties:

| Currents | Properties |
|---|---|
| Peru current | Peru current also called Humboldt current, low salinity Ocean current of cold that flow north along western coast of South America. |
| Canary current | It is wind –driven surface current that is part of the north Atlantic Gyre. |
| Labrador current | It is cold current in the North Atlantic Ocean Current which flow Arctic Ocean to the east coast of Nova Scotia. |
| Benguela current | It is the northward flowing ocean current that develop the eastern portion of the South Atlantic ocean gyre. |

**24. Tropic of Cancer and Capricorn:** The tropic of cancer is 23.5 degree north from the equator, and tropic of Capricorn is 23.5 degree south of the equator.

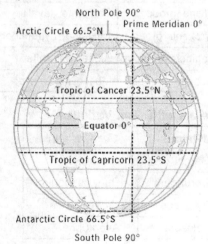

**25. Relative humidity:** It is defined as the amount of the water vapour in the air at a particular time that required to saturate the air. It is measured in the per cent with saturation humidity.

$$\text{Relative Humidity} = \frac{\text{actual vapour density}}{\text{saturation vapour density}} \times 100\%$$

**28. Contours and its Represents Topography:**

| Contour Direction | Features |
|---|---|
| Close interval | Step slop features |
| Long interval | Gentle slop features |

**29. Hurricanes:** It is the characterstics of the tropical cyclone which rotating low pressure weather system that has organized thunderstorms but no fronts due to different density of two air masses. When a tropical depression, tropical cyclone surface winds of less than 39 miles per hours (mph). The maximum sustained winds of 39 mph or higher are called tropical storms. When a storm's maximum sustained winds reach 74 mph, it is called a hurricane. Hurricanes originate in the Atlantic basin, which includes the Atlantic Ocean, Caribbean Sea, and Gulf of Mexico, the eastern North Pacific Ocean, and, less frequently, the central North Pacific Ocean. A six-year rotating list of names, updated and maintained by the World Meteorological Organization, is used to identify these storms.

**31. Landform formed by Wind:**

| Features | Characteristics |
|---|---|
| Yardang | Wind abrasion |
| Deflection hollows | Wind erosion feature, e.g. Ventifacts |
| Barchans | Wind directed downward form cresentic shaped. |
| Parabolic dunes | Opposite to the barchans dunes |

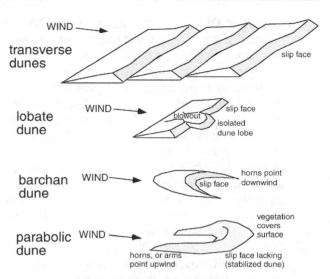

**32. Temperature, density, pressure and gravity variation with interior of the Earth:**

| Terms | Maximum | Minimum |
|---|---|---|
| Density | Core | Surface |
| Pressure | Core | Surface |
| Temperature | Core | Surface |

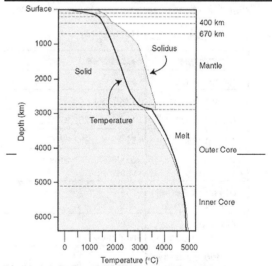

| Layer | Thickness (Km) | Density (g/cm³) | | Composition |
|---|---|---|---|---|
| | | Top | Bottom | |
| **Crust** | 30 | 2.2 | — | Silicic rocks |
| | | — | 2.9 | Andesite, basalt |
| **Upper mantle** | 720 | 3.4 | — | Peridotite, eclogite, olivine |
| | | — | 4.4 | Perovskite, oxides |
| **Lower mantle** | 2171 | 4.4 | — | Magnesium |
| | | — | 5.6 | Oxides |
| **Outer core** | 2259 | 9.9 | — | Iron + oxygen, sulphur |
| | | — | 12.2 | Nickel alloy |
| **Inner core** | 1221 | 12.8 | — | Iron + oxygen, sulphur |
| | | — | 13.1 | Nickel alloy |
| **Total thickness** | 6401 | | | |

33. **Celestial Objects:** Also called astronomical objects, different shape and size in our universe with empty space. Such as the Moon, the Sun, an asteroid, planet or star. Our universe contains an amazing array of celestial objects, sometimes referred to as celestial bodies or astronomical objects. Though most of the observable cosmos is composed of empty space, this cold, dark void that is sparsely populated by a number of astronomical objects that range from the common to the bizarre. Known collectively by astronomers as celestial objects, celestial bodies, astronomical objects, and astronomical bodies, they are the stuff that fills the empty space of the universe. Most of us are familiar with the stars, planets, and moons. But beyond these everyday celestial objects, lies an amazing collection of other wondrous sights. There are colorful nebulae, delicate star clusters, and massive galaxies. Pulsars and quasars add to the mystery, while black holes swallow up every bit of matter that comes too close. And now, the search is on to identify the mysterious, invisible objects known as dark matter. Join Sea and Sky for an intriguing journey as we discover these amazing celestial objects.

34. **Properties of the Hydrogen:**

| Properties | Remarks |
|---|---|
| Atomic number | 1 |
| Atomic weight | 1.007994 |
| Melting Point | 13.81 K (-252.87°C or -434.81°F) |
| Boiling point | 20.28 K (-252.87°C or -423.17°F) |
| Density | 0.00008988 grams per cubic centimetre |
| Phase at Room Temperature | Gas |
| Element Classification | Non-metal |
| Periodic number | 1 |
| Greek words | **Hydro** and **genes**, which together mean "water forming." |

35. **Kepler's Laws of Planetary motions:**

| Kepler's Law of Planetary Motion | |
|---|---|
| **First law** | The path of the planets about the sun is elliptical in shape, with the center of the sun being located at one focus. (The Law of Ellipses) |
| **Second law** | An imaginary line drawn from the center of the sun to the center of the planet will sweep out equal areas in equal intervals of time. (The Law of Equal Areas) |

| **Third law** | The ratio of the squares of the periods of any two planets is equal to the ratio of the cubes of their average distances from the sun. (The Law of Harmonies) |
|---|---|

37. **Equation of State to the Dwarf:** In the stellar interior, as we shall see, the temperature is so high that most elements are completely ionised. Therefore we have electrons, ions and photons at any radius $r$. They collide with each other very frequently and exchange energy, and thus local thermal equilibrium is achieved very quickly. So electrons, ions and photons have identical temperature locally. Notice that there is still a large-scale temperature gradient across the star, $T(r)$. However, a temperature gradient exists but we assume that it is small enough to be neglected for thermodynamic purposes. The local thermal equilibrium simplifies the problems tremendously. The equation of state describes how the pressure changes with density and temperature

$$P = P(\rho, T, Xi) \quad (1)$$

We already know the equation of state for an ideal gas, $P = nkT$, (2)

Where n is the number density of particles, k is the Boltzmann constant, and T is the temperature. The equation of state can depart from the classical ideal gas in three ways:

- The electrons can be highly relativistic.
- In some cases, the electrons are degenerate. In such cases, we have the so-called degenerate pressure to balance the gravity. The degenerate pressure is most important in very compact stars, such as white dwarfs and neutron stars.
- In massive stars, the pressure provided by radiation can be important.

38. **Charge Coupled Device (CCD):** The CCD is a integrated device which is join circuit etched onto a silicon surface. CCDs come in a wide variety of sizes and types and are used in many applications from cell phone cameras to high-end scientific applications. When Photons incident on this surface generate charge that can be ready by electronics and turned into a digital copy of the light patterns falling on the device. In the given below, the basic CCD consists of a closely spaced array of metal-oxide-semiconductor (MOS) diodes on a continuous insulator layer (oxide) that covers the semiconductor substrate.There are three gate electrodes on the top of Silicon dioxide, and the voltage applied can control the actions of charge

storage and transfer of CCD, as the surface depletion can be controlled: a slight higher bias applied on the center electrode will induce the center of MOS a greater depletion and formed a potential well, while a higher bias on the side electrode will cause the transfer of minority carriers in n-type semiconductor. Thus the quiescent storage site of MOS can be adjusted by the potential on the electrodes.

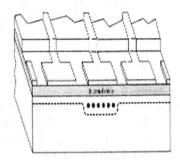

**Fig.** *Cross section of a three-phase charge-coupled device.*

**39. Colour Index of the Spectral:** The colour index of the spectral use to spectrum variation from objects. Based on the emphirical formula there are different class, spectra classes such as the Ao and B5 and G2.

| Stellar Spectral Class | | |
|---|---|---|
| Spectral Class | Approximate Surface Temperature | Example |
| O | 30,000 | Mintaka (O9) |
| A | 10,000 | Vega (A0), Sirius (A1) |
| B | 20,000 | Rigel (B8) |
| F | 7000 | Canopus (F0) |
| G | 6000 | Sun (G2), Alpha Centauri (G2) |
| K | 4000 | Areturus (K2) Aldebarna (K5) |
| M | 3000 | Betelgeuse (M2), Barnard's Star (M5) |

**41. Telescope and its properties:** There are two basic types of telescopes, refractors and reflectors. The part of the telescope that gathers the light, called the **objective**, determines the type of telescope. A **refractor** telescope uses a glass lens as its objective. The glass lens is at the front of the telescope and light is bent (refracted) as it passes through the lens. A **reflector** telescope uses a mirror as its objective. The mirror is close to the rear of the telescope and light is bounced off (reflected) as it strikes the mirror.

**Refractor Telescopes:** The refractor telescope uses a lens to gather and focus light. The first telescopes built were refractors. The small telescopes sold in department stores are refractors, as well as, those used for rifle scopes.

**Merits:**
- Refractor telescopes are rugged. After the initial alignment, their optical system is more resistant to misalignment than the reflector telescopes.
- The glass surface inside the tube is sealed from the atmosphere so it rarely needs cleaning.
- Since the tube is closed off from the outside, air currents and effects due to changing temperatures are eliminated. This means that the images are steadier and sharper than those from a reflector telescope of the same size.

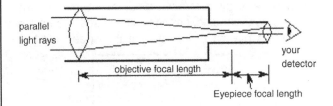

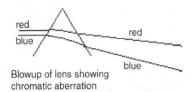

Blowup of lens showing chromatic aberration

**Demerits:**
- Though excellent refractors are still made, the disadvantages of the refractor telescope have blocked the construction of very large refractors for use in astronomical research.
- All refractors suffer from an effect called **chromatic aberration** ("color deviation or distortion") that produces a rainbow of colors around the image. Because of the wave nature of light, the longer wavelength light (redder colors) is bent less than the shorter wavelength light (bluer colors) as it passes through the lens. This is used in prisms to produce pretty rainbows, but can it ruin an image.

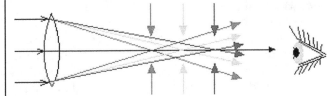

There a couple of ways to reduce chromatic aberration. One way uses multiple compensating lenses to counteract chromatic aberration. The other way uses a very long objective *focal length* (distance between the focus and the objective) to minimize the effect. This is why the early refracting telescopes were made very long.

42. **Wave-length photons:** A **photon** is the quantum of electromagnetic radiation. The term **quantum** is the smallest elemental unit of a quantity, or the smallest discrete amount of something. Thus, one quantum of electromagnetic energy is called a photon. The plural of quantum is quanta. The concept of photons and quanta comes from **quantum mechanics** and quantum theory. Quantum mechanics is a mathematical model that describes the behaviour of particles on an atomic and subatomic scale. It demonstrates that matter and energy are quantized, or come in small discrete bundles, on the smallest scales imaginable. A photon propagates at the speed of light.

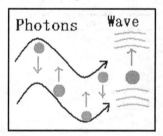

A photon describes the particle properties of an electromagnetic wave instead of the overall wave itself. In other words, we can picture an electromagnetic wave as being made up of individual particles called photons. Both representations are correct and reciprocal views of electromagnetic waves. For example, light exhibits wave properties under conditions of refraction or interference. Particle properties are exhibited under conditions of emission or absorption of light.

43. **Precession of the Earth's Axis:** The Earth's axis rotates (precesses) just as a spinning top does. The period of precession is about 26,000 years. Therefore, the North Celestial Pole will not always be point towards the same star field. Precession is caused by the gravitational pull of the Sun and the Moon on the Earth.

44. **Barnard's Star:** This star is red, very low mass dwarf about six light year from the earth. It is fourth closest known individual star to the Sun. Despite its proximity, at a dim apparent magnitude of about nine, it is not visible with the unaided eye; it is much brighter in the infrared than it is in visible light. The star is named after the American astronomer E. E. Barnard. He was not the first to observe the star (it appeared on Harvard University plates in 1888 and 1890), but in 1916 he measured its proper motion (which is a function of its close proximity to earth, and not of its actual space velocity) as 10.3 arcseconds per year, which remains the largest proper motion of any star relative to the Sun. In 2016, the International Astronomical Union organized a Working Group on Star Names (WGSN) to catalogue and standardize proper names for stars. The WGSN approved the name *Barnard's Star* for this star on 1 February 2017 and it is now so entered in the IAU Catalog of Star Names.

46. **Northeast Monsoon and Southwest Monsoon in India:** Northern Monsoon season over peninsular India in October to December, also called Post Monsoon Season or "Retreating southwest Monsoon Season". Northeast Monsoon season is the major period of rainfall activity over south peninsula, particularly in the eastern half comprising of the meteorological subdivisions of Coastal Andhra Pradesh, Rayalaseema and Tamil Nadu-Pondicherry. For Tamil Nadu this is the main rainy season accounting for about 48% of the annual rainfall. Coastal districts of the State get nearly 60% of the annual rainfall and the interior districts get about 40-50% of the annual rainfall. The period October-December (Northeast Monsoon) contributing about 20 % of the annual total.

47. **Western Disturbance monsoon:** The western disturbance is a low pressure area or a trough over surface or the upper air in the westerly winds regime, 20 degree North, causing changes in pressure, wind pattern and temperature fields by the R.M. Saxena a meteorologist. It is frequently used terminology for the weather of the Indian

continent. It mainly moves from the west to east direction. It is originated in the Caspian Sea or the Mediterranean Sea as tropical cyclones. WD also affects the weather system and agriculture of the Indian subcontinents.

49. **Distribution of the Ocean and Land on Earth's surface:** The Earth is called blue planets due to most abundant of the waters in different forms, about 70.8% bout cover.

| Different part of the earth | % (Earth's Total Surface Area) | Area (Sq. Kms) |
|---|---|---|
| Earth's Surface Area Covered by Water | 70.8 | 361,132,000 |
| Earth's Surface Area Covered by Land | 29.2% | 148,940,000 |
| Total | 100% | |

**Earth's Surface Area Covered by Water**

| Oceans | Percent (%) | Area (Sq Kms) |
|---|---|---|
| Pacific Ocean | 30.5% | 155,557,000 |
| Atlantic Ocean | 20.8% | 76,762,000 |
| Indian Ocean | 14.4% | 68,556,000 |
| Southern Ocean | 4.0% | 20,237,000 |
| Arctic Ocean | 2.8% | 14,056,000 |

50. **Turbulent zone of the Earth's Atmosphere:** The Earth's atmosphere is a zone of the irregular air motion in a small scale by the wind speed and direction. It is a mixture of the different substance, water vapour, smoke as a horizontal as well as vertical direction. The turbulence zone differs from the different height from the surface of the earth. Due to solar radiation heats the surface and its become warmer and more buoyant than the height.

51. **Coriolis force with its effect to Earth's Rotation:** The term Coriolis force is named in nineteen century by Gustave Coriolis a French mathematician. The Coriolis force deflect the wind, it also effect the rotating body, it is measured by the mass of the object and the object's rate of rotation. The Coriolis force effect ninety degree to the body's axis. In the respect of the earth the spins on its axis from west to east, and the coriolis force act in north to south direction. At the earth's equator the Coriolis force is zero.

52. **Humidity and its Types:** The humidity is defined as the amount of the water vapour in the air. There is different type of humidity like absolute, specific etc. Absolute humidity is equal to the mass of water vapour divided by the total volume of air, or water vapour density. It also changes due to the

volume of an air parcel changes. **Specific humidity** is equal to the mass of water vapour in the air divided by the *total* mass of the air parcel (including the water vapour).

The relative humidity is defined as the:

**Relative humidity** = water vapour content/ water vapour capacity.

**Relative humidity** = actual vapour pressure/ saturation vapour pressure × 100%

**Relative humidity** = actual mixing ratio/ saturation mixing ratio × 100%

55. **Types of Ocean and Its Cover Area:**

**Earth's Surface Area Covered by Water**

| Oceans | Percent (%) | Area (Sq Kms) |
|---|---|---|
| Pacific Ocean | 30.5% | 155,557,000 |
| Atlantic Ocean | 20.8% | 76,762,000 |
| Indian Ocean | 14.4% | 68,556,000 |
| Southern Ocean | 4.0% | 20,237,000 |
| Arctic Ocean | 2.8% | 14,056,000 |

58. **Warmest region in the Ocean:** Sea Surface Temperature varies from the 27–30 degree near the equator, generally maximum value found about few degree of latitude north of the equator and low (about 19 degree) polar oceans. Sea surface temperature also change the longitude. The Warmer water projects poleward along the western boundaries of the ocean. The eastern tropical regions of each ocean are cooler than the western tropical margin. These are due to the movement of seawater in the horizontal (ocean currents) and vertical (upwelling/sinking) directions. Temperature and density of ocean water are related inversely: warm water means low density, cold water means denser seawater. The salt content of the water also affects Ocean density.

59. **Density of the Different Ocean:** The density of the pure water is 1000 kg/m³. The density of the ocean water is more dense due to the salt, the sea surface density is about 1027 kg/m³. There are two main factors that make ocean water more or less dense than about 1027 kg/m³: the temperature of the water and the salinity of the water. Ocean water gets more dense as temperature goes down. So, the colder the water, the more dense it is. Increasing salinity also increases the density of sea water. Less dense water floats on top of more dense water. Given two layers of water with the same salinity, the warmer water will float on top of the colder water. Temperature has a greater effect on the density

of water than salinity does. So a layer of water with higher salinity can actual float on top of water with lower salinity if the layer with higher salinity is quite a bit warmer than the lower salinity layer.

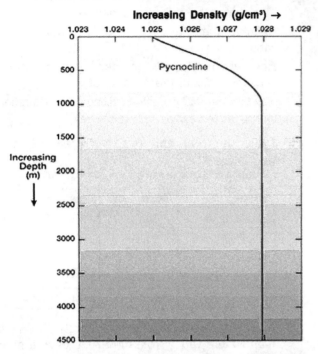

60. **Gulf Stream:** The Gulf Stream System is one of the world's most intensely studied current systems. This extensive western boundary current plays an important role in the pole-ward transfer of heat and salt and serves to warm the European subcontinent. The Gulf Stream begins upstream of Cape Hatteras, where the Florida Current ceases to follow the continental shelf. The position of the Stream as it leaves the coast changes throughout the year. In the fall, it shifts north, while in the winter and early spring it shifts south.

Compared with the width of the current (about 100-200 km), the range of this variation (30-40 km) is relatively small. However, recent studies by Mariano et al. (2002), suggests that the meridional range of the annual variation in stream path may be closer to 100 km. Other characteristics of the current are more variable. Significant changes in its transport, meandering, and structure can be observed through many time scales as it travels northeast.

63. **Deep Ocean Circulation and its Causes:** The circulation pattern are determined by wind direction, coriolis force from the Earth's rotation, and the position of landforms that interact with the currents, surface currents generally generated by the wind. Surface wind current generate upwelling current in with landforms creating deep water currents. The Currents may also be generated by density differences in water masses caused by temperature and salinity variations. These currents move water masses through the deep ocean— taking nutrients, oxygen, and heat with them.

64. **Unit of the Speed of Ships:** The **knot** is a unit of speed equal to one nautical mile (1.852 km) per hour, approximately 1.151 mph. The ISO Standard symbol for the knot is **kn**. The same symbol is preferred by the IEEE; **kt** is also common. The knot is a non-SI unit that is "accepted for use with the SI". Worldwide, the knot is used in meteorology, and in maritime and air navigation—for example, a vessel travelling at 1 knot along a meridian travels approximately one minute of geographic latitude in one hour.

1 international knot =

1 nautical mile per hour (by definition),
1.852 kilometres per hour (exactly),
0.514 metres per second (approximately),
1.151 miles per hour (approximately),
20.254 inches per second (approximately).

**Conversions Between Common Units of Speed**

|        | *m/s* | *km/h* | *Mph* | *Knot* | *Ft/s* |
|--------|-------|--------|-------|--------|--------|
| **1 m/s** | 1 | 3.6 | 2.236936 | 1.943844 | 3.280840 |
| **1 km/h** | 0.277778 | 1 | 0.621371 | 0.5399957 | 0.911344 |
| **1 mph** | 0.44704 | 1.609344 | 1 | 0.868976 | 1.466667 |
| **1 knot** | 0.514444 | 1.852 | 1.150779 | 1 | 1.687810 |
| **1 ft/s** | 0.3048 | 1.09728 | 0.681818 | 0.592484 | 1 |

66. **Velocity of sound in Seawater:** The speed of sound in sea water depends on its temperature, as well as on the salinity and hydrostatic pressure.

67. **Marine algae and its Causes:** The marine algae also known as the seaweeds with different shape

and size, look like as a plants but it is not. The classification of the algae can be confusing on the different purpose, although they are all referred to as algae, the red, green and brown algae are classified into three different kingdoms: the protists, chromists and Plantae, respectively. The algae all have cell wall structures and are capable of photosynthesis like our plants on land.

68. **Biological Oxygen demand:** This is a measure of the amount of molecular oxygen in milligrams required to convert organic molecules contained in 1.0 liter of a water sample to $CO_2$ Micro-organisms such as bacteria are responsible for decomposing organic waste. When organic matter such as dead plants, leaves, grass clippings, manure, sewage, or even food waste is present in a water supply, the bacteria will begin the process of breaking down this waste. When this happens, much of the available dissolved oxygen is consumed by aerobic bacteria, robbing other aquatic organisms of the oxygen they need to live. BOD level is a common metric for water pollution.

The BOD level is determined by comparing the dissolved oxygen levels of a water sample before and after 5 days of incubation in the dark. The difference between the two DO levels represents the amount of oxygen required for the deco-mposition of any organic material in the sample and is a good approximation of the BOD level.

Biological Oxygen Demand (BOD) = Initial dissolved oxygen – Final dissolved oxygen

BOD values are usually reported in either ppm values or in mg/L values. Unpolluted rivers typically have a BOD below 1 mg/L. Moderately polluted rivers vary between 2 to 8 mg/L. Untreated sewage averages between 200 and 600 mg/L while efficiently treated municipal sewage would be 20 mg/L or less.

70. **Mass of the atmosphere with height**: The gaseous layers on the earth planet have different layers or strata. The 99% of the mass of the atmosphere lies first about 35 km from the earth's surface. The layer of the atmosphere is remarks by the temperature, pressure, absorption and also a solar radiation of the spectrum. Atmosphere have different layer with its own characteristics.

**Troposphere:** It is the closest layer in the atmosphere to the earth planet, its have largest about 80% of the total mass of the atmosphere. In this layer the temperature and water vapour content in the troposphere decrease rapidly with altitude. All weather phenomena occur within the troposphere, although turbulence may extend into the lower portion of the stratosphere. Troposphere means "region of mixing" and is so named because of vigorous convective air currents within the layer. The upper boundary

of the layer, known as the tropopause, ranges in height from 5 miles (8 km) near the poles up to 11 miles (18 km) above the equator. Its height also varies with the seasons; highest in the summer and lowest in the winter.

**Stratosphere:** This is the second major layer in the atmosphere, extended above tropopause to an altitude of about 50 km from earth's surface. Air temperature in stratosphere increases with altitude. Ozone is main role play to the thermal regime of the stratosphere. Solar energy is converted to kinetic energy when ozone molecules absorb ultraviolet radiation then heating of the stratosphere.

The *ozone layer* is centered at an altitude between 10-15 miles (15-25 km). Approximately 90 % of the ozone in the atmosphere resides in the stratosphere. Ozone concentration in this region is about 10 parts per million by volume (ppmv) as compared to approximately 0.04 ppmv in the troposphere. Ozone absorbs the bulk of solar ultraviolet radiation in wavelengths from 290 nm - 320 nm (UV-B radiation). These wavelengths are harmful to life because they can be absorbed by the nucleic acid in cells. Increased penetration of ultraviolet radiation to the planet's surface would damage plant life and have harmful environmental consequences. Appreciably large amounts of solar ultraviolet radiation would result in a host of biological effects, such as a dramatic increase in cancers.

*Mesosphere:* The layer about 50 to 80 km above the surface, the temperature decreasing with heights. The coldest temperature in the atmosphere in this region. Earth's atmosphere occur at the top of this layer, the mesopause, especially in the summer near the pole.

*Thermosphere:* The layer above the mesosphere is called the thermosphere. The temperature in this layer generally increase with altitude. This increase in temperature is due to the absorption of intense solar radiation by the limited amount of remaing molecular oxygen. In this height gas molecules are widely separated.

*Exosphere.* The exosphere is the most distant atmospheric region from the earth's surface. In the exosphere upward trawelling molecules can escape to space. The upper boundary defined as theoretically by the altitude at which in influence of solar radiation pressure on atomic hydrogen velocities exceeds that of the earth's gravitational pull. This layer is observable from space as the geocorona is seen to extend to at least 60,000 miles from the earth's surface.

**MAGNETO-ELECTRONIC STRUCTURE:** The upper atmosphere is also divided into regions based on the behaviour and number of free electrons and other charged particles.

*Ionosphere:* The ionosphere is defined as the atmospheric effects on radiowave propogation as a result of the presence and variation in concentration of free electrons in the atmosphere.

- *D-region* is about 35 to 55 miles (60 - 90 km) in altitude but disappears at night.
- *E-region* is about 55 to 90 miles (90 - 140 km) in altitude.
- *F-region* is above 90 miles (140 km) in attitude. During the day it has two regions known as the $F_1$-region from about 90 to 115 miles (140 to 180 km) altitude and the $F_2$-region in which the concentration of electrons peaks in the altitude range of 150 to 300 miles (around 250 to 500 km).
- Most recent map of the Height of Maximum (hmF2). The ionosphere above the peak electron concentration is usually referred to as the *Topside Ionosphere.*

### 71. Fossils and its Geological Age:

| Fossils | Geological age |
|---|---|
| Dinosaur | Late Triassic to Present |
| Trilobites | Early Cambrian to late Permian |
| Bird | Jurassic to present |

### 73. Himalia:
Himalia [hih-MAL-yuh] is the tenth known satellite of Jupiter and is the brightest of Jupiter's outer satellites. Himalia is most likely an irregularly shaped asteroid that was captured into orbit around Jupiter.

| Information about Himalia satellite | |
|---|---|
| Discovery | 1904 |
| Mass (Earth=1) | 1.597e-06 |
| Equatorial radius | 93 km |
| Mass | 9.56e+18 kg |
| Mean density | 2.8 gm/cm³ |
| Mean distance from Jupiter | 11480000 km |
| Orbital period | 250.5662 days |
| Rotational period | 0.4 days |
| Mean orbital velocity | 3.34 km/s |
| Orbital eccentricity | 0.1580 |
| Orbital inclination | 27.63 degree |
| Escape velocity | 0.117 km/s |

### 75. Average depth of the Ocean:
Its average depth is about 3,688 meters (12,100 ft), and its maximum depth is 10,994 meters (6.831 mi) at the Mariana Trench. Nearly half of the world's marine waters are over 3,000 meters (9,800 ft) deep. The vast expanses of deep-ocean (anything below 200 meters or 660 feet) cover about 66% of Earth's surface.

### 78. Component of the Earth:
- Atmosphere: the gases.
- Hydrosphere: liquid water.
- Cryosphere: ice.
- Biosphere: living things.
- Geosphere (lithosphere): sediments, rocks and magma.
- Pyschosphere: defined as that connected to the humanity.

### 79. Electromagnetic Spectrum:
The sun radiates energy in a wide range of wavelengths, most of which are invisible to human eyes. The shorter the wavelength, the more energetic the radiation, and the greater the potential for harm. Ultraviolet (UV) radiation that reaches the Earth's surface is in wavelengths between 290 and 400 nm (nanometers, or billionths of a meter). This is shorter than wavelengths of visible light, which are 400 to 700 nm.

### The Electromagnetic Spectrum

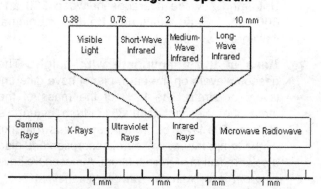

### 80. Greenhouse effect:
The greenhouse effect is a natural process that warms the Earth's surface. When the Sun's energy reaches the Earth's atmosphere, some of it is reflected back to space and the rest is absorbed and re-radiated by greenhouse gases. Greenhouse gases include water vapour, carbon dioxide, methane, nitrous oxide, ozone and some artificial chemicals such as chlorofluorocarbons (CFCs).

| Permanent Gases | | | Variable Gases | | |
|---|---|---|---|---|---|
| **Gas** | **Symbol** | **%age** | **Gas** | **Symbol** | **%age by volume** |
| Nitrogen | $N_2$ | 78 % | Water vapour | $H_2O$ | 0 – 4 |
| Oxygen | $O_2$ | 21 % | Carbon dioxide | $CO_2$ | 0.038 |
| Argon | Ar | 0.9 % | Ozone | $O_3$ | 0.000004 |
| Neon | Ne | 0.0018 % | Carbon monoxide | CO | 0.00002 |
| Helium | He | 0.0005 % | Sulphur dioxide | $SO_2$ | 0.000001 |
| Methane | $CH_4$ | 0.0001 % | Nitrogen dioxide | $NO_2$ | 0.000001 |
| Hydrogen | $H_2$ | 0.00005 % | Particles (dust, pollen) | — | 0.00001 |

**81. Ecosystem and its component:** The term ecosystem was coined in 1935 by the Oxford ecologist Arthur Tansley to encompass the interactions among biotic and abiotic components of the environment at a given site. The living and non-living components of an ecosystem are known as biotic and abiotic components, respectively. Ecosystem was defined in its presently accepted form by Eugene Odum as, "an unit that includes all the organisms, *i.e.*, the community in a given area interacting with the physical environment so that a flow of energy leads to clearly defined trophic structure, biotic diversity and material cycles, *i.e.*, exchange of materials between living and non-living, within the system".

Smith (1966) has summarized common characteristics of most of the ecosystems as follows:

- The ecosystem is a major structural and functional unit of ecology.
- The structure of an ecosystem is related to its species diversity in the sense that complex ecosystem have high species diversity.
- The function of ecosystem is related to energy flow and material cycles within and outside the system.
- The relative amount of energy needed to maintain an ecosystem depends on its structure. Complex ecosystems needed less energy to maintain themselves.
- Young ecosystems develop and change from less complex to more complex ecosystems, through the process called succession.
- Each ecosystem has its own energy budget, which cannot be exceeded.
- Adaptation to local environmental conditions is the important feature of the biotic components of an ecosystem, failing which they might perish.

- The function of every ecosystem involves a series of cycles, e.g., water cycle, nitrogen cycle, oxygen cycle, etc. These cycles are driven by energy. A continuation or existence of ecosystem demands exchange of materials/ nutrients to and from the different components.

**Types of Ecosystem:**

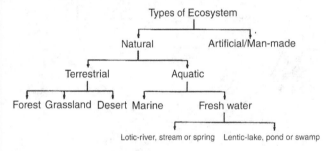

**82. Air Circulation Pattern:** The movement of air at all levels of the atmosphere all parts of the planet is atmospheric circulation. The driving force behind atmospheric circulation is solar energy, which heats the atmosphere with different intensities at the equator, the middle latitudes, and the poles. The rotation of Earth on its axis and the unequal arrangement of land and water masses on the planet also contribute to various features of atmospheric circulation.

At about 30 degrees latitude north and south, the cooled air descends back to the surface, pushing the air below it toward the equator, since air flows always move toward areas of low pressure. When the north and south trade winds meet at the equator and rise again, an area of calm develops because of the lack of cross-surface winds. Early mariners called this area the doldrums (from an Old English word meaning dull) because they feared their sailing ships would be stranded by the lack of wind.

While most of the trade-wind air that sinks at 30 degrees latitude returns to the equator, some of it flows poleward. At about 60 degrees latitude north and south, this air mass meets much colder polar air (the areas where this occurs are known as polar fronts). The warmer air is forced upward by the colder air to the tropopause, where most of it moves back toward the equator, sinking at about 30 degrees latitude to continue the cycle again. These second circulation belts over the middle latitudes between 30 degrees and 60 degrees are the prevailing westerlies or Ferrell cells, named after the American meteorologist William Ferrell.

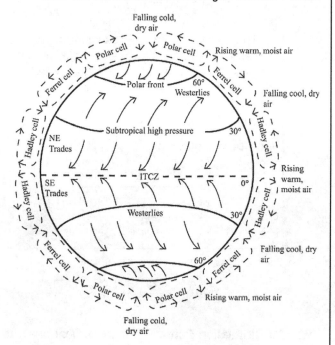

83. **Landmass of the Pangaea:** The Earth have not seven continents when the formation of the continents occur. About 300 million years ago one single and massive supercontinent called Pangaea, which exists surrounded by a single ocean called Panthalassa. We study formation of the Pangaea's due to plate tectonics, which posits that the Earth's outer shell is broken up into several plates that slide over Earth's rocky shell, the mantle, which makes up most of planet's volume. This breakup and formation of supercontinents has dramatically altered the planet's history. Pangaea formed through a gradual process spanning a few hundred million years. Beginning about 480 million years ago, a continent called Laurentia, which includes parts of North America, merged with several other micro-continents to form Euramerica. Euramerica eventually collided with Gondwana, another supercontinent that included Africa, Australia, South America and the Indian subcontinent.

About 200 million years ago, the supercontinent began to break up. Gondwana (what is now Africa, South America, Antarctica, India and Australia) first split from Laurasia (Eurasia and North America).

84. **ISRO Mangalayan Misson:** Marking India's first venture into the interplanetary space, MOM will explore and observe Mars surface features, morphology, mineralogy and the Martian atmosphere. Further, a specific search for methane in the Martian atmosphere will provide information about the possibility or the past existence of life on the planet. The enormous distances involved in interplanetary missions present a demanding challenge; developing and mastering the technologies essential for these missions will open endless possibilities for space exploration. After leaving Earth, the Orbiter will have to endure the Interplanetary space for 300 days before Mars capture. Apart from deep space communications and navigation-guidance-control capabilities, the mission will require autonomy at the spacecraft end to handle contingencies. Once India decided to go to Mars, ISRO had no time to lose as the nearest launch window was only a few months away and it could not afford to lose the chance, given the next launch would present itself after over 780 days, in 2016. Thus, mission planning, manufacturing the spacecraft and the launch vehicle and readying the support systems took place swiftly.

85. **Continental Drift Theory:** The continental drift hypothesis was developed in the early part of the 20th century, mostly by Alfred Wegener. Wegener said that continents move around on Earth's surface and that they were once joined together as a single supercontinent. While Wegener was alive, scientists did not believe that the continents could move. Find a map of the continents and cut each one out. Better yet, use a map where the edges of the continents show the continental shelf. That's the true size and shape of a continent and many can be pieced together like a puzzle. The easiest link is between the eastern Americas and western Africa and Europe, but the rest can fit together too.

Alfred Wegener proposed that the continents were once united into a single supercontinent named Pangaea, meaning all earth in ancient Greek. He suggested that Pangaea broke up long ago and that the continents then moved to their current positions. He called his hypothesis continental drift.

## Evidence for Continental Drift

- Besides the way the continents fit together, Wegener and his supporters collected a great deal of evidence for the continental drift hypothesis. For one, identical rocks of the same type and age are found on both sides of the Atlantic Ocean.

- Wegener said the rocks had formed side-by-side and that the land had since moved apart. Mountain ranges with the same rock types, structures, and ages are now on opposite sides of the Atlantic Ocean. The Appalachians of the eastern United States and Canada, for example, are just like mountain ranges in eastern Greenland, Ireland, Great Britain, and Norway. Wegener concluded that they formed as a single mountain range that was separated as the continents drifted.

- Ancient fossils of the same species of extinct plants and animals are found in rocks of the same age but are on continents that are now widely separated. Wegener proposed that the organisms had lived side by side, but that the lands had moved apart after they were dead and fossilized. He suggested that the organisms would not have been able to travel across the oceans. For example, the fossils of the seed fern *Glossopteris* were too heavy to be carried so far by wind. The reptile Mesosaurus could only swim in fresh water was a swimming reptile but could only swim in fresh water *Cyno-gnathus* and *Lystrosaurus* were land reptiles and were unable to swim.

- Grooves and rock deposits left by ancient glaciers are found today on different continents very close to the equator. This would indicate that the glaciers either formed in the middle of the ocean and/or covered most of the Earth. Today glaciers only form on land and nearer the poles. Wegener thought that the glaciers were centered over the southern land mass close to the South Pole and the continents moved to their present positions later on.

- Coral reefs and coal-forming swamps are found in tropical and subtropical environments, but ancient coal seams and coral reefs are found in locations where it is much too cold today. Wegener suggested that these creatures were alive in warm climate zones and that the fossils and coal later had drifted to new locations on the continents.

- Although Wegener's evidence was sound, most geologists at the time rejected his hypothesis of continental drift. Scientists argued that there was no way to explain how solid continents could plow through solid oceanic crust. Wegener's idea was nearly forgotten until technological advances presented even more evidence that the continents moved and gave scientists the tools to develop a mechanism for Wegener's drifting continents.

**87. Mass Extinction with geological time:**

| Geological time | Time (millions years) | Mass Extinction name |
|---|---|---|
| Ordovician – silurian | 450 – 440 | End–Ordovician O-S |
| Late Devonian | 375 – 360 | End–Devonian |
| Permian – Triassic | 251 | End–Permian |
| Triassic – Jurassic | 205 | End–Triassic |
| Cretaceous – Paleogene | 65.5 | End–Cretaceous K–Pg (K – T ) |

**88. Stromatolites**: Stromatolites are layered mounds, columns, and sheet-like sedimentary rocks. They were originally formed by the growth of layer upon layer of cyanobacteria, a single-celled photosynthesizing microbe that lives today in a wide range of environments ranging from the shallow shelf to lakes, rivers, and even soils. Cyanobacteria are prokaryotic cells (the simplest form of modern carbon-based life) in that they lack a DNA-packaging nucleus. Bacteria, including the photosynthetic cyanobacteria, were the only form of life on Earth for the first 2 billion years that life existed on Earth.

**89.** Arsenic contamination in India with state wise: Arsenic in ground water, as per the recommendations of the Bureau of Indian Standards (BIS), the permissible limit of Arsenic in drinking water is **0.01mg/l with no relaxation.** Chronic exposure to drinking water having arsenic contamination beyond permissible limit may cause several skin problems including arsenicoses characterised by dark spots on body and limbs, thickening of palms and soles etc, Bowen's disease non healing ulcers etc.

- Elevated levels (>0.05 mg/l) of Arsenic in ground water was reported from parts of 10 States of West Bengal, Assam, Bihar, Jharkhand, Uttar Pradesh, Punjab, Haryana, Chhattisgarh, Karnataka & Manipur .

- A recent survey by CGWB has shown Arsenic concentration in excess of 0.01 mg/l from patches from additional 11 States. In these areas arsenic occurrence is reported from only limited samples and resampling is envisaged.

**Uttar Pradesh:** Arsenic in ground water (0.05 mg/l) in Balia district was reported in 2003 and further survey indicated the presence of contamination in 7 blocks of the district of Gazipur, Balia and Varanasi (School of Environmental studies (SOES), Jadavpur University). The Arsenic affected districts are mainly aligned along a linear tract along the river Ganga as observed in Bihar and West Bengal. However the reasons for same are not established. The presence of Arsenicin ground water has been observed by CGWB and state agencies.

**Chhattisgarh:** Arsenic contamination in ground water is reported along the N-S trending 80 km stretch of Kotri lineament from Chhattisgarh State. The severity is found in eastern part of Ambagarh Chowki block of Rajnandgaon district. The high Arsenic in ground water is restricted to small isolated area and are in cluster of few villages extended over 330 sqkm area and is confined to the Proterozoic rocks. The worst Arsenic affected villages are Kaurikasa, Joratari, Sonsaytola, Jadutola, Muletitola.

**Bihar:** Arsenic groundwater contamination in Bihar was initially detected in the year 2002 from Semariya-Ojhapatti villages of Bhojpur district. Detailed investigations in the Gangetic Plain of Bihar revealed its wide occurrence on both the banks of the river Ganga. Arsenic distribution is marked with wide spatial variability resulting in patchyness in distribution. Fifty seven blocks, in 15 districts, located on both the banks of Ganga are affected (CGWB & PHED, 2005). The list of affected blocks of high Arsenic in ground water in Bihar revealed through survey by CGWB & State agencies.

**West Bengal:** The occurrence of high Arsenic in ground water was first reported in 1978 in West Bengal in India. In West Bengal, 79 blocks in 8 districts have Arsenic beyond the permissible limit of 0.05 mg/l. The most affected areas are on the eastern side of Bhagirathi river in the districts of Malda, Murshidabad, Nadia, North 24 Parganas and South 24 Parganas and western side of the districts of Howrah, Hugli and Bardhman. Arsenic in ground water is confined mainly in the aquifers upto 100 m depth. The deeper aquifers are free from Arsenic contamination. At present about 162.6 lakh people (35.48% of the total population of the state) live in the risk zone of potential threat in terms of Arsenic related diseases. The details of affected blocks with maximum concentration of Arsenic. (Source: CGWB)

93. **Rock Charecterstics with Example:**

| Characteristics | Example |
|---|---|
| Schistosity | Metamorphic terrain of schist belt |
| Bedding | Sedimentary terrain of the sediments beds |
| Foliation | Mica |
| Lineation | Any linear arrangement of the objects, like in grain, structures etc. |

94. **Rock types with Mineral Deposit:**

| Rock Types | Economic deposits |
|---|---|
| Metamorphic Rock | Manganese deposits of the Mansar formation of MP and Maharastra |
| Igneous Rock | Magnetite deposits of the Orissa and Tamil Nadu |
| Sedimentary Rock | Hematite deposits of Jharkhand and Bihar |

95. **Trench with Depth:**

| Trench | Depth |
|---|---|
| Owens Trench | 10,911 km |
| Mariana Trench | 10,994 km |
| San Andreas Trench | 10,809 km |

97. **Polymetallic Nodules:** The name of Polymetallic nodule comes because it contains multiple metals like copper, nickel, cobalt, manganese, iron, lead, zinc, aluminium, etc. Of these, cobalt, copper and nickel are of much importance and in great demand in the country and abroad. In fact, these three metals of strategic needs are fast depleting from the face of the earth. Hence a world-wide search is on for the potato-shaped nodules.

India is entirely dependent on imports to meet its requirements of cobalt, which is the most strategic of the three metals. As for copper and nickel, India will be in a precarious position by the year 2015. Fortunately, polymetallic nodules containing these three metals are lying scattered on the ocean floor in the Indian Ocean in abundant quantity.

Under an agreement, India has been allotted an area of 1.50 lakh sq km in the Central Indian Ocean basin by the International Seabed Authority to conduct its explorations. At present the activities are confined to half of this area. Similar agreements have been signed by some other countries which are engaged in sea-bed search of polymetallic nodules in their respective oceans. India is among the four recognised regional pioneers in this field, the others being France, Russia and Japan. The status has been accorded by the International Seabed Authority (IBM).

98. **Weathering and its climatic condition:** **Weathering** is a term which describes the general process by which rocks are broken down at the Earth's surface into such things as sediments, clays, soils and substances that are dissolved in water due to natural agencies. The process of weathering typically begins when the earth's crust is uplifted by tectonic forces. After the physical breakup and chemical decay of exposed rocks by weathering, the loosened rock fragments and alterations products are carried away through the process of **erosion**. Erosion relies on transporting agents such as wind, rivers, ice, snow and downward movement of materials to carry weathered products away from the source area. As weathered products are carried away, fresh rocks are exposed to further weathering. Over time, that mountain or hill is gradually worn down.

There are two types of weathering:

(a) **Chemical Weathering** results from chemical reactions between minerals in rocks and external agents like air or water. Oxygen oxidizes minerals to alteration products whereas water can convert minerals to clays or dissolve minerals completely.

(b) **Physical Weathering** is when rocks are broken apart by mechanical processes such as rock fracturing, freezing and thawing, or breakage during transport by rivers or glaciers.

**Factors Which Control the Rates of Weathering**
- Properties of the Parent Rock
- Climate
- Soil
- Length of Exposure

100. **Classification of Himalaya from North to South:**

The Himalayas can be divided into four divisions:
1. The Trans or Tethys Himalayas
2. The Greater Himalayas
3. The Lesser Himalaya
4. The Outer Himalayas or the Siwalik Range.

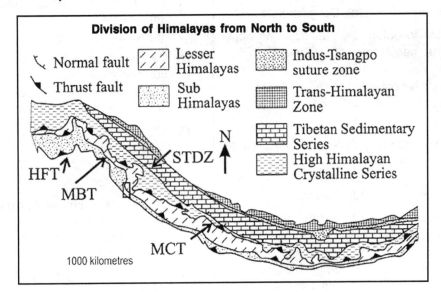

# International Earth Science Olympiad (IESO)
## Entrance Exam, 2014

**Total Marks : 100**                                    **Time : 90 minutes**

1. Long huge mountain ranges on the ocean floor are known as:
   (a) Orogenic Belts
   (b) Mid-Oceanic Ridges
   (c) Oceanic Mountains
   (d) Transoceanic Ridges

2. The region marked by two adjoining plates moving away from each other is expressed by:
   (a) Subduction Zone
   (b) Trench
   (c) Mid-Oceanic Ridge
   (d) Island arc

3. An igneous rock predominantly composed of quartz and alkali feldspars often with some mica is known as:
   (a) Gabbro            (b) Granite
   (c) Andesite          (d) Dacite

4. Which sedimentary rock is widely used in the manufacture of cement?
   (a) Shale             (b) Limestone
   (c) Sandstone         (d) Conglomerate

5. Which of the following raw materials find application in the manufacture of fertilizers?
   (a) Barite
   (b) Stromatolitic phosphorite
   (c) Pyrites
   (d) Mica

6. Which of the following mineral is used as an abrasive?
   (a) Felspars          (b) Micas
   (c) Corundum          (d) Olivine

7. Large volcanic eruptions from Western India that occurred around late Cretaceous to Eocene times are known as:
   (a) Panjal Traps      (b) Sylhette Traps
   (c) Deccan Traps      (d) Nidar volcanic

8. Which of the following rocks in India contain raw materials used for the extraction of aluminium?
   (a) Limestone         (b) Basalts
   (c) Bauxites          (d) Granites

9. A metamorphic rock composed of bands of different mineral composition is known as:
   (a) Schist            (b) Gneiss
   (c) Slate             (d) Marble

10. A rock essentially composed of pyroxene and plagioclase feldspars is known as:
    (a) Granite           (b) Syenite
    (c) Gabbro            (d) Gneiss

11. Which mineral group is most frequently represented in the earth's crust?
    (a) Quartz            (b) Feldspars
    (c) Micas             (d) Amphiboles

12. Which are the most abundant rocks in the mantle of the earth?
    (a) Granite           (b) Peridotites
    (c) Basalts           (d) Rhyolites

13. A high temperature and pressure meta-morphic rock common in South India is known as:
    (a) Marble            (b) Granulite
    (c) Slate             (d) Quartzite

14. Which metamorphic rock is the most abundant component of the deep crust of the Earth?
    (a) Marble            (b) Slate
    (c) Granulite         (d) Phyllite

15. Magma that erupts on the surface of the earth is called:
    (a) Geyser            (b) Lava
    (c) Fumarole          (d) Hot springs

16. 'Fools gold' is a mineral belonging to the following group of minerals:
    (a) Oxides            (b) Sulphides
    (c) Arsenides         (d) Tellurides

17. Asthenosphere is the following type of layer of the Earth:
    (a) Outer Ductile     (b) Inner Brittle
    (c) Inner ductile     (d) Outer Brittle

18. Final phase of the uplift of the Himalaya is the result of the following type of collision:
 (a) Ocean-Continent
 (b) Continent-Continent
 (c) Ocean-Island-Arc
 (d) Ocean-Continental Arc

19. Crustal dynamics is controlled by the following processes:
 (a) Weathering (b) Vulcanism
 (c) Plate tectonics (d) Sedimentation

20. Bauxites are the following type of deposits:
 (a) Igneous (b) Sedimentary
 (c) Residual (d) Metamorphic

21. What is the third largest abundant gas in Earth's atmosphere?
 (a) Hydrogen (b) Methane
 (c) Carbon dioxide (d) Argon

22. The Earth escapes from much of solar UV radiation because of the presence of ozone in the Earth's atmosphere:
 (a) Uniformly at all heights
 (b) Mostly in the lower atmosphere (< 10 km)
 (c) Mostly in the middle atmosphere (10 to 50 km)
 (d) Mostly in the upper atmosphere (above 50 km)

23. Lightning in the Earth's atmosphere helps in:
 (a) Getting nitrogen to plants
 (b) Radio broadcast
 (c) Causing more rain to occur,
 (d) Transmission of electrical signals from place to place

24. In India, monsoon season starts from:
 (a) End of May (b) Beginning of April
 (c) Beginning of July (d) Mid October

25. The average rainfall in the Indian plains due to the southwest monsoon is:
 (a) 1000 cm (b) 1000 inches
 (c) 1000 mm (d) 1000 m

26. Maximum rain occurs in India over:
 (a) Meghalaya (b) Manipur
 (c) Karnataka (d) Arunachal Pradesh

27. Which of India's neighboring countries gets the least share of southwest monsoon rains?
 (a) Sri Lanka (b) Bangladesh
 (c) Pakistan (d) Nepal

28. Cyclones do not occur at very low latitudes.
 (a) This statement is not true
 (b) Because of low atmospheric moisture
 (c) Because of intense solar radiation
 (d) Because of lack of Coriolis force

29. The annual average cloud cover over the Earth is
 (a) 50% (b) 10%
 (c) 30% (d) 80%

30. Western Disturbance occurs over:
 (a) Northern parts of India during summer
 (b) Northeastern part of India during April-May
 (c) Northern parts of India during winter
 (d) Southern parts of India during winter

31. The instrument that measures relative humidity is called a:
 (a) Barometer (b) Hygrometer
 (c) Thermometer (d) Clinometer

32. Isohyets refer to line connecting places of same:
 (a) Temperature (b) Rainfall
 (c) Humidity (d) Pressure

33. Earth's climate is mainly controlled by:
 (a) The Sun
 (b) The orbital variations of the Earth
 (c) Greenhouse gas concentrations
 (d) All the above

34. What percentage of the Solar radiation received by the Earth is reflected by it, on the average?
 (a) 10% (b) 20%
 (c) 30% (d) 40%

35. Which of the following is a good reflector of solar radiation?
 (a) Deserts (b) Oceans
 (c) Ice caps (d) Atmosphere

36. Rainfall measurements from Satellites is possible by the use of:
 (a) Visible light (b) Infra-red
 (c) Ultraviolet (d) Microwave

37. The Indian Satellite Kalpana is for the remote sensing of the:
 (a) Atmosphere (b) Oceans
 (c) Land surface (d) Vegetation

38. Planes fly at:
 (a) Upper tropospheric height
 (b) Upper stratospheric height
 (c) Lower exospheric height
 (d) Lower ionospheric height

39. The little Ice age occurred during:
 (a) Harappan times (b) The 17th Century
 (c) The 8th Century (d) 21000 years ago

40. Sun spot activity becomes low, generally associated with:
 (a) Dry climate (b) Wet climate
 (c) Hot climate (d) Cool climate

**41.** Fossils of Foraminifera found in _____ sediment.
(a) Lake
(b) River
(c) Marine
(d) Glacial

**42.** The deepest part of the ocean lies in:
(a) Northern Atlantic Ocean
(b) Southern Indian Ocean
(c) Bay of Bengal
(d) Northern Pacific

**43.** The winds blowing from subtropical high pressure to sub-polarlow pressure are:
(a) Jet Stream
(b) Polar Winds
(c) Easterlies
(d) Westerlies

**44.** Which is the most powerful and effective erosive agent of coastal areas:
(a) Sea waves
(b) Tidal waves
(c) Oceanic current
(d) Tsunamis

**45.** High flux of fresh water in Bay of Bengal makes it:
(a) Less saline and colder
(b) Less saline and warmer
(c) High saline and warmer
(d) High saline and colder

**46.** The largest, highest and most extensive reefs of all type of coral reefs are:
(a) Fringing reefs
(b) Atoll
(c) Barrier reefs
(d) Lagoon reefs

**47.** Temperature of sea surface depends on:
(a) Upwelling
(b) Evaporation
(c) Fresh water mixing
(d) All of the above

**48.** Isohalines are:
(a) The lines that join the places of equal precipitation
(b) The lines that join the places of equal temperature
(c) The lines that join the places of equal salinity
(d) The lines that join the places of equal humidity

**49.** Which one of the following is the oldest ocean?
(a) Indian Ocean
(b) Pacific Ocean
(c) Atlantic Ocean
(d) Arctic Ocean

**50.** High tides are formed when:
(a) The Sun and the earth at the position of 45° with reference to the moon.
(b) The Sun and the moon at the position of 45° with reference to the Earth.
(c) The Sun the earth and the moon are in the same line.
(d) The Sun and the moon are at the position of right angle with reference to the Earth.

**51.** Highest sea surface salinity is found in:
(a) The polar region
(b) The tropics
(c) The equator
(d) Both (a) and (b)

**52.** Coriolis forces are caused by:
(a) Rotation of the Moon
(b) Rotation of the Saturn
(c) Rotation of the Earth
(d) Rotation of the Sun

**53.** Which one of the following is a cold current:
(a) California current
(b) Kuroshio current
(c) Brazil current
(d) Gulf Stream

**54.** An iceberg is floating in sea. How much of its mass will remain above the surface of water:
(a) One –fourth
(b) One –tenth
(c) One –fifth
(d) One –eight

**55.** Coral reefs developed along the continental margins or along the islands are called:
(a) Fringing reefs
(b) Atoll
(c) Barrier reefs
(d) Lagoon reefs

**56.** The height of spring tides is:
(a) 20 % more than the normal tides
(b) 10 % more than the normal tides
(c) 15 % more than the normal tides
(d) 30 % more than the normal tides

**57.** Temperate cyclones move towards:
(a) Easterly direction
(b) Northerly direction
(c) Westerly direction
(d) Southerly direction

**58.** The surface layer of the ocean where light is sufficient for plant growth is called:
(a) Aphotic zone
(b) Photic zone
(c) Twilight zone
(d) Dysphotic zone

**59.** Which among the following has the largest Mass (per cent) of the earth?
(a) Mantle
(b) Hydrosphere
(c) Core
(d) Crust

**60.** Penetration of seismic profiling under the sea at a point depends on:
(a) Nature of the deposit beneath
(b) Depth of water from the sea level
(c) Distance from the coast
(d) Salinity of sea water

**61.** In which of the following islands is the Mid-Atlantic Ridge clearly evident?

(a) Fiji         (b) Iceland
(c) Bahamas     (d) Hawaii

62. Rifting and Plate separation is best seen within a continent in:
(a) Western United States
(b) East Africa
(c) Indian subcontinent
(d) Northern Europe

63. Which among the following is a volcanic rock?
(a) Termite      (b) Stalagmite
(c) Rhyolite     (d) Monazite

64. In which of the following States of India is lignite mined?
(a) Madhya Pradesh  (b) Tamil Nadu
(c) West Bengal     (d) Kerala

65. In agriculture practice, contour ploughing is resorted to in the hills with slopes:
(a) To increase percolation of water
(b) To inhibit erosion
(c) For better growth of crops
(d) For easier harvesting

66. Aquicludes are:
(a) Potential reservoirs of water
(b) Artificial canals passing over natural streams
(c) Hard rocks with very low permeability
(d) Body of water within the lagoon

67. Which among the following is the most pollutant of ground water within granites?
(a) Arsenic      (b) Fluoride
(c) Iron         (d) Chloride

68. Volcano 'Etna' is located in:
(a) Mexico      (b) Indonesia
(c) Colombia    (d) Italy

69. Which of the following rivers in India exhibits 'cuspate' delta?
(a) Godavari     (b) Narmada
(c) Subarnarekha  (d) Cauvery

70. Crevasse are characteristic features in:
(a) Rocky river bed  (b) Transverse dunes
(c) Glaciers     (d) Fractured limestone

71. Barren Island is an active volcano located in:
(a) Andaman Islands
(b) Nicobar Islands
(c) Maldives Islands
(d) Lakshadweep Islands

72. 'Ablation' refers to:
(a) Rounding of grains in a flowing stream
(b) Weathering of a rock by a chemical process
(c) Snow or ice lost from a glacier
(d) Process of 'yardang' formation in an arid region

73. Which among the following represents a correct sequence of sedimentary particles from the largest to the smallest?
(a) Cobble, boulder, sand
(b) Pebble, silt, cobble
(c) Grit, sand, silt
(d) Grit, sand, pebble

74. Calcium carbonate pellets and nodules get precipitated mostly under:
(a) Limestone bedrock
(b) Wet climate
(c) Temperate climate
(d) Dry climate

75. Classification of cyclones (type of disturbances) is based on the intensity of the wind-speed in kmph. In the following four which disturbance is correctly matched against its wind-speed?
(a) Depression <31
(b) Severe cyclonic storm >220
(c) Deep depression 50 to 61
(d) Hurricane 62 to 88

76. In which of the following cities the day is the longest on June 21?
(a) Thiruvanandapuram
(b) Chandigarh
(c) Hyderabad
(d) Jabalpur

77. The air that contains moisture to its full capacity is referred to as:
(a) Relative humidity  (b) Saturated air
(c) Specific humidity  (d) Absolute humidity

78. Which among the following terms refers to equality in rainfall?
(a) Isograd      (b) Isotope
(c) Isohyet      (d) Isohel

79. Echo-sounder is an instrument used to:
(a) Measure the hearing capacity of an individual
(b) Measure distance between two hills
(c) Locate mineral deposits in ocean
(d) Measure ocean water depths

80. A tide occurring at the first and third quarters of the Moon is called:
(a) Neap tide     (b) Spring tide
(c) High tide     (d) Low tide

81. Salinity is expressed as the amount of salt, in grams, dissolved in sea water per:
(a) 10 gm      (b) 100 gm
(c) 1000 gm    (d) 10,000 gm

82. Both canyons and trenches are found in:
    (a) Continental shelf
    (b) Abyssal hills
    (c) Plateaus
    (d) Continental slopes

83. Guyot is a feature associated with:
    (a) Submarine landforms
    (b) Karst topography
    (c) Volcanic landforms
    (d) Dune topography

84. Earliest evidences of glaciation in India has been found in:
    (a) Permian          (b) Pleistocene
    (c) Cretaceous       (d) Precambrian

85. Which among the following minerals weathers fastest?
    (a) Calcite          (b) Muscovite
    (c) Quartz           (d) Gibsite

86. En echelon pattern of faulting indicates:
    (a) Series of parallel normal faults
    (b) Series of parallel thrust faults
    (c) Series of small faults in a staggered arrangement
    (d) Those emanating from the uplift of a structural dome

87. The density of sun is:
    (a) Very high
    (b) More than that of earth
    (c) Less than that of earth
    (d) Cannot be calculated

88. All stars become red giants:
    (a) After 1 billion years
    (b) When hydrogen is completely exhausted
    (c) When helium is completely exhausted
    (d) When 10% of the hydrogen at the core is exhausted

89. The nuclear reactions taking place in the sun are:
    (a) Proton-proton reactions
    (b) CNO reactions
    (c) Uranium fission
    (d) Not operating when the sun becomes a red giant

90. After 10 billion years the sun will become a:
    (a) White dwarf      (b) Neutron star
    (c) Black hole       (d) Blue star

91. The Sun is called a yellow star because:
    (a) It looks red at rise and set
    (b) It emits white light
    (c) It emits maximum energy in yellow light
    (d) Sometimes it looks blue

92. Red giants appear brighter because:
    (a) CNO cycle is producing energy
    (b) p-p reactions have stopped
    (c) The stars swell to a larger size
    (d) Hydrogen is exhausted

93. Nebulae implies:
    (a) Galaxies like Andromeda
    (b) Crab nebula
    (c) Orion nebula
    (d) Cloud like tenuous material of Milky Way

94. Globular clusters are:
    (a) Star forming regions
    (b) Young clusters
    (c) Very rich in metal content
    (d) Spread across the halo region of the Galaxy

95. Novae are:
    (a) Faint explosion of stars
    (b) New stars that are born million years ago
    (c) Death of a massive star in another galaxy
    (d) Temporary increase in brightness caused by accretion disc in a binary

96. The distance to farther galaxies is estimated by:
    (a) Method of parallax
    (b) Measuring luminosities
    (c) Cepheid variables
    (d) Supernovae

97. Inter stellar matter may be identified:
    (a) By optical spectroscopy
    (b) By reddening
    (c) By parallax
    (d) From radio observations

98. Metallicity means:
    (a) Iron content
    (b) Ratio of Fe/H abundances
    (c) Fraction of all elements other than hydrogen and helium
    (d) Ratio of inorganic metal content to organic content

99. Andromeda galaxy is:
    (a) A spiral galaxy
    (b) An elliptical galaxy
    (c) A nebula in our Galaxy
    (d) A super nova remnant

100. Red shift implies:
    (a) Galaxies are moving away
    (b) The star or galaxy looks red
    (c) There is no blue light emitted from the star or galaxy
    (d) The source of light is moving away from us

## ANSWERS

| 1 | 2 | 3 | 4 | 5 | 6 | 7 | 8 | 9 | 10 |
|---|---|---|---|---|---|---|---|---|---|
| (b) | (c) | (b) | (b) | (c) | (c) | (c) | (c) | (b) | (c) |

| 11 | 12 | 13 | 14 | 15 | 16 | 17 | 18 | 19 | 20 |
|---|---|---|---|---|---|---|---|---|---|
| (b) | (b) | (b) | (c) | (b) | (b) | (c) | (b) | (c) | (c) |

| 21 | 22 | 23 | 24 | 25 | 26 | 27 | 28 | 29 | 30 |
|---|---|---|---|---|---|---|---|---|---|
| (d) | (c) | (a) | (a) | (c) | (a) | (c) | (d) | (a) | (c) |

| 31 | 32 | 33 | 34 | 35 | 36 | 37 | 38 | 39 | 40 |
|---|---|---|---|---|---|---|---|---|---|
| (b) | (b) | (d) | (c) | (c) | (d) | (a) | (a) | (b) | (d) |

| 41 | 42 | 43 | 44 | 45 | 46 | 47 | 48 | 49 | 50 |
|---|---|---|---|---|---|---|---|---|---|
| (c) | (d) | (d) | (a) | (b) | (c) | (d) | (c) | (b) | (c) |

| 51 | 52 | 53 | 54 | 55 | 56 | 57 | 58 | 59 | 60 |
|---|---|---|---|---|---|---|---|---|---|
| (b) | (c) | (a) | (b) | (a) | (a) | (b) | (b) | (a) | (a) |

| 61 | 62 | 63 | 64 | 65 | 66 | 67 | 68 | 69 | 70 |
|---|---|---|---|---|---|---|---|---|---|
| (b) | (b) | (c) | (b) | (b) | (c) | (b) | (d) | (c) | (c) |

| 71 | 72 | 73 | 74 | 75 | 76 | 77 | 78 | 79 | 80 |
|---|---|---|---|---|---|---|---|---|---|
| (a) | (c) | (c) | (d) | (c) | (b) | (b) | (c) | (d) | (a) |

| 81 | 82 | 83 | 84 | 85 | 86 | 87 | 88 | 89 | 90 |
|---|---|---|---|---|---|---|---|---|---|
| (c) | (d) | (a) | (d) | (a) | (c) | (c) | (d) | (a) | (a) |

| 91 | 92 | 93 | 94 | 95 | 96 | 97 | 98 | 99 | 100 |
|---|---|---|---|---|---|---|---|---|---|
| (c) | (c) | (d) | (d) | (d) | (d) | (b) | (c) | (a) | (d) |

## HINTS AND SOLUTIONS

1. **Mid–Oceanic Ridge:** MOR formed due to divergent plate boundaries, new ocean floor is formed by the geological earth's tectonics plates spread apart. The divergent plate setting, molten material comes on the sea floor due to volcanic activity of basaltic compositions. This is the longest chain of the volcanoes in the World. The rate of spreading, plate varies from mm to cm. In general the rate is slow (1 – 3 cm) fast (10 – 20 cm) per year. They also effect irregular topography, narrow and fast to slow movements.

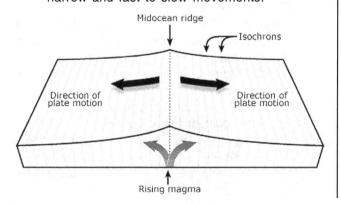

Two of the most carefully studied mid-ocean ridges are the Mid-Atlantic Ridge and the East Pacific Rise. The Mid-Atlantic Ridge runs down the center of the Atlantic Ocean, slowly spreading at a rate of two to five centimeters (0.8 to 2 inches) per year and forming a rift valley that is about the depth and width of the Grand Canyon. In contrast, the East Pacific Rise spreads fast at rates of 6 to 16 centimeters (three to six inches) per year. Due to the fast spreading rates, there is no rift valley in the Pacific, just a smooth volcanic summit with a crack along the crest that is much smaller than the Atlantic rift valley.

2. **Plate movement direction:**

| Plate Setting | Movement Direction | Example |
|---|---|---|
| Convergent plate | Plates move in each other | Island – Arc |
| Divergent plate | Two plates away from each other | Mid-Oceanic ridge |
| Transform plate | Plate slide each other | Strike – slip faults |

### 3. Rocks type with essential minerals:

| Rock Types | Essential Minerals |
|---|---|
| Gabbro | Calcium-rich plagioclase feldspar (usually labradorite or bytownite) and clinopyroxene (augite). Minor amounts of olivine and orthopyroxene might also be present and quartz absent in the rock. |
| Granite | Granite is composed mainly of quartz and feldspar with minor amounts of mica, amphiboles, and other minerals. This mineral composition usually gives granite a red, pink, gray, or white colour with dark mineral grains visible throughout the rock. |
| Andesite | Andesite is rich in plagioclase-feldspar minerals and may contain biotite, pyroxene, or amphibole. Andesite usually does not contain quartz or olivine. |

### 4. Cement and its Constituents:
Portland cement gets its strength from chemical reactions between the cement and water. The process is known as hydration. This is a complex process that is best understood by first understanding the chemical composition of cement.

**Manufacture of Cement**: Portland cement is manufactured by crushing, milling and proportioning the following materials:

- Lime or calcium oxide, CaO: from limestone, chalk, shells, shale or calcareous rock
- Silica, $SiO_2$: from sand, old bottles, clay or argillaceous rock
- Alumina, $Al_2O_3$: from bauxite, recycled aluminium, clay
- Iron, $Fe_2O_3$: from from clay, iron ore, scrap iron and fly ash
- Gypsum, $CaSO_4.2H_2O$: found together with limestone

**Chemical Shorthand**: Due to complex chemical reaction for the nature of cement, generally form is used to chemical compounds. The shorthand for the basic compounds is:

| Compounds | Formula | Short hand form |
|---|---|---|
| Calcium oxide (lime) | CaO | C |
| Silicon dioxide (silica) | $SiO_2$ | S |
| Sulphate | $SO_3$ | S |
| Water | $H_2O$ | H |
| Iron Oxide | $Fe_2O_3$ | F |
| Aluminium oxide (alumina) | $Al_2O_3$ | A |

| Composition of Cement | |
|---|---|
| Calcium Oxide (CaO) | 60 – 65 % |
| Silica ($SiO_2$) | 20 – 25 % |
| Aluminium Oxide | 4 – 8 % |
| Ferrous Oxide | 2 – 4 % |
| Magnesium Oxide | 1 – 3 % |

### 5. Raw Materials for Fertilizer:
The fertilizer is very important in agricultural industry for the any developing country, where farmer sucide in own crops. The main causes for that is not a suitable constituents for the farmimg. Fertilizer is a substance added to soil to improve plants' growth and yield. First used by ancient farmers, fertilizer technology developed significantly as the chemical needs of growing plants were discovered. Modern synthetic fertilizers are composed mainly of nitrogen, phosphorous, and potassium compounds with secondary nutrients added. The use of synthetic fertilizers has significantly improved the quality and quantity of the food available today, although their long-term use is debated by environmentalists. Phosphatic fertilizers containing phosphorous as a base element, which is expressed by $P_2O_5$%. Phosphate rock is considered the main raw material for the production of phosphate type fertilizers, Super phosphate $Ca(H_2PO_4)_2$ and Triple super phosphate.

### 6. Abrasive Minerals:
An abrasive is a mineral or material used to change the appearance of an object. Abrasives can be naturally made or synthetic. There are many minerals used as abrasives, but each mineral are used for different purposes. There are a variety of abrasives today, but one thing they all have in common is their hardness. All abrasive minerals have a hardness of seven or more. Synthetic stones are used as abrasives, but they are not considered minerals because they are not naturally made. Examples of naturally made abrasives are calcite, novaculite, rouge, diamond dust, sand, garnet and emery. In contrast man made abrasives include ceramic, dry ice, glass powder, steel abrasives, and silicon carbide. Many factors determine if the specific mineral or synthetic stone will make a good abrasive. Factors such as hardness, grain size, Adhesion, contact force, Loading: the worn out abrasive gets filled by the object it is cutting making it less effective, and use of fluids. The fluid or coolant will help prevent loading, and prevent the abrasive from heating up.

| Minerals | Uses |
|----------|------|
| Feldspar | Glassmaking, ceramics, filler and in paint, plastics, and rubber. |
| Micas | Thermal insulation, and in electronic equipment as electrical insulators. |
| Corundum | Abrasive and gemstones. |
| Olivine | Slag conditioner, blast furnaces as metallurgical uses. |

## 7. Volcanic Eruption and its Geological Age:

| Traps | Geological Age | Location state |
|-------|----------------|----------------|
| Panjal Traps | Early to middle Permian | North -western India |
| Sylhete Traps | Jurassic | Southern part of the Shillong Plateau in north-eastern India |
| Deccan Traps | Tertiary | West – central India |
| Nidar volcanoes | Lower Cenozoic | Laddakh |

## 8. Raw materials for Aluminium extraction: The main raw materials for the aluminium as compound of aluminium and oxygen, it is obtained from the bauxite by different process. The Bayer process – hydrated alumina is first precipitated from a solution of bauxite in concentrated caustic soda. Two parts by weight of alumina in powder form are extracted from four to five parts by weight of bauxite; subsequently, one part by weight of pure

aluminium is obtained using the Hall-Héroult process (fused-salt electrolysis). Over 90% of the alumina is used in the extraction of aluminium.

Alumina also refered to aluminium oxide ($Al_2O_3$), hard, high melting point. It is also used for the starting material for chemicals, precious stones, ceramics and abrasives. Alumina is a white, electrically non-conductive compound of low solubility whose hardness approaches that of diamond in certain crystal forms; its melting point is 2050 °C and thus very high. Alumina occurs naturally in crystalline form as precious stones such as corundum, sapphire and ruby.

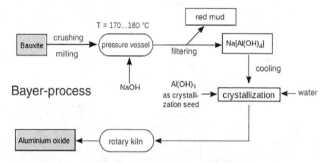

Bayer-process

## 11. Component of Earth and its composition:

| Continental Crust | Silicic Rocks |
|-------------------|---------------|
| Oceanic Crust | Basaltic Rocks |
| Mantle | Peridotite, eclogite, olivine |
| Core | Iron, oxygen, sulphur, nickel alloy |

| Layer | Thickness (Km) | Density (g/cm³) Top | Density (g/cm³) Bottom | Composition |
|-------|----------------|-----|--------|-------------|
| Crust | 30 | 2.2 | — | Silicic rocks |
| | | — | 2.9 | Andesite, basalt |
| Upper mantle | 720 | 3.4 | — | Peridotite, eclogite, olivine |
| | | — | 4.4 | Perovskite, oxides |
| Lower mantle | 2171 | 4.4 | — | Magnesium |
| | | — | 5.6 | Oxides |
| Outer core | 2259 | 9.9 | — | Iron + oxygen, sulphur |
| | | — | 12.2 | Nickel alloy |
| Inner core | 1221 | 12.8 | — | Iron + oxygen, sulphur |
| | | — | 13.1 | Nickel alloy |
| Total thickness | 6401 | | | |

| Different layers of the earth | Elements |
|-------------------------------|----------|
| Crust | O > Si > Al > Fe > Ca > Na |
| Lithosphere | O > Si > Al > Fe > Ca > Na |
| Atmosphere | $N_2$ > $O_2$ > Ar > $CO_2$ |
| Earth | Fe > O > Si > Mg |
| Universe | H > He > O |

## 12. Mantle rock composition: Mantle rocks mainly consists of the peridotite, eclogite, olivine, spinel, pyroxene, perovaskite, oxide. Mantle rocks rich in magnesium (Si, Mg, Fe, O). Crustal rocks are much less rich in Mg and comparatively more rich in Ca and Al. It is the increasing trend in the silicon content from mantle to oceanic crust to continental crust.

### 13. Metamorphic Rocks and Its Pressure, Temperature:

| Type of Metamorphism | Dominant Agent | Geological situation in which most likely to occur | Nature of process | Typical minerals formed | Characteristic Rocks | Texture |
|---|---|---|---|---|---|---|
| Thermal - including contact | High or moderate temperature + igneous emanations (liquids and gases) | Close to igneous intrusions and extrusions | Recrystallization-Replacement from invading liquids and gases | Andalusite Garnet Wollastanite | Hornfels Quartzite Marble | N O N F O L I A T E S |
| Cataclastic | Directed pressure – low temperature | Belts of folding crush zones thrust planes | Crushing pulverising Brecciation | Micas | Breccia, Mylonite | |
| Regional | Strong directed pressure – High Temperature | Regions of great earth movement (tectonic belts) | Recrystallization under different temperatures and pressures Progressive recrystallization | Micas Kyanite Staurolite | Phyllites Schists Gneiss | F O L I A T E S |
| | Strong hydrostatic pressure High temperature | In deeper parts of tectonic belts | Recrystallization | Augite Feldspar Garnet | Gneiss | |
| Injection | Magma, Gases and liquids at High temperature | Regions invaded by batholithic intrusions | Recrystallization Replacement of minerals in invaded rocks by material from invading substances | Feldspars Augites Hornblendes Micas Garnets | Banded Gneiss Migmatites | |

### 14. Metamorphism with Depth: 
Temperature, pressure and chemical active fluids is an agent of the metamorphism.

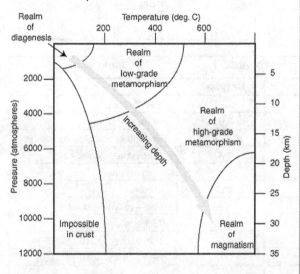

### 16. 'Fools gold': 
The mineral **pyrite**, or **iron pyrite**, also known as **fool's gold**, is an iron sulfide with the chemical formula $FeS_2$. This mineral's metallic luster and pale brass-yellow hue give it a superficial resemblance to gold, hence the well-known nickname of *fool's gold*. The colour has also led to the nicknames *brass*, *brazzle*, and *Brazil*, primarily used to refer to pyrite found in coal.

### 17. Mechanical behaviour of the Earth's layer:

| Mechanical Layers | Behaviour |
|---|---|
| Lithosphere | Brittle to ductile |
| Crust | Brittle |
| Mantle | Brittle to ductile |

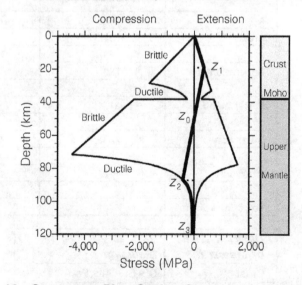

### 18. Convergent Plate Setting:
Convergent boundaries are the zones where two tectonic plates moving towards each other come together at their plate boundaries. At convergent boundaries tectonic plates collide and crust is destroyed as one plate

is pulled beneath the other, the type of collision depends on the types of plates involved. These can be categorised as:

- Oceanic – Continental Plate Convergence
- Oceanic – Oceanic Plate Convergence
- Continental – Continental Plate Convergence

| Types of Convergence | Features |
|---|---|
| Ocean – continent | Volcanic Arc |
| Ocean – ocean | Island Arc |
| Continent – continent | Mountain range |

## 20. Type of Deposits with Example:

| Types of Deposits | Example |
|---|---|
| Igneous deposit | Magnetite deposits of Mayurbhanj, Orissa |
| Sedimentary deposit | Siderite deposits of Madhya Pradesh |
| Residual deposit | Manganese deposits of Madhya Pradesh |
| Metamorphic deposit | Manganese deposits of Maharashtra |

## 21. Earth's Atmospheric Gases:

| Permanent Gases | | | Variable Gases | | |
|---|---|---|---|---|---|
| Gas | Symbol | %age | Gas | Symbol | %age by volume |
| Nitrogen | $N_2$ | 78 % | Water vapour | $H_2O$ | 0 – 4 |
| Oxygen | $O_2$ | 21 % | Carbon dioxide | $CO_2$ | 0.038 |
| Argon | Ar | 0.9 % | Ozone | $O_3$ | 0.000004 |
| Neon | Ne | 0.0018 % | Carbon monoxide | CO | 0.00002 |
| Helium | He | 0.0005 % | Sulphur dioxide | $SO_2$ | 0.000001 |
| Methane | $CH_4$ | 0.0001 % | Nitrogen dioxide | $NO_2$ | 0.000001 |
| Hydrogen | $H_2$ | 0.00005 % | Particles (dust, pollen) | — | 0.00001 |

## 22. Earth's Atmospheric Layers:

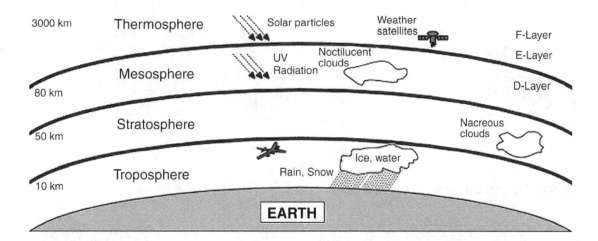

## 23. Atmospheric's Layer with Charecters:

| Layers of the Atmosphere | Remarks |
|---|---|
| Troposphere | Flight |
| Stratosphere | Clouds |
| Mesosphere | UV radiation, D-layer |
| Thermosphere | Weather satellites, E-layer |

## 24. Monsoon season in India with Time: A monsoon is a seasonal change in the direction of the prevailing, or strongest, winds of a region. Monsoons cause wet and dry seasons throughout much of the tropics. Monsoons are most often associated with the Indian Ocean. Monsoons always blow from cold to warm regions. The summer monsoon and the winter monsoon determine the climate for most of India and Southeast Asia.

**Indian Summer Monsoon:** The Indian summer monsoon typically lasts from June-September, with large areas of western and central India receiving more than 90% of their total annual precipitation during the period, and southern and north-western India receiving 50%-75% of their total annual rainfall. Overall, monthly totals average 200-300 mm over the country as a whole, with the largest values observed during the heart of the monsoon season in July and August.

**Winter Monsoon**: The Indian Oceans winter monsoon, which lasts from October to April, is less well-known than its rainy summer equivalent. The dry winter monsoon blows from the northeast. These winds start in the air above Mongolia and north-western China. Winter monsoons are less powerful than summer monsoons in Southeast Asia, in part because the Himalaya Mountains prevent much of the wind and moisture of the monsoons from reaching the coast. The Himalayas also prevent much of the cool air from reaching places like southern India and Sri Lanka, keeping them warm all year. Winter monsoons are sometimes associated with droughts.

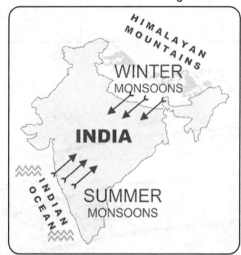

27. **Southwest Monsoon Effect in India:** Southwest Monsoon brings humid climate and torrential rainfall to India and Southeast Asia. The warm and moist air from the southwest Indian Ocean blows towards countries like Sri Lanka, Bangladesh, Myanmar, Thailand, Cambodia, Indonesia, Malaysia and Myanmar. A weak current also reaches Pakistan, bringing minimal rain over the country during the Monsoon season.

The negative impact of Southwest Monsoon is very heavy showers can cause great damage. In urban areas like Mumbai, flooding is a common phenomenon. In rural areas, mudslides caused by excessive rain can bury villages and destroy crops. In the year 2005, a strong Monsoon devastated western part of India. Southwest Monsoon first hit the state of Gujarat, claiming more than 100 lives. The monsoon rains also hit the state of Maharashtra, where flooding killed more than 1,000 people. On July 26, 2005, Mumbai received 39.1 inches or 993.14 mm of rain. However, both the states received rain from two different monsoon systems. East and Northeast India is blessed with huge rivers but in the absence of proper network of rivers, heavy showers invariably lead to bouts of flooding and inundation.

31. **Instruments with Uses:**

| Instruments | Applications |
|---|---|
| Barometer | This is a scientific instrument used in meteorology to measure atmospheric pressure. |
| Hygrometer | This instruments used for measuring the water vapour in the atmosphere, in soil, or in confined spaces. |
| Thermometer | Measuring a temperature |
| Clinometer | A clinometer or inclinometer is an instrument for measuring angles of slope (or tilt), elevation or depression of an object. |

32. **Isohytes:** A line drawn on a map connecting points that receive equal amounts of rainfall.

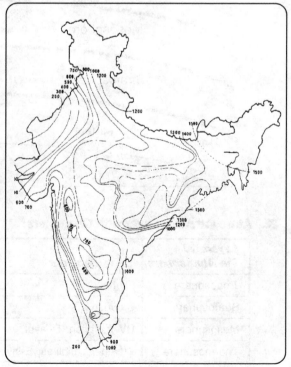

33. **Earth's climate controlled:** The climate of any particular place is influenced by a host of interacting factors. These include latitude, elevation, nearby water, ocean currents, topography, vegetation, and prevailing winds. The global climate system and any changes that occur within it also influence local climate. Consider how each factor illustrated by the thumbnail images might control climate at your location.

34. **Solar radiation received and reflected:** Once the Earth's atmosphere receives shortwave solar radiation, the energy is referred to as insolation. This insolation is the energy input responsible to moving the various Earth-atmosphere systems like the energy balance described above but also weather events, oceanic currents, and other Earth cycles. Insolation can be direct or diffuse.

   • Direct radiation is solar radiation received by the Earth's surface and/or atmosphere that has not been altered by atmospheric scattering. Diffused radiation is solar radiation that has been modified by scattering.

   • Scattering itself is one of five pathways solar radiation can take when entering the atmosphere.

   • It occurs when insolation is deflected and/or redirected upon entering the atmosphere by dust, gas, ice, and water vapour present there. If the energy waves have a shorter wave-length, they are scattered more than those with longer wavelengths. Scattering and how it reacts with wavelength size are responsible for many things we see in the atmosphere such as the sky's blue colour and white clouds.

   • Transmission is another solar radiation pathway. It occurs when both shortwave and longwave energy pass through the atmosphere and water instead of scattering when interacting with gases and other particles in the atmosphere.

   • Refraction can also occur when solar radiation enters the atmosphere. This pathway happens when energy moves from one type of space to another, such as from air into water. As the energy moves from these spaces, it changes its speed and direction when reacting with the particles present there. The shift in direction often causes the energy to bend and release the various light colours within it, similar to what happens as light passes through a crystal or prism.

   • Absorption is the fourth type of solar radiation pathway and is the conversion of energy from one form into another.

   • For example, when solar radiation is absorbed by water, its energy shifts to the water and raises its temperature. This is common of all absorbing surfaces from a tree's leaf to asphalt.

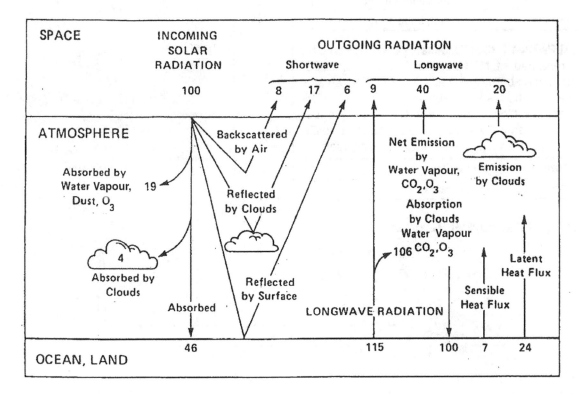

### 35. Albedo of the Different Surface:

| Part of the Solar System | % solar reflectance |
|---|---|
| Sand | 15 – 45 |
| Water | 10 |
| Ice | 30 – 40 |
| Fresh snow | 75 – 95 |
| Forest | 3 – 10 |

### 36. Classification of the Spectrum:

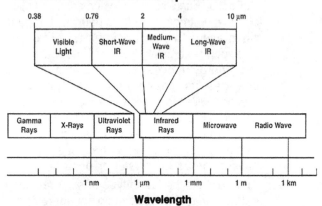

| Satellite Spectrum | Application |
|---|---|
| Visible light | Detection of subsurface features soil and vegetation discrimination. |
| Infra – red | Areal photography |
| Ultraviolet | UV light from the Sun |
| Microwave | Cloud, fog study |

### 37. KALPANA-1 Indian Satellite:
The Kalpana satellite is renamed of METSAT on February 5, 2003, after Indian born American Astronaut Dr. Kalpana Chawla, who died on February 1, 2003 in the US Space Shuttle Columbia disaster. This is the first in the series of exclusive meteorological satellite built by Indian Space Research organization.

| Terms | Remarks |
|---|---|
| Mission | Meteorological |

| Spacecraft Mass | 1060 kg mass (at Lift-off), 498 kg (Dry mass) |
|---|---|
| Onboard Power | 550 W |
| Launch date | 12 September 2002 |
| Payload | Very High Resolution Radiometer (VHRR), Data Relay Transponder (DRT) |
| Launch vehicle | PSLV – C4/ KALPANA-1 |
| Launch site | SHAR, Sriharikota |
| Orbit | Geostationary (74 degree East longitude) |
| Mission | 7 years |
| **Owner** | ISRO |
| **Launch Mass** | 1060 kg |
| Power | 550 W |
| Manufacture | ISRO |
| Orbital | GSO |
| Application | Climate and environment |

### 38. Planes Fly in Atmospheric Heights:

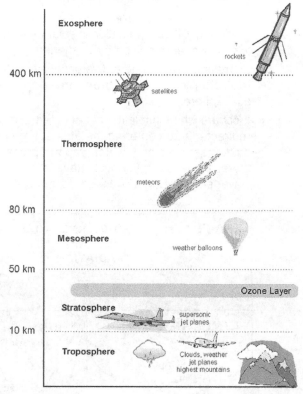

### 39. Ice age in Geological Records:

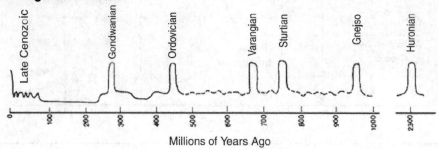

**40. Sun Spot:** Sunspots are darker, cooler areas on the surface of the sun in a region called the photosphere. The photosphere has a temperature of 5,800 degrees Kelvin. Sunspots have temperatures of about 3,800 degrees K. They look dark only in comparison with the brighter and hotter regions of the photosphere around them. Sunspots can be very large, up to 50,000 kilometers in diameter. They are caused by interactions with the Sun's magnetic field which are not fully understood. But a sunspot is somewhat like the cap on a soda bottle: shake it up, and you can generate a big eruption. Sunspots occur over regions of intense magnetic activity, and when that energy is released, solar flares and big storms called coronal mass ejections erupt from sunspots.

**41. Foraminifera Fossils:** Foraminifera is a type of microfossils which exists in marine environments, in intertidal to the deepest ocean trenches and from tropics to the poles, but species of foraminifera can be very particular about the environments where they live. Some are abundant only in the deep Ocean, others are found only in brackish estuaries or salt marshes along the shore, and most live at certain depths and water temperatures in between. Foraminifera are an important part of the marine food chain. On the continental shelf there can be tens of thousands of living individuals per square meter of ocean bottom. Many larger animals (including snails, sand dollars, and fish) eat forams, and some are very selective about which species they eat.

**42. Deepest part of the Ocean:** The Mariana Trench or Mariansa Trench is the deepest part of the world's ocean. It is located in the western Pacific Ocean, an average of 200 km to the east of the Mariana Island, in the Western Pacific East of Philippines.

**47. Sea surface temperature conditions:** The temperature of the sea surface is totally depends on its waters, the water temperature is also a part of the air masses in the Earth's atmosphere. Warm sea surface temperatures cause the tropical cyclogenesis over the earth. Tropical cyclones can also cause a cool wake, due to turbulent mixing of the upper 30 metres (100 ft) of the ocean. SST changes diurnally, like the air above it, but to a lesser degree. There is less SST variation on breezy days than on calm days. In addition, ocean currents such as the Atlantic Multidecadal Oscillation (AMO), can effect SST's on multi-decadal time scales, a major impact results from the global thermohaline circulation, which affects average SST significantly throughout most of the world's oceans. In the offshore region the winds also effect the cool and warm enviro-nments due to the movements in the form of the coastal sea surface temperatures.

**48. Isohaline:** Isohalines are lines (or contours) that join points of equal salinity in an aquatic system. There are different isolines:

| Types of Isolines | Remarks |
| --- | --- |
| Isoheights | It is a line of the equal elevation or also called topographic contours. |
| Isobars | It is a line of the equal atmospheric pressure also called weather maps. |
| Isotherm | A line of equal temperature |
| Isobaths | A line of equal depth |
| Isohaline | A line of equal salinity |
| Isotachs | A line of equal wind speed |
| Isopycnals | A line of equal rainfall |

**50. Low and High Tides:** Based on the number of high and low tides and their relative heights each tidal day, tides are described as semi-diurnal, mixed, or diurnal. When the moon is directly over Earth's equator, its associated tidal bulges are centered on the equator. In theory, all locations on the planet except at the highest latitudes would rotate through the two tidal bulges and experience two equal high tides and two equal low tides per tidal day; this is known as a **semi-diurnal tide**. Semi-diurnal tides have a period of 12 hrs and 25 min, and theoretically have a wavelength of more than half the circumference of Earth.

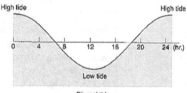

Diurnal tide

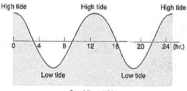

Semidiurnal tide

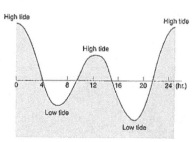

Mixed tide

### 53. Current and its Feaures:

| Currents | Types |
|----------|-------|
| California current | Cold current |
| Kuroshio current | Warm current |
| Brazil current | Warm current |
| Gulf current | Warm current |
| Canary current | Cold current |
| Peru current | Cold current |

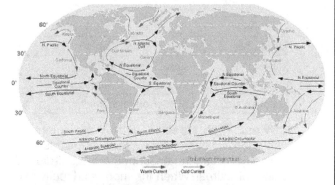

### 55. Type of Reefs:

| Types of Reefs | Remarks |
|----------------|---------|
| Fringing reef | **Fringing reefs** grow near the coastline around islands and continents. |
| Atoll | **Atolls** are rings of coral that create protected lagoons and are usually located in the middle of the sea. |
| Barrier reef | **Barrier reefs** also parallel the coastline but are separated by deeper, wider lagoons. At their shallowest point, they can reach the water's surface forming a "barrier" to navigation. |

### 57. Temperate Cyclone:
**Temperate Cyclone:** The systems developing in the mid and high latitude **(35° latitude and 65° latitude in both hemispheres)**, beyond the tropics are called the Temperate Cyclones or Extra Tropical Cyclones or Mid-Latitude Cyclones or Frontal Cyclones or Wave Cyclones. The temperate cyclones occur mostly in winter, late autumn and spring. They are generally associated with rainstorms and cloudy weather.

- During summer, all the paths of temperate cyclones shift northwards and there are only few temperate cyclone over sub-tropics and the warm temperate zone, although a high concentration of storms occurs over Bering Strait, USA and Russian Arctic and sub-Arctic zone.

### 58. Zone with character:

| Zones | Character |
|-------|-----------|
| Aphotic zone | No Sun's light |
| Photic zone | Receive Sun's light |

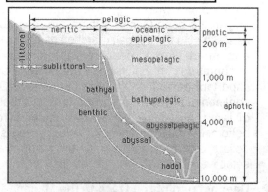

### 59. Mass Percentage of the Earth:

| Component of the Earth | Mass Percentage | Volume Percentage |
|------------------------|-----------------|-------------------|
| Crust | < 1 | 1 |
| Mantle | 70 | 83 |
| Core | 30 | 16 |

| ELEMENT (symbol) | CRUST | | HYDROSPHERE | TROPOSPHERE |
|------------------|-------|---|-------------|-------------|
| | Per cent by mass | Per cent by volume | Per cent by volume | Per cent by volume |
| Oxygen (O) | 46.10 | 94.04 | 33.0 | 21.0 |
| Silicon (Si) | 28.20 | 0.88 | | |
| Aluminum (Al) | 8.23 | 0.48 | | |
| Iron (Fe) | 5.63 | 0.49 | | |
| Calcium (Ca) | 4.15 | 1.18 | Per cent by volume | |
| Sodium (Na) | 2.36 | 1.11 | | |
| Magnesium (Mg) | 2.33 | 0.33 | | |
| Potassium (K) | 2.09 | 1.42 | | |
| Nitrogen (N) | | | | 78.0 |
| Hydrogen (H) | | | 66.0 | |
| Other | 0.91 | 0.07 | 1.0 | 1.0 |

60. **Seismic profiling under Sea depend:** Seismic waves propagate and its develop of the profiling is due to the emition of the waves in different time interval. The energy reflected from different boundaries with different composition in multiple layers. Acoustic impedance is defined by the bulk density of medium times the velocity of the sound within that medium. The reflected acoustic signals is received either by a ship towed hydrophone. The receiver converts it into the different signal and we use our objectives within the computer with suitable software.

61. **Mid–Atlantic Ridge:** The North American and Eurasian Plates are moving away from each other along the line of the **Mid Atlantic Ridge**. The Ridge extends into the South Atlantic Ocean between the South American and African Plates. The ocean ridge rises to between 2 to 3 km above the ocean floor, and has a **rift valley** at its crest marking the location at which the two plates are moving apart. The Mid Atlantic Ridge, like other ocean ridge systems, has developed as a consequence of the divergent motion between the Eurasian and North American, and African and South American Plates. As the mantle rises towards the surface below the ridge the pressure is lowered (decompression) and the hot rock starts to partially melt. This produces basaltic volcanoes when an eruption occurs above the surface (**Eyjafjallajökull** in Iceland) and characteristic basalt "**pillow lava**" in underwater eruptions. In this way, as the plates move further apart new ocean lithosphere is formed at the ridge and the ocean basin gets wider. This process is known as "**sea floor spreading**" and results in a symmetrical alignment of the rocks of the ocean floor which get older with distance from the ridge crest.

63. **Terms with Remarks:**

| Terms | Remarks |
|---|---|
| Termite | Cockroach |
| Stalagmite | Depositional landform by underground water |
| Rhyolite | Volcanic equivalent of the granite |
| Monazite | Ore of the thorium |

64. **Lignite and Bituminous Mines in India:**

| Lignite Mines | States |
|---|---|
| Kachchh, Bharuch, Bhavnagar, Surat | Gujarat |
| Kupwara | J & K |
| Kannur | Kerala |
| Bikaner, Barmer, Jaiselmer, Nagaur | Rajasthan |
| Cuddolore, Ariyalur, Ramnad | Tamil Nadu |

| Bituminous mines | States |
|---|---|
| Sohagpur, Sonhat, Hasdeo-Arand | Chattisgarh |
| Raniganj, Jharia, Hutar, Ramgarh | Jharkhand |
| Singrauli, Umaria | MP |
| Kamthi, Vardha valley | Maharashtra |

66. **Types of Aquifer:**

| Types of Aquifer | Character | Example |
|---|---|---|
| Aquifer | Porous and permeable | Sandy formation |
| Aquiclude | Porous but not permeable | Clay bed |
| Aquifuge | Neither porous nor permeable | Solid granite |
| Aquitard | Porous but less permeable | Sandy clay |

68. **Etna Volcano:** This is a type of the active strato – volcanoes, which on the east coast of Sicily, Italy. This lies on convergent plate setting in between African and Eurasian plates, tallest (3,329 km) active volcanoes in the Europe. Etna covers an area of 1,190 $km^2$ (459 sq mi) with a basal circumference of 140 km. This makes it by far the largest of the three active volcanoes in Italy, being about two and a half times the height of the next largest, Mount Vesuvius. Only Mount Teide in Tenerife (owned by Spain) surpasses it in the whole of the European–North-African region. In Greek Mythology, the deadly monster Typhon was trapped under this mountain by Zeus, the god of the sky and thunder and king of gods, and the forges of Hephaestus were said to also be located underneath it.

Mount Etna is one of the most active volcanoes in the world and is in an almost constant state of activity. The fertile volcanic soils support extensive agriculture, with vineyards and orchards spread across the lower slopes of the mountain and the broad Plain of Catania to the south. Due to its history of recent activity and nearby population, Mount Etna has been designated a Decade Volcano by the United Nations. In June 2013, it was added to the list of UNESCO World Heritage Sites.

70. **Crevasse:** A *crevasse* is a deep crack, or fracture, found in an ice sheet or glacier, as opposed to a crevice that forms in rock. *Crevasses* form as a result of the movement and resulting stress associated with the shear stress generated when two semi-rigid pieces above a plastic substrate have different rates of movement.

### 73. Particle size:

| Particle Name | Size |
|---|---|
| Boulder | >256 mm |
| Cobble | 64 – 256 mm |
| Pebble | 4 – 64 mm |
| Granule | 2 – 4 mm |
| Sand | 2 – 1/16 mm |
| Silt | 1/16 – 1/256 mm |
| Clay | <1/256 mm |

### 75. Classification of Cyclone:
- Polar cyclone – polar region
- Polar lows – Short polar region
- Extratropical cyclone – mid –latitude cyclone
- Subtropical cyclone – between the equator and 50 degree North and South
- Mesocyclone
- Tropical cyclone – tropics

### 79. Echo-sounder instruments:
Echo sounding is a type of sonar used to determine the depth of water by transmitting sound pulses into water. The time interval between emission and return of a pulse is recorded, which used to determine the depth of water along with the speed of sound in water at the time. This information is then typically used for navigation purposes or in order to obtain depths for charting purposes. Echo sounding can also refer to hydroacoustic "echo sounders" defined as active sound in water (sonar) used to study fish. Hydroacoustic assessments have traditionally employed mobile surveys from boats to evaluate fish biomass and spatial distributions. Conversely, fixed-location techniques use stationary transducers to monitor passing fish.

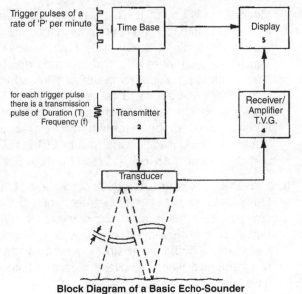

**Block Diagram of a Basic Echo-Sounder**

The word *sounding* is used for all types of depth measurements, including those that don't use sound, and is unrelated in origin to the word *sound* in the sense of noise or tones. Echo sounding is a more rapid method of measuring depth than the previous technique of lowering a sounding line until it touched bottom.

### 80. Types of Tides:
There are different tide based on shape, size and its origin.

**Bore Tide:** A tidal bore (or simply bore in context, or also aegir, eagre, or eygre) is a tidal phenomenon in which the leading edge of the incoming tide forms a wave (or waves) of water that travels up a river or narrow bay against the direction of the river or bay's current.

**Neap Tide:** When the Sun and Moon form a right angle, as when we see a half moon, their gravitational pulls fight each other and we notice a smaller difference between high and low tides. These are called neap tides.

**Spring Tide:** When the Moon, Earth, and Sun fall in a straight line, which we call syzygy (siz-eh-gee), we notice the greatest difference between high and low tide water levels. These spring tides occur twice each month, during the full and new Moon. If the Moon is at perigee, the closest it approaches Earth in its orbit, the tides are especially high and low.

**Rip Tide:** A rip current, commonly referred to simply as a rip, or by the misnomer rip tide, is a strong channel of water flowing seaward from near the shore, typically through the surf line. Typical flow is at 0.5 meter-per-second, and can be as fast as 2.5 meters-per-second (8 feet-per-second), which is faster than any human swimmer. They can occur at any beach with breaking waves, including oceans, seas and even large lakes.

**Low Tide:** In both senses also called low water. The time at which the tide is lowest. The lowest level of the tide.

**High Tide:** (HT)
*a)* The tide at its fullest, when the water reaches its highest level.
*b.)* The time at which this tide occurs. Also called high water.

**Brown Tide:** Brown Tide is a bloom (excessive growth) of small marine algae (Aureococcus anophagefferens). Although algae of many types are found in all natural freshwater and marine ecosystems, blooms of the Brown Tide organism literally turn the water deep brown, making it unappealing to swimmers and fishermen alike. While not harmful to humans, the presence of the Brown Tide is a problem for bay scallops and eelgrass, and to a lesser degree other finfish and shellfish. Brown Tide is unlike most other algal blooms because of its unusually high concentrations, the extent of area it covers and the length of time it persists.

**Red Tide:** Harmful algal blooms, (HAB) occur when colonies of algae grow out of control while producing toxic or harmful effects on people, fish, shellfish, marine mammals and birds. The human illnesses caused by HABs, though rare, can be debilitating or even fatal. Many people call HABs 'red tides,' scientists prefer the term harmful algal bloom. One of the best known HABs in the nation occurs nearly every summer along Florida's Gulf Coast.

**Crimson Tide:** Trademarked name for the University of Alabama Athletics.

**Semidiurnal Tide:** These are tides occurring twice a day. This means a body of water with semi-diurnal tides, like the Atlantic Ocean, will have two high tides and two low tides in one day, much like the eastern seaboard of North America.

**Diurnal Tide:** These tides occur once a day. A body of water with diurnal tides, like the Gulf of Mexico, has only one high tide and one low tide in a 25-hour period.

**Mixed Tide:** Some bodies of water, including most of North America that in contact with the Pacific Basin, have mixed tides, where a single low tide follows two high tides.

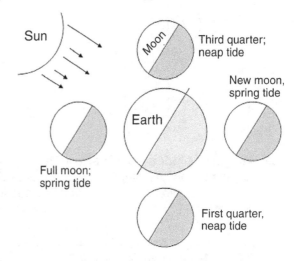

82. **Trench:** A *trench* is a type of excavation or depression in the ground that is generally deeper than it is wide (as opposed to a wider gully, or ditch), and narrow compared with its length (as opposed to a simple hole).

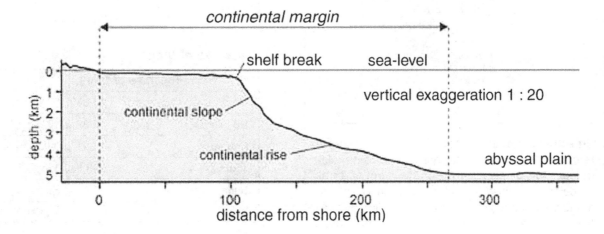

83. **Guyot:** Seamounts and Guyots are volcanoes that have built up from the ocean floor, sometimes to sea level or above. Guyots are seamounts that have built above sea level. Erosion by waves destroyed the top of the seamount resulting in a flattened shape. Due to the movement of the ocean floor away from oceanic ridges, the sea floor gradually sinks and the flattened guyots are submerged to become undersea flat-topped peaks. We know that the tops of guyots were once at the surface because they contain evidence of fossils such as coral reefs that only live in shallow water. Seamounts conversely represent volcanoes that did not reach sea level so their tops remain intact and are shaped like volcanoes on land.

84. **Glaciation with geological time: What is an ice age?** An ice age is a long interval of time (millions to tens of millions of years) when global temperatures are relatively cold and large areas of the Earth are covered by continental ice sheets and alpine glaciers. Within an ice age are multiple shorter-term periods of warmer temperatures when glaciers retreat (called interglacials or interglacial cycles) and colder temperatures when glaciers advance (called glacials or glacial cycles).

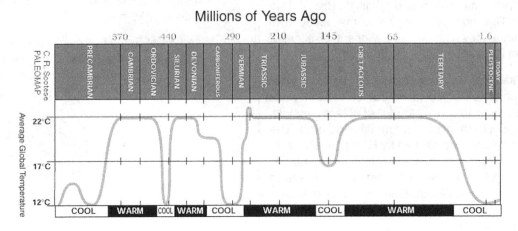

85. **Weathering Index of the Minerals:** The wea-thering is defined as the stability on the basis of the Bowen's reaction series. The least susceptible is quartz (end crystallization mineral) and the most susceptible is olivine.

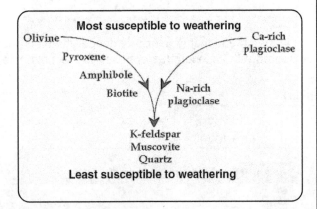

86. **En echelon pattern faulting:** The term 'en echelon' refers to closely-spaced, parallel or sub-parallel, overlapping or step-like minor structural features in rock (faults, tension fractures), which lie oblique to the overall structural trend. Conjugate deforma-tion structures are related in deformational origin.

Extensional stresses create fractures that can infill with calcite. When rocks deform in a brittle manner, the fracture pore can subsequently infill with some form of cement, such as calcite. Typically, crystals will nucleate on the fracture wall and grow into the opening. (Sometimes apparent fracture are completely reduced by a prismatic or fibrous mineral that is oriented long axis normal to the wall. In this case, the force of crystallization of the

'filling' material may be the actual cause of the opening of the fracture.)

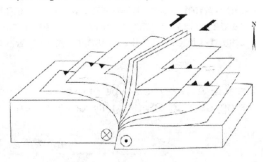

87. **Properties of Sun:**

| Properties of Sun | |
|---|---|
| Mass | 1.98892 x $10^{30}$ kg |
| Density | 1.622 x $10^5$ kg/m³ |
| Diameter | 1,391,000 kilometers |
| Radius | 695,500 km |
| Surface gravity of the Sun | 27.94 g |
| Volume of the Sun | 1.412 x $10^{18}$ km³ |

89. **Nuclear reaction:** A nuclear reaction, very simply, is a reaction that affects the nucleus of an atom. This is different from a chemical reaction, which has nothing to do with the nucleus of an atom but rather involves changes in atoms' electrons that orbit the nucleus. In chemical reactions, the electrons are exchanged from one or more substances to produce a different substance, and the elements are the same in the products and

reactants. In nuclear reactions, the particles in the nucleus are changed, and one element is transformed into another element when particles in the nucleus are gained or lost.

93. **Nebula:** A nebula is a truly wondrous thing to behold. Named after the Latin word for "cloud", nebulae are not only massive clouds of dust, hydrogen and helium gas, and plasma; they are also often "stellar nurseries"–*i.e.,* the place where stars are born. And for centuries, distant galaxies were often mistaken for these massive clouds.

Alas, such descriptions barely scratch the surface of what nebulae are and what there significance is. Between their formation process, their role in stellar and planetary formation, and their diversity, nebulae have provided humanity with endless intrigue and discovery.

For some time now, scientists and astronomers have been aware that outer space is not really a total vacuum. In fact, it is made up of gas and dust particles known collectively as the Interstellar Medium (ISM). Approximately 99% of the ISM is composed of gas, while about 75% of its mass takes the form of hydrogen and the remaining 25% as helium.

98. **Metallicity:** Astronomers call all elements more massive than Helium 'metals', and denote them by Z, X and Y being the hydrogen and helium abundance by mass, respectively). These are produced in stars. For some elements, like e.g. Carbon, we don't really know which stars are the dominant source. Super Novae (SNe) are a major source of metals. There are two basic types:

SNe of type II are explosions of very massive stars. Nuclear fusion during the explosion is responsible for many elements of the $\alpha$-type, like Oxygen and Silicon.

SNe of type I, on the other hand, are thought to occur during mass-transfer in binary stars - these are the dominant producers of Iron, Fe. The chemical mix of the stars is therefore a fossil relict of the relative fractions of type I and type II SNe. Typically though, one measures just one metallicity, for example the Fe abundance since that is often the easiest to measure, and then assumes that the other elements scale with Fe. But we know for a fact that some stellar systems have a rather different relative abundance pattern of the elements.

For the Sun, the total amount of metals by mass, is about $Z_0 = 0.02$, or 2 per cent of the mass in the solar system is *not* hydrogen or helium. This is inferred not just from observations of the Sun, but also from the composition of comets. For other stars, one usually compares the metallicity in units of the solar value, on a logarithmic scale,

$Fe/H = \log_{10} [(Fe/H) / (Fe/H)_0 ]$

So if a star has [Fe/H]=0, it has the same Iron abundance as the Sun, for [Fe/H]=-1, it has one tenth the solar value.

99. **Andromeda galaxy:** The Andromeda Galaxy (M31) is the closest large galaxy to the Milky Way and is one of a few galaxies that can be seen unaided from the Earth. In approximately 4.5 billion years the Andromeda Galaxy and the Milky Way are expected to collide and the result will be a giant elliptical galaxy. Andromeda is accompanied by 14 dwarf galaxies, including M32, M110, and possibly M33 (The Triangulum Galaxy).

| Properties of Andromeda | |
|---|---|
| *Designation* | *M31/ NGC 224* |
| Type | Spiral |
| Diameter | 220,000 ly |
| Distance | 2.54 Mly |
| Mass | 1,230 billion |
| Number of stars | 1 trillion |
| Constellation | Andromeda |

100. **Red Shift:** The light from distant stars and more distant galaxies is not featureless, but has distinct spectral features characteristic of the atoms in the gases around the stars. When these spectra are examined, they are found to be shifted toward the red end of the spectrum. This shift is apparently a Doppler shift and indicates that essentially all of the galaxies are moving away from us. Using the results from the nearer ones, it becomes evident that the more distant galaxies are moving away from us faster. This is the kind of result one would expect for an expanding universe. The red line of the spectrum below is the transition from n=3 to n=2 of hydrogen and is famous as the H-alpha line seen throughout universe.

# International Earth Science Olympiad (IESO)
## Entrance Exam, 2013

**Total Marks : 100**                                    **Time : 90 minutes**

1. What is the chemical composition of the mineral *talc* commonly used in paper, paint, ceramic and other industries?
   (a) Hydrous silicate of aluminium
   (b) Hydrous silicate of potassium
   (c) Hydrous silicate of magnesium
   (d) Aluminium oxide

2. The purple variety of quartz known as *amethyst* owes its colour to _____.
   (a) Manganese        (b) Magnesium
   (c) Titanium         (d) Calcium

3. _____ is the plane of weakness along which a mineral can be easily split.
   (a) Fracture         (b) Cleavage
   (c) Crack            (d) Pitch

4. An igneous rock with a mixture of fine and large grains of minerals is called _____.
   (a) Porphyry         (b) Pegmatite
   (c) Pitchstone       (d) Breccia

5. Which of the following rocks floats on water?
   (a) Pumice           (b) Dunite
   (c) Obsidian         (d) Basalt

6. What is the term used to describe a mixture of minerals, gases and molten rock found underneath the earth's crust?
   (a) Melt             (b) Lava
   (c) Magma            (d) Mantle

7. A wall like intrusive of an igneous rock is called a _____.
   (a) Sill             (b) Batholith
   (c) Dyke or dike     (d) Boss

8. _____ is a rock characterised by parallel to sub parallel arrangement of platy minerals.
   (a) Schist           (b) Gneiss
   (c) Granite          (d) Dolerite

9. _____ is a metamorphic rock with bands of light and dark minerals (usually quartz-feldspar and micas).
   (a) Slate            (b) Schist
   (c) Phyllite         (d) Gneiss

10. What is the common term used to describe the changes in mineralogy a rock undergoes when it is intensely heated by an igneous intrusive?
    (a) Hydrothermal metamorphism
    (b) Contact metamorphism
    (c) Cataclastic metamorphism
    (d) Regional metamorphism

11. A measure of the energy released during an earthquake is measured on a scale known as the _____ .
    (a) Richter scale       (b) Mercalli scale
    (c) Beaufort scale      (d) Mohorovicic scale

12. _____ is the shape that the surface of the oceans would take under the influence of gravity alone.
    (a) Geoid               (b) Reference ellipsoid
    (c) Geode               (d) Spheroid

13. What type of a tectonic boundary exists between the Indian-Australian plate and the Eurasian plate?
    (a) Constructive
    (b) Conservative
    (c) Destructive
    (d) Continent/ continent collision

14. A combination of shallow earthquakes, volcanism and contact metamorphism characterises _____.
    (a) Transform fault boundary
    (b) Spreading center
    (c) Subduction zone
    (d) Continent/ continent margin

15. _____ is an example of a chemical sedimentary rock.
    (a) Sandstone           (b) Shale
    (c) Conglomerate        (d) Halite

16. Cross-beds form when sediment is deposited in a _____ current of water or air.
    (a) Weak                (b) Very Weak
    (c) Moderate            (d) Strong

17. The two important constituents of limestone are _____ .
    (a) Calcite and Aragonite
    (b) Calcite and Gypsum
    (c) Calcite and Dolomite
    (d) Aragonite and Dolomite

18. The rock composed of large (> 2mm dia.) angular particles is known as _____ .
    (a) Sandstone          (b) Limestone
    (c) Conglomerate       (d) Breccia

19. Corals belong to _____ class.
    (a) Scyphozoa          (b) Hydrozoa
    (c) Anthozoa           (d) Bryozoa

20. The first land plants appeared in _____ .
    (a) Cambrian           (b) Ordovician
    (c) Silurian           (d) Devonian

21. The main source of limestone is _____ .
    (a) Gastropod Shells
    (b) Lamellibranch Shells
    (c) Inorganic Material
    (d) Coral Reefs

22. Gastropods are also known as _____ .
    (a) Snails             (b) Lamellibranchs
    (c) Scaphopods         (d) Pelecypods

23. Giant reptiles and ammonites disappeared at the end of _____ .
    (a) Triassic           (b) Jurassic
    (c) Cretaceous         (d) Permian

24. Fossils are found mainly in _____ rocks.
    (a) Igneous            (b) Sedimentary
    (c) Metamorphic        (d) Volcanic

25. The winter season in the Northern Hemisphere is shorter than summer because:
    (a) The Earth is closer to the Sun during winter in the Northern Hemisphere
    (b) The Earth is farthest from the Sun during winter in the Northern Hemisphere
    (c) The Northern Hemisphere has more land area than the Southern Hemisphere
    (d) There is no continent at the North Pole

26. This most common mineral on the Earth is used in chronometers.
    (a) Diamond            (b) Quartz
    (c) Calcite            (d) Ruby

27. If the distance between two villages on the ground is 15 km and the distance between the same two villages on a map is 3 cm, then the scale of the map is:
    (a) 1:5.000            (b) 1:50,000
    (c) 1:500,000          (d) 1:5000,000

28. Excessive _____ in soil will result in good drainage.
    (a) Gravel             (b) Sand
    (c) Silt               (d) Clay

29. Acid-generating cations in soil solution include ions of:
    (a) Aluminum, Potassium Sodium
    (b) Aluminum, Hydrogen
    (c) Hydrogen, Potassium, Calcium
    (d) Hydrogen, Magnesium, Sodium

30. A line connecting points of equal precipitation is a:
    (a) Contour            (b) Isohyet
    (c) Isohaline          (d) Isobar

31. If the contour interval of a topographic map is doubled, how many contour lines are needed to show the same increase in elevation?
    (a) Half as many
    (b) Twice as many
    (c) The same number
    (d) Variable depending upon the terrain

32. In the cross section of a sand dune given below, the wind was blowing from _____ .

    (a) Left to right      (b) Right to left
    (c) Bottom to top      (d) Top to bottom

33. Which of the following is not a likely impact of deforestation and increased grazing intensity?
    (a) Reduced infiltration capacity
    (b) Increased infiltration capacity
    (c) Greater infiltration-excess overland flow generation
    (d) Increased stream discharge variability

34. In the sub-tropics, the driest hot deserts are found in the:
    (a) Western coastal regions of the continents
    (b) Eastern coastal regions of the continents
    (c) Continental interiors
    (d) Highland plateaux

35. According to Darcy's law, groundwater flow is assumed to be _____ .
    (a) Laminar            (b) Turbulent
    (c) Zigzag             (d) Both (a) and (b)

36. The ability of a saturated rock to hold water after drainage due to gravity is called _____ .
    (a) Specific storage
    (b) Specific retention
    (c) Specific yield
    (d) Storativity

**37.** A perched aquifer occurs in _____ zone.
(a) Saturated
(b) Aerated
(c) Artesian
(d) Confined

**38.** The main source of freshwater on the earth is _____.
(a) Polar ice caps
(b) Oceans
(c) Rivers
(d) Groundwater

**39.** Runoff results after _____.
(a) Saturation of soil
(b) Satisfying the losses
(c) Infiltration
(d) All of the above

**40.** The structure shown below forms in a _____ environment.

(a) Glacial
(b) Tidal mud flat
(c) Deep ocean
(d) Shallow sea

**41.** The primary structure shown below is known as _____.

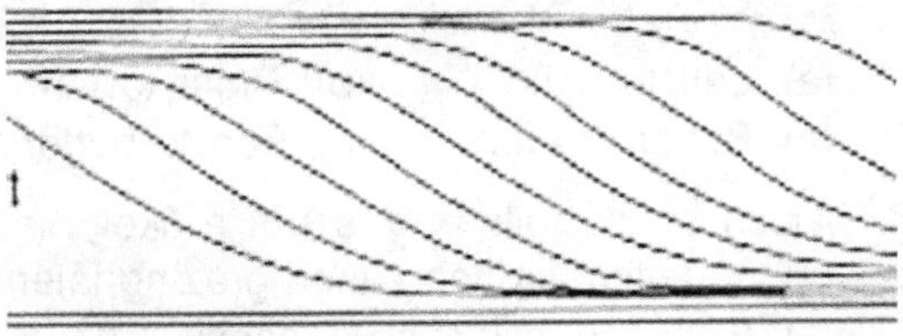

(a) Graded bedding
(b) Current bedding
(c) Rhythmic bedding
(d) Cross bedding

**42.** Which of the following is a type of stress?
(a) Compression
(b) Tension
(c) Shear
(d) All of the above

**43.** Folding occurs when rocks behave as _____.
(a) Ductile solids
(b) Frozen solids
(c) Fluids
(d) Brittle solids

**44.** A structural basin is a special case of _____.
(a) A freak of nature
(b) An anticline
(c) A syncline
(d) A dome

**45.** Faults where displacement is both vertical and horizontal are called
(a) Oblique faults
(b) Slippery faults
(c) Complex faults
(d) Ordinary faults

**46.** An extra-tropical storm originating in the Mediterranean that brings sudden winter rain and snow to the north-western parts of India is called _____.
(a) North-west Monsoon
(b) Anticyclone
(c) Westerly disturbance
(d) Tropical cyclone

**47.** The rate of change of temperature with height is called _____.
(a) Troposphere
(b) Vertical velocity
(c) Global warming
(d) Lapse rate

**48.** Geostrophic flow is the balance between the following forces:
(a) Coriolis and curvature
(b) Coriolis and friction
(c) Coriolis and pressure gradient
(d) Coriolis and gravity

**49.** The sky appears blue because of _____.
(a) Refraction
(b) Reflection
(c) Scattering
(d) Cosmic rays

**50.** Condensation results in the release of _____
(a) Sensible heat
(b) Long-wave radiation
(c) Photons
(d) Latent heat

**51.** The atmospheric circulation which features rising motion near the equator, pole-ward flow 10–15 kilometers above the surface, descending motion in the subtropics, and equator-ward flow near the surface is known as the _____ .
(a) Walker cell
(b) Hadley cell
(c) Ferrel cell
(d) Equator cell

**52.** Which of the following is NOT a greenhouse gas?
(a) $N_2O$
(b) $O_3$
(c) $N_2$
(d) $H_2O$

**53.** The fraction of incoming solar radiation reflected by the earth is called _____.
(a) Albedo
(b) Alameda
(c) Absorptivity
(d) Attenuation

**54.** The jet streams move from _____.
(a) West to east
(b) East to west
(c) South to north
(d) North to south

**55.** Chlorofluorocarbons (CFC's) were banned because they were found to _____.
(a) Produce ozone
(b) Produce $NO_x$
(c) Produce poisonous gases
(d) Deplete ozone

56. The annual temperature range of Delhi is greater than that of Mumbai because _____.
    (a) Delhi is at a higher latitude
    (b) Delhi is not on the coast
    (c) Delhi is at a higher altitude
    (d) Delhi is at a higher longitude.

57. Large volcanic eruptions result in a large amount of _____ in the stratosphere which scatter solar radiation causing cooling of the surface.
    (a) $CO_2$
    (b) Sulphate aerosols
    (c) Carbonaceous aerosols
    (d) Water droplets

58. As temperature increases, the _____ of air increases exponentially.
    (a) Lifting condensation level
    (b) Cloud condensation nuclei
    (c) Saturation vapour pressure
    (d) Density

59. Tropical cyclones are formed over _____.
    (a) Warm desert regions
    (b) Warm tropical oceans
    (c) Cold tropical ocean regions
    (d) Warm equatorial oceans

60. The _____ appears as a band of clouds, usually thunderstorms, which circle the globe near the equator.
    (a) South Pacific Convergence Zone
    (b) Monsoon
    (c) Inter-Tropical Convergence Zone
    (d) Ferrel Cell.

61. A bathythermograph measures which of the following parameters:
    (a) Temperature and salinity
    (b) Temperature and density
    (c) Depth and temperature
    (d) Depth and density

62. The interface between rivers and oceans is called a _____.
    (a) Continental rise      (b) Continental margin
    (c) Continental slope    (d) Estuary

63. Which is the main source of protein from the oceans for humans?
    (a) Fish                 (b) Sea weed
    (c) Corals               (d) Sea shells

64. Diurnal tides occur:
    (a) Once a day
    (b) Twice a day
    (c) Once in two days
    (d) Once in two weeks

65. Knot is a measure of:
    (a) The strength of a rope
    (b) A sailor's ability
    (c) Speed
    (d) A nautical mile

66. Which of the following is NOT dangerous for swimmers in the sea?
    (a) Sea shells           (b) Tsunami
    (c) Sharks               (d) Rip currents

67. The maximum depth to which sunlight penetrates the ocean depends on which of the following properties of sea water?
    (a) Temperature          (b) Turbidity
    (c) Salinity             (d) Density

68. Dissolved carbon dioxide in the oceans is measured in units of _____.
    (a) Gram                 (b) Millimole/kg
    (c) cc                   (d) ml/m$^2$

69. In an ocean map, contours connecting points of equal density are known as _____.
    (a) Isotherms            (b) Isopycnals
    (c) Isohyets             (d) Isohalines

70. The typical mass of a 10 cc volume of sea water is _____ grams.
    (a) 9.9                  (b) 12.0
    (c) 5.3                  (d) 10.2

71. Surface ocean currents are driven by _____.
    (a) Winds
    (b) Earth's rotation
    (c) Sea floor topography
    (d) Direct solar heating

72. Equatorial excess heat is transported polewards mainly by _____.
    (a) Trade winds
    (b) Cold deep ocean currents
    (c) Coriolis force
    (d) Warm ocean surface currents

73. Measurement of conductivity of sea water helps in determining its_____.
    (a) Temperature
    (b) Salinity
    (c) Depth
    (d) Density

74. The most abundant positive ion in sea water is _____.
    (a) Ca$^{++}$            (b) Na
    (c) K$^+$                (d) Al$^{+++}$

**75.** The most abundant anion in sea water is _____.
    (a) $CO_3^-$
    (b) $Cl^-$
    (c) $SO_4^-$
    (d) $NO_3^-$

**76.** Carbon fixation by marine plankton happens because of the presence of _____.
    (a) Chlorophyll-a
    (b) Bacteria
    (c) Viruses
    (d) Fungi

**77.** The highest phytoplankton bloom occurs in the Arabian Sea during _____.
    (a) Spring
    (b) Winter
    (c) Monsoon
    (d) Autumn

**78.** Oceans in the Northern Hemisphere receive maximum solar heat during _____.
    (a) July
    (b) January
    (c) March
    (d) October

**79.** Surface waters of the Bay of Bengal are less saline compared to the surface waters of the Arabian Sea because of _____.
    (a) More fresh water discharge from rivers to the Bay of Bengal
    (b) Higher evaporation from the Bay of Bengal
    (c) Less evaporation from the Arabian Sea
    (d) More rain over the Arabian Sea

**80.** The saltiest sea in the world is the _____.
    (a) Black Sea
    (b) Dead Sea
    (c) Yellow Sea
    (d) Red Sea

**81.** Stars on the Main Sequence _____.
    (a) Convert helium to hydrogen in their centres.
    (b) Convert helium to carbon in their centres
    (c) Convert hydrogen to helium in their centres
    (d) Have no fusion in their centres

**82.** Venus is closest to the Earth when:
    (a) It is full (bright side faces the Earth)
    (b) It is dark (dark side faces the Earth)
    (c) It is half lit
    (d) None of the above

**83.** Constellations are groups of stars related by:
    (a) Brightness
    (b) Spectral type
    (c) Apparent position in the sky
    (d) Physical location in the Galaxy

**84.** Polaris was not the North Star in the past. This is because of:
    (a) The motion of the Earth around the Sun.
    (b) The rotation of the Earth.
    (c) The motion of the Sun through the Galaxy.
    (d) The precession of the Earth's rotation axis

**85.** Energy from the Sun is due to:
    (a) Fusion of hydrogen in the core
    (b) Gravitational contraction
    (c) Chemical reactions
    (d) Fission of uranium in the core

**86.** Voyager is now about:
    (a) 1 A.U. from the Sun
    (b) 100 A.U. from the Sun
    (c) 1 light year from the Sun
    (d) 1 pc from the Sun

**87.** A sunspot is a region of the Sun's surface that is:
    (a) Hotter than its surroundings
    (b) Cooler than its surroundings
    (c) Higher than its surroundings
    (d) Deeper than its surroundings

**88.** Paris is about 1/4 of the way around Earth from Chicago. On a night when people in Chicago see a first quarter moon, people in Paris see:
    (a) A new moon
    (b) A first quarter moon
    (c) A full moon
    (d) Any of the above, depending upon the time of night

**89.** The Moon is receding from the Earth because of:
    (a) Pressure from escaping gases in the Earth's atmosphere
    (b) Tidal forces between the Earth and the Moon
    (c) Pressure from the Solar wind
    (d) It is not receding from the Earth

**90.** In order to evaluate Hubble's constant, what quantities should we measure?
    (a) Redshift and distance
    (b) Flux and redshift
    (c) Flux and distance
    (d) Radial velocity and flux

**91.** Which of the following is NOT a piece of evidence in favour of the Big Bang theory?
    (a) The discovery of heavier elements in the oldest stars
    (b) The background radiation
    (c) The abundance of helium in the universe
    (d) The expansion of the galaxies

**92.** Pluto is not a planet because:
    (a) It is too small
    (b) It is too far away
    (c) It has not cleared its neighbourhood of other objects
    (d) It is a planet

**93.** The Earth's core is made up of iron because:
  (a) The early Earth was molten
  (b) The mantle and crust were deposited after the core formation from meteor impact
  (c) It was magnetically attracted to the center of the Earth
  (d) Volcanic action

**94.** The apparent path of the Sun across our sky, day by day throughout the year is known as:
  (a) The celestial equator
  (b) The celestial meridian
  (c) The Tropic of Cancer
  (d) The ecliptic

**95.** The autumnal equinox is that time of the year when:
  (a) The Sun crosses the equatorial plane, moving south
  (b) The Sun crosses the galactic equator
  (c) The earth is at its closest point to the Sun
  (d) The Sun crosses the ecliptic plane, moving south

**96.** A star with a temperature of 10,000 K will have a surface brightness:
  (a) Twice that of the Sun
  (b) Half that of the Sun
  (c) Sixteen times that of the Sun
  (d) Four times that of the Sun

**97.** The Milky Way is:
  (a) The asteroid belt
  (b) The disk of the Galaxy
  (c) The ecliptic plane
  (d) The nearest galaxy to ours

**98.** A total solar eclipse occurs when:
  (a) The Moon is full
  (b) The Moon is new
  (c) The Earth is closest to the Sun
  (d) Can occur at any time

**99.** The danger to satellites is greatest:
  (a) When the Moon is closest to the Earth
  (b) In the daytime
  (c) When there are many sunspots
  (d) When the Earth is closest to the Sun

**100.** The evidence for dark energy comes from:
  (a) The rotation curves of galaxies
  (b) The motion of the planets
  (c) Hubble's Law
  (d) Supernovae at high redshifts

## ANSWERS

| 1 | 2 | 3 | 4 | 5 | 6 | 7 | 8 | 9 | 10 |
|---|---|---|---|---|---|---|---|---|---|
| (c) | (a) | (b) | (a) | (a) | (c) | (c) | (a) | (d) | (b) |
| **11** | **12** | **13** | **14** | **15** | **16** | **17** | **18** | **19** | **20** |
| (a) | (a) | (d) | (b) | (d) | (d) | (a) | (d) | (c) | (c) |
| **21** | **22** | **23** | **24** | **25** | **26** | **27** | **28** | **29** | **30** |
| (d) | (a) | (c) | (b) | (a) | (b) | (c) | (a) | (b) | (b) |
| **31** | **32** | **33** | **34** | **35** | **36** | **37** | **38** | **39** | **40** |
| (a) | (b) | (b) | (a) | (a) | (b) | (b) | (a) | (a) | (b) |
| **41** | **42** | **43** | **44** | **45** | **46** | **47** | **48** | **49** | **50** |
| (d) | (d) | (a) | (c) | (a) | (c) | (d) | (c) | (c) | (d) |
| **51** | **52** | **53** | **54** | **55** | **56** | **57** | **58** | **59** | **60** |
| (b) | (c) | (a) | (a) | (d) | (b) | (b) | (c) | (b) | (c) |
| **61** | **62** | **63** | **64** | **65** | **66** | **67** | **68** | **69** | **70** |
| (c) | (d) | (a) | (a) | (c) | (a) | (b) | (b) | (b) | (d) |
| **71** | **72** | **73** | **74** | **75** | **76** | **77** | **78** | **79** | **80** |
| (a) | (d) | (b) | (b) | (b) | (a) | (c) | (a) | (a) | (b) |
| **81** | **82** | **83** | **84** | **85** | **86** | **87** | **88** | **89** | **90** |
| (c) | (b) | (c) | (d) | (a) | (b) | (b) | (b) | (b) | (a) |
| **91** | **92** | **93** | **94** | **95** | **96** | **97** | **98** | **99** | **100** |
| (a) | (c) | (a) | (a) | (a) | (c) | (b) | (b) | (c) | (d) |

## HINTS AND SOLUTIONS

### 1. Physical Properties of Talc:

| Chemical Composition | Mg6 [Si₈O₂₈] (OH)₄ |
|---|---|
| Crystal system | Monoclinic system |
| Colour | White |
| Streak | White |
| Cleavage | Perfect |
| Lustre | Pearly |
| Hardness | 1 |
| Specific gravity | 2.58 – 2.83 |
| Diagnostic property | Feel Greasy |

### 2. Colour of the Minerals:

| Different Minerals | Colours |
|---|---|
| Manganese | Grey |
| Magnesium | Shiny grey |
| Titanium | Dark grey |
| Calcium | White |

### 3. Fractures:

| Types of fractures | Example |
|---|---|
| Mode I | Opening (extension) |
| Mode II | Sliding (shear) |

| Types of fractures | Example |
|---|---|
| Mode III | Tearing |
| Mode IV | Closing |

### 4. Terms and its Features:

| Terms | Remarks |
|---|---|
| Porphyry | It is a textural in used in igneous rocks |
| Pegmatite | It is a type of course grain igneous rock |
| Pitchstone | Felsic volcanic rocks |
| Breccia | Clastic sedimentary rocks that are composed of large angular fragments (over two millimeters in diameter). |

### 5. Rock Type with Specific Feature:

| Rocks | Remarks |
|---|---|
| Pumice | Light weight volcanic rocks |
| Dunite | Plutonic course grain igneous rock which contain largly olivine |
| Obsidian | Extrusive igneous rock formed due to sudden crystallization. |
| Basalt | Volcanic igneous rock |

### 6. Layer and its Composition:

| Layer | Thickness (Km) | Density (g/cm³) | | Composition |
|---|---|---|---|---|
| | | Top | Bottom | |
| Crust | 30 | 2.2 | — | Silicic rocks |
| | | — | 2.9 | Andesite, basalt |
| Upper mantle | 720 | 3.4 | — | Peridotite, eclogite, olivine |
| | | — | 4.4 | Perovskite, oxides |
| Lower mantle | 2171 | 4.4 | — | Magnesium |
| | | — | 5.6 | Oxides |
| Outer core | 2259 | 9.9 | — | Iron + oxygen, sulphur |
| | | — | 12.2 | Nickel alloy |
| Inner core | 1221 | 12.8 | — | Iron + oxygen, sulphur |
| | | — | 13.1 | Nickel alloy |
| Total thickness | 6401 | | | |

## 7. Igneous bodies with its Designation:

| Igneous bodies | Designation |
|---|---|
| Sill | Concordant igneous bodies |
| Batholith | Discordant igneous bodies |
| Dyke | Discordant igneous bodies |
| Boss | Discordant igneous bodies |

## 8. Rocks with Arrangements:

| Rocks | Arrangement of minerals |
|---|---|
| Schist | Course grain metamorphic rocks of different layers of the minerals |
| Gneiss | High grade metamorphic rocks with light and dark colour banding |
| Granite | Course grain igneous rock |
| Dolerite | Dark, medium grain igneous rock show a ophitic texture |

## 9. Grade of Metamorphic Rocks:

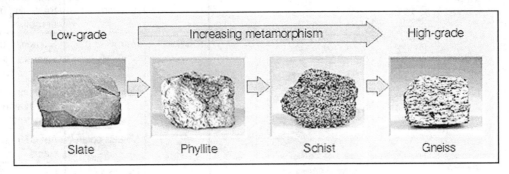

## 10. Metamorphic Products:

| Types of metamorphism | Products |
|---|---|
| Hydrothermal metamorphism | Serpentinite |
| Contanct metamorphism | Hornfels |
| Cataclastic metamorphism | Mylonites |
| Regional metamorphism | Hornblende |

## 11. Earthquake Scale:
The scale of the earthquake is only two type, magnitude (richter scale) and intensity (mircalli scale).

| Earthquake Scale | Remarks |
|---|---|
| Richter scale | Magnitude scale ( 0 to 9) |
| Mercalli scale | Intensity scale (1 – 12 ) |

## 13. Plate setting with its Features:

| Plate Setting | Character |
|---|---|
| Convergent | Trench |
| Conservative | San Andreas fault |
| Divergent | MOR |
| Continent / Continent collision | Himalayas |

## 14. Earthquake Type and Plate Boundaries:

| Plate boundary | Earthquake type |
|---|---|
| Transform fault boundary | Shallow earthquake |
| Spreading center | Deep earthquake |
| Subduction zone | Deep earthquake |
| Continent-continent margin | Intermediate earthquake |

## 15. Rocks and Its Classification:

| Rock type | Classification |
|---|---|
| Sandstone | Arenaceous rock |
| Shale | Argillaceous rock |
| Conglomerate | Rudaceous rock |
| Halite | Chemical recipitate salt rock |

## 17. Constituents of limestone:
Calcite (calcium carbonate and dolomite (calcium–magnesium carbonate) are the two most important carbonate minerals.

## 18. Particle Size and name of Sedimentary Rocks:

| Particle size (mm) | Sediment | Rock |
|---|---|---|
| <1/256 | Clay | Shale/claystone |
| 1/256 – 1/16 | Silt | Shale/siltstone |
| 1/16 – 2 | Sand | Sandstone |
| 2 – 64 | Pebble | Conglomerate / breccia |
| 64 – 256 | Cobble | Conglomerate / breccia |
| >256 | Boulder | Conglomerate / breccia |

### 19. Phylum with Example:

| Class | Example |
|---|---|
| Scyphozoa | Jellyfish |
| Hydrozoa | Jellyfish |
| Anthozoa | Coral |
| Bryozoa | Moss animals |

### 20. Evolution of Plants through Geological Time Scale:

| GEOLOGIC TIME SCALE | | | | |
|---|---|---|---|---|
| Time Units of the Geologic Time Scale | | | | Development of Plants and Animals |
| Eon | Era | Period | Epoch | |
| Phanerozoic | Cenozoic | Quaternary | Holocene 0.01 / Pleistocene 1.6 | Earliest *Homo sapiens* |
| | | Tertiary | Pliocene 5.3 | Earliest hominids |
| | | | Miocene 23.8 | "Age of Mammals" |
| | | | Oligocene 33.7 | |
| | | | Eocene 55 | |
| | | | Palaeocene 65 | Extinction of dinosaurs and many other species |
| | Mesozoic | Cretaceous 145 | "Age of Reptiles" | First flowering plants First birds Dinosaurs dominant First mammals |
| | | Jurassic 208 | | |
| | | Triassic 248 | | |
| | Palaeozoic | Permian 286 | "Age of Amphibians" | Extinction of trilobites and many other marine animals |
| | | Carboniferous — Pennsylvanian 320 | | First reptiles Large coal swamps |
| | | Carboniferous — Mississippian 360 | | Amphibians abundant |
| | | Devonian 410 | "Age of Fishes" | First amphibians First insect fossils Fishes dominant |
| | | Silurian 438 | | |
| | | Ordovician 505 | "Age of Invertebrates" | First land plants First fishes Trilobites dominant |
| | | Cambrian 545 | | First organisms with shells |
| | | Vendian 650 | "Soft-bodied faunas" | Abundant Ediacaran faunas |
| Archean Proterozoic | 2500 | Collectively called Precambrian comprises about 87% of the geological time scale | | First multicelled organisms |
| | 3800 | | | First one-celled organisms Age of oldest rocks |
| Hadean | 4600 Ma | | | Origin of the earth |

### 22. Gastropod Morphology: Different features of the Shell

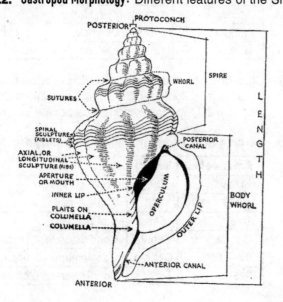

### 23. Evolution of the Invertebrate in Geological Records:

| Era | Periods | Remarks (Life development through geological time) |
|---|---|---|
| Cenozoic | Quaternary | Appearance of man |
| | Tertiary | Rise of modern mammals and birds |
| Mesozoic | Cretaceous | Extinction of dinosaurs and other reptile group |
| | Jurassic | Domination by giant reptiles Beginning of birds and mammals |
| | Triassic | Beginning of dominance of reptiles |
| Paleozoic | Permian | Extinction of the many invertebrate groups and primitive type plants |
| | Pennsylvanian | Many coal forests of spore bearing plants First reptiles |
| | Mississippian | Abundant spore bearing plants |
| | Devonian | First amphibians Numerous marine fishes |
| | Silurian | First land plants First land animals |
| | Ordovocian | First indication of vertibrates (fishes) |
| | Cambrian | Invertibrates numerous and varied Trilobite |
| Precambrian | | Bacteria, algae and a few primitive invertebrates |

**24. Condition of Fossilization:** One of the keys to preservation is resistance. Either the conditions are mild enough (calm water, little oxygen) not to destroy much of the organism, or those parts that do get preserved are the most resistant to chemical and physical damage. Good examples of this are the shells of clams and the teeth of mammals. Both of these examples demonstrate that there is a preservational bias for hard parts compared to soft parts.

The nature of preservation is dependent upon the interaction of several factors. The composition of the organism and its structure play vital roles in how the body will react to the physical and chemical activities that normally break down or damage dead organisms. Intimately related to this is the sedimentary environment in which the organism lived. It will determine the type and intensity of the physical and chemical processes. These all contribute to the post-depositional changes (such as replacement, recrystallization, carbonization, the formation of casts, etc.) that take place during fossilization. And finally, numerical abundance will affect the nature of preservation by increasing or decreasing the chances of something being preserved, simply because of the sheer numbers or lack of certain organisms (this does make sense, if you think about it for a while).

25. **Season in Northern and Southern Hemisphere:**
A season is a period of the year that is distinguished by special climate conditions. The four seasons—spring, summer, rainy, and winter—follow one another regularly. Each has its own light, temperature, and weather patterns that repeat yearly. In the Northern Hemisphere, winter generally begins on December 21 or 22. This is the winter solstice, the day of the year with the shortest period of daylight. Summer begins on June 20 or 21, the summer solstice, which has the most daylight of any day in the year. Spring and rainy, or autumn, begin on equinoxes, days that have equal amounts of daylight and darkness. The vernal, or spring, equinox falls on March 20 or 21, and the autumnal equinoxis on September 22 or 23.

The seasons in the Northern Hemisphere are the opposite of those in the Southern Hemisphere. This means that in Argentina and Australia, winter begins in June. The winter solstice in the Southern Hemisphere is June 20 or 21, while the summer solstice, the longest day of the year, is December 21 or 22. Seasons occur because Earth is tilted on its axis relative to the orbital plane, the invisible, flat disc where most objects in the solar system orbit the sun. Earth's axis is an invisible line that runs through its center, from pole to pole. Earth rotates around its axis.

In June, when the Northern Hemisphere is tilted toward the sun, the sun's rays hit it for a greater part of the day than in winter. This means it gets more hours of daylight. In December, when the Northern Hemisphere is tilted away from the sun, with fewer hours of daylight. Seasons have an enormous influence on vegetation and plant growth. Winter typically has cold weather, little daylight, and limited plant growth. In spring, plants sprout, tree leaves unfurl, and flowers blossom. Summer is the warmest time of the year and has the most daylight, so plants grow quickly. In autumn, temperatures drop, and many trees lose their leaves.

27. The distance between two village on the ground is = 15 km

The distance between same two village on the map is = 3 cm
Scale of the map = Distance of two points on the map/ actual ground distance
= 3/1500000
= 1 : 500000

29. **Anion and Cation in the Soil:**

**Cations and Anions in the Soil**

| Cations | Formula | Anions | Formula |
|---|---|---|---|
| Hydrogen (acid) | $H^+$ | Phosphate | $H_2PO_4^-$ |
| Ammonium | $NH_4^+$ | Nitrate | $NO_3^-$ |
| Sodium | $Na^+$ | Chloride | $Cl^-$ |
| Potassium | $K^+$ | Sulfate | $SO_4^-$ |
| Calcium | $Ca^{++}$ | Boran | $H_3BO_3^-$ |
| Magnesium | $Mg^{++}$ | Bicarbonate | $HCO_3^-$ |
| Copper | $Cu^{++}$ | | |
| Iron | $Fe^{+++}$ | | |
| Aluminium | $Al^{+++}$ | | |

30. **Terms with Remark:**

| Terms | Remark |
|---|---|
| Contour | It is an imaginary line connecting points of equal elevation from the mean sea level (fixed point). |
| Isohyet | A line drawn on a weather map connecting points of equal amounts of precipitation during a given period of time. |
| Isohaline | A line that join equal salinity of the system |
| Isobar | A line of the equal pressure |

31. **Contour Intervals**:

| Contour intervals | Remarks |
|---|---|
| Low | Step slop |
| High | Gentle slop |

33. **Causes of Deforestation:**
- Conversion of forests
- Forest fires
- Illegal and unsustainable logging
- Fuel wood harvesting
- Mining
- Climate change

35. **Darcy's law:** what drives groundwater flow:
- ❑ Water flows from high elevation to low elevation and from high pressure to low

pressure, gradients in potential energy drive groundwater flow

❑ Groundwater flows from high to low head

❑ How do you measure the head or potential? = > drill an observation well, the elevation of the water level in the well is a measure of the potential energy at the opening of the well

• In 1856, a French hydraulic engineer named Henry Darcy published an equation for flow through a porous medium that today bears his name.

• $Q = KA (h_1 - h_2)/L$ or $q = Q/A = -K \, dh/dl$, h: *hydraulic head*, $h = p/g + z$

### Condition of Darcy's Law:

• The steady state is laminar flow with no changes in hydraulic gradient.

• 100% saturation and no air bubbles in the soil voids.

• Flow fulfilling continuity conditions.

• No volume changes occur during or as a result of flow.

• The total cross sectional area of soil mass is considered.

### 36. Hydrological Properties:

| Terms | Remarks |
|---|---|
| Specific storage | Physical properties of the aquifer to storage capacity. |
| Specific retention | Volume of the water retained/ total volume of the aquifer. |
| Specific yield | Volume of the water drained/ total volume of the aquifer. |
| Storativity | Storativity / storage coefficient is the volume of water released from storage per unit decline in hydraulic head in the aquifer, per unit area of the aquifer. |

### 37. Types of Aquifer:

| Terms | Remarks |
|---|---|
| Aquifer | It is saturated geological formation that contains and transmits "significant" quantities of water under normal field conditions. |
| Aquiclude | It is a formation that may contain water but does not transmit significant quantities (clays and shales). |
| Aquitard | It is a formation with relatively low permeability. |

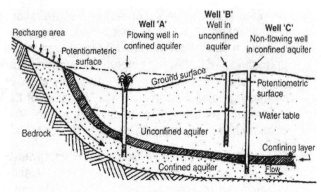

Types of Aquifers

• Confined and unconfined (water-table) aquifers

❑ An unconfined aquifer has a water table (water table aquifer).

❑ A confined aquifer does not have a water table. If you drill a well, water will rise (in the well) above the top of the aquifer.

❑ Perched groundwater is groundwater sitting on top of a poorly permeable layer with an unconfined aquifer underneath.

• The height to which water rises in a well defines the *piezometric* or *potentiometric* surface.

### 38. Water Distribution on the Earth:

| Source | Volume, in cubic kilometers | |
|---|---|---|
| | Fresh water | Salt water |
| Oceans, Seas, & Bays | 0 | 1,338,000,000 |
| Ice Sheets, Glaciers, & Permafrost | 24,364,000 | 0 |
| Groundwater | 10,530,000 | 12,870,000 |
| Surface Water | 122,210 | 85,400 |
| Atmosphere | 12,900 | 0 |
| Totals | 35,029,110 | 1,350,955,400 |

Grand Total (rounded) = 1,386,000,000

### Water distribution in Words

| Location | Percentage (%) |
|---|---|
| Ocean | 97.2 % |
| Inland salt | 0.008% |
| Glaciers and permafrost | 2.15 |
| Rivers | 0.009 |
| Groundwater | 0.63 |
| Soil water | 0.005 |
| Atmosphere | 0.001 |
| **Total** | **100** |

## 39. Hydrological Cycle:

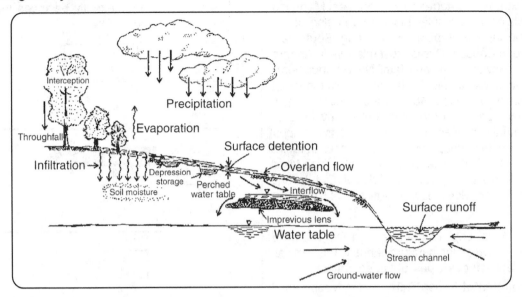

## 41. Sedimentary Structures with Significance:

| Sedimentary Structure | Remarks |
|---|---|
| Graded bedding | Top and bottom |
| Current bedding | Flow direction |
| Rhythmic bedding | Cyclic variation due to climatic condition |
| Cross bedding | Flow direction |

## 42. Stress Components:

| Type of stress | Character |
|---|---|
| Compression | Force direction in same |
| Tension | Force in opposite direction |
| Shear | Force slide each other |

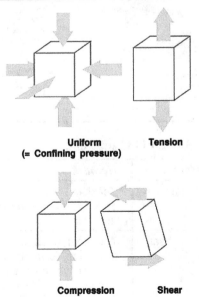

## 43. Rock's Behaviour:

| Types of Rocks Behaviour | Example Feature |
|---|---|
| Ductile solids | Folds |
| Fluids | Fluid flow structures (lava) |
| Brittle solids | Faults and joints |

## 44. Structures with Example:

| Type of Structure | Remarks |
|---|---|
| Basin | Synclinal structures |
| Dome | Anticlinal structures |
| Syncline | Concave upward structure |
| Anticline | Convex upward structure |

## 45. Fault and Its Displacement:

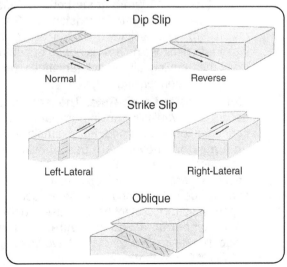

46. **Northwest Monsoon in India:** The month October to December is referred to as Northeast Monsoon season over peninsular India. This is also called Post Monsoon Season/ Retreating Southwest Monsoon Season. This is most effective in Andhra Praesh Royalaseema and Tamil Nadu-Pondicherry. For Tamil Nadu this is the main rainy season accounting for about 48% of the annual rainfall. Coastal districts of the State get nearly 60% of the annual rainfall and the interior districts get about 40-50% of the annual rainfall. The increase in rainfall activity over Andhra-Tamil Nadu coasts which takes place sometime around middle of October is generally considered as the "setting in of Northeast Monsoon".

47. **Lapse Rate:** Lapse Rate is a term that refers to the rate at which temperature varies in the vertical. There are various types of Lapse Rates.

    **Environmental Lapse Rate:** The environmental lapse rate is the rate at which temperature changes in the vertical in the troposphere, as observed by an upwards moving radiosonde. This varies greatly from day to day. When this lapse rate is averaged out for all places and times, it is called the Standard (or Average) Lapse Rate, which is around 3.0F/1000 ft. It's important to keep in mind that this lapse rate is determined by a vertically moving radiosonde. The air itself is not moving up or down.

    **Dry Adiabatic Lapse Rate:** The lapse rate that occurs in a vertically moving air parcel in which no condensation is occurring. The temperature change is related to the expansional cooling (compressional warming) that occurs when the air moves upward (downward). It is entirely determined by the pressure distribution in the atmosphere in question. For earth's atmosphere, in the troposphere, for example, the pressure is 200 mb at the top and 1000 mb at the bottom. Thus, the dry adiabatic lapse rate is constant, 5.5F/1000 ft (1C/100m). This is known as the dry adiabatic lapse rate because no heat is added or subtracted from the moving air parcel (adiabatic) and no moisture is condensing (dry).

    **Wet Adiabatic Lapse Rate:** The lapse rate that occurs in a vertically moving air parcel in which condensation is occurring. For example, although an upwards moving air parcel will always experience expansional cooling as a dominant effect, a certain amount of heating offsets that cooling due to latent heat release associated with condensation. This latent heat release is dependent upon temperature and pressure, so the wet adiabatic rate is not a constant. It averages around 3.5 F/1000 ft in the lower troposphere.

48. **Geostrophic Flow:** A form of gradient flow where the Coriolis force exactly balances the horizontal pressure force.

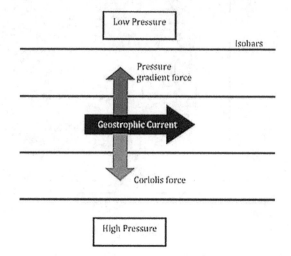

49. **Scattering:** In the air, part of the sunlight is scattered. The small particles (molecules, tiny water droplets and dust particles) scatter photons the more, the shorter their wavelength is. Therefore, in the scattered light, the short wavelengths predominate, the sky appears blue, while direct sunlight is somewhat yellowish, or even reddish when the sun is very low. Goethe believed this to be the basic phenomenon to generate colours ("Urphänomen").

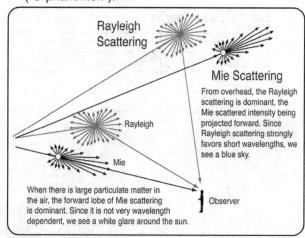

50. **Sensible and Latent heat:**

| Terms | Remark |
|---|---|
| Sensible heat | Sensible heat is heat that can be felt and measured by a thermometer. |
| Latent heat | The heat needed to change from one form of matter to another, which doesn't change temperature. |

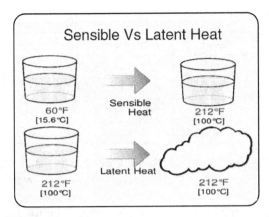

Sensible Vs Latent Heat

**52. Greenhouse Gas:** Role of Atmospheric Greenhouse Gases (man-made and natural) as a % of Relative Contribution to the "Greenhouse Effect"

| Based on concentrations (ppb) adjusted for heat retention characteristics | Per cent of Total | Per cent of Total — adjusted for water vapour |
|---|---|---|
| **Water vapour** | — | 95.000% |
| Carbon Dioxide ($CO_2$) | 72.369% | 3.618% |
| Methane ($CH_4$) | 7.100% | 0.360% |
| Nitrous oxide ($N_2O$) | 19.000% | 0.950% |
| CFC's (and other misc. gases) | 1.432% | 0.072% |
| **Total** | **100.000%** | **100.000%** |

**53. Albedo**: Albedo is the fraction of solar energy (shortwave radiation) reflected from the Earth back into space. It is a measure of the reflectivity of the earth's surface. Ice, especially with snow on top of it, has a high albedo: most sunlight hitting the surface bounces back towards space. Water is much more absorbent and less reflective. So, if there is a lot of water, more solar radiation is absorbed by the ocean than when ice dominates.

**54. Jet Stream:** Jet streams are relatively narrow bands of strong wind in the upper levels of the atmosphere. The winds blow from west to east in jet streams but the flow often shifts to the north and south. Jet streams follow the boundaries between hot and cold air. Since these hot and cold air boundaries are most pronounced in winter, jet streams are the strongest for both the northern and southern hemisphere winters.

**55. Chlorofluorocarbons (CFC's):** Chlorofluorocarbons (**CFCs**) contain **C**arbon and some combination of **F**luorine and **C**hlorine atoms.

- Hydrofluorocarbons (**HFCs**) contain **H**ydro-gen, **F**luorine, and **C**arbon (no chlorine).
- Hydrochlorofluorocarbons (**HCFCs**) contain **H**ydrogen, **C**hlorine, **F**luorine, and **C**arbon atoms.

- Hydrobromofluorocarbons (HBFCs) contain Hydrogen, Bromine, Fluorine, and Carbon atoms.
- Perfluorocarbons contain Fluorine, Carbon, and Bromine atoms, and some contain Chlorine and/or Hydrogen atoms.
- These compounds are often designated by a combination of letters and numbers (e.g., CFC-11, HCFC-142b).

**59. Tropical Cyclones:** A tropical cyclone is the generic term for a low pressure system over tropical or sub-tropical waters, with organised convection (*i.e.,* thunderstorm activity) and winds at low levels circulating either anti-clockwise (in the northern hemisphere) or clockwise (in the southern hemisphere).

**60. Inter–Tropical Convergence Zone (ITCZ):** The Inter-Tropical Convergence Zone (ITCZ - pronounced "itch") appears as a band of clouds consisting of showers, with occasional thunderstorms, that encircles the globe near the equator. The solid band of clouds may extend for many hundreds of miles and is sometimes broken into smaller line segments. It exists because of the convergence of the trade winds. In the northern hemisphere the northeast trade winds converge with southeast winds from the Southern Hemisphere. The point at which the trade winds converge forces the air up into the atmosphere, forming the ITCZ.

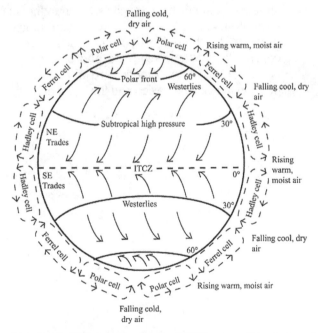

**61. Bathythermograph:** An XBT is a small instrument probe that is dropped over the side of a ship. As it falls through the water, it measures temperature. Small wires transmit the temperate data back to the ship where it is recorded for further analysis. Because the probe falls through the water at a known rate, the depth of the probe can be inferred from the time of launch. Scientists then plot temperature as a function of depth to create a temperature profile of the water.

### 62. Classification of Ocean to Land:

| Terms | Dip angle |
|---|---|
| Continental shore | >1 |
| Continental shelf | 1 |
| Continental slop | 1 – 5 |
| Abyssal plain | <1 |

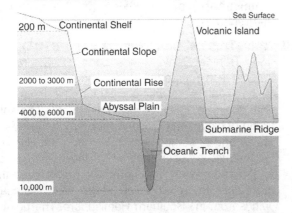

### 64. Diurnal tide:
Ocean tides are caused by the pull of gravity of the moon and the sun on the ocean's surface. As the moon is much closer than the sun to earth, its influence is far greater. Diurnal tides occur when there is so much interference by continents, only one high tide and one low tide occur per day. In the Americas, diurnal tides only occur in the Gulf of Mexico and the coast of Alaska.

### 67. Sunlight in Ocean and Its Conditions:

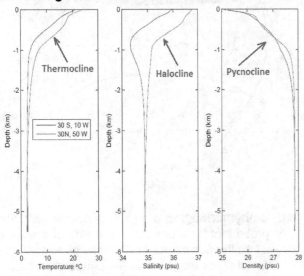

### 69. Terms with Different Character:

| Terms | Character |
|---|---|
| Isotherms | A line of equal temperature |
| Isopycnal | A line of the equal density |
| Isohyets | A line of the equal rainfall |
| Isohalines | A line of the equal salinity |

### 71. Cause of Surface Ocean Current:
Surface currents are generated largely by wind. Their patterns are determined by wind direction, Coriolis forces from the Earth's rotation, and the position of landforms that interact with the currents. Surface wind-driven currents generate upwelling currents in conjunction with landforms, creating deepwater currents.

### 73. Conductivity of Sea Water:

| Type | Electrical Conductivity (µS/cm) |
|---|---|
| Pure water | 0.05 |
| Distilled water | 1 |
| Rain or Snow | 2 – 100 |
| Surface/Ground water | 50 – 50,000 |
| Seawater | 50,000 |

### 74. Anion and Cation in Sea Water:

**Seawater Composition (by mass) (Salinity = 3.5%)**

| Elements | Percentage | Elements | Percentage |
|---|---|---|---|
| Oxygen | 85.84 | Sulphur | 0.091 |
| Hydrogen | 10.82 | Calcium | 0.04 |
| Chloride | 1.94 | Potassium | 0.04 |
| Sodium | 1.08 | Bromine | 0.0067 |
| Magnesium | 0.1292 | Carbon | 0.0028 |
| Vanadium | 1.5 – 3.3 µg/kg | | |

### 81. Stars Composition:
- Stars vary in their chemical composition.
- Most are about 73% hydrogen, 25% helium, and 2% other elements.
- Astronomers use a spectrograph to determine the elements present in the star.
- Gases in the atmosphere absorb some wavelength of light, each absorbed wavelength is see as a dark band on the spectrum.
- Each element has a unique spectral pattern.

## 82. Planets distance from Sun:

### Planet Distance from Sun

| Planet | Distance from Sun (km) | No of years of Travel from the Sun (yrs) | Distance from Earth (km) | No of Years of Travel From Earth (Yrs) |
|---|---|---|---|---|
| Mercury | 58,000,000 | 13 | 92,000,000 | 21 |
| Venus | 108,000,000 | 25 | 42,000,000 | 10 |
| Earth | 150,000,000 | 34 | — | —- |
| Mars | 228,000,000 | 52 | 78,000,000 | 18 |
| Jupiter | 778,000,000 | 178 | 628,000,000 | 143 |
| Saturn | 1,427,000,000 | 326 | 1,277,000,000 | 292 |
| Uranus | 2,870,000,000 | 655 | 2,720,000,000 | 621 |
| Neptune | 4,497,000,000 | 1,027 | 4,347,000,000 | 992 |

## 83. Constellations:
A group of stars that forms a particular shape in the sky and has been given a name. A **constellation** is simply defined as a recognisable group of conspicuous stars that are placed together as imaginary patterns or outlines on the celestial sphere.

## 85. Source of Sun's energy:
In a typical nuclear reaction, several sub atomic particles come together, interact and several (possibly different) particles emerge. There are a series of reactions going on in the sun, but the net result is the following combination of particles:

$$4_1H^1 + 4e - {_2}He^4 + 2e$$

## 86. Voyager:
The twin Voyager 1 and 2 spacecraft are exploring where nothing from Earth has flown before. Continuing on their more-than-39-year journey since their 1977 launches, they each are much farther away from Earth and the Sun than Pluto. In August 2012, Voyager 1 made the historic entry into interstellar space, the region between stars, filled with material ejected by the death of nearby stars millions of years ago. Scientists hope to learn more about this region when Voyager 2, in the "heliosheath" — the outermost layer of the heliosphere where the solar wind is slowed by the pressure of interstellar medium — also reaches interstellar space. Both spacecraft are still sending scientific information about their surroundings through the Deep Space Network, or DSN. The primary mission was the exploration of Jupiter and Saturn. After making a string of discoveries there — such as active volcanoes on Jupiter's moon Io and intricacies of Saturn's rings — the mission was extended. Voyager 2 went on to explore Uranus and Neptune, and is still the only spacecraft to have visited those outer planets. The adventurers' current mission, the Voyager Interstellar Mission (VIM), will explore the outermost edge of the Sun's domain.

## 87. Sunspot:
Sunspots are darker, cooler areas on the surface of the sun in a region called the photosphere. The photosphere has a temperature of 5,800 degrees Kelvin. **Sunspots** have temperatures of about 3,800 degrees K. They look dark only in comparison with the brighter and hotter regions of the photosphere around them.

## 91. Big Bang Theory and Its Evidence:

What are the major evidences which support the Big Bang theory?

- First of all, we are reasonably certain that the universe had a beginning.
- Second, galaxies appear to be moving away from us at speeds proportional to their distance. This is called "Hubble's Law," named after Edwin Hubble (1889-1953) who discovered this phenomenon in 1929. This observation supports the expansion of the universe and suggests that the universe was once compacted.
- Third, if the universe was initially very, very hot as the Big Bang suggests, we should be able to find some remnant of this heat. In 1965, Radioastronomers Arno Penzias and Robert Wilson discovered a 2.725 degree Kelvin (−454.765 degree Fahrenheit, −270.425 degree Celsius) Cosmic Microwave Background radiation (CMB) which pervades the observable universe. This is thought to be the remnant which scientists were looking for. Penzias and Wilson shared in the 1978 Nobel Prize for Physics for their discovery.

- Finally, the abundance of the "light elements" Hydrogen and Helium found in the observable universe are thought to support the Big Bang model of origins.

### 93. Mineral Composition of the Earth:

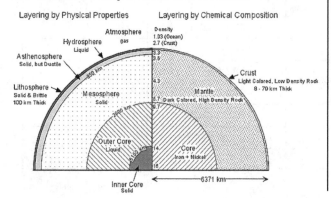

### 94. Different Location:

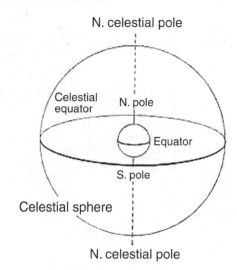

97. **Milky Way:** Our Sun (a star) and all the planets around it are part of a galaxy known as the Milky Way Galaxy. A galaxy is a large group of stars, gas, and dustbound together by gravity. They come in a variety of shapes and sizes. The Milky Way is a large barred spiral galaxy. All the stars we see in the night sky are in our own Milky Way Galaxy. Our galaxy is called the Milky Way because it appears as a milky band of light in the sky when you see it in a really dark area.

98. **Solar eclipse:** Total Solar eclipses occur when the New Moon comes between the Sun and Earth and casts the darkest part of its shadow, the umbra, on Earth. A full solar eclipse, known as totality, is almost as dark as night. During a total eclipse of the Sun, the Moon covers the entire disk of the Sun. In partial and annular solar eclipses, the Moon blocks only part of the Sun.

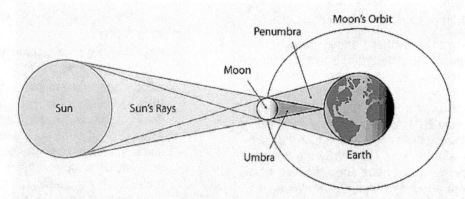

100. **Dark Energy:** A mysterious quantity known as dark energy makes up nearly three-fourths of the universe, yet scientists are unsure not only what it is but how it operates. How, then, can they know this strange source exists.

Previous Paper (Solved)

# International Earth Science Olympiad (IESO)
## Entrance Exam, 2012

**Total Marks : 100**                                    **Time : 90 minutes**

1. What is the basic difference between terrestrial planets and giant planets?
   (a) Terrestrial planets have an atmosphere whereas giant planets do not have one.
   (b) Terrestrial planets have a core which is not present in giant planets.
   (c) Terrestrial planets are made up of rocks whereas giant planets are made up of gases.
   (d) Terrestrial planets have a larger number of moons when compared to giant planets.

2. What is the molten rock material that occurs beneath the earth's crust called?
   (a) Magma        (b) Lava
   (c) Melt         (d) Mantle

3. When did the earth's atmosphere become oxygen rich like the present day atmosphere?
   (a) With the first appearance of land plants
   (b) With the first appearance of dinosaurs
   (c) With the first appearance of marine algae
   (d) It was always oxygen rich

4. Which of the following best defines a mineral and a rock?
   (a) A rock has an orderly, repetitive, geometrical, internal arrangement of minerals; a mineral is a lithified or consolidated aggregate of rocks.
   (b) A mineral consists of its constituent atoms arranged in a geometrically repetitive structure; in a rock, the atoms are randomly bonded without any geometric pattern.
   (c) In a mineral the constituent atoms are bonded in a regular, repetitive, internal structure; a rock is a lithified or consolidated aggregate of different mineral grains.
   (d) A rock consists of atoms bonded in a regular, geometrically predictable arrangement; a mineral is a consolidated aggregate of different rock particles.

5. Why basalt is finer grained than gabbro?
   (a) Gabbro formed at greater depths
   (b) Basalt formed from quick cooling of lava
   (c) Basalt has a mafic composition
   (d) Gabbro has a felsic composition

6. Visible quartz and potassium feldspar grains are the main constituents in a ____.
   (a) Gabbro        (b) Basalt
   (c) Rhyolite      (d) Granite

7. When did land plants first appear on earth?
   (a) 600 million years ago
   (b) 400 million years ago
   (c) 2500 million years ago
   (d) 20 million years ago

8. Which of the following rocks is porous but not permeable?
   (a) Sandstone     (b) Siltstone
   (c) Shale         (d) Marble

9. The Andaman Island is a good example of ____.
   (a) Atolls        (b) Fringing reefs
   (c) Coral island  (d) Shingle beach

10. Which of the following statements about oceanic and continental rocks is true?
    (a) Oceanic rocks are older than continental rocks
    (b) Continental rocks are younger than oceanic rocks
    (c) Continental rocks are older than oceanic rocks
    (d) Continental and oceanic rocks are of the same age

11. Among the following, the softest mineral is ____
    (a) Mica         (b) Talc
    (c) Gypsum       (d) Halite

12. In the correct order from the centre outward, the Earth has ____.
    (a) Core, inner mantle, outer mantle, crust
    (b) Inner core, outer core, mantle, crust
    (c) Inner core, crust, mantle, hydrosphere
    (d) Core, crust, mantle, hydrosphere

13. What is the rate at which tectonic (crustal) plates of the earth move?
    (a) A few kilometres a year

(b) A few centimetres a year

(c) A few micrometres a year

(d) That the earth's plates move is a fallacy

14. What type of volcanoes form by eruptions dominated by basaltic lava flows?
(a) Composite     (b) Stratospheric
(c) Cinder cone     (d) Shield

15. What is the main difference between a conglomerate and a sedimentary breccia?
(a) Breccia clasts are angular; conglomerate clasts are rounded.
(b) A breccia is well stratified; a conglomerate is poorly stratified.
(c) Breccia clasts are the size of baseballs; conglomerate clasts are larger.
(d) Breccia has a compacted, clay-rich matrix; conglomerate has no matrix.

16. Which of the following is the most common type of chemical sedimentary rock?
(a) Limestone     (b) Chert
(c) Phosphate rock     (d) Quartz sandstone

17. What is the name of a rock that is composed largely of abundant mica flakes arranged in a parallel manner?
(a) Gneiss     (b) Schist
(c) Shale     (d) Silt

18. Which of the following geological era is the youngest in the geologic time scale?
(a) Precambrian     (b) Mesozoic
(c) Paleozoic     (d) Quaternary.

19. _____ is a residue left behind after the weathering of rocks?
(a) Coal     (b) Pyrite
(c) Bauxite     (d) Gypsum

20. Which one of the following metallic elements is contained in monazite sands?
(a) Calcium     (b) Uranium
(c) Thorium     (d) Platinum

21. Which of the following statements about the equator is incorrect?
(a) The sun is always directly overhead at noon on the Equator
(b) Equator is a great circle
(c) No cyclones form at the Equator
(d) Snow cover is present on the Equator

22. Desert sand dunes are commonly asymmetrical. The steeper leeward side _____.
(a) Faces the downwind direction
(b) Faces the upwind direction
(c) Is oriented parallel to wind direction
(d) Is not oriented in any direction

23. Which of the following surface ocean currents transports warm water from low to high latitudes?
(a) The Peru and Canary Currents
(b) The Labrador and Benguela Currents
(c) The Gulf Stream and Kuroshio Currents
(d) The Falkland and Brazil Currents

24. Relative humidity is "relative" to _____.
(a) Moisture
(b) Temperature
(c) Water vapour pressure
(d) Altitude

25. One of the following statements is NOT true of a wave approaching the shore.
(a) The wavelength increases because of frictional drag.
(b) The orbital motion of water in a wave decreases with depth.
(c) The wave height increases.
(d) The wave becomes asymmetrical.

26. Circular, concentric contours that show decreasing values towards the centre represent a _____ .
(a) Elevation     (b) Depression
(c) River valley     (d) Scarp

27. _____ is characterized by sink-holes, disappearing streams and caves, and shaped by the dissolution of layers of soluble bedrock such as limestone or dolomite.
(a) Yardang
(b) Hummock
(c) Karst
(d) Barchan

28. It is known that the Himalaya is rising, though at a very slow rate. Which of the following statements is true?
(a) The rate at which it grows is compensated equally by erosion.
(b) It started growing about 40 to 50 million years ago
(c) It is not eroded because there are no rivers at that height.
(d) It has stopped growing because the Tethys Sea is closed.

29. The region between ~ 30°-35° north and 30°-35° south latitudes is characterized by weak winds. This region is called _____.
(a) The tropics
(b) The doldrums
(c) The Inter-tropical Convergence zone
(d) The horse latitudes

30. _____ is the scale used to measure the intensity of earthquakes.
    (a) Richter Scale
    (b) Modified Mercalli Scale
    (c) Fujita Scale
    (d) Beaufort Scale

31. The focus of an earthquake is also known as _____.
    (a) Hypocenter        (b) Epicenter
    (c) Antipode          (d) Seismicentric

32. Which type of earthquake waves causes the maximum damage and destruction?
    (a) P waves
    (b) S waves
    (c) P-S waves
    (d) Raleigh and Love waves

33. This rock is made of crystals of quartz, feldspar and mica and is used as a common building stone.
    (a) Pegmatite         (b) Granite
    (c) Diorite           (d) Gabbro

34. _____ are crystals with the same composition but with a different crystal structure.
    (a) Isomorphs         (b) Polymorphs
    (c) Polymers          (d) Amorphous

35. Which of the following pairs of elements is the most abundant in the Earth?
    (a) Fe and Mg         (b) Fe and $O_2$
    (c) Fe and Ni         (d) Si and $O_2$

36. On a Survey of India toposheet number 57D/11, a distance of four centimetres represents an actual ground distance of _____
    (a) 1 Km              (b) 2 Km
    (c) 3 Km              (d) 16 Km

37. What is the rigid outer layer (about 75–150 km thick) of the earth called?
    (a) Asthenosphere     (b) Mesosphere
    (c) Crust             (d) Lithosphere.

38. Identify the fossil in this picture.

    (a) Gastropod         (b) Brachiopod
    (c) Ammonite          (d) Tetrapod

39. _____ is a process by which empty spaces within a dead organism (spaces were filled with liquid or gas during life) get filled with mineral-rich groundwater from which minerals precipitate and occupy the empty spaces.
    (a) Permineralization  (b) Cast
    (c) Mold               (d) Impression

40. What is paleoichnology?
    (a) Study of fish
    (b) Study of trace fossils
    (c) Study of ferns
    (d) Study of tree rings

41. Lahar is a type of _____.
    (a) Sea wave          (b) Wind
    (c) Debris flow       (d) Lava flow

42. I lived in the last Ice Age. I am a herbivore. I am a Siberian. Who am I?
    (a) Saber tooth tiger
    (b) Woolly mammoth
    (c) Mastodon
    (d) Giant sloth

43. Former floodplains along a river are represented by _____.
    (a) River terraces    (b) Meanders
    (c) River valleys     (d) Canyons

44. _____ refers to the material deposited by a stream.
    (a) Alluvium
    (b) Lacustrine sediment
    (c) Aeolian sediment
    (d) Submarine sediment

45. The Great East Japan Earthquake was because of a _____
    (a) Normal fault
    (b) Strike slip fault
    (c) Mega thrust fault
    (d) Submarine volcanic eruption

46. The average depth of the oceans is about _____.
    (a) 1000 m            (b) 2000 m
    (c) 3000 m            (d) 4000 m

47. Which is the most abundant dissolved gas in the ocean surface water?
    (a) Carbon dioxide    (b) Nitrogen
    (c) Argon             (d) Oxygen

48. Which of the following clouds is likely to give rain?
    (a) Cirrus            (b) Tratus
    (c) Altostratus       (d) Cumulonimbus

49. The direction of winds in western India during the main rainy season is from the
    (a) East              (b) North
    (c) South-west        (d) North-east

**50.** How are fresh water resources distributed on the earth's surface?
(a) Evenly
(b) Unevenly
(c) Abundantly
(d) Scarcely

**51.** What is the ratio between land and ocean in the Northern Hemisphere?
(a) Almost equal
(b) Not equal
(c) 1 : 2
(d) 1:3

**52.** Fresh groundwater constitutes _____of the total water present in the earth?
(a) 33%
(b) 29%
(c) 0.29%
(d) 0.76%

**53.** The amount of fresh water trapped in polar ice and glaciers is roughly _____ per cent of the total fresh water available on earth.
(a) 14
(b) 75
(c) 0.3
(d) 11

**54.** The average annual precipitation is the highest in _____.
(a) Temperate regions
(b) Tundra regions
(c) Polar regions
(d) Tropical regions

**55.** Precipitation is normally enhanced in the vicinity of _____.
(a) Oceans
(b) Forests
(c) Mountains
(d) Cities

**56.** In the water cycle, evaporated water _____.
(a) Precipitates as rain or snow
(b) Becomes groundwater
(c) Runs into lakes, streams, and oceans
(d) Condenses into clouds

**57.** The general term for the transfer of moisture from the earth's surface to the atmosphere is _____.
(a) Evapo-transpiration
(b) Vaporization
(c) Evaporation
(d) Evaporative cooling

**58.** "Hydrosphere" is one of Earth's major spheres. It includes _____.
(a) All of the water above and below the continents
(b) All of the fresh water on the planet
(c) All forms of the water on the planet
(d) All of the water in the oceans, sea, lakes and rivers

**59.** _____ is the process of water loss from plants through stomata.

(a) Humidity
(b) Transpiration
(c) Evaporation
(d) Evapo-transpiration

**60.** What per cent of the total freshwater on earth is present in Lake Baikal, Russia?
(a) 25%
(b) 20%
(c) 15%
(d) 10%

**61.** Oceans, seas, lakes, and rivers provide nearly _____ of the moisture in our atmosphere due to evaporation.
(a) 40%
(b) 50 %
(c) 80%
(d) 90%

**62.** Only _____ of the moisture in the atmosphere is contributed due to transpiration by plants.
(a) 10%
(b) 20%
(c) 30%
(d) 40%

**63.** The total water resources of the world are about _____.
(a) 1.6 billion km$^3$
(b) 1.4 billion km$^3$
(c) 1.2 billion km$^3$
(d) 2.0 billion km$^3$

**64.** Water table drop in India is due to _____.
(a) Overexploitation
(b) Less rainfall
(c) Drought
(d) Floods

**65.** _____ is the highest rainfall receiving state in India.
(a) Kerala
(b) Karnataka
(c) Goa
(d) Assam

**66.** The average annual rainfall over India is _____ cm.
(a) 125
(b) 250
(c) 400
(d) 500

**67.** The Hubble's law states that _____
(a) The Universe is accelerating
(b) The farther the galaxy is, the greater is the velocity of recession
(c) Galaxies are expanding
(d) The Sun will be thrown out of the Milky Way

**68.** The rotation of the earth on its axis causes _____.
(a) A small drift of the pole star in 25000 years
(b) The summer and winter
(c) The revolution of the moon around the earth
(d) The rising and setting of stars every day

**69.** We have seasons because _____.
(a) The earth's orbit is elliptical and the sun is one of the foci
(b) The Arctic and Antarctic regions get sunshine only for six months
(c) Circulation of air is very slow
(d) The earth's rotation axis is inclined to its orbital plane

**70.** If we beat a drum on the earth and an astronaut who is doing a spacewalk beats an identical drum, what will be the difference in the effects?
(a) There will be no vibration in the drum in space.
(b) The drum on the earth will vibrate for a longer time.
(c) There will be vibration in space but no sound.
(d) There will be no difference in terms of sound.

**71.** Star A has a temperature of 4000 K and star B 40,000 K. If the two stars have the same radii, which of the following is NOT true?
(a) Star B is more luminous than A.
(b) Star A emits more in infrared than in UV.
(c) Star B emits more in UV than in infrared.
(d) Star A emits more in infrared than B.

**72.** Consider the following two statements:
P. One can see absorption lines in the solar spectrum.
Q. The core of the Sun has a temperature of more than 1 million degree Celsius and the solar surface has a temperature of about 6000 degree Celsius.
Which of the following is correct?
(a) Statement 'P' is correct but 'Q' is incorrect.
(b) Statement 'P' is incorrect but 'Q' is correct.
(c) Both the statements are correct and 'Q' is the correct reason of 'P'.
(d) Both the statements are correct and 'Q' is not the reason of 'P'.

**73.** Which of the following statement(s) is true of the outer core of the earth?
i. It is in a molten state
ii. It does not transmit 'S' (seismic waves)
iii. Is mostly made of silicates of iron and magnesium
iv. Is mostly made of sulphide of iron and nickel.
(a) i and ii      (b) i, ii and iii
(c) i, ii and iv      (d) ii, iii and iv

**74.** All stars become red giants _____.
(a) After 1 billion years
(b) When hydrogen is completely exhausted
(c) When helium is completely exhausted
(d) When 10% of the hydrogen at the core is exhausted

**75.** The sun is called a yellow star because _____
(a) It looks red at rise and set
(b) It emits white light
(c) It emits the maximum energy in yellow light
(d) Its color changes from white to red

**76.** The energy produced in the core of the sun is by _____.
(a) Nuclear fusion of protons p-p reactions
(b) Nuclear fusion C-N-O cycle
(c) Triple alpha reactions
(d) Nuclear fission reactions

**77.** The distance to farther galaxies is estimated by _____.
(a) The method of parallax
(b) Measuring luminosities
(c) Cepheid variables
(d) Supernovae

**78.** Astronomers prefer larger telescopes because _____.
(a) Of a larger field of view
(b) Of a brighter image
(c) Of a larger image
(d) They are more sensitive to visible wavelengths.

**79.** All locations in the Northern Hemisphere have the most daylight on _____.
(a) March 21      (b) July 21
(c) September 21      (d) June 21

**80.** Increasing the size of the telescope mirror _____.
(a) Improves the clarity
(b) Increases the magnification of the image
(c) Increases the brightness of the image
(d) Makes the stars look bigger

**81.** On open water, evaporation increases when the saturation deficit _____.
(a) Increases and the wind speed increases
(b) Increases and the wind speed decreases
(c) Decreases and the wind speed increases
(d) Decreases and the wind speed decreases

**82.** Given below is the geologic map of an area with little relief. Rock units A through D represent the oldest to the youngest. What structure is shown on the map?

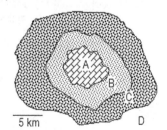

(a) Dome      (b) Basin
(c) Anticline      (d) Syncline

**83.** Which of the diagrams below correctly shows sites of erosion and deposition on a river meander?

**84.** Water molecules absorb energy during _____.
(a) The formation of ice from water
(b) The formation of clouds from vapour
(c) Runoff on land surface
(d) Evaporation from sea surface

**85.** Any of the various small, mostly tailless, extinct flying reptiles is called_____.
(a) Pterodactyls      (b) Archaeopteryx
(c) Flying squirrel    (d) Flying fox

**86.** In general, the probability of flooding decreases when there is an increase in the amount of _____.
(a) Precipitation      (b) Infiltration
(c) Runoff             (d) Snowmelt

**87.** Liquid water can store more heat energy than an equal amount of any other naturally occurring substance because liquid water _____.
(a) Covers 71% of the Earth's surface
(b) Has a higher specific heat
(c) Has a greater density at 4° C.
(d) Changes into its gaseous phase quickly

**88.** Which reference line passes through both the geographic North Pole and the geographic South Pole?
(a) 0° latitude
(b) 0° longitude
(c) Tropic of Cancer (23.5°N)
(d) Tropic of Capricorn (23.5°S)

**89.** Which of these is not a green-house gas?
(a) Water vapour      (b) Methane
(c) Ozone             (d) Nitrogen

**90.** Which of the following represents a metamorphic rock?

(a) Rock 1            (b) Rock 2
(c) Rock 3            (d) Rock 4

**91.** There are absorption lines in the spectrum of stars that help us in identifying the chemical elements present in these stars. What are these lines called?
(a) Fraunhofer lines   (b) Red shift
(c) Blue shift         (d) Doppler lines

**92.** To measure the distance to an object, astronomers use "parallax"-the distance an object seems to make when viewed from opposite sides of the Earth's orbit. What is this unit called?
(a) Light year         (b) Parsec
(c) Pardegree          (d) Arcsine

**93.** A layer of ozone in the _____ absorbs ultraviolet light from the sun.
(a) Troposphere        (b) Stratosphere
(c) Mesosphere         (d) Exosphere

**94.** A hypothetical supercontinent that included all the landmasses of the earth is called _____.
(a) Laurasia           (b) Gondwanaland
(c) Pangea             (d) Tethysia

**95.** We see the same face of the Moon always, because
(a) The Moon does not rotate on its axis
(b) The phases of the Moon make it appear so.
(c) The rotation period of the Moon is the same as the period of revolution of Moon around the earth
(d) Magnetic forces due to material on Earth and Moon keep them locked in the same orientation

**96.** A cyclone is a system of wind in which the wind blows spirally _____.
(a) Towards the centre of low pressure
(b) Towards the central high pressure region
(c) Towards a region of low pressure
(d) Outward from a region of high pressure

**97.** For a time difference of one hour, the longitudinal distance is equal to _____.
(a) 15°                (b) 30°
(c) 45°                (d) 60°

**98.** Which of the following types of coal is smokeless and contains 90% carbon?
(a) Anthracite         (b) Lignite
(c) Peat               (d) Bituminous coal

**99.** _____ is the largest salt water lake in the world.
(a) Caspian Sea        (b) Dead Sea
(c) Red Sea            (d) Sargasso Sea

**100.** Temperature decreases with increasing altitude because of a _____.
(a) Decrease in air pressure
(b) Increase in distance from centre of the earth
(c) Decrease in $CO_2$
(d) Decrease in $O_2$.

# ANSWERS

| 1 | 2 | 3 | 4 | 5 | 6 | 7 | 8 | 9 | 10 |
|---|---|---|---|---|---|---|---|---|---|
| (c) | (a) | (c) | (c) | (b) | (d) | (b) | (c) | (b) | (c) |
| 11 | 12 | 13 | 14 | 15 | 16 | 17 | 18 | 19 | 20 |
| (b) | (b) | (b) | (d) | (a) | (a) | (b) | (d) | (c) | (c) |
| 21 | 22 | 23 | 24 | 25 | 26 | 27 | 28 | 29 | 30 |
| (a) | (a) | (c) | (b) | (a) | (b) | (c) | (b) | (d) | (b) |
| 31 | 32 | 33 | 34 | 35 | 36 | 37 | 38 | 39 | 40 |
| (a) | (d) | (b) | (b) | (b) | (b) | (d) | (c) | (a) | (b) |
| 41 | 42 | 43 | 44 | 45 | 46 | 47 | 48 | 49 | 50 |
| (c) | (b) | (a) | (a) | (c) | (d) | (b) | (d) | (d) | (b) |
| 51 | 52 | 53 | 54 | 55 | 56 | 57 | 58 | 59 | 60 |
| (b) | (d) | (b) | (d) | (c) | (d) | (a) | (c) | (b) | (b) |
| 61 | 62 | 63 | 64 | 65 | 66 | 67 | 68 | 69 | 70 |
| (d) | (a) | (b) | (a) | (c) | (a) | (b) | (d) | (d) | (c) |
| 71 | 72 | 73 | 74 | 75 | 76 | 77 | 78 | 79 | 80 |
| (d) | (d) | (c) | (d) | (c) | (a) | (d) | (b) | (d) | (c) |
| 81 | 82 | 83 | 84 | 85 | 86 | 87 | 88 | 89 | 90 |
| (a) | (a) | (b) | (d) | (a) | (b) | (b) | (b) | (d) | (a) |
| 91 | 92 | 93 | 94 | 95 | 96 | 97 | 98 | 99 | 100 |
| (a) | (b) | (b) | (c) | (c) | (a) | (a) | (a) | (a) | (a) |

# HINTS AND SOLUTIONS

1. **Terrestrial and Giant Planets:**

| Jovian Planets | Terrestrial Planets |
|---|---|
| Far from the Sun | Close to the Sun |
| Large mass and radii | Small mass with radii |
| Low density | High density |
| Faster rotation | Slow rotation |
| They are beyond the orbit of mars | They are closer to Sun and lie between Sun and the Jupiter |
| They have structure silimar to Jupiter | They have structure similar to Earth |
| They have large number of moons bigger in size | They have less number of moons which are smaller in size |
| They are bigger in size but have less density | They are smaller in size and dense |
| Most of them possess rings around them | They do not have rings around them |
| Jupiter, Saturn, Neptune, Uranus | Mercury, Venus, Earth, Mars |

2. **Terms with Composition:**

| Terms | Compositions |
|---|---|
| Magma | Solid + liquid + gas |
| Lava | Liquid + gas |
| Melt | Solid + liquid + gas |
| Mantle | Peridotite |

3. **Composition of Atmosphere:**

**Seawater Composition (by mass) (salinity = 3.5%)**

| Elements | Percentage | Elements | Percentage |
|---|---|---|---|
| Oxygen | 85.84 | Sulphur | 0.091 |
| Hydrogen | 10.82 | Calcium | 0.04 |
| Chloride | 1.94 | Potassium | 0.04 |

| Elements | Percentage | Elements | Percentage |
|----------|-----------|----------|-----------|
| Sodium | 1.08 | Bromine | 0.0067 |
| Magnesium | 0.1292 | Carbon | 0.0028 |
| Vanadium | 1.5 – 3.3 µg/kg | | |

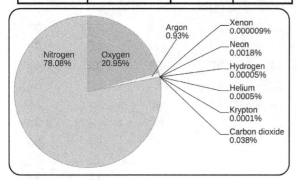

4. **Minerals**: Mineral is defined as a natural occurruing, solid with inorganic substance, definite chemical composition, commonly crystalline forms.
   ***Example:*** Quartz, feldspar, mercury, olivine, pyroxene.

   **Rocks:** Rock is a aggregate of the minerals.
   ***Example:*** Granite, basalt, carbonatite, schist, Shale, Limestone, Sandstone, marble.

5. **Basalt:** Fine grain volcanic igneous rock which contain plagioclase and pyroxene.
   **Gabbro:** Course grain plutonic igneous rocks with same as basaltic composition.

6. **Rocks with Compositions:**

| Rocks | Compositions |
|-------|-------------|
| Gabbro | Gabbro is composed mainly of calcium-rich plagioclase feldspar (usually labradorite or bytownite) and clinopyroxene (augite). Minor amounts of olivine and orthopyroxene might also be present in the rock. |
| Basalt | Volcanic equivalent of the grabbro. |
| Rhyolite | Volcanic equivalent of the granite. |
| Granite | Granites are coarse-grained rocks, comprise a mixture of glassy quartz, white, pink or red alkali feldspar, minor amounts of dark minerals, and often white, sodic plagioclase. |

Generalized Composition Ranges of Common Igneous Rocks

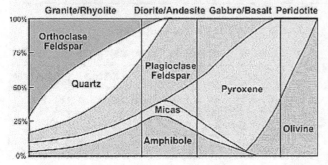

7. **Evolutions of Plants:**

| Era | Periods | Remarks (Life development through geological time) |
|-----|---------|--------------------------------------------------|
| Cenozoic | Quaternary | Flourishing of angiosperms |
| | Tertiary | |
| Mesozoic | Cretaceous | Appearance of gymnosperms |
| | Jurassic | Flourishing of conifers |
| | Triassic | Appearance of cycads |
| Paleozoic | Permian | — |
| | Carboniferous | Tree ferns from large forests, appearance of gymnosperms |
| | Devonian | — |
| | Silurian | Appearance of terrestrial plants |
| | Ordovocian | Flourishing of algea |
| | Cambrian | — |
| Precambrian | | Appearance of green algae and cyanobacteria Appearance of bacteria |

8. **Hydrological Properties of the Sedimentary Materials:**

| Rocks | Hydrological properties (Porosity %) |
|-------|-------------------------------------|
| Soils | 50 – 60 |
| Clay | 45 – 55 |
| Silt | 40 – 50 |
| Uniform sand | 30 – 40 |
| Gravel | 30 – 40 |
| Sandstone | 10 – 20 |
| Shale | 1 – 10 |

9. **Types of Coral Reefs:**

   **Fringing Reef:** It is directly attached to a shore or borders with an intervening shallow channel or lagoon.
   ***Example:*** Greater Caribbean region

   **Barrier Reef:** It is separated from a mainland or island shores by deep channel or lagoon.
   ***Example:*** Great Barrier reef

   **Atoll Reef:** More or less circular or continuous barrier reefs extends all the way around a lagoon without a central island
   ***Example:*** The Pacific Ocean

10. **Oceanic and Continental Crust:** The oceanic and continental crust is the lower and upper layer of the crust respectiviely.

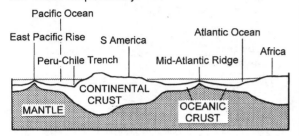

11. **Hardness of the Minerals:**

| Minerals | Hardness |
|----------|----------|
| Mica | 2.5 – 3 |
| Talc | 1 |
| Gypsum | 2 |
| Halite | 2.0 – 2.5 |
| Kyanite | 5 – 7 |

12. **Composition of the Earth's Interior:**

| Earth's Interior | Compositions |
|------------------|--------------|
| Crust | Granitic to granodioritic |
| Mantle | Peridotite |
| Core | Ni and Fe alloy |

| Different Layers of the Earth | Elements |
|-------------------------------|----------|
| Crust | O > Si > Al > Fe > Ca > Mg > Na > K |

| Lithosphere | O > Si > Al > Fe > Ca > Mg > Na > K |
|-------------|-------------------------------------|
| Atmosphere | $N_2$ > $O_2$ > Ar > $CO_2$ |
| Earth | Fe > O > Si > Mg |
| Universe | H > He > O |

13. **Movements of Crustal Plate:** The plate movement is a natural phenomenon which also called the plate tectonic. The movement of the plate is not in uniform with time and direction, it changes time to time. Some plate move very fast and some very slow.

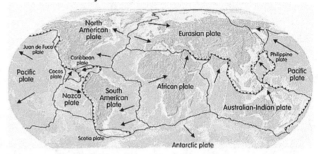

14. **Different type of the Volcanic Features:**

| Terms | Remarks |
|-------|---------|
| Composite cone | It is a type of the alternatively pyroclastic and lava. |
| Lava cone | It is the lava flow |
| Cinder cone | Central type of eruption with steep side, uniform slope |
| Shield | Very quite type eruption only lava |

15. **Difference between conglomerate and breccia:**

| Conglomerate | Breccia |
|--------------|---------|
| Conglomerate is a sedimentary rock which forms from rounded gravel and boulder sized clasts which are cemented together in a matrix. | Breccia is a rock consisting of angular fragments of stones which are cemented by finer calcareous material. |
| Durable Rock, Soft Rock Coarse Grained Rock, Opaque Rock | Durable Rock, Hard RockCoarse Grained Rock, Medium Grained Rock, Opaque Rock |
| Clastic | Brecciated, Clastic |
| Beige, Black, Brown, Buff, Light to Dark Grey, Orange, Rust, White, Yellow. | Beige, Black, Blue, Brown, Buff, Green, Grey, Orange, Pink, Purple, Red, Rust, White, Yellow. |
| Conglomerate forms where sediments consisting mainly of pebble and cobble-size clasts at least two millimeters in diameter starts accumulating. | Breccia is a clastic sedimentary rock which is composed of broken fragments of minerals or rock which are cemented together by a fine-grained matrix and it forms where broken, angular fragments of rock or mineral debris accumulate. |
| NaCl, CaO | Aluminium Oxide, Ca, NaCl, CaO, Iron(III) Oxide, Potassium Oxide, Sodium Oxide, Silicon Dioxide, Titanium Dioxide |
| Clay, Sand, Silica, Silt | Calcite, Clay, Feldspar, Phosphates, Quartz, Silica |

## 17. Rocks and Its Charecters:

| Rocks Type | Remarks |
|---|---|
| Gneiss | High grade metamorphic rock |
| Schist | Medium grade metamorphic rock |
| Shale | Sedimentary rock |
| Silt | Sediment size |

## 18. Geological time Scale:

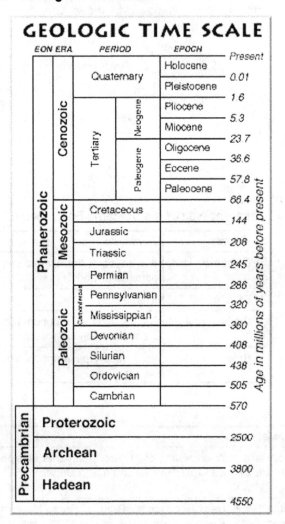

## 19. Economic Deposits:

| Rocks | Origin |
|---|---|
| Coal | Sedimentary origin |
| Pyrite | Igneous origin |
| Bauxite | Sedimentary origin |
| Gypsum | Sedimentary origin |

**22. Sand Dunes:** The dune is defined as the wind direction and its faces. Transverse, barchans, parabolic, and Seif types.

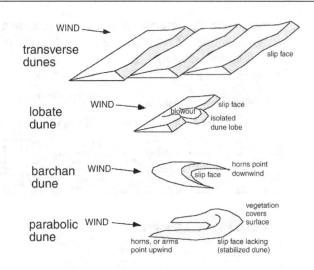

## 23. Currents and Its Nature:

| Name of Current | Nature of Current |
|---|---|
| North Equatorial Current | Hot or Warm |
| Kuroshio Current | Warm |
| North Pacific Current | Warm |
| Alaskan Current | Warm |
| Counter Equatorial Current | Warm |
| El Nino Current | Warm |
| Tsushima Current | Warm |
| South Equatorial Current | Warm |
| East Australian Current | Warm |
| Humboldt or Peruvian Current | Cold |
| Kuril or Oya shio Current | Cold |
| California Current | Cold |
| Antarctica Current | Cold |
| Okhotsk Current | Cold |
| Florida Current | Warm |
| Gulf Stream | Warm |
| Norwegian Current | Warm |
| Irminger Current | Warm |
| Rannell Current | Warm |
| Antilles Current | Warm |
| Brazilian Current | Warm |
| Labrador Current | Cold |
| Canary Current | Cold |
| Eastern Greenland Current | Cold |
| Benguela Current | Cold |
| Antarctica Current | Cold |
| Falkland Current | Cold |

| Name of Current | Nature of Current |
|---|---|
| Mozambique Current | Warm and Stable |
| Agulhas Current | Warm and Stable |
| South-West Monsoon Current | Warm and unstable |
| North-East Monsoon Current | Cold and unstable |
| Somali Current | Cold and unstable |
| Western Australian Current | Cold and Stable |
| South Indian Ocean Current | Cold |

**24. Relative Humidity:** The amount of water vapour in the air at any given time is usually less than required to saturate the air. The relative humidity is the per cent of saturation humidity.

Relative Humidity = Actual vapour density/ saturation vapour density x 100%

**29. Latitudes Variation and Its Character:**

### Latitudinal Variation in Precipitation and Evaporation

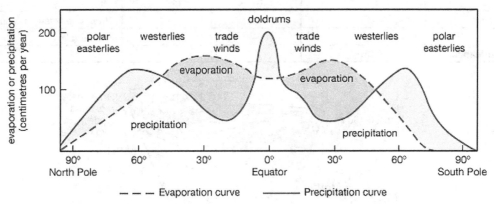

- - - Evaporation curve ——— Precipitation curve

**30. Earthquake Scale:**

| Scales | Remarks |
|---|---|
| Richter scale | Logarithmic scale (0 – 9) |
| Modified mercalli Scale | Intensity scale (1 – 12) |

**31. Focus of the Earthquake:** The hypocenter is the point within the earth where an earthquake rupture starts. The epicenter is the point directly above it at the surface of the Earth, also commonly termed the focus.

**Epicenter:** The epicenter is the point on the earth's surface vertically above the hypocenter (or focus), point in the crust where a seismic rupture begins.

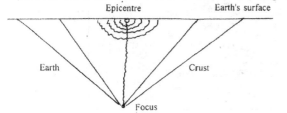

**26. Contour and Its Directions:**

| Features | Contours Direction |
|---|---|
| Elevation | Circular |
| Step slope | Close interval |
| River valley | Tapper in any direction |
| Gantle slope | Distance interval |

**27. Geomorphological Features:**

| Features | Characteristics |
|---|---|
| Yardang | Wind abrasion features |
| Hummocky | Sedimentary Cross stratification |
| Karst | Landform formed by limestone |
| Barchan | Wind depositional features |

**32. Type of Seismic Waves:**

| Primary waves | Secondary waves |
|---|---|
| P –Wave | S – wave |
| Fastest moving seismic wave | Slower moving wave |
| Arrive at recording stations first | Arrives at recording station after the P waves |
| Move in a spring like way | Moves in up and down way |
| Travel through solid and liquid | Only solid |

**34. Terms with Example:**

| Terms | Remarks | Example |
|---|---|---|
| Isomorphs | A group of minerals with the same atomic structure but different chemical formulas | Plagioclase feldspar |
| Polymorphs | A group of minerals which have sameof $SiO_2$ chemical formulas but different atomic structures | Polymorph |

## 35. Different layer with Elements:

| Different Layers of the Earth | Elements |
|---|---|
| Crust | O > Si > Al > Fe > Ca > Mg > Na > K |
| Lithosphere | O > Si > Al > Fe > Ca > Mg > Na > K |
| Atmosphere | $N_2$ > $O_2$ > Ar > $CO_2$ |

| Earth | Fe > O > Si > Mg |
|---|---|
| Universe | H > He > O |

## 36. Toposheet number: 57D/11
Toposheet division – 57
Scale = 1 : 50000
Area – Karnataka

## 37. Mechanical Layers of the Earth: The mechanical behaviour of the rocks/minerals with depth.

| Layer | Thickness (Km) | Density (g/cm³) | | Composition |
|---|---|---|---|---|
| | | Top | Bottom | |
| Crust | 30 | 2.2 | — | Silicic rocks |
| | | — | 2.9 | Andesite, basalt |
| Upper mantle | 720 | 3.4 | — | Peridotite, eclogite, olivine |
| | | — | 4.4 | Perovskite, oxides |
| Lower mantle | 2171 | 4.4 | — | Magnesium |
| | | — | 5.6 | Oxides |
| Outer core | 2259 | 9.9 | — | Iron + oxygen, sulphur |
| | | — | 12.2 | Nickel alloy |
| Inner core | 1221 | 12.8 | — | Iron + oxygen, sulphur |
| | | — | 13.1 | Nickel alloy |
| Total thickness | 6401 | | | |

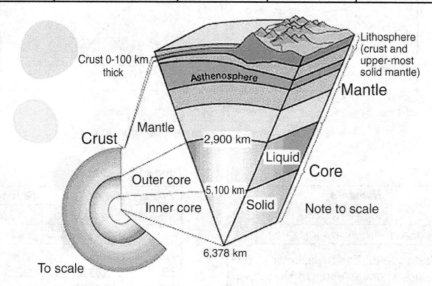

## 38. Fossils and its Morphology:

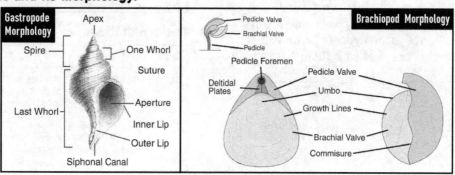

**39. Condition of Fossilization:** Only two main fundamental conditions for the fossilization

- **Quick burial**
- **Hard part**

**40. Paleoichnology:** Fossilized tracks and trackways (ichnofossils) are the only direct evidence of what extinct animals did when they were alive. They are like snapshots from the animal's life and can provide us with important information about locomotion (e.g., posture, kinematics), behaviour (e.g., herding), and even soft tissues (e.g., foot scales, body feathers). These advantages, however, are balanced by difficulties we have in establishing trackmaker identity, which must be inferred because vertebrate bones are rarely (if ever) preserved in direct association with tracks. For example, discovery of a fossilized track resembling the one pictured above would provide us with information about sidewinding locomotion, but without Crotales bones preserved with it, we would have difficulty establishing the identity of the trackmaker. Clues such as scale impressions, lack of limbs, and other features might identity the trackmaker as a snake, but lower-level determinations might prove more difficult.

**42. Ice Age in Geological Age:**

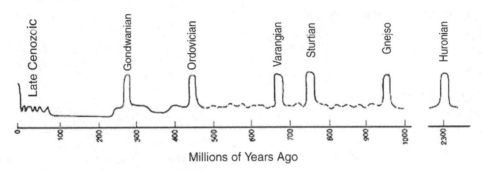

Millions of Years Ago

**46. Average Depth of the Ocean:** The average depth of the ocean is about 12,100 feet. The deepest part of the ocean is called the Challenger Deep and is located beneath the western Pacific Ocean in the southern end of the Mariana Trench, which runs several hundred kilometers southwest of the U.S. territorial island of Guam. Challenger Deep is approximately 36,200 feet deep. It is named after the HMS *Challenger*, whose crew first sounded the depths of the trench in 1875.

**Ocean Depth:**

| Ocean | Average depth (mtrs) |
|---|---|
| Pacific | 4188 |
| Atlantic | 3872 |
| Indian | 3872 |
| Arctic | 1038 |
| Average overall | 4000 |

**Deepest Point of Each Ocean:**

| Ocean | Deepest Point | Depth (feet) | Depth (meters) |
|---|---|---|---|
| Pacific | Mariana Trench | 36,200 | 11,033 |
| Atlantic | Puerto Rico Trench | 28,374 | 8,648 |
| Indian | Java Trench | 25,344 | 7,725 |
| Arctic | Eurasia basin | 17,881 | 5,450 |

**47. Composition of the Ocean water:** The ocean contains every known naturally occuring element plus various gases, chemical compounds, and minerals.

| Element | Parts per Million |
|---|---|
| Chloride | 18,980.0 |
| Sodium | 10,560.0 |
| Sulphate | 2,560.0 |
| Magnesium | 1,272.0 |
| Calcium | 400.0 |
| Potassium | 380.0 |
| Bicarbonate | 142.0 |
| Bromide | 65.0 |
| Strontium | 13.0 |
| Boron | 4.6 |
| Flouride | 1.4 |

**48. Types of Clouds:** The visible part of the droplets/ ice crystal, from cloud, rain and snowfall. If there is no cloud, there is water in the air in invisible form. Warm air is capable of holding more water vapor than cold air.When air rises as in storms, ahead of fronts or when forced over mountains, it cools and becomes less able to hold water in vapour form. The vapour condenses into droplets, forming clouds. As it continues to rise, the drops grow in number and size. When the drops get sufficiently large and heavy, they begin to fall through the rising air. They may collide with rising droplets and increase in size. When they reach the ground, we call it rain. In winter, when the air is cold, ice crystals form in the cloud. They tend to grow faster than the water droplets in the cloud. When the air is very cold, they may fall as tiny snowflakes. When the air is not as cold, the snowflakes are wetter and tend to stick together as they fall, forming the bigger snowflakes that flutter as they fall. The some type of clouds as follow:

### HIGH CLOUDS (18000 feet and above)

- CIRRUS
- CIRROSTRATUS
- CIRROCUMULUS

### MIDDLE CLOUDS (7000-18000 feet)

- ALTOSTRATUS
- ALTOCUMULUS
- ALTOSTRATUS LENTICULARIS

### LOW CLOUDS (below 7000 feet)

- STRATUS
- STRATOCUMULUS
- CUMULUS
- *MULTILAYERED CLOUDS*
- NIMBOSTRATUS
- CUMULONIMBUS

49. **Wind Direction in India in Different Seasons:** The season in any part of the world totally based on the wind pattern. The wind flow high pressure to low pressure. The word monsoon is derived from the Arabic word 'Mausim' which means season. Monsoon refers to the ***seasonal reversal in the wind direction*** during a year. During summer, the interior parts of North Indian Plains covering Rajasthan, Punjab, Haryana, and Western Uttar Pradesh are intensely hot. The daily maximum temperature in some of these parts is as high as 45° to 47° C.

**Summer Monsoon:** The average maximum temperature is above 33°C in the month of May at Delhi, Jodhpur and Jaisalmer. Such high temperature heats up the air of that region. Hot air rises and due to this a low pressure area is created under it. This low pressure is also known as **monsoonal trough**. It lies between western Rajasthan to Odisha.

**Winter Monsoon:** During the winter season, **North-East trade winds** prevail over India. They blow from land to sea and that is why that for most part of the country, it is a dry season. A part of North-East trade winds blow over Bay of Bengal. They gather moisture which causes rainfall in the Coromandal coast while the rest of the country remains dry. Strictly speaking these winds are planetary winds known as **Northeast Trades**. In India they are essentially land bearing winds.

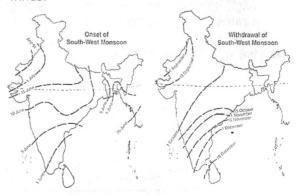

50. **Water distribution on the earth's surface:** Water Facts - Worldwide Water Supply

- Water covers about 71% of the earth's surface.
- 326 million cubic miles of water on the planet
- 97% of the earth's water is found in the oceans (too salty for drinking, growing crops, and most industrial uses except cooling).
- 320 million cubic miles of water in the oceans
- 3% of the earth's water is fresh.
- 2.5% of the earth's fresh water is unavailable: locked up in glaciers, polar ice caps, atmosphere, and soil; highly polluted; or lies too far under the earth's surface to be extracted at an affordable cost.
- 0.5% of the earth's water is available fresh water.
- If the world's water supply were only 100 liters (26 gallons), our usable water supply of fresh water would be only about 0.003 liter (one-half teaspoon).
- In actuality, that amounts to an average of 8.4 million liters (2.2 million gallons) for each person on earth.
- This supply is continually collected, purified, and distributed in the natural hydrologic (water) cycle.

Where Water is to be found on different location:

| Location/area | Percent (%) |
|---|---|
| Oceans | 97.2% |
| Ice Caps/Glaciers | 2.0% |
| Groundwater | 0.62% |
| Freshwater Lakes | 0.009% |
| Inland seas/salt lakes | 0.008% |
| Atmosphere | 0.001% |
| Rivers | 0.0001% |
| TOTAL | 99.8381% |

56. **Water Cycle:** Only water present on our earth in all three stage; solid, liquid and gas. We can observed due to some processes because Earth's water is present in all three states, it can get into a variety of environments around the planet. The movement of water around Earth's surface is the **hydrologic (water) cycle**. The **water cycle** is a cycle that describes the use, storage, and recycling process (transformation of water in medium to medium) of water on Earth. It is arguably the most important of all the cycles because the way water is spread across the globe and redistributed is critical to life on our planet. A very basic explanation of the water cycle is that the majority of water is stored in our oceans. With added energy from the sun, much of that liquid water turns into gas, or water vapor, and is absorbed by the atmosphere in a process called **evaporation** Then, the water vapor gathers and cools down in a process called **condensation**. When enough water condenses in the atmosphere, it falls back to the earth during a process called **precipitation**, also known as rain, snow, and hail. A lot of that precipitation then makes its way, above or underground, back to major bodies of water like lakes and oceans. There is more to this cycle as we'll see shortly, but it's important to know the basics.

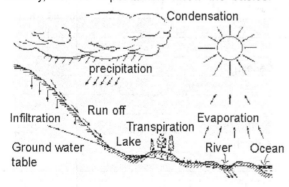

59. **Terms and its Explanation:**
   * **Condensation:** The process where water vapour changes from a gas to liquid water.

* **Water Cycle:** The movement of water between the atmosphere and Earth. It includes: Evaporation, Condensation, Precipitation, Surface Runoff, Transpiration and Perspiration.
* **Transpiration:** When plants release water through pores in their leaves back into the atmosphere.
* **Groundwater:** All the water that soaks into the ground, found under the Earth's surface.
* **Cloud:** Millions of tiny water droplets or crystals. They form when water vapor in the air condenses to form liquid water or ice crystals. They can only form when dust particles and cool air are present.
* **Evaporation:** The process where liquid water changes to a gas as water vapour.
* **Cool Air:** Cool air is necessary for condensation to occur in the atmosphere and clouds to form.
* **Surface Runoff:** Water that cannot be absorbed into the surface (the ground is too dense) but runs along it.
* **Water Vapor:** When water is in the gas state.
* **Precipitation:** Any form of water that falls from clouds and reaches Earth's surface. Rain, snow, sleet or hail.
* **Humidity:** The amount of water vapour in the air; warm air can hold more water vapour than cool air.
* **Relative Humidity:** The percentage of water vapor in the air compared to the maximum amount of water that the air can hold at a particular temperature.
* **Dew Point:** The temperature at which condensation begins.
* **Perspiration:** When animals release water through pores in their skin back into the atmosphere. It is commonly known as sweat.

64. **Causes of water table drop in India:** The main causes of the water table drop as follow:
   * Land degradation
   * Climate change
   * Population growth

65. **Rainfall distribution in India:** The process of continuous condensation in free air helps the condensed particles to grow in size. When the resistance of the air fails to hold them against the force of gravity, they fall on to the earth's surface. So after the condensation of water vapour, the release of moisture is known as precipitation. This may take place in liquid or solid form.

**Types of Rainfall:** On the basis of origin, rainfall may be classified into three main types :
   * Convectional                 • Orographic or relief
   * Cyclonic or frontal.

## 66. Average Annual Rainfall of the States in India

| Sl. No. | State | Meteorological Divisions | Average annual rainfall (mm) |
|---|---|---|---|
| 1. | Andaman & Nicobar Islands | Andaman and Nicobar Islands | 2,967 |
| 2. | Arunachal Pradesh | Arunachal Pradesh | 2,782 |
| 3. | Assam | Assam and Meghalaya | 2,818 |
| 4. | Meghalaya | Assam and Meghalaya | 2,818 |
| 5. | Nagaland | Nagaland, Manipur, Mizoram and Tripura | 1,881 |
| 6. | Manipur | Nagaland, Manipur, Mizoram and Tripura | 1,881 |
| 7. | Mizoram | Nagaland, Manipur, Mizoram and Tripura | 1,881 |
| 8. | Tripura | Nagaland, Manipur, Mizoram and Tripura | 1,881 |
| 9. | West Bengal | Sub-Himalayan West Bengal and Sikkim Gangetic | 2,739 |
|  |  | West Bengal | 1,039 |
| 10. | Sikkim | Sub-Himalayan West Bengal and Sikkim | 2,739 |
| 11. | Odisha | Odisha | 1,489 |
| 12. | Bihar | Bihar Plateau | 1,326 |
|  |  | Bihar Plains | 1,186 |
| 13. | Uttar Pradesh | Uttar Pradesh | 1,025 |
|  |  | Plain of West Uttar Pradesh | 896 |
|  |  | Hills of West Uttar Pradesh | 1,667 |
| 14. | Haryana | Haryana, Chandigarh and Delhi | 617 |
| 15. | Delhi | Haryana, Chandigarh and Delhi | 617 |
| 16. | Chandigarh | Haryana, Chandigarh and Delhi | 617 |
| 17. | Punjab | Punjab | 649 |
| 18. | Himachal Pradesh | Himachl Pradesh | 1,251 |
| 19. | Jammu and Kashmir | Jammu and Kashmir | 1,011 |
| 20. | Rajasthan | West RajasthanEast Rajasthan | 313675 |
| 21. | Madhya Pradesh | Madhya Pradesh | 1,017 |
|  |  | East Madhya Pradesh | 1,338 |
| 22. | Gujarat | Gujarat region | 1,107 |
|  |  | Saurashtra and Kachchh | 578 |
| 23. | Goa | Konkan and Goa | 3,005 |
| 24. | Maharashtra | Konkan and Goa | 3,005 |
|  |  | Madhya Maharashtra | 901 |
|  |  | Marathwada | 882 |
|  |  | Vidarbha | 1,034 |
| 25. | Andhra Pradesh | Coastal Andhra Pradesh | 1,094 |
|  |  | Telengana | 961 |
|  |  | Rayalaseema | 680 |
| 26. | Tamil Nadu | Tamil Nadu and Pondicherr | 998 |
| 27. | Pondicherry | Tamil Nadu and Pondicherry | 998 |
| 28. | Karnataka | Coastal Karnataka | 3,456 |
|  |  | North Interior Karnataka | 731 |
|  |  | South Interior Karnataka | 1,126 |
| 29. | Kerala | Kerala | 3,055 |
| 30. | Lakshadweep | Lakshadweep | 1,515 |

67. **Hubble's Law:** The dominant motion in the universe is the smooth expansion known as **Hubble's Law**.

Recessional Velocity = Hubble's constant times distance

$$V = H_o D$$

Where,

V is the observed velocity of the galaxy away from us, usually in km/sec

H is Hubble's "constant", in km/sec/Mpc

D is the distance to the galaxy in Mpc

In 1929, Hubble estimated the value of the expansion factor, now called the Hubble constant, to be about 500 km/sec/Mpc. Today the value is still rather uncertain, but is generally believed to be in the range of 45-90 km/sec/Mpc.

While in general galaxies follow the smooth expansion, the more distant ones moving faster away from us, other motions cause slight deviations from the line predicted by Hubble's Law.

This diagram shows a typical plot of distance versus recessional velocity, with each point showing the relationship for an individual galaxy. In the example shown here, two things should be apparent:

68. **Rotation of the Earth on its Axis:** The earth rotates about an imaginary line that passes through the North and South Poles of the planet. This line is called the axis of rotation. Earth rotates about this axis once each day (appro-ximately 24 hours). More specifically, our rotation period (the time elapsed for one rotation) with respect to the stars is called a sidereal day. A sidereal day is 24 sidereal hours, or 23 hours and 56 minutes on a normal clock. Our clock time is based on the earth's rotation with respect to the sun from solar noon to solar noon. This is a solar day, and it is divided into 24 hours. Because Earth travels about 1/365 of the way around the sun during one day, there is a small difference between solar time and sidereal time.

73. **Earth's layer and its Composition:**

| Layer | Thickness (Km) | Density (g/cm³) | | Composition |
|---|---|---|---|---|
| | | Top | Bottom | |
| Crust | 30 | 2.2 | — | Silicic rocks |
| | | — | 2.9 | Andesite, basalt |
| Upper mantle | 720 | 3.4 | — | Peridotite, eclogite, olivine |
| | | — | 4.4 | Perovskite, oxides |
| Lower mantle | 2171 | 4.4 | — | Magnesium |
| | | — | 5.6 | Oxides |
| Outer core | 2259 | 9.9 | — | Iron + oxygen, sulphur |
| | | — | 12.2 | Nickel alloy |
| Inner core | 1221 | 12.8 | — | Iron + oxygen, sulphur |
| | | — | 13.1 | Nickel alloy |
| Total thickness | 6401 | | | |

82. **Terms and its Significance:**

| Features | Remarks |
|---|---|
| Dome | Anticlinal structures |
| Basin | Synclinal depression |
| Anticline | Convex upward features |
| Syncline | Concave upward features |

88. **Lines Passes through Different Latitude:** Three of the most significant imaginary lines running across the surface of the Earth are the equator, the Tropic of Cancer, and the Tropic of Capricorn. While the equator is the longest line of latitude on the Earth (the line where the Earth is widest in an east-west direction), the tropics are based on the sun's position in relation to the Earth at two points of the year. All three lines of latitude are significant in their relationship between the Earth and the sun.

**THE EQUATOR:** The equator is located at zero degrees latitude. The equator runs through Indonesia, Ecuador, northern Brazil, the Democratic Republic of the Congo, and Kenya, among other countries. It is 24,901.55 miles (40,075.16 kilometers) long. On the equator, the Sun is directly overhead at noon on the two equinoxes - near March and September 21. The equator divides the planet into the Northern and Southern Hemispheres. On the equator, the length of day and night are equal every day of the year - day is always twelve hours long and night is always twelve hours long.

**THE TROPIC OF CANCER AND THE TROPIC OF CAPRICORN:** The Tropic of Cancer and the Tropic of Capricorn each lie at 23.5 degrees latitude. The Tropic of Cancer is located at 23.5° North of the equator and runs through Mexico, the Bahamas, Egypt, Saudi Arabia, India, and southern China. The Tropic of Capricorn lies at 23.5° South of the equator and runs through Australia, Chile, southern Brazil (Brazil is the only country that passes through both the equator and a tropic), and northern South Africa. The tropics are the two lines where the sun is directly overhead at noon on the two solstices - near June and December 21. The sun is directly overhead at noon on the Tropic of Cancer on June 21 (the beginning of summer in the Northern Hemisphere and the beginning of winter in the Southern Hemisphere) and the sun is directly overhead at noon on the Tropic of Capricorn on December 21 (the beginning of winter in the Northern Hemisphere and the beginning of summer in the Southern Hemisphere).

The reason for the location of the Tropic of Cancer and the Tropic of Capricorn at 23.5° north and south respectively is due to the axial tilt of the Earth. The Earth is titled 23.5 degrees from the plane of the Earth's revolution around the sun each year.

**PRIME MERIDIAN:** While the equator divides the Earth into Northern and Southern Hemispheres, it is the Prime Meridian at zero degrees longitude and the line of longitude opposite the Prime Meridian (near the International Date Line) at 180 degrees longitude that divides the Earth into the Eastern and Western Hemispheres. The Eastern Hemisphere consists of Europe, Africa, Asia, and Australia while the Western Hemisphere includes North and South America. Some geographers place the boundaries between the hemispheres at 20° West and 160° East so as to not run through Europe and Africa. Unlike the equator and the Tropic of Cancer and the Tropic of Capricorn, the Prime Meridian and all lines of longitude are completely imaginary lines and have no significance with regard to the Earth or to its relationship with the sun.

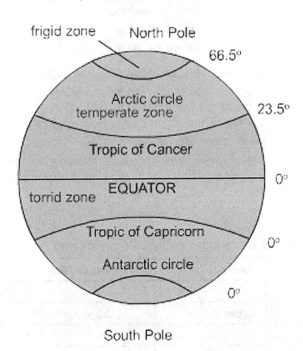

**89. Green House Gasses:**

| Gas | Concentration |
|---|---|
| Carbon dioxide | 345 ppm |
| Methane | 1.65 ppm |
| Nitrous oxide | 305 ppb |
| CFC – 11 | 220 ppt |
| CFC – 12 | 380 ppt |

**93. Layers in Atmosphere:** The atmosphere has 4 distinct layers: 1) Troposphere, 2) Stratosphere, 3) Mesosphere, and 4) the Thermosphere. These layers are distinguished from one another by the a) mass budget [total amounts and types of elemental and molecular species], and b) changes in air motion that occur within each layer c) changes in temperature with change in altitude. These changes in the physical characteristics of air exhibit how Earth interacts with the Sun to produce our atmosphere, control our climate, distribute elements and molecules, and protect the biosphere of Earth.

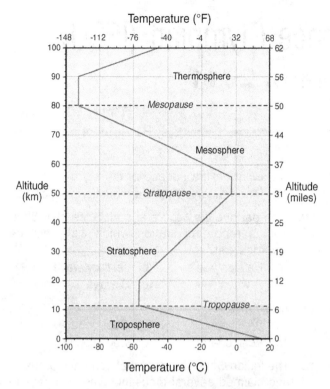

## 98. Coal Types and its Compositions: The composition of the coal (Lignite, Bituminous and Anthracite) as follow:

| Rank: | Lignite | Sub-bituminous | Bituminous | Anthracite |
|---|---|---|---|---|
| | ----------Low Rank-------------- | | ----------High Rank--------- | |
| Age: | ------------------------------Increase-------------------------- | | | |
| % Carbon: | 65-72 | 72-76 | 76-90 | 90-95 |
| % Hydrogen: | ~5----------------------------decreases----------------------- | | | ~2 |
| % Nitrogen: | -----------------------~1-2------------------------- | | | |
| % Oxygen: | ~30----------------------------decreases---------------------- | | | ~1 |
| % Sulphur: | ~0-----------------increase----------~4 ------- decreases----------~0 | | | |
| % Water: | 70-30 | 30-10 | 10-5 | ~5 |
| Heating value (BTU/lb) : | ~7000 | ~10,000 | 12,000-15,000 | ~15,000 |

## 100. Temperature variation in atmosphere: Based on the variation of temperature with height, the atmosphere can be divided to different layers.

- Troposphere
- Stratosphere
- Mesosphere
- Thermosphere

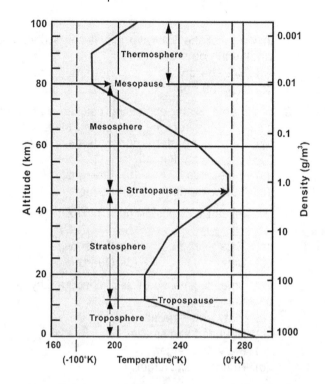

**Lapse Rate:** A rate of change in temperature observed while moving upward through the Earth's atmosphere. The lapse rate is positive when temperature increasing with altitude, zero in case of isothermal stratification and negative when temperature decreasing with height.

# International Earth Science Olympiad (IESO)
## Entrance Exam, 2011

**Total Marks : 100**                                                     **Time : 90 minutes**

1. In which of the following climates will chemical weathering be most rapid?
   (a) Hot and dry        (b) Hot and humid
   (c) Cold and dry       (d) Cold and humid

2. In caverns, water containing calcium carbonate solution drips from the ceiling, and thereby long, cylindrical, pendent concretions known as _____ are formed.
   (a) Stalactites        (b) Stalagmites
   (c) Speleothems        (d) Caves

3. Mineral that is commonly used in glazing porcelain is _____.
   (a) Mica               (b) Feldspar
   (c) Clay               (d) Quartz

4. With time, sediment particles transported by rivers become _____.
   (a) Platy and smaller
   (b) Rounded and smaller
   (c) Platy and larger
   (d) Rounded and larger

5. In which rock type do Karst topography and caves develop?
   (a) Silicate           (b) Felsic
   (c) Carbonate          (d) Ferric

6. This mineral is commonly known by the name "fool's gold".
   (a) Pyrite             (b) Chalcopyrite
   (c) Galena             (d) Bronzite

7. The most abundant element in the earth is:
   (a) Oxygen             (b) Magnesium
   (c) Iron               (d) Silicon

8. An igneous rock which is characterized by very large crystals of minerals is called a:
   (a) Granite            (b) Basalt
   (c) Pegmatite          (d) Obsidian

9. The epicentre of an earth describes the _____.
   (a) Place of origin of the earthquake inside the earth
   (b) Point on the fault on which the earthquake occurs
   (c) Point on the surface of the earth
   (d) Place at which the earthquake is recorded

10. If an earthquake occurs at a distance of 118 km from a recording station which wave will be recorded first?
    (a) Raleigh wave      (b) Tertiary wave
    (c) P wave            (d) S wave

11. *Nautilus* is a:
    (a) Brachiopod        (b) Gastropod
    (c) Echinoderm        (d) Cephalopod

12. The Indian Ocean tsunami that damaged property and claimed several thousand lives was caused due to an earthquake off the:
    (a) Andaman Islands
    (b) Indonesian island of Sumatra
    (c) Indonesian island of Java
    (d) Malaysia

13. The rigid upper layer of the earth (known as lithosphere) rides over a mobile but viscous layer called _____.
    (a) The core          (b) The Asthenosphere
    (c) The Mesosphere    (d) The Exosphere

14. This mineral is popularly also known as "lodestone".
    (a) Hematite          (b) Magnetite
    (c) Pyrite            (d) Barite

15. A metamorphic rock which shows alternate bands of dark and light colored minerals is called:
    (a) Slate             (b) Schist
    (c) Gneiss            (d) Marble

16. Two hundred and fifty million years ago, the land masses of the Earth were clustered into a single super-continent known as:
    (a) Tethys            (b) Gondwanaland
    (c) Pangea            (d) Eurasia

17. A linear lowland between mountain ranges created by the action of a fault is known as:
    (a) Rift valley       (b) Horst
    (c) Thrust belt       (d) Subduction Zone

**18.** Most of the rocks in tropical regions are often covered by an extensive layer of a product of chemical leaching called:
(a) Laterite     (b) Bauxite
(c) Alluvium     (d) Clays

**19.** Ancient fossils characterised by layers of calcium carbonate precipitated over bacterial filaments in shallow marine environments are called:
(a) Lime muds     (b) Stromatolites
(c) Corallites     (d) Coprolites

**20.** What is the term that is used for the layer of loose, heterogeneous weathered material lying on top of rocky hill slopes?
(a) Soil     (b) Weathering profile
(c) Regolith     (d) Alluvium

**21.** Granite is essentially composed of:
(a) Quartz and mica
(b) Quartz and feldspar
(c) Quartz and pyroxene
(d) Pyroxene and plagioclase

**22.** What are detrital sedimentary rocks with large pebbles of other rocks or minerals called?
(a) Arenites     (b) Conglomerates
(c) Grit     (d) Sandstone

**23.** When did dinosaurs become extinct?
(a) End of Cretaceous
(b) End of Permian
(c) End of Jurassic
(d) End of Holocene

**24.** Which biome is often transitional between tropical rainforests and deserts?
(a) Deciduous     (b) Temperate forest
(c) Chaparral     (d) Savanna

**25.** In which of the following unconsolidated sediments is porosity the highest?

(a)      (b)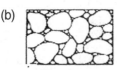

(c) 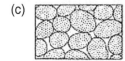     (d)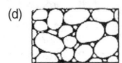

**26.** Which of the following statements regarding dry lands is NOT correct?
(a) Dry lands are often characterized by infrequent but intense rainfall events.
(b) Coarse and sandy soil cover results in high rate of infiltration.

(c) Because of high evaporation and infiltration rates, runoff is negligible during high intensity rainfall events.
(d) Due to the absence of vegetation cover, transpiration is very low.

**27.** Identify the type of fault in the figure on the right.

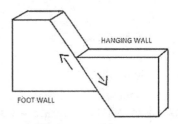

(a) Normal fault     (b) Reverse fault
(c) Strike slip fault     (d) Transform fault

**28.** In India which is the most earthquake-prone zone?
(a) The Indian Peninsula
(b) The Indo-Gangetic Plain
(c) The Himalaya
(d) Gujarat

**29.** It is horse-shoe shaped; it is home to most active volcanoes in the world and is characterized by frequent earthquakes.
(a) Marianna's trench
(b) Java (Sunda) trench
(c) The Pacific ring of fire
(d) Peru – Chile trench

**30.** The property of a mineral to show a bright band of scattered light because of the presence of small inclusions of a different mineral is known as:
(a) Lustre     (b) Iridescence
(c) Asterism     (d) Chatoyancy

**31.** Fossilization needs:
(a) Quick burial within sediments
(b) Quick drowning in water
(c) Quick transportation
(d) Slow burial within

**32.** What are the two important mineral constituents of limestone?
(a) Calcite and aragonite
(b) Calcite and gypsum
(c) Calcite and dolomite
(d) Aragonite and dolomite

**33.** Which of the following is NOT a tectonic plate boundary?
(a) Mid-Oceanic Ridge
(b) Subduction Zone
(c) Transform fault
(d) Continental margin

34. What is a "downward" fold in which younger rock layers occur at the inward portion or the centre of the structure called?
    (a) Synform
    (b) Syncline
    (c) Antiform
    (d) Anticline

35. Which of the following is least expected in a desert?
    (a) Playa
    (b) Rounded hills
    (c) Gorges
    (d) Wide stream channels

36. In plate tectonics, plates move and collide with one another. When one plate goes down below another, it is known as a:
    (a) Collision boundary
    (b) Subduction boundary
    (c) Suture zone
    (d) Contact point

37. In which case does a seismic wave travel faster?
    (a) Travelling through rocks
    (b) Travelling through water
    (c) Travelling through air
    (d) Travelling through vacuum

38. A dendritic drainage pattern will tend to develop in regions:
    (a) Underlain by regularly spaced joints
    (b) Of folded rocks
    (c) Along the flanks of isolated volcanoes
    (d) Of flat-lying sedimentary rocks

39. Egyptian Mummy is not a fossil because:
    (a) It is a human remnant
    (b) It is not naturally preserved
    (c) It has soft parts
    (d) None of the above

40. Arrange the following natural calamities in a chronological sequence.
    i. Indian Ocean Tsunami
    ii. Gujarat Earthquake
    iii. Kosi Flood
    iv. Icelandic volcanic eruption
    (a) i, ii, iv, iii
    (b) ii, iii, i, iv
    (c) ii, i, iii, iv
    (d) i, ii, iii, iv

41. Which of the following came first in the stratigraphic record?
    (a) Dinosaurs
    (b) Birds
    (c) Flowering plants
    (d) Conifers

42. Where would you go to see lava lakes?
    (a) Andamans
    (b) Java
    (c) Iceland
    (d) Hawaii

43. Phosphorite or rock phosphate deposits are a type of:
    (a) Non-detrital sedimentary formation
    (b) Detrital sedimentary formation
    (c) Metamorphic rocks
    (d) Igneous rocks

44. Intense structural deformation of the earth's crust associated with plate tectonics is referred to as:
    (a) Continental drift
    (b) Folding
    (c) Faulting
    (d) Orogeny

45. Are magnitude and intensity of an earthquake the same?
    (a) Yes
    (b) May be
    (c) No
    (d) None of the above

46. The most important gas responsible for the greenhouse effect is:
    (a) Carbon dioxide
    (b) Methane
    (c) Water vapour
    (d) Nitrous oxide

47. The annual range of temperature over Siberia (located in the northern part of Asia in Russia) is larger than that at Mumbai because:
    (a) It is not a developing country
    (b) Of Greenhouse effect
    (c) It is at a higher latitude
    (d) It is a larger area

48. Without the greenhouse effect, the surface temperature of the earth would be lower by:
    (a) 18° C
    (b) 15° C
    (c) 33° C
    (d) 255° K

49. The hydrological cycle describes the transport of:
    (a) Nitrogen
    (b) Carbon
    (c) Water
    (d) Hydrogen

50. The region of the ocean where temperature decreases rapidly with depth is called the:
    (a) Thermocline
    (b) Pycnocline
    (c) Isoline
    (d) Incline

51. Cooling sea-water results in its sinking because:
    (a) It increases the buoyancy
    (b) It increases the salinity
    (c) It decreases the entropy
    (d) It increases the density

52. The geostrophic approximation is a balance between:
    (a) Coriolis and hydrostatic forces
    (b) Coriolis and pressure gradient forces
    (c) Frictional and hydrostatic forces
    (d) Frictional and pressure gradient forces

53. The El Niño impacts the Indian summer monsoon through:
    (a) Teleconnections    (b) Telekinesis
    (c) Viscous effects    (d) Dipole effect

54. The glacial-interglacial cycles due to orbital variations are also known as:
    (a) Carnot cycles
    (b) Rabinowitz cycles
    (c) Milankovich cycles
    (d) Solar cycles

55. Most tropical cyclones originate _____.
    (a) Between 0° and 5° north and south of the equator
    (b) In the centre of sub-tropical highs
    (c) Between 10° and 20° north and south of equator
    (d) To the west of westerly winds

56. The concentration of nitrogen in the Earth's atmosphere at sea level is about:
    (a) 4%     (b) 21%
    (c) 78%    (d) 96%

57. _____ of the earth's atmosphere shields the earth from harmful ultraviolet radiation.
    (a) Equatorial bulge    (b) Ionic layer
    (c) Ozone layer         (d) Protective layer

58. The layer of the earth that reflects radio waves back to the earth is called the:
    (a) Ionosphere       (b) Radiation zone
    (c) Aurora borealis  (d) Ozone layer

59. The phenomenon of polar lights (aurora) commonly occurs in the:
    (a) Stratosphere    (b) Ionosphere
    (c) Troposphere     (d) Mesosphere

60. The atmospheric pressure at mean sea level is:
    (a) 1.03 kg/cm$^2$    (b) 10.3 kg/cm$^2$
    (c) 14.7 kg/cm$^2$    (d) 0.017 kg/cm$^2$

61. The temperature is minimum:
    (a) Just after sunset
    (b) Around midnight
    (c) About 2:00 to 3:00 am
    (d) Just before sunrise

62. The portion of the atmosphere which extends from the earth's surface up to 8 miles and experiences decrease in temperature at constant rate is:
    (a) Stratosphere    (b) Tropopause
    (c) Troposphere     (d) Mesosphere

63. A northerly wind means a _____.
    (a) Wind coming from the north
    (b) Wind going towards the north
    (c) Wind in the northern hemisphere
    (d) Wind in northern India

64. An empirical measure for describing wind speed based mainly on observed sea conditions is called the:
    (a) Beaufort scale    (b) Richter scale
    (c) Fujita scale      (d) Storm scale

65. A strong tropical cyclone that developed in the Northern Indian Ocean Basin and caused the worst natural disaster in Burma, killing nearly 100,000 people, was named:
    (a) Katrina    (b) Nargis
    (c) Sidr       (d) Irrawady

66. Relative to the horizon, as seen from the earth's southern hemisphere, the sun daily:
    (a) Rises in the east and sets in the west.
    (b) Rises in the west and sets in the east.
    (c) Moves mainly in a northward direction.
    (d) Moves mainly in a southward direction.

67. When Venus has reached its maximum eastern elongation from the sun as viewed from the earth, it is visible in the sky:
    (a) In opposition to the sun.
    (b) As an evening "star".
    (c) As a morning "star".
    (d) In conjunction with the sun.

68. In order to have a solar eclipse, you need to have:
    (a) A full moon.
    (b) A new moon.
    (c) The moon on or close to the ecliptic.
    (d) Both (b) and (c)

69. From where on the Earth will we see the North Star at the horizon?
    (a) North pole
    (b) South pole
    (c) On the Equator
    (d) Nowhere— it is not possible.

70. We see the same face of the Moon always, because:
    (a) The Moon does not rotate on its axis
    (b) The phases of the Moon make it appear so.
    (c) The rotation period of the Moon is the same as the period of revolution of Moon around the Earth
    (d) Magnetic forces due to material on Earth and Moon keep them locked in the same orientation

71. Which planet can't be seen high in the sky at midnight?
    (a) Venus      (b) Mars
    (c) Jupiter    (d) Saturn

72. The river channels observed on Mars are estimated to be about 3.9 billion years old. How did astronomers arrive at this age estimate?
    (a) By radioactive age dating of rock samples from the channels.
    (b) By calculating the time it would take for that much water to evaporate on Mars.
    (c) By assuming they are the same age as dry river channels on the Earth.
    (d) By counting the number of craters in the now-dry channels.

73. Refracting telescopes always contain which of the following?
    (a) Mirrors    (b) Lenses
    (c) Film    (d) CCD

74. According to Kepler's Law, the cube of the mean distance of a planet from the Sun is proportional to the:
    (a) Area that is swept out
    (b) Cube of the period
    (c) Square of the period
    (d) Fourth power of the mean distance

75. In our solar system which planet has a moon with a mass closest to its own?
    (a) Earth    (b) Mars
    (c) Jupiter    (d) Saturn

76. By what factor would the brightness of a star decrease if an observer moved from 1 to 3 light years from the star?
    (a) 3 times    (b) 9 times
    (c) 27 times    (d) 81 times

77. Which of the following devices would not work on the Moon?
    (a) Thermometer    (b) Spectrometer
    (c) Spring balance    (d) Siphon

78. Which of the following planets has no moons?
    (a) Ceres    (b) Mars
    (c) Venus    (d) Neptune

79. The planet Neptune was discovered by studying the deviations in the orbit of _____
    (a) Jupiter    (b) Uranus
    (c) Saturn    (d) Pluto

80. Which planet seems to be turned on its side with an axis tilt of 98 degrees?
    (a) Jupiter    (b) Venus
    (c) Neptune    (d) Uranus

81. What is the essential difference between X-ray, radio waves and infrared radiation?
    (a) Wave amplitude
    (b) Temperature
    (c) Wavelength
    (d) Wave velocity

82. The apparent daily path of the Sun in the sky during winter is different from that in summer, because:
    (a) The Sun revolves
    (b) Earth's distance from the Sun changes
    (c) The Sun rotates
    (d) Earth's axis is tilted

83. The following instrument demonstrates the rotation of the Earth around its axis.
    (a) Pendulum clock
    (b) Foucault's pendulum
    (c) Spectrometer
    (d) Photomultiplier tube

84. If you were to stand on the Moon, then the position of the Earth in the moon sky:
    (a) Will remain the same with time
    (b) Will change with time
    (c) Will not be able to see the Earth from the Moon
    (d) None of the above

85. The distance of the star nearest to the solar system is:
    (a) A few million light years
    (b) A few light days
    (c) A few light years
    (d) A few thousand light years

86. Semi-diurnal tides have:
    (a) One high and one low daily
    (b) Two highs and one low daily
    (c) One high and two lows daily
    (d) Two highs and two lows daily

87. Water entrapped in sediments during their formation is known as:
    (a) Connate water    (b) Meteoric water
    (c) Juvenile water    (d) Magmatic water

88. Lysimeter is used to measure:
    (a) Evaporation
    (b) Evapo-transpiration
    (c) Transpiration
    (d) Humidity

89. Isohyet is a line joining points having:
    (a) The same atmospheric pressure
    (b) The same amount of rainfall
    (c) The same temperature
    (d) The same depth of water table

90. A water-bearing formation sandwiched between two layers of impermeable geological formation is called _____.

(a) Confined aquifer
(b) Unconfined aquifer
(c) Semi-confined aquifer
(d) Aquifer

**91.** In drinking water, the upper limit of fluoride content is _____.
(a) 1 mg/l
(b) 1.5 mg/l
(c) 15 mg/l
(d) 20 mg/l

**92.** The evaporation through plants and from the surrounding soil together is known as:
(a) Transpiration
(b) Evaporation
(c) Evapo-transpiration
(d) Both (a) and (b)

**93.** _____ has the highest porosity.
(a) Clay
(b) Gravel
(c) Silt
(d) Sandstone

**94.** Water holding capacity is more in _____ soils.
(a) Sandy
(b) Clayey
(c) Loamy
(d) Red

**95.** An unconfined aquifer is also known as _____ aquifer.
(a) An artesian
(b) A Leaky
(c) A Water table
(d) Perched

**96.** The amount of salt present in 1 kg of sea water is:
(a) 3.5g
(b) 35mg
(c) 35g
(d) 350mg

**97.** Thermocline is the region where:
(a) Temperature increases rapidly with depth
(b) Temperature decreases rapidly with depth
(c) Temperature remains uniform
(d) Temperature is lowest

**98.** Because of the Coriolis force, a southward ocean current in the southern hemisphere deflects:
(a) Westward
(b) Eastward
(c) Downward
(d) Not affected

**99.** Sinking motion in the thermohaline circulation takes place:
(a) Along the Gulf Stream
(b) Near the equator
(c) Near polar regions
(d) Off the coast of Peru

**100.** Altimeter is used for measuring:
(a) Sea level
(b) Sea surface temperature
(c) Sea surface salinity
(d) Ocean colour

## ANSWERS

| 1 | 2 | 3 | 4 | 5 | 6 | 7 | 8 | 9 | 10 |
|---|---|---|---|---|---|---|---|---|---|
| (b) | (b) | (b) | (b) | (c) | (a) | (c) | (c) | (c) | (c) |
| **11** | **12** | **13** | **14** | **15** | **16** | **17** | **18** | **19** | **20** |
| (d) | (b) | (b) | (b) | (c) | (c) | (a) | (a) | (b) | (c) |
| **21** | **22** | **23** | **24** | **25** | **26** | **27** | **28** | **29** | **30** |
| (b) | (b) | (a) | (d) | (c) | (c) | (a) | (c) | (c) | (d) |
| **31** | **32** | **33** | **34** | **35** | **36** | **37** | **38** | **39** | **40** |
| (a) | (c) | (d) | (b) | (b) | (b) | (a) | (d) | (b) | (c) |
| **41** | **42** | **43** | **44** | **45** | **46** | **47** | **48** | **49** | **50** |
| (a) | (d) | (a) | (d) | (c) | (c) | (c) | (c) | (c) | (a) |
| **51** | **52** | **53** | **54** | **55** | **56** | **57** | **58** | **59** | **60** |
| (d) | (b) | (a) | (c) | (c) | (c) | (c) | (a) | (b) | (a) |
| **61** | **62** | **63** | **64** | **65** | **66** | **67** | **68** | **69** | **70** |
| (d) | (c) | (a) | (a) | (b) | (a) | (b) | (d) | (c) | (c) |
| **71** | **72** | **73** | **74** | **75** | **76** | **77** | **78** | **79** | **80** |
| (a) | (d) | (b) | (c) | (a) | (b) | (d) | (c) | (b) | (d) |
| **81** | **82** | **83** | **84** | **85** | **86** | **87** | **88** | **89** | **90** |
| (c) | (d) | (b) | (a) | (c) | (d) | (a) | (b) | (b) | (a) |
| **91** | **92** | **93** | **94** | **95** | **96** | **97** | **98** | **99** | **100** |
| (b) | (c) | (a) | (b) | (c) | (c) | (b) | (b) | (c) | (a) |

## HINTS AND SOLUTIONS

1. **Agent of Chemical Weathering:** The decomposition and disintegration of the rocks/minerals due to chemically is called the chemical weathering. The reasons rocks look so varied in their appearance is because they are subjected to chemical weathering, which is the process by which rocks are broken down by chemical reactions. In this lesson, you will learn about the different types of chemical weathering and how exposure to things such as water, oxygen, carbon dioxide and acids can alter the minerals found in rocks.

**The agent of the Chemical Weathering:**
- Water
- Oxygen
- Carbon dioxide
- Living organisms
- Acid rain

**Water:** Weathers rock by dissolving it.

**Oxygen:** Rocks that contain iron will oxidize or rust. Rust makes rocks soft and crumbly and gives it a red or brown color.

**Carbon dioxide:** Becomes dissolved in rain water and in water that sinks through air pockets in the soil becoming carbonic acid which will easily weather marble and limestone.

**Living organisms (ex. Lichen):** Produce weak acids that weather rock.

**Acid rain:** Burning fossil fuels produce this, causing rapid chemical weathering.

2. **Different Karst Topography:** The development of all karst landforms requires the presence of rock which is capable of being dissolved by surface water or ground water. The term karst describes a distinctive topography that indicates dissolution (also called chemical solution) of underlying soluble rocks by surface water or ground water. Although commonly associated with carbonate rocks (limestone and dolomite) other highly soluble rocks such as evaporates (gypsum and rock salt) can be sculpted into karst terrain.

The degree of development of karst landforms varies greatly from region to region. Large drainage systems in karst areas are likely to have both fluvial (surface) and karst (underground) drainage components. As stated in the introduction, the term karst describes a distinctive topography that indicates **dissolution** of underlying rocks by surface water or ground water. Limestone is a sedimentary rock consisting primarily of calcium carbonate in the form of the mineral calcite. Rainwater dissolves the limestone by the following reaction: Calcite + Carbonic acid = Calcium ions dissolved in ground water + Bicarbonate ions dissolved in ground water.

*Karst Landform:*
- Terra Rosa
- Karst Plain
- Stalagmites
- Karst Solution Valley
- Polje
- Karst cockpits
- Sinkholes
- Stalactites
- Pillars
- Uvala
- Karst Tower

3. **Minerals and its Uses:** Different minerals have uses in others purpose.

| Minerals | Uses |
|----------|------|
| Mica | **Thermal insulation**, and in electronic equipment as electrical insulators. |
| Feldspar | **Feldspars** are used widely in the glass and ceramics industries. |
| Clay | Used in ceramics. |
| Quartz | Quartz and its varieties is frequently used in different commercial aspects. |

4. **Properties of the Particles Transported by Rivers:** Sediment refers to the conglomerate of materials, organic and inorganic, that can be carried away by water, wind or ice. While the term is often used to indicate soil-based, mineral matter (e.g. clay, silt and sand), decomposing organic substances and inorganic biogenic material are also considered sediment. Most mineral sediment comes from erosion and weathering, while organic sediment is typically detritus and decomposing material such as algae. These particulates are typically small, with clay defined as particles less than 0.00195 mm in diameter, and coarse sand reaching up only to 1.5 mm in diameter. However, during a flood or other high flow event, even large rocks can be classified as sediment as they are carried downstream. Sediment is a naturally occurring element in many bodies of water, though it can be influenced by anthropogenic factors.
- Bedload
- Suspended Load
- Wash Load

5. **Conditions for development of Karst Topography:** The main process as follow:
- Soluble rock (Dolomite, limestone)
- Dense highly jointed
- Moderate rain fall region

## 6. Minerals and its Significance:

| Minerals | Names |
|---|---|
| Pyrite | $FeS_2$ (Iron sulphide) |
| Chalcopyrite | $CuFeS_2$ (Copper sulphide) |
| Galena | PbS (Lead sulphide) |
| Bronzite | $(Mg,Fe)SiO_3$ Pyroxene group of minerals |

## 7. Earth's Layer with Elements:

| Different layers of the earth | Elements |
|---|---|
| Crust | O > Si > Al > Fe > Ca > Mg > Na |
| Lithosphere | O > Si > Al > Fe > Ca > Mg > Na |
| Atmosphere | $N_2 > O_2 > Ar > CO_2$ |
| Earth | Fe > O > Si > Mg |
| Universe | H > He > O |

## 8. Rocks with its grains:

| Rocks | Crystal/ grain size |
|---|---|
| Granite | Course grain |
| Basalt | Fine grain |
| Pegmatite | Course grain |

## 10. Earthquake Wave: The mainly earthquake wave two type; body and surface waves.

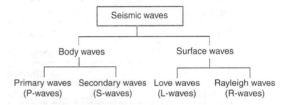

| P – waves | S – waves |
|---|---|
| Primary waves | Secondary waves |
| Fastest | Slower |
| 7 – 8 km/s | 4 – 5 km/s |
| Longitudinal waves | Transverse waves |

## 13. Mechanical behaviour of Earth's Interior:

| LAYERS | Thickness | Density | Composition |
|---|---|---|---|
| CRUST | Outer most layer, thinnest under ocean and thickest under continents | Oceanic crust more dense than continental crust | Solid rocks with silicon and oxygen. Oceanic crust – basalt, continental crust – granite |
| LITHOSPHERE | Crust and top of mantle | | |
| MANTLE | Middle layer, also called thickest layer | Density increases with depth because of increasing pressure | Hot soft rocks with iron and magnesium rock |
| ASTHENOSPHERE | Top layer of the mantle | — | — |
| CORE | Inner most layer outer and inner core | Heavy density material | Mostly iron and nickel, outer core slow flowing liquid, inner core solid |

### Some Earth's Interior

| Crust | 0 – 100 km | 0.5 % Earth's volume | Sial |
|---|---|---|---|
| Mantle | 100 – 2900 km | 16% of Earh's volume | Sima |
| Core | 2900 – 6400 km | 83% of Earth's volume | Nife |
| Earth's Density = 5.517 g/cm³ | | | |

## 14. Minerals and its Significance: Ores and its minerals.

| Minerals | Remarks |
|---|---|
| Hematite | Iron oxide |
| Magnetite | Iron oxide |
| Pyrite | Iron sulphide |
| Barite | Barium sulphate |

## 15. Grade of Metamorphic Rocks: A formation of the rocks when change pressure and temperature its called metamorphis. When rocks are subjected to elevated temperatures and pressures, for example due to deep burial in orogenic (mountain building) zones when two continents collide, they may becomemetamorphosed (metamorphism is from the Greek, to change in form). They slowly

recrystallize while remaining in the solid state. This may takes thousands or millions of years. Metamorphism is essentially an isochemical process, *i.e.*, the bulk chemical composition of a rock body is more or less unchanged from the protolith, or original rock. But the minerals may be largely recrystallized into a new mineral assemblage. In addition, new structural features are frequently imparted to the rocks, such as **slaty cleavage** or **schistosity**.

| | Very Low Grade | Low Grade | Medium Grade | High Grade |
|---|---|---|---|---|
| Parent Rock/ Approximate Temperature Ranges | 150-300°C | 300-450°C | 450-550°C | Above 550°C |
| Mudrock | Slate | Phyllite | schist | Gneiss |
| Granite | no change | no change | no change | granite gneiss |
| Basalt | chlorite schist | chlorite schist | amphibolite | amphibolite |
| Sandstone | no change | little change | quartzite | Quartzite |
| Limestone | little change | Marble | marble | Marble |

## Scheme for Metamorphic Rock Identification

| TEXTURE | GRAIN SIZE | COMPOSITION | TYPE OF METAMORPHISM | COMMENTS | ROCK NAME | MAP SYMBOL |
|---|---|---|---|---|---|---|
| FOLIATED / MINERAL ALIGNMENT | Fine | MICA QUARTZ FELDSPAR AMPHIBOLE GARNET PYROXENE | Regional (Heat and pressure increase with depth) | Low-grade metamorphism of shale | Slate | |
| | Fine to medium | | | Foliation surfaces shiny from microscopic mica crystals | Phyllite | |
| | | | | Platy mica crystals visible from metamorphism of clay or feldspars | Schist | |
| BANDING | Medium to coarse | | | High-grade metamorphism; some mica changed to feldspar; segregated by mineral type into bands | Gneiss | |
| NONFOLIATED | Fine | Variable | Contact (Heat) | Various rocks changed by heat from nearby magma/lava | Hornfels | |
| | Fine to coarse | Quartz | Regional or Contact | Metamorphism of quartz sandstone | Quartzite | |
| | | Calcite and/or dolomite | | Metamorphism of limestone or dolostone | Marble | |
| | Coarse | Various minerals in particles and matrix | | Pebbles may be distorted or stretched | Metaconglomerate | |

## 16. Continents and its Geological Age:

| Supercontinent name | Age (Mya: Millions Years ago) |
|---|---|
| Vaalbara | ~3,636–2,803 |
| Ur | ~2,803–2,408 |
| Kenorland | ~2,720–2,114 |
| Arctica | ~2,114–1,995 |
| Atlantica | ~1,991-1,124 |
| Columbia (Nuna) | ~1,820–1,350 |

| Supercontinent name | Age (Mya: Millions Years ago) |
|---|---|
| Rodinia | ~1,130–750 |
| Pannotia | ~633-573 |
| Gondwana | ~596-578 |
| Laurasia and Gondwana | ~472-451 |
| Pangaea | ~336-173 |

## 19. Term with remark:

| Terms | Remarks |
|-------|---------|
| Stramatolites | Stromatolites are layered mounds, sheet like columnar sedimentary rocks, developed due to growth of the layer of the cyanobacteria, single celled photosynthesizing microbe. |
| Corallites | The skeleton of a single coral polyp consisting of a septate investing wall or theca and an underlying basal plate and being imbedded in the general structure of the corallum. |
| Coprolites | A *coprolite* is fossilized feces. *Coprolites* are classified as trace fossils as opposed to body fossils, as they give evidence for the animal's behaviour (in this case, diet) rather than morphology. The name is derived from the Greek words (kopros, meaning "dung") and (lithos, meaning "stone"). |

## 21. Granites:
Granite is a light-colored igneous rock with grains large enough to be visible with the unaided eye. It forms from the slow crystallization of magma below Earth's surface. Granite is composed mainly of quartz and feldspar with minor amounts of mica, amphiboles, and other minerals. This mineral composition usually gives granite a red, pink, gray, or white colour with dark mineral grains visible throughout the rock.

**Types of Granites:** S-I-A-M Classification given by Chappell and White

- S-type granites
- I-type granites
- A-type granitoids
- M-type granitoids

**S-type granites** Occur in regional metamorphic terranes, partial melting of metasediments and High Al but contain no hornblende with Biotite, muscovite, cordierite, & garnet.

**I-type granites:** This type granite occur in Subduction zone continental margin, High Ca and Na – Contain hornblende and sphene, Hornblende-rich inclusions with Melting of deep crustal igneous rocks.

**A-type granites:** Anorogenic origin, High in $SiO_2$, up to 77%, High alkalies, Fe/Mg, halogens with stable craton environment.

**M-Type Granitoids:** Originate as fractionated mantle melts, underplated mantle melts – may assimilate crustal materials, may mix with crustal melts with low Rb, Th, U.

## 22. Classification of the sedimentary rocks:
Sedimentary rocks form at or near the Earth's surface. Rocks made from particles of eroded sediment are called clastic sedimentary rocks, those made from the remains of living things are called biogenic sedimentary rocks, and those that form by minerals precipitating out of solution are called evaporites.

Sedimentary rock is classified into two groups based on how they form. They are clastic and chemical. Clastic sedimentary rock is formed as bits of weathered rock become cemented together. Because all kinds of rock are subject to weathering many different minerals can make up this group of rocks. Clays and quartz are the most common.

| Name of Rock | Texture | Sedimentary type |
|--------------|---------|------------------|
| Conglomerate | Coarse (>2 mm | Rounded fragment |
| Breccia | Coarse (>2 mm | Angular fragment |
| Sandstone | Medium (1/16 to 2 mm) | Sandstone |
| Siltstone | Fine (1/256 to 1/16 mm) | Mud |
| Shale | Very fine (less than 1/256) | Shale |

Chemical sedimentary rocks form from dissolved minerals that are precipitated or separated from water. This happens most frequently when water evaporates leaving the minerals behind. At the right is a cube of table salt, also called halite or sodium chloride, formed when sea water evaporates. You can see this process taking place in your own home. The white deposits that form around the faucets in your bathroom or kitchen are from minerals left behind as water evaporates. Below is a list of chemical sedimentary rocks with some of their characteristics:

## Chemical Sedimentary Rocks

| Name of Rock | Composition | Texture |
|--------------|-------------|---------|
| Crystalline Limestone | Calcite - $CaCo_3$ | coarse to fine Crystalline |
| Fossiliferous Limestone | Calcite - $CaCo_3$ | visible fragments of shells |
| Chalk | Calcite - $CaCo_3$ | microscopic shells and clay |
| Chert | Quartz - $SiO_2$ | very fine crystalline |
| Gypsum | Gypsum - $CaSO_4–2H_2O$ | fine to coarse crystalline |
| Rock Salt | Halite – NaCl | fine to coarse crystalline |
| Bituminous Coal | Organic Matter | fine |

23. **Geological history of the Dinosaurs:** Evolution of the life through geological records.

| EON | ERA | PERIOD | | EPOCH | MYA | |
|---|---|---|---|---|---|---|
| PHANEROZOIC | CENOZOIC | QUATERNARY | | RECENT | 0.01 | ICE AGE ENDS |
| | | | | PLEISTOCENE | 1.6 | ICE AGE BEGINS / EARLIEST HUMANS |
| | | TERTIARY | NEOGENE | PLIOCENE | 5.3 | |
| | | | | MIOCENE | 23.7 | |
| | | | PALEOGENE | OLIGOCENE | 36.6 | |
| | | | | EOCENE | 57.8 | FORMATION OF HIMALAYAS |
| | | | | PALEOCENE | 66 | DINOSAUR EXTINCTION / ROCKY MTS. FORMED |
| | MESOZOIC | CRETACEOUS | | | 144 | |
| | | JURASSIC | | | 208 | FIRST MAMMALS |
| | | TRIASSIC | | | 245 | PANGEA BREAK UP / FIRST DINOSAURS |
| | PALEOZOIC | PERMIAN | | | 286 | |
| | | PENNSYLVANIAN | | | 320 | FIRST REPTILES |
| | | MISSISSIPPIAN | | | 360 | FIRST ANPHIBIANS |
| | | DEVONIAN | | | 408 | |
| | | SILURIAN | | | 438 | FIRST LAND PLANTS |
| | | ORDOVICIAN | | | 505 | FIRST FISH |
| | | CAMBRIAN | | | 570 | |
| PRECAMBRIAN | | PROTEZOIC EON | | | | EARLIEST SHELLED ANIMALS |
| | | | | | 2500 | |
| | | ARCHEAN EON | | | | EARLIEST FOSSIL RECORDED OF LIFE |
| | | | | | 3800 / 4600 | |

25. **Porosity of the Rocks:** Porosity ($\phi$) is defined as the nonsolid or pore-volume fraction.

$$\text{Porosity} = \frac{\text{Pore Volume}}{\text{Total Volume}} = \Phi$$

The ratio of the pore volume in a rock to the bulk volume of that rock. Express in per cent. Mathematical form is: $\phi = Vp/Vb$. Porosity is a volume ratio and thus dimensionless, and is usually reported as a fraction or per cent. To avoid confusion, particularly when variable or changing porosities are involved, it is often reported in porosity units (1 PU = 1%).

27. **Fault and its features:**

| Types of Faults | Remarks |
|---|---|
| Normal fault | The hanging wall moved downward relative to footwall. |
| Reverse fault | The hanging wall moved upward relative to footwall. |
| Strike Slip Fault | A strike slip fault is a fault zone where two blocks of land move horizontally rather than vertically along a fault plane. These faults can form between two small blocks of land or crustal plates. They also sometimes develop within a continental plate. The Alpine Fault in New Zealand is an example of this type of tectonic plate movement. |

28. **Earthquake Distribution in India:** An earthquake is caused by a sudden slip on a fault. Stresses in the earth's outer layer push the sides of the fault together. Stress builds up and the rocks slips suddenly, releasing energy in waves that travel through the earth's crust and cause the shaking. An Earthquake occurs when plates grind and scrape against each other.

Bureau of Indian Standards, based on the past seismic history, grouped the country into four seismic zones, viz. Zone-II, -III, -IV and –V. Of these, Zone V is the most seismically active region, while zone II is the least. The Modified Mercalli (MM) intensity, which measures the impact of the earthquakes on the surface of the earth, broadly associated with various zones, is as follows:

**Seismic Zone Intensity on MM scale:**

| Seismic Zone | Intensity on MMI scale | % of total area |
|---|---|---|
| II (Low intensity zone) | VI (or less) | 43% |
| III (Moderate intensity zone) | VII | 27% |
| IV (Severe intensity zone) | VIII | 18% |
| V (Very severe intensity zone) | IX (and above) | 12% |

**Zone-V** comprises of entire northeastern India, parts of Jammu and Kashmir, Himachal Pradesh, Uttarakhand, Rann of Kutch in Gujarat, parts of North Bihar and Andaman & Nicobar Islands.

**Zone-IV** covers remaining parts of Jammu & Kashmir and Himachal Pradesh, Union Territory of Delhi, Sikkim, northern parts of Uttar Pradesh, Bihar and West Bengal, parts of Gujarat and small portions of Maharashtra near the west coast and Rajasthan.

**Zone-III** comprises of Kerala, Goa, Lakshadweep islands, and remaining parts of Uttar Pradesh, Gujarat and West Bengal, parts of Punjab, Rajasthan, Madhya Pradesh, Bihar, Jharkhand, Chhattisgarh, Maharashtra, Orissa, Andhra Pradesh, Tamil Nadu and Karnataka.

**Zone-II** covers remaining parts of the country.

30. **Mineral properties:** Physical Properties of the Minerals

| Properties | Remarks | Example |
|---|---|---|
| Lustre | Amount and intensity of light reflected from the surface of the minerals. | Gold is a example of metallic lustre. |
| Iridescence | A mineral show rainbow colour | Pearls |
| Asterism | A star like reflection/refraction show a particular minerals | Rubies and shaphire |
| Chatoyancy | This is like cat's eye effect, is an optical reflectance effect seen in certain gemstones. | Chrysoberyl, quartz |

**31. Condition of Fossilization:** For a fossil to form, different conditions have to be met. First of all, the animal had to live in the given area! Animals live in many environments on Earth, but not everywhere. The water above many lake bottoms and many areas of the deep ocean bottom are stagnant. The bottom water is never exchanged with surface waters, so the water contains no dissolved oxygen. Animals cannot live without oxygen, so no animals live there. In these situations, the only possibility of fossilization is if a fish or other swimming animal dies in oxygen-rich waters above, sinks down into the stagnant muddy bottom, and is buried by sediments. Most environments on the land surface are populated with animals. Marine is the best sutable place for the preservation.

- Possession of Hard parts
- Quick burial

**33. Types of Tectonic Plate Boundary:** There are different plate movements through different differential forces.

**Divergent Plate Setting:** A divergent boundary occurs when two tectonic plates move away from each other. Along these boundaries, lava spews from long fissures and geysers spurt superheated water. Frequent earthquakes strike along the rift. Beneath the rift, magma—molten rock—rises from the mantle. It oozes up into the gap and hardens into solid rock, forming new crust on the torn edges of the plates. Magma from the mantle solidifies into basalt, a dark, dense rock that underlies the ocean floor. Thus at divergent boundaries, oceanic crust, made of basalt, is created.

**Convergent Plate Setting:** When two plates come together, it is known as a convergent boundary. The impact of the two colliding plates buckles the edge of one or both plates up into a rugged mountain range, and sometimes bends the other down into a deep seafloor trench. A chain of volcanoes often forms parallel to the boundary, to the mountain range, and to the trench. Powerful earthquakes shake a wide area on both sides of the boundary.

If one of the colliding plates is topped with oceanic crust, it is forced down into the mantle where it begins to melt. Magma rises into and through the other plate, solidifying into new crust. Magma formed from melting plates solidifies into granite, a light colored, low-density rock that makes up the continents. Thus at convergent boundaries, continental crust, made of granite, is created, and oceanic crust is destroyed.Convergent boundaries

plates may converge directly or at an angle. Three types of convergent boundaries are recognized:

- Continent continent
- Ocean continent
- Ocean ocean

**Transform Plate Boundaries:** A transform boundary is a fault or a series of parallel faults (fault zone) along which plates slide past each other via strike slip movements. As previously discussed, transform faults connect offset mid-oceanic ridges (including the rift valleys). The motion between the two ridge segments is in opposite directions; beyond the transform fault, crustal movement is strike slip in the same direction. Thus, the transform fault "transforms" into a fault that has different motions along the same fault plane. Transform faults can connect diverging and converging boundaries or two converging boundaries (such as two oceanic trenches). Transform faults are thought to form because the original line of divergence is slightly curved. As an adjustment to mechanical constraints, the tectonic forces break the curved or irregular plate boundary into a series of pieces. The segments are separated by transform faults that are parallel to the spreading direction, allowing the ridge crest to be perpendicular to the spreading direction, which is the easiest way for two plates to diverge. Transform faults allow the divergent boundary to be in a structural equilibrium.

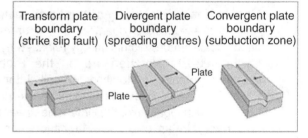

Transform plate boundary (strike slip fault)   Divergent plate boundary (spreading centres)   Convergent plate boundary (subduction zone)

**37. Velocity of Seismic Waves in Different Medium:** Primary (P) and Secondary (S) waves travel in different medium with different velocity.

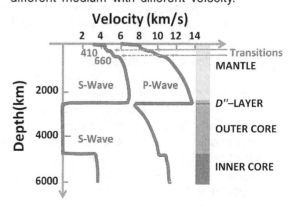

38. **Dendritic Drainage Pattern:** This type of drainage pattern developed due to tributary divides just like a tree's branches, found in horizontal sedimentary or in intrusive igneous rocks where the rock mass is in homogeneous. The tributaries in steep terrains tend to be subparallel and join at acute angles. Joints, faults will tend to development of the dendritic drainage pattern.

44. **Terrain with example:**

| Terms | Example |
|---|---|
| Non–detrital sedimentary formation | Phosphorite deposits |
| Detrital sedimentary formation | Sandstone formations |
| Metamorphic rocks | Phyllite formation |
| Igneous rocks | Granite terrain |

45. **Magnitudes and Intensity of the Earthquakes:** An earthquake size is a quantitative measurement on the scale where seismic energy released by an earthquake. Which measure on the Richter Magnitude Scale or Modified Mercalli Intensity Scale. On the magnitude scale the numerical values from 0 – 10 in logrithimic, high intensities near the epicentre. In an example, Magnitude can be likened to the power of radio or television waves sent out from a broadcasting station. Intensity is how well you receive the signal, which can depend on your distance from the energy source, the local conditions, and the pathway the signal has to take to reach you.

**Intensities of the Earthquakes:** The intensity is a number (written as a Roman numeral) describing the severity of an earthquake in terms of its effects on the earth's surface and on humans and their structures. Several scales exist, but the ones most commonly used in the United States are the Modified Mercalli scale and the Rossi-Forel scale. There are many intensities for an earthquake, depending on where you are, unlike the magnitude, which is one number for each earthquake. The severity of earthquake shaking is assessed using a *descriptive* scale – the Modified Mercalli Intensity Scale.

46. **Green Houses Gases:**

| Greenhouse gases | Chemical Formula | Sources |
|---|---|---|
| Carbon Dioxide | $CO_2$ | Fossils fuel combustion |
| Methane | $CH_4$ | Fossils fuels, Waste dumps |
| Nitrous Oxide | $N_2O$ | Fertilizer |
| Tropospheric Ozone | $O_3$ | Industrial emissions, Fossils fuel |
| CFC-12 | $CCL_2F_2$ | Liquid coolants, Foams |
| HCFC-22 | $CCl_2F_2$ | Refrigerants |
| Sulphur Hexafluoride | $SF_6$ | Dielectric fluid |

49. **Hydrological Cycle:** This is defined as the movement of water to one medium to another.

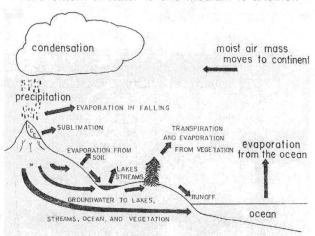

50. **Terms with Example:**

| Terms | Character |
|---|---|
| Isotherms | A line of equal temperature |
| Isopycnal | A line of the equal density |
| Isohyets | A line of the equal rainfall |
| Isohalines | A line of the equal salinity |

54. **Carnot Cycle:** The Carnot cycle in this heat engine consists of two isentropic and two isothermal processes.

- **Process: 1a** Reversible Isothermal Expansion ($T_H$ = const) During this process, heat is absorbed. Gas expands reversibly at the constant temperature $T_H$.

- **Process: 1b** Reversible Adiabatic (Isentropic) Expansion, This process is isentropic. The engine is perfect insulated so that no heat is lost and absorbed. Gas continues expanding slowly until the temperature drops from $T_H$ to $T_L$.

- **Process: 1c** Reversible Isothermal Compression ($T_L$ = const) After gas reaches the low temperature $T_L$, some external force is applied on the engine in order that gas can be compressed.

- Since the temperature remains constant at $T_L$, no change of internal energy of gas occurs, if we assume that gas is ideal gas. Knowing from the 1st law of thermodynamics, we obtain a conclusion that heat must be transferred from engine to low-temperature reservoir.

- **Process: 2a** Reversible Adiabatic (Isentropic) Compression. This process is isentropic. The engine is perfect insulated so that no heat is lost and absorbed. Gas continues being compressed slowly until the temperature rises from $T_L$ to $T_H$. The process comes to an end when reaching its initial state.

56. **Composition of the Atmosphere:** Earth's relatively thin atmosphere primarily consists of a mixture of nitrogen (78%) and oxygen (21%) gases. The remaining 1% contains several inactive gases (*i.e.*, argon, neon, helium, hydrogen, and xenon) and several other gases that vary in con-centration (*i.e.*, water vapor, carbon dioxide, methane, nitrous oxide, ozone, and chlorofluorocarbons). Although water vapor and carbon dioxide make up a very small amount of the gases in Earth's atmosphere, they are very important because of their ability to absorb heat. Throughout the upcoming modules, you will learn much more about why and how the concentrations of water vapor and carbon dioxide vary.

| *Permanent Gases* | | | *Variable Gases* | | |
|---|---|---|---|---|---|
| *Gas* | *Symbol* | *%age* | *Gas* | *Symbol* | *%age by volume* |
| Nitrogen | $N_2$ | 78 % | Water vapour | $H_2O$ | 0 – 4 |
| Oxygen | $O_2$ | 21 % | Carbon dioxide | $CO_2$ | 0.038 |
| Argon | Ar | 0.9 % | Ozone | $O_3$ | 0.000004 |
| Neon | Ne | 0.0018 % | Carbon monoxide | CO | 0.00002 |
| Helium | He | 0.0005 % | Sulphur dioxide | $SO_2$ | 0.000001 |
| Methane | $CH_4$ | 0.0001 % | Nitrogen dioxide | $NO_2$ | 0.000001 |
| Hydrogen | $H_2$ | 0.00005 % | Particles (dust, pollen) | — | 0.00001 |

58. **Different Layers of the Atmosphere:**

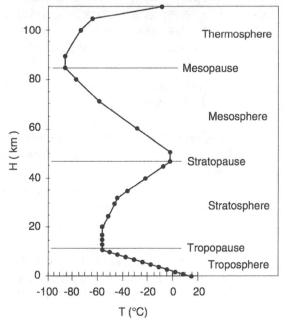

60. **Atmospheric Pressure:** Pressure and Temp-erature variation with height:

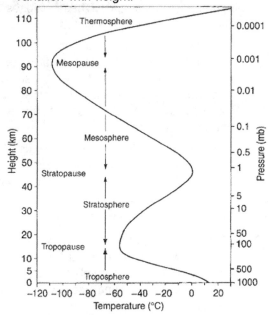

## 65. Cyclone Names:

| Cyclone Names | Remarks |
|---|---|
| Katrina | Catogary – 5 (Gulf of Mexico) |
| Nargis | Catogary – 4 (Mayanmar, Indian Ocean) |
| Sidr | Catogary – 5 (Bangladesh, Indian Ocean) |
| Irrawady | Delta name in Myanmar |

## 68. Solar Eclipse:
Eclipses of the Sun can only occur when the Moon is near one of its two orbital nodes during the New Moon phase. It is then possible for the Moon's penumbral, umbral or antumbral shadows to sweep across Earth's surface thereby producing an eclipse. There are four types of solar eclipses:

1. **Partial** : Moon's penumbral shadow traverses Earth (umbral and antumbral shadows completely miss Earth).

2. **Annular** : Moon's antumbral shadow traverses Earth (Moon is too far from Earth to completely cover the Sun).

3. **Total** : Moon's umbral shadow traverses Earth (Moon is close enough to Earth to completely cover the Sun).

4. **Hybrid** : Moon's umbral and antumbral shadows traverse Earth (eclipse appears annular and total along different sections of its path). Hybrid eclipses are also known as annular-total eclipses.

Total eclipses are visible from within the Moon's umbral shadow while annular eclipses are seen within the antumbral shadow. These eclipses can be classified as central or non-central as:

1. **Central (two limits)** - The central axis of the Moon's shadow cone traverses Earth thereby producing a central line in the eclipse track. The umbra or antumbra falls entirely upon Earth so the ground track has both a northern and southern limit.

2. **Central (one limit)** - The central axis of the Moon's shadow cone traverses Earth. However, a portion of the umbra or antumbra misses Earth throughout the eclipse and the resulting ground track has just one limit.

**Non-Central (One Limit) :** The central axis of the Moon's shadow cone misses Earth. However, one edge of the umbra or antumbra grazes Earth thereby producing a ground track with one limit and no central line.

## 73. Refracting Telescopes:
Telescopes were first created by Dutch for use of the boats's flags, after Italian scientist Galileo Galilei was first person to use a telescope for sky objective. There are two types of telescopes: refractors and reflectors. The refractor telescope is a tube that contains two lenses: one at the front end with little magnification, which is called the 'objective lens', and another at the bottom end, that is closest to the user's eye, called the 'eyepiece'.

The larger objective lens collects lots of light from an object far away and then refracts or 'bends' that light, bringing it to a point near the bottom end of the telescope. The smaller eyepiece lens then magnifies that point and brings it into focus at the user's eye. The tube itself holds the lenses at just the right distance from each other. It also keeps out light, dust and moisture that might interfere with the image.

It is very difficult to build big lenses since they weigh a lot and have to be supported around their edges, the thinnest, most fragile part. They are also difficult to move around (you want to be able to point your telescope at any point in the sky!). The light can also bend too much with a big lens, which distorts the image.

## 74. Kelper's Law:
In the early 1600s, Johannes Kepler proposed three laws of planetary motion. Kepler was able to summarize the carefully collected data of his mentor - Tycho Brahe - with three statements that described the motion of planets in a sun-centered solar system. Kepler's efforts to explain the underlying reasons for such motions are no longer accepted; nonetheless, the actual laws themselves are still considered an accurate description of the motion of any planet and any satellite.

Kepler's three laws of planetary motion can be described as follows:

1. The path of the planets about the sun is elliptical in shape, with the center of the sun being located at one focus. (The Law of Ellipses)

2. An imaginary line drawn from the center of the sun to the center of the planet will sweep out equal areas in equal intervals of time. (The Law of Equal Areas)

3. The ratio of the squares of the periods of any two planets is equal to the ratio of the cubes of their average distances from the sun. (The Law of Harmonies)

**75. Planets from the Sun:**

| Planets | Diameter (Km) | Mass (Earth = 1) | Density (gm/cm³) (Water = 1) | Length of the day (Earth hours) | Period of one revolution around Sun (Earth years) | Average distance from Sun (millions of km) |
|---------|---------------|------------------|------------------------------|----------------------------------|---------------------------------------------------|-------------------------------------------|
| Mercury | 4880 | 0.0558 | 5.44 | 1416 | 0.24 | 58 |
| Venus | 12104 | 0.815 | 5.20 | 5832 | 0.62 | 108 |
| Earth | 12756 | 1.0 | 5.52 | 24 | 1.00 | 150 |
| Mars | 6787 | 0.108 | 3.93 | 24.6 | 1.88 | 228 |
| Jupiter | 142800 | 317.8 | 1.30 | 9.8 | 11.86 | 778 |
| Saturn | 120000 | 95.2 | 0.69 | 10.2 | 29.50 | 1427 |
| Uranus | 51800 | 14.4 | 1.28 | 17.2 | 84.00 | 2870 |
| Neptune | 49500 | 17.2 | 1.64 | 16.1 | 164.90 | 4497 |

### Distance of Planets from Sun in Astronomical Units

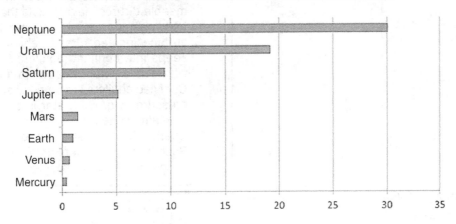

**76. Light Year:**

The light-year is a measure of distance, not time. It is the total distance that a beam of light, moving in a straight line, travels in one year. To obtain an idea of the size of a light-year, take the circumference of the earth (24,900 miles), lay it out in a straight line, multiply the length of the line by 7.5 (the corresponding distance is one light-second), then place 31.6 million similar lines end to end. The resulting distance is almost 6 trillion (6,000,000,000,000) miles / 10,000,000,000 km.

**78. Planets and its Moons:**

| Planets | Number of Moons |
|---------|-----------------|
| Mercury | 0 |
| Venus | 0 |
| Earth | 1 |
| Mars | 2 |
| Jupiter | 69 |
| Saturn | 62 |

| Uranus | 27 |
|--------|-----|
| Neptune | 14 |
| Pluto | 0 |

**81. Electromagnetic Spectrum:** The electromagnetic spectrum describes all the wavelengths of light. The *electromagnetic spectrum* is the term used by scientists to describe the entire range of light that exists. From radio waves to gamma rays, most of the light in the universe is, in fact, invisible to us. Light is a wave of alternating electric and magnetic fields. The propagation of light isn't much different than waves crossing an ocean. Like any other wave, light has a few fundamental properties that describe it. One is its *frequency*, measured in Hertz, which counts the number of waves that pass by a point in one second. Another closely related property is *wavelength*: the distance from the peak of one wave to the peak of the next. These two attributes are inversely related. The larger the frequency, the smaller the wavelength – and vice versa.

| Type of radiation | Wavelenght (m) | Frequency (Hz) | Speed (m/s) |
|---|---|---|---|
| Radio Waves | $10^3$ | $10^4$ | 299,792,485 |
| Microwave | $10^{-2}$ | $10^8$ | 299,792,458 |
| Infrared | $10^{-5}$ | $10^{12}$ | 299,792,458 |
| Visible | $0.5 \times 10^{-6}$ | $10^{15}$ | 299,792,458 |
| Ultraviolet | $10^{-8}$ | $10^{16}$ | 299,792,458 |
| X-Ray | $10^{-10}$ | $10^{18}$ | 299,792,458 |
| Gamma Ray | $10^{-12}$ | $10^{20}$ | 299,792,458 |

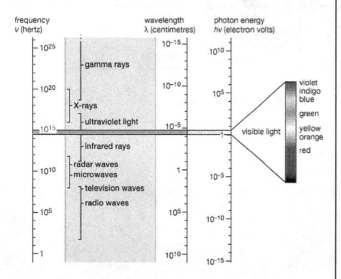

## 87. Types of Water: Different water have its own chemical formation.

| Types of Water | Properties |
|---|---|
| Connate water | Sedimentary rocks origin |
| Meteoric water | Water from lakes, rivers, and icemelts, which all originate from precipitation indirectly. |
| Juvenile water | Magmatic water |
| Magmatic water | Derived from magma/ magmatic process |

## 88. Lysimeter: Lysimeter (noun) an apparatus for measuring change due to moisture loss, percolation, etc. undergone by a body of soil under controlled conditions.

## 89. Terms with Characters:

| Terms | Character |
|---|---|
| Isotherms | A line of equal temperature |
| Isopycnal | A line of the equal density |
| Isohyets | A line of the equal rainfall |
| Isohalines | A line of the equal salinity |

## 90. Types of Aquifers: Aquifer is made of two words 'aqua' and 'ferre' from Latin language. 'Aqua' means water and 'ferre' means 'produce or bear'. Thus, aquifer is a geological composition which is porous and permeable. There is storage and transmission of water in it, as well as yielding of water to wells and springs in sufficient quantity. Aquifers come in two types which are shown below: unconfined and confined.

Unconfined aquifers are those into which water seeps from the ground surface directly above the aquifer. In such types of aquifers, ground-water level works like the upper layer of the zone of saturation. It is also called free or non-artesian groundwater. Wavy form and slope of groundwater is changeable, which depends on replenishing of groundwater, abandoned area and permeability.

Confined aquifers are those in which an impermeable dirt/rock layer exists that prevents water from seeping into the aquifer from the ground surface located directly above. Instead, water seeps into confined aquifers from farther away where the impermeable layer doesn't exist. Confined aquifers are found at such places where pressure of groundwater is comparatively more than atmospheric pressure due to non-permeable layers. They are also called 'artesian aquifers'. Such types of aquifers are found above the base of confined beds of water level in punctured wells.

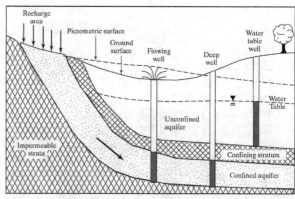

*Schematic cross section illustrating unconfined and confined aquifers.*

## 91. Element Contents in Drinking Water:

### WHO Standards for Drinking Water

| Parameter | WHO Standards |
|---|---|
| Colour | Acceptable |
| Odour | Unobjectionable |
| Taste | Agreeable |
| Turbidity | 5 NTU |
| pH | 7 – 8.5 |
| Electrical conductivity | 1000 µmhos/cm |

| Parameter | WHO Standards |
|---|---|
| Total Dissolved Solids | 500 |
| Chloride | 250 |
| Alkalinity | 120 |
| Hardness | 300 |
| Sulphate | 200 |
| Nitrate | 45 |
| Fluoride | 1 |
| Dissolved Oxygen | 5 |
| BOD | 3 |

All values except Turbidity, pH and Electrical conductivity are expressed in mg/l.

## 94. Percentage Porosity of The Different Soils:

### Porosity of Common Rocks

| Rocks/ soils | Maximum porosity (%) |
|---|---|
| Soil | >50 |
| Sand and gravel | 20 – 47 |
| Clay | >49 |
| Sandstone | 10 – 15 |
| Limestone | 5 |
| Chalk | Up to 50 |
| Igneous rocks | <1.5 |
| Metamorphic rocks | Very low |

**95. Perched Eater Table:** A perched water table is an accumulation of groundwater that is above the water table in the unsaturated zone. The groundwater is usually trapped above an impermeable soil layer, such as clay, and actually forms a lens of saturated material in the unsaturated zone. A perched water table is generally insufficient to supply domestic groundwater needs, and often runs dry after being drilled. If the perched water table intersects a sloping surface, it may be manifested by springs or seeps along the line of intersection.

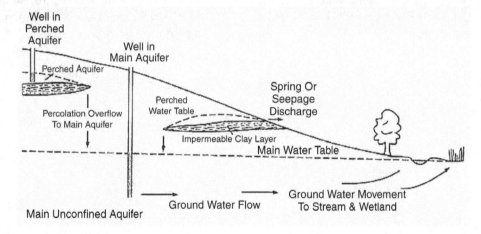

## 96. Elements in Sea Water:

**Major Elements in Seawater**: Elements present in amounts greater than 1 mg/litre are called major elements. These elements determine the salinity of seawater. Their ratios with salinity or with each other are nearly constant. They are also known as conservative elements. Common salt (sodium chloride) is the principal ingredient of seawater that makes it salty. It exists in solution as separate hydrated sodium ions ($Na^+$) and hydrated chloride ions ($Cl^-$).

**Major Elements present in seawater of 34.5 ppt salinity, their ionic forms, and their levels**

| Elements | Concentration (mg/lit) | % weight |
|---|---|---|
| Cations | | |
| $Na^+$ | 10500 | 30.42 |

| Elements | Concentration (mg/lit) | % weight |
|---|---|---|
| $Mg^{2+}$ | 1350 | 3.91 |
| $Ca^{2+}$ | 400 | 1.16 |
| $K^+$ | 380 | 1.10 |
| $Sr^{2+}$ | 8 | 0.02 |
| Anions | | |
| $Cl^+$ | 19000 | 55.04 |
| $SO_4^{2-}$ | 2665 | 7.69 |
| $CO_3^{2-}$ | 140 | 0.41 |
| $Br^-$ | 65 | 0.19 |
| $BO_3^{3-}$ | 20 | 0.06 |
| $SiO_3^{2-}$ | 8 | 0.02 |
| $F^-$ | 1 | 0.003 |

**97. Thermocline:** The thermocline is the transition layer between the mixed layer at the surface and the deep water layer. The definitions of these layers are based on temperature. The mixed layer is near the surface where the temperature is roughly that of surface water. In the thermocline, the temperature decreases rapidly from the mixed layer temperature to the much colder deep water temperature. The mixed layer and the deep water layer are relatively uniform in temperature, while the thermocline represents the transition zone between the two.

**98. Causes of Ocean Current Deflection:**
- The factors relating to the earth's nature and its rotation include the gravitational force and deflective force by earth's rotation also known as Coriolis force.
- Oceanic factors include the pressure gradient, temperature variations and salinity differences. Ex-oceanic factors are atmospheric pressure and winds, evaporation and precipitation.
- Tides caused by the gravitational pull of the Moon and the Sun also play role in the forming of oceanic currents.

**100. Altimeter:** Aircraft altimeters tell pilots how high they're flying. It's a simple and basic flight instrument, yet it is often misinterpreted by pilots - sometimes with grave consequences. Understanding how your aircraft altimeter works is necessary for safe flight. The instrument itself is simple enough, but its operation comes with a few caveats. Newer altimeters use high-tech sensors to detect altitude. Altitude can also be accurately attained with an IFR-certified GPS system on board.

**Barometric Altimeter:** A barometric altimeter consists of a barometric capsule linked to a pointer by a suitable mechanical or electronic system. The pointer moves across the dial in response to changes in barometric pressure. The dial is calibrated in feet, or (less commonly) in metres. Barometric altimeters are provided with a pressure setting control and sub-scale (Kollsman window) so that the altimeter may be calibrated according to the appropriate pressure setting to indicate flight level, altitude above mean sea level, or altitude above ground level.

---

# International Earth Science Olympiad (IESO)
## Entrance Exam, 2010

**Total Marks : 100**                                          **Time : 90 minutes**

---

**1.** The age of the Earth is _____ million years.
- (a) 3900
- (b) 4200
- (c) 4600
- (d) 4800

**2.** Which is the most abundant element in the Earth's crust?
- (a) Silica
- (b) Iron
- (c) Oxygen
- (d) Aluminium

**3.** Which is the most common mineral in the Earth's crust?
- (a) Quartz
- (b) Mica
- (c) Amphibole
- (d) Feldspar

**4.** _____ is commonly referred to as "fool's gold".
- (a) Pyrite
- (b) Chalcopyrite
- (c) Pyrrhotite;
- (d) None of these – It is a joke!

**5.** What is emery powder used as?
- (a) A filler in ceramic material;
- (b) For the manufacture of fine crystal glass
- (c) As abrasive
- (d) A mixture in paints

**6.** The general process by which rocks and minerals are broken down at or near the Earth's surface is called _____.
- (a) Weathering
- (b) Denudation
- (c) Erosion
- (d) Corrosion

**7.** Which is the most widespread mineral group distributed in sedimentary, igneous and metamorphic rocks?
- (a) Quartz
- (b) Feldspars
- (c) Clay minerals
- (d) Carbonates

**8.** _____ rocks form at great depths inside the earth.
- (a) Volcanic
- (b) Plutonic
- (c) Hypabyssal
- (d) Hypogene

**9.** _____ is the principal raw material for manufacturing steel.
- (a) Pyrite
- (b) Magnetite
- (c) Bauxite
- (d) Both (a) and (b)

**10.** Limestone is used for manufacturing _____.
- (a) Bricks
- (b) Cement
- (c) Glass
- (d) Both (a) and (c)

**11.** India is an exporter of _____.
- (a) Diamonds
- (b) Gold
- (c) Copper ore
- (d) Iron ore

**12.** An igneous rock containing coarse mineral grains indicates _____.
- (a) Slow cooling
- (b) Fast cooling
- (c) Not related to cooling rate
- (d) Magma composition

**13.** Sedimentary rocks form because of _____.
- (a) Chemical precipitation
- (b) Sediment deposition;
- (c) Both (a) and (b)
- (d) Weathering

**14.** Metamorphic rocks form due to the action of _____
- (a) Water
- (b) Pressure
- (c) Temperature
- (d) Both (b) and (c)

**15.** The fossils recovered from a sedimentary rock are shown below.

These are:
- (a) Brachiopod and Ammonite
- (b) Coral and Lamellibranch
- (c) Ammonite and Coral
- (d) Lamellibranch and Ammonite

**16.** The possible depositional environment of the rock containing fossils shown above was:
- (a) Fluvial
- (b) Aeolian
- (c) Glacial
- (d) Marine

**17.** Which of the following is a non-clastic sedimentary rock?
(a) Conglomerate    (b) Chalk
(c) Sandstone    (d) Shale

**18.** During which geological period did most of the coal deposits form?
(a) Ordovician    (b) Carboniferous
(c) Jurassic    (d) Pleistocene

**19.** The oldest fossil recorded on the earth is about _____ billion years old.
(a) 3    (b) 2
(c) 1    (d) 0.5

**20.** The clasts of a sedimentary rock are between 5 mm and 10 mm in size. So, the rock will be named as _____.
(a) Shale    (b) Sandstone
(c) Conglomerate    (d) Siltstone

**21.** The Deccan volcanism in India took place _____ million years ago.
(a) 55    (b) 65
(c) 75    (d) 85

**22.** A typical sedimentary rock indicating glaciation in the past is:
(a) Shale    (b) Tillite
(c) Limestone    (d) Lignite

**23.** A large number of animals got extinct at the end of the Cretaceous time.
This extinction was caused by _____.
(a) Meteorite impact    (b) Tsunami
(c) Volcanism    (d) Both (a) and (c)

**24.** If a piece of rock is crushed into very fine particles, it leads to _____.
(a) An increase in surface area;
(b) A decrease in surface area;
(c) An increase in the volume of rock;
(d) A decrease in the volume of rock

**25.** Rocks containing fossils of _____ would be the oldest.
(a) Dinosaur bones
(b) Trilobites
(c) Bird bones
(d) Woolly mammoth bones

**26.** Which of the following can form in the shortest length of time?
(a) Soil profile    (b) Coral reef
(c) Volcano    (d) River valley

**27.** Which of the following statements about transpiration and river runoff in India is correct?
(a) The amount of water that is lost through vegetation is greater than the amount of water carried away by rivers

(b) The amount of water carried away by rivers is at least three orders of magnitude higher than the amount of water that is lost through vegetation
(c) The amount in each case is approximately the same
(d) The amount of water that escapes through vegetation is insignificant compared to the amount of water carried away by rivers

**28.** On an eroded sedimentary dome, the drainage pattern is usually _____.
(a) Dendritic    (b) Trellis
(c) Annular    (d) Parallel

**29.** Marine influence upon climate is responsible for:
(a) An increase in the annual temperature range
(b) An increase in the annual rainfall totals
(c) A decrease in the annual temperature range
(d) A decrease in the annual rainfall totals

**30.** Most tropical cyclones originate _____.
(a) Between 0° and 5° north and south of the equator
(b) In the centres of sub-tropical highs
(c) Between 10° and 20°
(d) To the west of westerly winds

**31.** Rain-shadow zone occurs on the lee (or leeward side) of a mountain because _____.
(a) Adiabatic warming lowers the relative humidity
(b) Air forced to rise is warmed by the adiabatic process
(c) Condensation has a drying effect upon the air
(d) No water vapour remains in the descending air.

**32.** The temperature is minimum typically _____.
(a) Just after sunset
(b) Around midnight
(c) About 2:00 to 3:00 am
(d) Just before sunrise

**33.** The following diagram shows the contour pattern of an area. Identify the features labelled A, B and C:

Contours in m

(a) A, B and C represent valleys.

(b) A, B and C represent spurs.

(c) A and C represent valleys and B is a spur.

(d) B is a valley and A and C are spurs.

**34.** Which lawn would need more frequent watering?

(a) One with clayey soil

(b) One with sandy-silty loam soil

(c) One with silty soil

(d) One with sandy soil

**35.** Movement of groundwater is most rapid _____.

(a) Within acquicludes

(b) Beneath streams in valley bottoms

(c) Where the land surface is highest

(d) Where the water table is highest

**36.** Crevasse splays are associated with:

(a) Glaciers

(b) Waterfalls

(c) Natural levees

(d) Moraines

**37.** Which of the following statements about tides is **FALSE?**

(a) Most places on Earth experience two high and two low tides each day

(b) Most places on Earth experience one high tide and one low tide each day

(c) Each month there are two spring tides and two neap tides

(d) The primary body that influences the tides is the Moon

**38.** The following graph shows the daily temperature cycle at a station for two days.

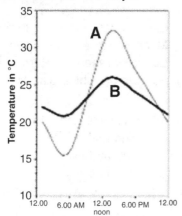

Which of the following statements is correct?

(a) Graphs A and B represent the temperature cycle of an overcast day

(b) Graphs A and B represent the temperature cycle of a clear day

(c) Graph A represents the temperature cycle of a clear day and graph B represents the temperature cycle of an overcast day

(d) Graph A represents the temperature cycle of an overcast day and Graph B represents the temperature cycle of a clear day

**39.** Which of the following criteria is **NOT** used to establish marine life zones?

(a) Availability of sunlight

(b) Distance from shore

(c) Seawater depth

(d) Seawater salinity

**40.** Adiabatic cooling occurs when a parcel of air:

(a) Rises without exchanging heat with the surroundings

(b) Rises on exchanging heat with the surroundings

(c) Rises from equator to poles

(d) Rises from ground to mountain top

**41.** Psychrometer is an instrument to measure:

(a) Rainfall          (b) Humidity

(c) Pressure          (d) Wind direction

**42.** Albedo is the fraction of:

(a) Greenhouse gas in the atmosphere

(b) Moisture content of the atmosphere

(c) Radiation reflected by the earth

(d) Momentum received by the atmosphere

**43.** Which of the following is not a tropical storm?

(a) Cyclone          (b) Hurricane

(c) Typhoon          (d) Tornado

**44.** Radiation fog occurs during a _____.

(a) Long night with clear sky

(b) Long night with cloudy sky

(c) Long day with clear sky

(d) Long day with cloudy sky

**45.** Dynes/cm² is the unit of _____.

(a) Force          (b) Acceleration

(c) Momentum          (d) Pressure

**46.** A northerly wind means a _____.

(a) Wind coming from the north

(b) Wind going towards the north

(c) Wind in the northern hemisphere

(d) Wind in northern India

**47.** The most abundant gas in the atmosphere is _____.

(a) Oxygen          (b) Hydrogen

(c) Nitrogen          (d) Carbon dioxide

48. The temperature of a dry air parcel at a hill top is 30 °C. If the adiabatic lapse rate of dry air is 1 °C/100 m, what will be the temperature of the air at 1 km height from the top of the hill?
    (a) 20 °C    (b) 25 °C
    (c) 30 °C    (d) 40 °C

49. For a black body radiation, which of the following relations is correct? (E is the energy and T the temperature).
    (a) E directly proportional to T
    (b) E directly proportional to $T^2$
    (c) E directly proportional to $T^3$
    (d) E directly proportional to $T^4$

50. Troposphere is that part of the atmosphere where temperature _____.
    (a) Increases with height
    (b) Increases with height in the day but decreases with height in the night
    (c) Decreases with height
    (d) Remain constant

51. Trade winds occur in the _____.
    (a) Polar region
    (b) Tropical region
    (c) Extra-tropical region
    (d) Southern Ocean

52. Isobaric surface refers to a surface of equal _____.
    (a) Humidity    (b) Temperature
    (c) Pressure    (d) Wind

53. To track the movement of cyclone we need _____.
    (a) An aircraft with meteorological sensors
    (b) A polar orbiting satellite
    (c) A lunar orbiting satellite
    (d) A geostationary satellite

54. An anemometer is used for measuring _____.
    (a) Humidity    (b) Rainfall
    (c) Wind    (d) Radiation

55. Which of the following states receives northeast monsoon rainfall?
    (a) Goa    (b) Maharashtra
    (c) Karnataka    (d) Tamil Nadu

56. El Nino refers to _____.
    (a) Cooling of the eastern Pacific Ocean
    (b) Warming of the eastern Pacific Ocean
    (c) Warming of the western Pacific Ocean
    (d) Warming of the Indian Ocean

57. Which of the following is **NOT** associated with global warming?

(a) Melting of polar ice caps
(b) Increase in $CO_2$ concentration;
(c) Acid rain
(d) Sea level rise

58. Depletion of ozone in the atmosphere will lead to _____.
    (a) Increase in atmospheric temperature
    (b) Decrease in atmospheric temperature
    (c) Increase in the earth's UV radiation
    (d) Decrease in the earth's UV radiation

59. During precipitation, the atmosphere _____.
    (a) Gains heat through sensible heat
    (b) Loses heat through sensible heat
    (c) Gains heat through latent heat
    (d) Loses heat through latent heat

60. With increasing depth the ocean temperature _____.
    (a) Increases
    (b) Decreases
    (c) Remains constant
    (d) First increases and then decreases

61. The speed of sound in the oceans is close to _____.
    (a) 1.5 m/s    (b) 15 m/s
    (c) 150 m/s    (d) 1500 m/s

62. Tides in the ocean are the result of balance of force between
    (a) Gravitational force and centrifugal force
    (b) Gravitational force and centripetal force
    (c) Gravitational force and frictional force
    (d) Gravitational force and buoyancy force

63. Neap tide occurs when the _____.
    (a) Earth is between the Sun and the Moon
    (b) Moon is between the Earth and the Sun
    (c) Sun is between the Earth and the Moon
    (d) Earth is at right angles to the Sun and the Moon

64. A semi-diurnal tide refers to _____.
    (a) One high and one low water in a month
    (b) Two high and two low waters in a month
    (c) One high and one low water in 24 hours
    (d) Two high and two low waters in 24 hours

65. In the oceans, the concentration of oxygen is highest in _____.
    (a) Bottom water
    (b) Intermediate water
    (c) Surface water
    (d) Sediment

66. Remote sensing the sea surface height makes use of _____.
    (a) An altimeter      (b) A scatterometer
    (c) A radiometer      (d) A current meter

67. Which of the following equipment can be used to determine the depth of the ocean?
    (a) Radar             (b) Sonar
    (c) Magnetometer      (d) Echosounder

68. When rain adds fresh water to the ocean, the surface density
    (a) Increases
    (b) Decreases
    (c) Remains constant
    (d) Initially increases but ultimately decreases

69. Which of the following processes will **NOT** change the salinity of ocean water?
    (a) Sensible heat loss
    (b) Wind-mixing
    (c) Evaporation
    (d) Precipitation

70. Thermohaline circulation is driven by _____.
    (a) Heat flux        (b) Fresh water flux
    (c) Momentum flux    (d) Density

71. A geostrophic current is a balance between _____.
    (a) Pressure gradient force and frictional force
    (b) Pressure gradient force and coriolis force
    (c) Pressure gradient force and centripetal force
    (d) Pressure gradient force and centrifugal force

72. Which of the following is **INCORRECT** about tsunami?
    (a) Occurs only in the ocean
    (b) Very long wave length
    (c) Very high amplitude in the open ocean
    (d) Is propagated very fast

73. With increasing ocean water depth, light intensity _____.
    (a) Diminishes exponentially
    (b) Diminishes linearly
    (c) Diminishes quadratically
    (d) Remains constant

74. Sound speed in the oceans does not depend on _____.
    (a) Temperature      (b) Salinity
    (c) Pressure         (d) Suspended sediment

75. Which of the following **DOES NOT** form a part of the hydrological cycle?
    (a) Evaporation      (b) Precipitation
    (c) Mixing           (d) River run off

76. When the ocean water is green, it contains a large amount of _____.
    (a) Suspended matter
    (b) Phytoplankton
    (c) Zooplankton
    (d) Bacteria

77. Knowing the sea water density and height, pressure can be calculated using _____.
    (a) Continuity equation
    (b) Conservation of mass equation
    (c) Hydrostatic equation
    (d) Conservation of energy equation

78. Which of the following travels a long distance in the oceans without much attenuation?
    (a) Microwave        (b) Acoustic wave
    (c) Gamma-ray        (d) X-ray

79. Planet Venus cannot be seen at mid-night in Bangalore's sky because:
    (a) Venus is very faint when it is away from the Sun
    (b) Venus is an inner planet of the solar system
    (c) Venus is in 'new moon' phase at midnight
    (d) Venus is hidden behind the moon late at night

80. A block of silver of 107g weight is kept in contact with a 1000 W power source in an otherwise completely isolated system. How long will it take for the silver to melt starting from 0 $^\circ$C? (Melting point of silver is 960 $^\circ$C; its specific heat is 25 J/mol C; Molecular weight is 107 g/mole; 1 Watt sec = 1 Joule)
    (a) 1 sec            (b) 12 sec
    (c) 24 sec           (d) 960 min

81. Calculate the angular size of India at the centre of the earth in an east – west direction.
    (a) 19.5°            (b) 14.5°
    (c) 20°              (d) 29°

82. In a sudden release of pressure, a volcano throws up a 1 tonne cubical stone (each side measuring 1 m) 1 km into the atmosphere. What was the pressure inside the volcano just when it exploded?
    (a) 105 N            (b) 107 N
    (c) 109 N            (d) 1011 N

83. A person looking at the sky at sunset sees a pattern of stars setting in the sky. At a later date, he notices that the same set of stars are now rising at sunset. What is the time difference between the two observations?
    (a) 14 days          (b) 88 days
    (c) 182 days         (d) 274 days

84. Two observatories on earth about 6000 km apart claim to have seen the *Chandrayaan* (which is still circling the moon) to be occulting two different stars at the same time. What is the angular separation of the stars, assuming them to be at infinity?
   (a) 0.5°
   (b) 0.05°
   (c) 0.005°
   (d) 0.0°

85. A hole is dug through the centre of the earth and a ball is thrown in. What is the expected behaviour exhibited by the ball?
   (a) It will fall to the centre of the earth
   (b) It will oscillate from surface to surface
   (c) It will come out at the other end and stay there
   (d) The problem is not fully defined

86. India's first moon mission, *Chandrayaan* 1, found that we can get 0.2 litre of water from 5 tons of soil. What is the total useful volume of water collected over an area of 1 km² on the Moon assuming that this dampness penetrates up to 1m and further assuming a lunar soil density of 5 g/cc?
   (a) $5 \times 10^4$ litres
   (b) $5 \times 10^5$ litres
   (c) $2 \times 10^4$ litres
   (d) $2 \times 10^4$ litres

87. Rajesh weighing 100 kg and Iqbal weighing 50 kg climb up the Mount Everest (9000 m) and return to find that their weights are still the same. Calculate the *minimum* difference in the energy consumed by Rajesh and Iqbal.
   (a) $4.5 \times 10^3$
   (b) $4.5 \times 10^4$
   (c) $4.5 \times 10^5$
   (d) $4.5 \times 10^6$

88. In the next Moon Mission, it is planned to take a seismograph to record quakes on the moon. If the mission is successful, then a quake on the moon can be recorded using a seismograph installed _____.
   (a) At the space station on the earth
   (b) On board the satellite orbiting the moon
   (c) On the moon
   (d) On the moon, the orbiting satellite and the earth

89. Earthquakes are caused due to sudden displacement along a fault zone, releasing energy. In the diagram below which is the most stressed block?

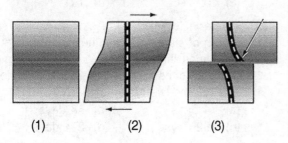

(1)          (2)          (3)

(a) 1 and 3
(b) 2 only
(c) 3 only
(d) 1 and 2

Study the diagram below and answer the following questions.

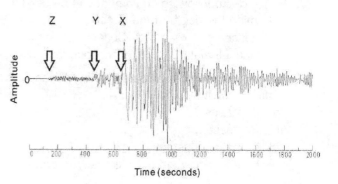

Time (seconds)

90. Study the diagram below and answer the following questions.
   Which is the shear wave in the above diagram?
   (a) X
   (b) Z
   (c) Y
   (d) None

91. The fastest waves recorded on the seismogram will have the largest amplitude.
   (a) False
   (b) True
   (c) Both
   (d) None

92. Sometimes you hear sounds when an earthquake occurs. If there was vacuum on the surface of the earth, can you hear the sound?
   (a) Yes
   (b) Yes, if close to the earthquake epicentre
   (c) No
   (d) Not defined

93. Which of the following earthquakes will cause a tsunami?
   (a) Magnitude 8.7 in Himalaya
   (b) Magnitude 8.6 in Shillong
   (c) Magnitude 8.2 in Burma
   (d) Magnitude 7.5 in Java

94. Where do you find island arcs?
   (a) The Himalaya
   (b) The Alps
   (c) Japan
   (d) Not defined

95. What is the epicentre of an earthquake?
   (a) Place of origin of the earthquake inside the earth
   (b) A point on the fault on which the earthquake occurs
   (c) A point on the surface of the earth
   (d) Place at which the earthquake is recorded

**96.** Which law defines the relationship between stress and strain?
(a) Boyle's law
(b) Snell's law
(c) Hooke's law
(d) Kepler's law

**97.** Primary (P) waves and Love (L) waves are:
(a) Body waves
(b) Surface waves
(c) Body and surface waves
(d) Shear waves

**98.** _____ waves cannot travel through fluids.
(a) P waves
(b) S waves
(c) Sound waves
(d) Fluids waves

**99.** The main greenhouse gas is _____.
(a) CFC
(b) $CO_2$
(c) N
(d) Ar

**100.** Dissolved salt can be removed by _____.
(a) Using a sieve
(b) Using UV light;
(c) Using water jets
(d) Using reverse osmosis

# ANSWERS

| 1 | 2 | 3 | 4 | 5 | 6 | 7 | 8 | 9 | 10 |
|---|---|---|---|---|---|---|---|---|---|
| (c) | (c) | (a) | (a) | (c) | (a) | (b) | (b) | (b) | (b) |
| 11 | 12 | 13 | 14 | 15 | 16 | 17 | 18 | 19 | 20 |
| (d) | (a) | (c) | (d) | (b) | (d) | (b) | (b) | (a) | (c) |
| 21 | 22 | 23 | 24 | 25 | 26 | 27 | 28 | 29 | 30 |
| (a) | (b) | (d) | (a) | (b) | (c) | (a) | (c) | (c) | (c) |
| 31 | 32 | 33 | 34 | 35 | 36 | 37 | 38 | 39 | 40 |
| (a) | (d) | (c) | (d) | (b) | (c) | (b) | (c) | (d) | (a) |
| 41 | 42 | 43 | 44 | 45 | 46 | 47 | 48 | 49 | 50 |
| (b) | (c) | (d) | (a) | (d) | (a) | (c) | (a) | (d) | (c) |
| 51 | 52 | 53 | 54 | 55 | 56 | 57 | 58 | 59 | 60 |
| (b) | (c) | (d) | (c) | (d) | (b) | (c) | (c) | (c) | (b) |
| 61 | 62 | 63 | 64 | 65 | 66 | 67 | 68 | 69 | 70 |
| (d) | (b) | (d) | (b) | (c) | (a) | (d) | (b) | (a) | (d) |
| 71 | 72 | 73 | 74 | 75 | 76 | 77 | 78 | 79 | 80 |
| (b) | (c) | (a) | (d) | (c) | (b) | (c) | (b) | (b) | (c) |
| 81 | 82 | 83 | 84 | 85 | 86 | 87 | 88 | 89 | 90 |
| (d) | (b) | (c) | (a) | (b) | (d) | (c) | (c) | (b) | (c) |
| 91 | 92 | 93 | 94 | 95 | 96 | 97 | 98 | 99 | 100 |
| (a) | (c) | (d) | (c) | (c) | (c) | (c) | (b) | (b) | (d) |

# HINTS AND SOLUTIONS

**1. Age of the Earth:** Scientists have not found a way to determine the exact age of the Earth directly from Earth rocks because Earth's oldest rocks have been recycled and destroyed by the process of plate tectonics. If there are any of Earth's primordial rocks left in their original state, they have not yet been found. Nevertheless, scientists have been able to determine the probable age of the Solar System and to calculate an age for the Earth by assuming that the Earth and the rest of the solid bodies in the Solar System formed at the same time and are, therefore, of the same age. The ages of Earth and Moon rocks and of meteorites are measured by the decay of long-lived radioactive isotopes of elements that occur naturally in rocks and minerals and that decay with half lives of 700 million to more than 100 billion years to stable isotopes of other elements. These dating techniques, which are firmly grounded in physics and are known collectively as radiometric dating, are used to measure the last time that the rock being dated was either melted or disturbed sufficiently to rehomogenize its radioactive elements.

2011 IESO (PP)–22

Ancient rocks exceeding 3.5 billion years in age are found on all of Earth's continents. The oldest rocks on Earth found so far are the Acasta Gneisses in northwestern Canada near Great Slave Lake (4.03 Ga) and the Isua Supracrustal rocks in West Greenland (3.7 to 3.8 Ga), but well-studied rocks nearly as old are also found in the Minnesota River Valley and northern Michigan (3.5-3.7 billion years), in Swaziland (3.4-3.5 billion years), and in Western Australia (3.4-3.6 billion years).

2. **Different Elements:** Elements in the earth's interior.

| Different layers of the earth | Elements |
|---|---|
| Crust | O > Si > Al > Fe > Ca > Mg > Na |
| Lithosphere | O > Si > Al > Fe > Ca > Mg > Na |
| Atmosphere | $N_2$ > $O_2$ > Ar > $CO_2$ |

3. **Different Elements in Interior of Earth:**

| Different Layers of the Earth | Elements |
|---|---|
| Crust | O > Si > Al > Fe > Ca > Na |
| Lithosphere | O > Si > Al > Fe > Ca > Na |
| Atmosphere | $N_2$ > $O_2$ > Ar > $CO_2$ |
| Earth | Fe > O > Si > Mg |
| Universe | H > He > O |

4. **"Fool's gold":** "Fool's Gold" is technically known as pyrite or iron sulfide ($FeS_2$) and is one of the most common sulfide minerals. Sulfide minerals are a group of inorganic compounds containing sulfur and one or more elements. Minerals are defined by their chemistry and crystalline structure. Minerals that have the same chemical composition but different crystal structures are called polymorphs. Pyrite and marcasite, for example, are polymorphs because they are both iron sulfide, but each has a distinct structure. Minerals can also have the same crystalline structure but different elemental compositions, but it's the crystal structure that determines the mineral's physical characteristics.

In addition to pyrite, common sulfides are chalco-pyrite (copper iron sulfide), pentlandite (nickel iron sulfide), and galena (lead sulfide). The sulfide class also includes the selenides, the tellurides, the arsenides, the antimonides, the bismuthinides, and the sulfosalts. Many sulfides are economically important as metal ores.

5. **Emery Powder:** A natural occurring odorless mineral having its broadest use as an abrasive in polishing applications. An intimate mix of corundum and magnetite. The higher amounts of impurities and weaker internal structure than naturally occurring minerals has restricted its growth in new applications. It is brownish-black or dark gray in colour. It is the hardest mineral after diamond, making it the second hardest mineral with a mohs hardness value of about 9. Chemical Formula: $Al_2O_3$ + an iron bearing mineral + trace impurities such as mullite, titania, silica, and magnesia.

6. **Different Process:**

| Different Processes | Remarks |
|---|---|
| Weathering | Disintegration and decompositions of the rocks due to naural agencies is called weathering. Chemical, Physical and Biological weathering. |
| Denudation | The combined effect of the weathering and erosion is called denudation. |
| Erosion | Process by removal of the soils/rocks from earth's crust. |

7. **Minerals with Example:**

| Minerals group | Example |
|---|---|
| Quartz | Quartz, tridymite, cristobalite, coesite |
| Feldspar | Orthoclase, albite, anorthite |
| Clay minerals | Kaolinite, Illite |
| Carbonates | Calcite, aragonite |

8. **Rocks with Mode of Occurrence:**

| Rocks | Depth | Particle size | Example |
|---|---|---|---|
| Volcanic | Surface on the earth | Fine | Basalt |
| Hypabyssal | Intermediate depth | Medium | Dolerite |
| Plutonic | Depth in the earth | Coarse | Gabbro |

9. **Raw Material for Manufacturing Steel:** The ores used in making iron and steel are iron oxides, which are compounds of iron and oxygen. The major iron oxide ores are hematite, which is the most plentiful, limonite, also called brown ore, taconite, and magnetite, a black ore. Magnetite is named for its magnetic property and has the highest iron content. Taconite, named for the Taconic Mountains in the northeastern United States, is a low-grade, but important ore, which contains both magnetite and hematite.

Ironmaking furnaces require at least a 50% iron content ore for efficient operation. Also, the cost of shipping iron ores from the mine to the smelter can be greatly reduced if the unwanted rock and other impurities can be removed prior to shipment. This requires that the ores undergo several processes called "beneficiation." These processes include crushing, screening, tumbling, floatation, and magnetic separation. The refined ore is enriched to over 60% iron by these processes and is often formed into pellets before shipping. Taconite ore powder, after beneficiation, is mixed with coal dust and a binder and rolled into small balls in a drum pelletizer where it is then baked to hardness. About two tons of unwanted material is removed for each ton of taconite pellets shipped.

10. **Raw Material for Manufacturing Cement:** If you happen to be a geologist, the raw materials quarry is probably the most interesting part of a cement works, maybe unless you view the clinkering process as igneous rocks in the making.

The most common raw rock types used in cement production are:

- Limestone (supplies the bulk of the lime)
- Clay, marl or shale (supplies the bulk of the silica, alumina and ferric oxide)
- Other supplementary materials such as sand, fly ash/pulverised fuel ash (PFA), or ironstone to achieve the desired bulk composition

**Raw Materials for Cement Manufacture:** The first step in the manufacture of portland cement is to combine a variety of raw ingredients so that the resulting cement will have the desired chemical composition. These ingredients are ground into small particles to make them more reactive, blended together, and then the resulting raw mix is fed into a cement kiln which heats them to extremely high temperatures.

Examples of raw materials for Portland cement manufacture.

| Calcium | Silicon | Aluminum | Iron |
|---|---|---|---|
| Limestone | Clay | Clay | Clay |
| Marl | Marl | Shale | Iron ore |
| Calcite | Sand | Fly ash | Mill scale |
| Aragonite | Shale | Aluminum ore refuse | Shale |
| Shale | Fly ash | | Blast furnace dust |
| Sea Shells | Rice hull ash | | |
| Cement kiln dust | Slag | | |

12. **Cooling and its Grain Size**

| Types of Cooling | Grain size | Example |
|---|---|---|
| Slow cooling | Coarse grain | Granite |
| Fast cooling | Fine grain | Basalt |

13. **Condition for Formation of Sedimentary Rocks:** Sedimentary rock is one of the three main rock groups (along with igneous and metamorphic rocks) and is formed in four main ways: by the deposition of the weathered remains of other rocks (known as 'clastic' sedimentary rocks); by the accumulation and the consolidation of sediments; by the deposition of the results of biogenic activity; and by precipitation from solution. Sedimentary rocks include common types such as chalk, limestone, sandstone, clay and shale. Sedimentary rocks cover 75% of the Earth's surface. Four basic processes are involved in the formation of a clastic sedimentary rock: weathering (erosion) caused mainly by friction of waves, transportation where the sediment is carried along by a current, deposition and compaction where the sediment is squashed together to form a rock of this kind.

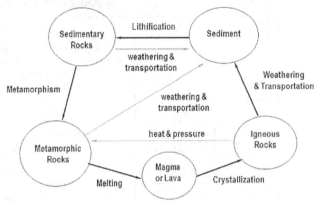

14. **Agents of Metamorphism:** THREE AGENTS OF METAMORPHISM AND THEIR EFFECTS

Recall that any rock can be changed to a metamorphic rock. Whatever the beginning rock is, it is called the ***PROTOLITH*** of the metamorphic rock it is transformed into. Three things contribute in varying proportions to the transformation from a protolith to a metamorphic rock: heat, pressure, and fluids (mostly water with dissolved ions).

- Heat
- Pressure
- Fluids

17. **Classification of Sedimentary Rocks:** Sedimentary rocks are rocks composed of sediment. Sediment is deposited in a number of environments of deposition, by both moving air and moving water. Sedimentary rock identification is primarily based on composition. Texture will still be used

but in a different sense than for igneous rocks.

- **Texture:** Texture of sedimentary rocks in this lab will be taken to indicate origin or type of sediment found in the rock. Three types of "texture" will be used - clastic, chemical, and biologic.
- **Clastic Rocks:** Clastic sedimentary rocks contain clasts. These are fragments or pieces of rock or minerals. The composition of clastic sedimentary rocks is divided into three types - clay/silt, sand and gravel. Clay and silt are less than 1/16 mm. These are not visible to the unaided eye. Sand is clasts between 1/16 and 2 mm in size, and gravel is greater than 2 mm.
- **Chemical Rocks:** Chemical sedimentary rocks are identified by identifying the mineral from which they are composed. In this lab there are four minerals that need to be identified—quartz, halite, gypsum and calcite. Quartz has a hardness of 7 and is very difficult to scratch, even with a good quality knife blade. Gypsum is relatively soft (Hardness =2) and

can be scratched easily with a fingernail. Halite is common table salt and is most easily identified by taste. However, this is not a sensible practice in a large lab with many different people handling the samples. Halite has a hardness of 2.5 and cannot be scratched by a fingernail (un-polished fingernail). Calcite readily reacts with a small drop of HCl.

- **Biologic Rocks:** Biologic sedimentary rocks are formed as the result of the accumu-lation of organic material or biologic activity. Coal is usually obvious to most students even though few people seem to have ever actually examined it up close. The dark brown to black colour is the most obvious charateristic. Coquina and limestone are both composed of calcite. Coquina is composed almost entirely of shell or fossil fragments. Lime-stone may or may not contain fossils fragments. Both will react to HCl. Lime-stone containing fossils is referred to as fossiliferous limestone.

**Sedimentary Rock Identification Chart**

| TEXTURE | GRAIN SIZE | COMPOSITION | ROCK NAME |
|---------|-----------|-------------|-----------|
| Clastic | >2 mm | Rounded quartz, feldspar and rock fragments | Conglomerate |
| | >2 mm | Angular quartz, feldspar and rock fragments | Breccia |
| | 1/16 - 2 mm | Quartz, feldspar | Sandstone |
| | >1/16 mm | Feldspar, quartz | Arkose |
| | <1/16 mm | Quartz, clay minerals | Siltstone (Mudstone, Shale) |
| | <1/256 mm | Quartz, clay minerals | Claystone |
| Chemical | | Silica (quartz) | Chert |
| | | Dolomite | Dolostone |
| | | Calcite | Limestone |
| | | Halite | Rock Salt |
| | | Gypsum | Rock Gypsum |
| Biologic | | Silica (quartz) | Chert |
| | | Loosely compacted organic material and plant fragments | Peat |
| | | Densely compacted organic material and plant fragments | Bituminous Coal |
| | | Calcite | Limestone |
| | | Calcite, micro-skeletal fragments | Chalk |
| | | Calcite, almost entirely shell and skeletal fragments | Coquina |
| | | Calcite with some shell and skeletal fragments | Fossiliferous Limestone |
| | | Dolomite with some shell and skeletal fragments | Fossiliferous Dolostone |

## 18. Coals Deposits in India through Geological Records:

**Important coal field of Gondwana**

| Coal fields | State |
|---|---|
| Raniganj, Bankura | West Bengal |
| Jharia, Giridih, Bokaro, Daltonganj, Karanpur, Ramgarh | Jharkhand |
| Talcher, Rampur Hingir (Sambalpur dist) | Orissa (Lower Gondawa) |
| Singareni, Kamavaram | A.P |
| Umaria, Singrauli, Korba, Chirmiri, Sohagpur, Bisrampur, Mohapani | M.P |
| Kota, Chikiyala, Rajur, Bandar | Maharashtra |
| Ghunkeri | Gujarat |

**Important Coal Field of Tertiary**

| Coal fields | State |
|---|---|
| Jarain, Charogaon, Umasor, Karaibari, Tura, Sogring | Assam |
| Ladda, Kalkoth, Methkha | Jammu & Kashmir |
| Palana (Bikaner) | Rajasthan |
| Neyvalley, Cuddalore | Tamil Nadu |
| Varkala, Quilon | Kerala |
| Umarsar in Kutch | Gujarat |

## 19. Geological records of origin of life:

| Era | Periods | Remarks (Life development through geological time) |
|---|---|---|
| **Cenozoic** | Quaternary | Appearance of man |
| | Tertiary | Rise of modern mammals and birds |
| **Mesozoic** | Cretaceous | Extinction of dinosaurs and other reptile group |
| | Jurassic | Domination by giant reptiles; Beginning of birds and mammals |
| | Triassic | Beginning of dominance of reptiles |
| **Paleozoic** | Permian | Extinction of the many invertebrate groups and primitive type plants |
| | Pennsylvanian | Many coal forests of spore bearing plants; First reptiles |
| | Mississippian | Abundant spore bearing plants |
| | Devonian | First amphibians; Numerous marine fishes |
| | Silurian | First land plants; First land animals |
| | Ordovocian | First indication of vertibrates (fishes) |
| | Cambrian | Invertibrates numerous and varied; Trilobite |
| **Precambrian** | | Bacteria, algae and a few primitive invertebrates |

## 20. Classification of sedimentary Rocks on Grain Size:

| Name of Rock | Texture | Sedimentary type |
|---|---|---|
| Conglomerate | Course (>2 mm | Rounded fragment |
| Breccia | Course (>2 mm | Angular fragment |
| Sandstone | Medium (1/16 to 2 mm) | Sandstone |
| Siltstone | Fine (1/256 to 1/16 mm) | Mud |
| Shale | Very fine (less than 1/256) | Shale |

## 28. Drainage Pattern and Its Features:

| Drainage Pattern | Remarks |
|---|---|
| Dendritic pattern | Irregular branching tributaries with main stream |
| Parallel pattern | Tributaries with main stream flow in same (Parallel) pattern. |
| Trellis pattern | This type of pattern develop in the folded structures like folded, faulted, joints. |
| Radial pattern | It is developed with dome/basin like a central points. |

### 35. Hydrological Terms with Example:

| Terms | Remarks | Example |
|---|---|---|
| Aquifer | A medium which have porous with permeable | Sandy formation |
| Aquiclude | Porous but not permeable | Clay bed |
| Aquitard | Porous but less permeable | Sandy clay |
| Aquifuge | Neither porous nor permeable | Solid granite |

### 36. Geomorphological features:

| Features | Characteristics |
|---|---|
| Glaciers | Cover of the Ice-sheet. |
| Waterfalls | Erosional feature of the rivers. |
| Natural levees | Parallel depositional to the river. |
| Moraines | Unstratified deposits of the glaciers. |

### 39. Life Zone in Sea:

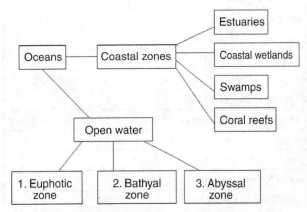

| Zone | Organisms of each Ocean life zone |
|---|---|
| Intertidal | Hermit crab, sea star, mussels, sea urchin, barnacles |
| Neritic | Loggerhead sea turtle, mackerel, cod, kelp, bottlenose, dolphin |
| Benthic | Sea urchins, sea cucumbers, crustaceans, squid, octopus |
| Bathyal | Jellies, crustaceans, sperm whales |
| Abyssal | Deep sea Anglerfish, giant squid, tripod fish |

### 41. Instruments and its uses:

| Measurements | Instruments |
|---|---|
| Rainfall | A **rain** gauge (also known as an udometer, pluviometer, or an ombrometer) is an instrumen used by meteorologists and hydrologists to gather and measure the amount of liquid precipitation over a set period of time. |

| Humidity | Hygrometer |
|---|---|
| Pressure | Barometer |
| Wind direction | Anemometer |

### 45. Terms with Units:

| Terms | Units |
|---|---|
| Force | Newton |
| Acceleration | Meter per second squared (m/Sec$^2$) |
| Momentum | kilogram meters per second (kg. m/s) |
| Pressure | Pascal (Pa), defined as a force of one Newton per square-meter. |

### 47. Composition of Atmosphere: Composition of the atmosphere is as follow:

- The atmosphere is made up of different gases, water vapour and dust particles.
- The composition of the atmosphere is not static and it changes according to the time and place.

**Gases of the Atmosphere**

**Permanent gases of the Atmosphere**

| Constituent | Per cent by Volume | Concentration in Parts Per Million (PPM) |
|---|---|---|
| $N_2$ | 78.084 | 780,840.0 |
| $O_2$ | 20.946 | 209,460.0 |
| Ar | 0.934 | 9,340.0 |
| $CO_2$ | 0.036 | 360.0 |
| Ne | 0.00182 | 18.2 |
| He | 0.000524 | 5.24 |
| Kr | 0.000114 | 1.14 |
| $H_2$ | 0.00005 | 0.5 |

- The atmosphere is a mixture of different types of gases.
- Nitrogen and oxygen are the two main gases in the atmosphere and 99 percentage of the atmosphere is made up of these two gases.
- Other gases like argon, carbon dioxide, neon, helium, hydrogen, etc. form the remaining part of the atmosphere.
- The portion of the gases changes in the higher layers of the atmosphere in such a way that oxygen will be almost negligible quantity at the heights of 120 km.

- Similarly, carbon dioxide (and water vapour) is found only up to 90 km from the surface of the earth.

**51. Trade Wind:** In the Northern Hemisphere, warm air around the equator rises and flows north toward the pole. As the air moves away from the equator, the Coriolis effect deflects it toward the right. It cools and descends near 30 degrees North latitude. The descending air blows from the northeast to the southwest, back toward the equator (Ross, 1995). A similar wind pattern occurs in the Southern Hemisphere; these winds blow from the southeast toward the northwest and descend near 30 degrees South latitude.

These prevailing winds, known as the trade winds, meet at the Intertropical Convergence Zone (also called the doldrums) between 5 degrees North and 5 degrees South latitude, where the winds are calm. The remaining air (air that does not descend at 30 degrees North or South latitude) continues toward the poles and is known as the westerly winds, or westerlies. The trade winds are so named because ships have historically taken advantage of them to aid their journies between Europe and the Americas (Bowditch, 1995).

**57. Causes of Global Warming:** Global warming is primarily a problem of too much carbon dioxide ($CO_2$) in the atmosphere—which acts as a blanket, trapping heat and warming the planet. As we burn fossil fuels like coal, oil and natural gas for energy or cut down and burn forests to create pastures and plantations, carbon accumulates and over-loads our atmosphere. Certain waste management and agricultural practices aggravate the problem by releasing other potent global warming gases, such as methane and nitrous oxide. See the pie chart for a breakdown of heat-trapping global warming emissions by economic sector.

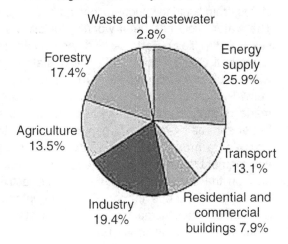

**63. Classification of Tides:** We will use two classi-fications to define the tide types. The first of them is the value awarded to the height of the tide and is the one reflected in the tide tables. The second is the lunar phase and is directly related to the average activity of fish in the solunar charts.

***According to the height of the tide***

- **High tide**: When the sea water reaches its greatest height within the tide cycle. They are shown in blue on the tide tables.
- **Low tide**: When the sea water reaches its lowest height within the tide cycle. They are shown in red on the tide tables.

Normally there are two high tides and two low tides for every lunar day as, at the same time as the Moon lifts the water over the Earth on the side facing it, it also separates the Earth from the water on the opposite side. The result is that the water lifts over the terrestrial surface on the two diametrically opposite sides of the planet.

**67. Equipment and its uses:**

| Equipment | Uses |
|---|---|
| Radar | Location or distance of the objects |
| Sonar | Sonar is a commonly used technique for communica-tion, detection of objects, and navigation in sea. |
| Magnetometer | A magnetometer is an instr-ument that measures mag-netism—either the magne-tization of a magnetic material like a ferromagnet, or the direction, strength, or relative change of a magnetic field at a particular location. |

**71. Geostrophic Currents:** Geostrophic currents, are the surface currents caused by the variability of sea surface elevation. Due to the difference in surface elevation there is a horizontal pressure gradient and subsequently a current (water) flow from areas with higher elevation to areas with lower elevation. Due to the large scale of geostrophic current coriolis is important and the current direction is such that a balance between pressure gradient and coriolis force is possible.

**73. Light Intensity in Ocean Water:** Visible radiation, or light, from the Sun is important to the world's ocean systems for several reasons. It provides the energy necessary for ocean currents and wind-driven waves. Conversion of some of that energy into heat helps form the thin layer of warm water near the ocean's surface that supports the majority of marine life. Most significantly, the transmission of light in sea water is essential to the productivity of the oceans. Visible wavelengths of light are captured by chlorophyll-bearing marine plants, which then make their own food through the process of **photosynthesis**. The organic molecules created by this process are an important energy source for many small organisms that are the base of the entire marine **food chain.** All life in the oceans is ultimately dependent upon the light and the process of photosynthesis that it initiates. Similarly, light transmission is a key factor in the **ecology** of lakes and streams, which are discussed elsewhere in this encyclopedia.

The ocean is divided into three zones based on depth and light level.

- Sunlight entering the water may travel about 1,000 meters (3,280 feet) into the ocean under the right conditions, but there is rarely any significant light beyond 200 meters (656 feet).

- The ocean is divided into three zones based on depth and light level. The upper 200 meters (656 feet) of the ocean is called the euphotic, or "sunlight," zone. This zone contains the vast majority of commercial fisheries and is home to many protected marine mammals and sea turtles. Only a small amount of light penetrates beyond this depth.

- The aphotic, or "midnight," zone exists in depths below 1,000 meters (3,280 feet). Sunlight does not penetrate to these depths and the zone is bathed in darkness. 'Photic' is a derivative of 'photon,' the word for a particle of light.

74. **Sound speed in ocean:** The speed of sound depends on the medium through which sound waves propagate. The speed of sound differs in air and water, with sound waves travelling faster in water. For example, in air at a temperature of 18°C (64°F), the speed of sound is approximately 341 meters (1,120 feet) per second. In contrast, in salt water at approximately the same temperature, the speed of sound is approximately 1,524 meters (5,000 feet) per second.

The state properties of water (temperature and pressure) and the degree of salinity also affect the speed of sound. The propagation of sound waves in sea water can be directly affected by suspensions of particulate matter that can scatter, absorb, or reflect the waves. Sound travels about 1500 meters per second in seawater. Sound travels much more slowly in air, at about 340 meters per second.

Here are the basic profiles of temperature, salinity and pressure for a mid-latitude location in the deep ocean.

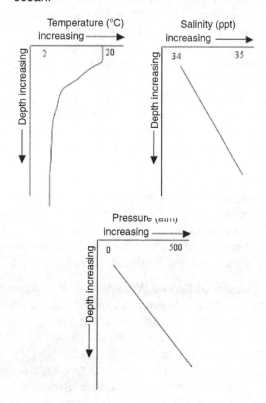

75. **Hydrological Cycle:** What is the water cycle? I can easily answer that—it is "me" all over! The water cycle describes the existence and movement of water on, in, and above the Earth. Earth's water is always in movement and is always changing states, from liquid to vapour to ice and back again. The water cycle has been working for billions of years and all life on Earth depends on it continuing to work; the Earth would be a pretty stale place without it. Where does all the Earth's water come from? Primordial Earth was an incandescent globe made of magma, but all magmas contain water. Water set free by magma began to cool down the Earth's atmosphere, and eventually the environment became cool enough so water could stay on the surface as a liquid. Volcanic activity kept and still keeps introducing water into the atmosphere, thus increasing the surface-water and groundwater volume of the Earth.

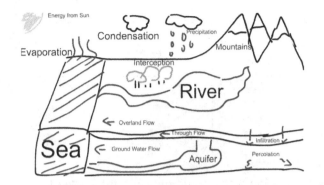

**90. Moving Pattern of Seismic Waves:** Earthquakes occur along a fracture in the Earth's crust where one side moves relative to the other. The location where Earthquakes originate is called the **focus**. Energy is released and travels through the Earth in the form of **seismic waves**. Seismic waves generate two types of wave motions: Body waves and surface waves. Body waves move through the interior of the Earth and are made up of P waves (red concentric) and S waves (white concentric lines). Body waves depart the point of origin at the same time, but P waves travel faster than S waves. P waves, also called *primary waves*, are **compressional waves** that arrive at distant locations first and have a push-pull type motion. S waves, also known as secondary waves, are **shear waves** that arrive after P waves and have a side-to-side motion. The **epicenter** is the surface location directly above the focus. **Surface waves** (yellow concentric lines) travel slower than body waves and along the surface of the Earth generating two types of waves: Love waves and Rayleigh waves. **Love waves** move side-to-side at right angles to the propagation direction. **Rayleigh waves** move in a circular pattern with the crest (highest point) moving up and forward and the trough (lowest point) moving down and backwards. Surface waves attenuate where they are strongest near the epicenter and dissipate as you move farther away.

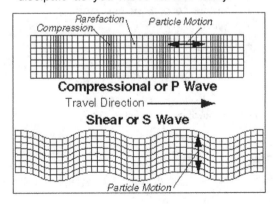

**93. Causes of Tsunamis:** What causes a tsunami?... A tsunami is a large ocean wave that is caused by sudden motion on the ocean floor. This sudden motion could be an earthquake, a powerful volcanic eruption, or an underwater landslide. The impact of a large meteorite could also cause a tsunami. Tsunamis travel across the open ocean at great speeds and build into large deadly waves in the shallow water of a shoreline.

**94. Formation of Island Arc:** Island arcs are volcanic islands that form parallel to ocean trenches in subduction zones. The Pacific Ring of Fire is home to many of these groups of islands. Volcanoes that form above hot spots like the Hawaiian islands are not volcanic arcs. There are two ways in which a group of islands can form.

1) As a lithospheric slab is being subducted, the slab melts when the edges reach a depth which is sufficiently hot. Hot, remelted material from the subducting slab rises and leaks into the crust, forming a series of volcanoes. These volcanoes can make a chain of islands called an "island arc". Examples of island arcs are the Japanese islands, the Kuril Islands, and the Aleutian Islands of Alaska.

2) The second way in which islands are formed is via plumes or hot spots in the lithosphere. The Hawaiian Islands are an example of this type of island formation. In this case, there is no associated subducting slab.

**95. Epicentre of Earthquake:** Earthquakes can cause huge amounts of death and destruction. For this reason, understanding them is vitally important. Like all major events, seismic or otherwise, they have to start somewhere. The **epicenter** is the place on the Earth's surface under which they start.

**Location of the Epicenter:** There are two important locations in any earthquake. The most important is the **hypocenter**, or focus of the earthquake. This is the point where the earthquake truly begins, deep under the ground and located at a tectonic plate boundary, the border between two of the fragments the Earth's crust is broken into. It is where the plate boundary begins to rupture.

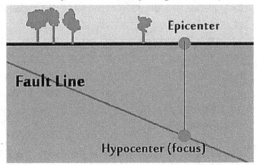

**96. Boyle's Law:** According to Boyle's Law, the pressure (P) of a given mass of gas is inversely proportional to its volume (V), provided that the temperature of the gas remains constant.

For an enclosed gas, at constant temperature (T);

$$P \alpha \frac{1}{V}$$

or,    P × V = constant

*i.e.;*   $P_1V_1 = P_2V_2$

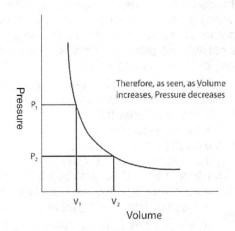

Therefore, as seen, as Volume increases, Pressure decreases

The quill tube is helpful in verifying Boyle's law.

Since the volume of gas inside the tube(V) = cross sectional area of the tube($a$) × length of air column(l),

V = $a$ × *l*

So, P × *l* = constant

**Learning outcomes**

- Students learn about the properties of gases and their relationships.
- Students understand Boyles law and its applications.
- Students understand the relation between pressure and volume of a given mass of the gas.

**Snell's Law:** When light travels from one medium to another, it generally bends, or *refracts*. The law of refraction gives us a way of predicting the amount of bend. This law is more complicated than that for reflection, but an understanding of refraction will be necessary for our future discussion of lenses and their applications. The law of refraction is also known as Snell's Law, named for Willobrord Snell, who discovered the law in 1621.

Snell's Law is given in the following diagram.

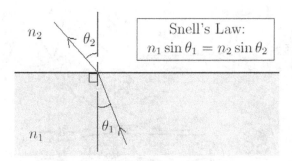

As in reflection, we measure the angles from the normal to the surface, at the point of contact. The constants *n* are the indices of refraction for the corresponding media.

Tables of refractive indices for many substances have been compiled.

***n*** **for Light of Wavelength 600 nm**

| Substance | Refractive Index, *n* |
|---|---|
| Air (1 atmosphere pressure, 0 degrees C) | 1.00029 |
| Water (20 degrees C) | 1.33 |
| Crown Glass | 1.52 |
| Flint Glass | 1.66 |

**97. Classification of Seismic Waves:** When you look at a seismogram the wiggles you see are an indication that the ground is being, or was, vibrated by seismic waves. Seismic waves are propagating vibrations that carry energy from the source of the shaking outward in all directions. You can picture this concept by recalling the circular waves that spread over the surface of a pond when a stone is thrown into the water. An earthquake is a more complicated process than a stone splashing into water, and the seismic waves that are set up during an earthquake are more varied than those on the pond. There are many different seismic waves, but all of basically of four types:

- Compressional or P (for primary)
- Transverse or S (for secondary)
- Love
- Rayleigh

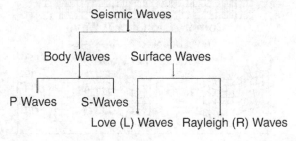

## 99. Greenhouse Gases:

| Greenhouse Gases | Chemical Formula | Sources |
|---|---|---|
| Carbon Dioxide | $CO_2$ | Fossils fuel combustion |
| Methane | $CH_4$ | Fossils fuels, Waste dumps |
| Nitrous Oxide | $N_2O$ | Fertilizer |
| Tropospheric Ozone | $O_3$ | Industrial emissions, Fossils fuel |
| CFC-12 | $CCl_2F_2$ | Liquid coolants, Foams |
| HCFC-22 | $CCl_2F_2$ | Refrigerants |
| Sulphur Hexafluoride | $SF_6$ | Dielectric fluid |

### Greenhouse Gases

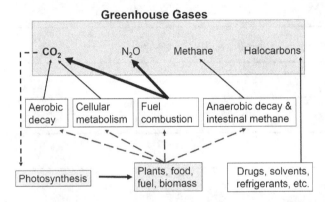

## 100. Process of removal of dissolved salt: Desalination/distillation is one of mankind's earliest forms of water treatment, and it is still a popular treatment solution throughout the world today. In ancient times, many civilizations used this process on their ships to convert sea water into drinking water. Today, desalination plants are used to convert sea water to drinking water on ships and in many arid regions of the world, and to treat water in other areas that is fouled by natural and unnatural contaminants. Distillation is perhaps the one water treatment technology that most completely reduces the widest range of drinking water contaminants.

In nature, this basic process is responsible for the water cycle. The sun supplies energy that causes water to evaporate from surface sources such as lakes, oceans, and streams. The water vapour eventually comes in contact with cooler air, where it re-condenses to form dew or rain. This process can be imitated artificially and more rapidly than in nature, using alternative sources of heating and cooling. Some desalination facts:

- It is estimated that some 30% of the world's irrigated areas suffer from salinity problems and remediation is seen to be very costly.
- In 2002 there were about 12,500 desalination plants around the world in 120 countries. They produce some 14 million cubic meters/day of freshwater, which is less than 1% of total world consumption.
- The most important users of desalinated water are in the Middle East, (mainly Saudi Arabia, Kuwait, the United Arab Emirates, Qatar and Bahrain), which uses about 70% of worldwide capacity; and in North Africa (mainly Libya and Algeria), which uses about 6% of worldwide capacity.

Among industrialized countries, the United States is one of the most important users of desalinated water, especially in California and parts of Florida. The cost of desalination has kept desalination from being used more often.

YOUR SPACE

# International Earth Science Olympiad(IESO)

# Study Material with MCQs

# CHAPTER 1

# GEOSPHERE

## Minerals

Mineral is defined as natural occurring substances, solid with fixed chemical composition and general atomic structure. Our earth's crust made a different mineral with varying colour, form, size, hardness, specific gravity and composition.

**Example:** Quartz, feldspar, mica, olivine, pyroxene, amphibole.

| Mineral name | Chemical formula | Uses |
|---|---|---|
| Halite | NaCl | Rock salt |
| Gold | Au | Gold jewellery |
| Chalcopyrite | $CuFeS_2$ | Copper ore |
| Barite | $BaSO_4$ | Drilling mud |
| Bauxite | $Al_2O_3$ | Aluminium ore |
| Magnetite | $Fe_3O_4$ | Iron ore |
| Uraninite | $UO_2$ | Uranium ore |
| Diamond | C | Gemstone |

**Table:** Different minerals with chemical composition

## Properties of Minerals

Minerals are physical and optical behaviour with respect to its own characteristics. Here we discuss physical properties of the minerals.

- ❏ Crystal form
- ❏ Fracture or cleavage
- ❏ Colour
- ❏ Density
- ❏ Hardness
- ❏ Lustre
- ❏ Streak

## Elements in the Earth's Crust

The earth is made up of different layers, the outer layer is called crust. The crust is composed of mainly oxygen, silicon, aluminium, iron, calcium, sodium, potassium. The elements concentration percentage is given below:

| Element name | Symbol | Percentage by weight of the Earth's crust |
|---|---|---|
| Oxygen | O | 47 |
| Silicon | Si | 28 |
| Aluminium | Al | 8 |
| Iron | Fe | 5 |
| Calcium | Ca | 3.5 |
| Sodium | Na | 3 |
| Potassium | K | 2.5 |
| Magnesium | Mg | 2 |
| All other elements | —— | 1 |

## Rocks and Its Classification

Our earth is made up of the different rocks types which show different behaviour on physical, chemical and biological parameters. The component of the crust is Sial (Continental crust) and Sima (Oceanic crust) which is consists of the granitic and basaltic rocks respectively. The main minerals in the sial are silica and alumina and the silica, iron and magnesium in the sima. Finally all rocks mainly classified in three major groups:

- ❏ Igneous rocks
- ❏ Sedimentary rocks
- ❏ Metamorphic rocks

**Igneous rocks:** Igneous rock is a primary rocks formed by the cooling and solidification of the magma. When the hot molten materials come on the surface and crystallize then igneous rocks formed. Fossils and sedimentary strata absent in the igneous rock. The classification of the igneous rocks is based on the colour, texture, silica composition, size etc.

The classification of the igneous rocks based on the origin:

1. **Plutonic rocks:** These igneous rocks formed in depth, these are also called intrusive rocks which show course grain.

   Example: Granite, gabbro, diorite

2. **Volcanic rocks:** The molten materials solidify on the earth's surfaTe those are also called the extrusive rocks. The volcanic rocks fine grain.

   Example: Rhayolite, basalt

**Sedimentary Rocks:** Sedimentary rocks are secondary rocks which formed due to sediments settling. The fragments (Sediments/particles) are transported by agencies and deposited in low level area. The different deposited materials converted into the sedimentary rocks by lithification (Soft sediments converted into hard material) processes. The sedimentary rocks are identified by the thickness of the strata, colours, grain size etc. Sedimentary rocks is a house of the fossils.

The classification of the mode of formation the sedimentary rocks are classified into three categories.

1. **Mechanically formed sedimentary rocks:** The sedimentary rocks formed by the mechanical process.

   **Example:** Sandstone, conglomerate, shale, loess, breccia.

2. **Organically formed sedimentary rocks:** These sedimentary rocks formed by the organisms such as corals, shellfish and other living organisms.

   **Example:** Chalk, geyserite, limestone, carbonaceous rocks.

3. **Chemically formed sedimentary rocks:** Such rocks formed by the precipitation of the chemically active fluids or solutions.

   **Example:** Rock salts, chert, potash, nitrates.

**Metamorphic Rocks:** The term metamorphic defined as (Meta- change, Morph- shape/form) "change of form". The rocks which are igneous or sedimentary change to metamorphic by pressure, temperature or chemically active fluids. Their original character changed due to forces which developed by earth movements. Some examples are given below:

| Before metamorphism | After metamorphism |
|---|---|
| Clay | Slate |
| Limestone | Marble |
| Sandstone | Quartzite |
| Granite | Gneiss |
| Shale | Schist |
| Coal | Graphite |
| Carbon | Diamond |

## Rock Cycle

The Rock Cycle is a group of changes. Igneous rock can change into sedimentary rock or into metamorphic rock. Sedimentary rock can change into metamorphic rock or into igneous rock. Metamorphic rock can change into igneous or sedimentary rock.

**Rock Cycle in Earth's Crust**

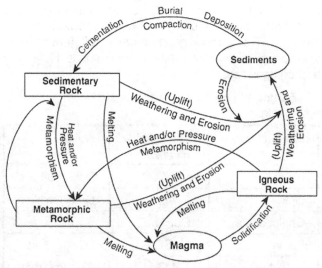

## Important Terminology related to Rock Cycle

❏ **Cementation**: The process by which clastic sediment is lithified by precipitation of mineral cement, such as calcite cement, among the grains of the sediment.

❏ **Compaction:** It is the processes by which tighter packing of sedimentary grains causing weak lithification and a decrease in porosity, usually from the weight of overlying sediment.

❏ **Deposition:** The settling of materials out of a transporting medium in low level area. Basin is the best suitable place for the deposition.

❏ **Erosion:** The processes that loosen sediment and move it from one place to another on Earth's surface by natural agencies. Agents of erosion include water, ice, wind, and gravity.

❑ **Lithification:** The processes by which soft sediment is converted into (hard) sedimentary rock. These processes include cementation and compaction.

❑ **Magma:** Molten rock, generally silicate melt with suspended crystals and dissolved gases. The medium is solid, liquid and gases.

❑ **Melting:** To go from a solid state to a liquid state (solid to liquid).

❑ **Metamorphism:** Alteration of the minerals and textures of a rock by changes in temperature and pressure, and/or by a gain or loss of chemical components.

❑ **Pressure:** The force per unit of area exerted upon something, such as on a surface.

❑ **Sediment:** Material/particles (such as gravel, sand, mud, and lime) that is transported and deposited by natural agencies (wind, water, ice, or gravity); material that is precipitated from solution; deposits of organic origin (such as coal and coral reefs).

❑ **Transportation:** The processes that carry sediment or other materials away from their point of origin. Transporting media include/natural agencies like wind, water and mantle convection currents.

❑ **Uplift:** A structurally high area in the crust, produced by movements that raise the rocks, as in a broad dome or arch.

❑ **Weathering:** The processes by which rocks are chemically altered or physically broken into fragments as a result of exposure to atmospheric agents and the pressures and temperatures at or near Earth's surface, with little or no transportation of the loosened or altered materials.

## PRINCIPAL OF STRATIGRAPHY

Stratigraphy is the study of strata (sedimentary layers) in the Earth's crust (depositional sequence). There are different principles to study the stratigraphic column. **Stratigraphic Laws** are basic principles that all geologists use in deciphering the spatial and temporal relationships of rock layers. These laws were developed in the 17th to 19th centuries based upon the work of Niels Steno, James Hutton and William Smith, among others. Stratigraphic principal include the following:

1. **Principal of Uniformitarianism**
2. **Principal of Original Horizontality**
3. **Principal of Lateral Continuity**
4. **Principal of Superposition**
5. **Principal of Cross-Cutting Relations**
6. **Principal of Inclusions**
7. **Principal of Faunal Succession**

## Geological Time Scale

The age of the earth to the present.

**Geologic Time Scale**

| Eon | Era | Period | Epoch | Age(my) |
|---|---|---|---|---|
| Phanerozoic (Visible Life) | Cenozoic (Recent Life) (Age of Mammals) | Quaternary | Holocene | 0.01 |
| | | | Pleistocene | 1.8 |
| | | Tertiary | Pliocene | 5.3 |
| | | | Miocene | 23.0 |
| | | | Oligocene | 33.9 |
| | | | Eocene | 55.8 |
| | | | Paleocene | 65.5 |
| | Mesozoic (Middle Life) (Age of Reptiles) | Cretaceous | | 145 |
| | | Jurassic | | 200 |
| | | Triassiac | | 251 |
| | Paleozoic (Ancient Life) | Permian | | 299 |
| | | Pennsylvanian | | 318 |
| | | Mississippian | | 359 |
| | | Devonian | | 416 |
| | | Silurian | | 444 |
| | | Ordovician | | 488 |
| | | Cambrian | | 542 |
| Proterozoic (Early Life) | | | Oldest Known Life | 2500 |
| Archean | | | Oldest Known Rocks | 3800 |
| Hadean | | | Age of the Earth | 4600 |

The Eras are divided into Periods. The Periods are often named after specific localities.

### The Palaeozoic Era has the following Periods:

- Cambrian
- Ordovician (first vertebrate organisms - fish)
- Silurian (first land plants)
- Devonian (first amphibians)
- Carboniferous (in the U.S. this is further divided into: Mississippian and Pennsylvanian (first reptiles)).
- Permian

### The Mesozoic Era has the following Periods:

- Triassic (first dinosaurs)
- Jurassic
- Cretaceous (first mammals. ended with extinction of dinosaurs).

**The Cenozoic Era has the following Periods:**

- Tertiary        • Quaternary

Further subdivisions of Periods are called Epochs. Only Epochs of the Cenozoic Era are shown in the Chart.

## Stratigraphic Classification

Criteria for classification; Classification based on the different properties.

- Lithology
- Fossiliferous / unfossiliferous
- Sequence
- Magnetic property
- Seismic property
- Isotope study

**Chronostratigraphy :** The element of stratigraphy that deals with the relative time relations and ages of rock bodies.

**Chronostratigraphic classification :** The organization of rocks into units on the basis of their age or time of origin.

**Chronostratigraphic unit :** A body of rocks that includes all rocks formed during a specific interval of geologic time, and only those rocks formed during that time span. Chronostratigraphic units are bounded by synchronous horizons.

**Chronostratigraphic horizon (Chronohorizon):** A stratigraphic surface or interface that is synchronous, everywhere of the same age.

| Chronostratigraphic Units | Geochronologic Units |
|---|---|
| Eonothem | Eon |
| Erathem | Era |
| System | Period |
| Series | Epoch |
| Stage | Age |
| Substage | Age / subage |

## SEDIMENTARY STRUCTURES

A structure seen in the sedimentary rocks formed at the time of the deposition in a particular environment. Stratification, laminations, ripples marks, current bedding, mud cracks are example of the sedimentary structures. These structures are very important for the depositional environments.

## Graded Bedding

The gradation of the sediments, sediment loaded currents (turbity currents) experience a relatively quick drop in velocity causing the sediment to deposit. The heavy sediments settle first than lighter materials then vertical beds formed. In the normal condition the fine grain particles at the top and coarse grain on bottom.

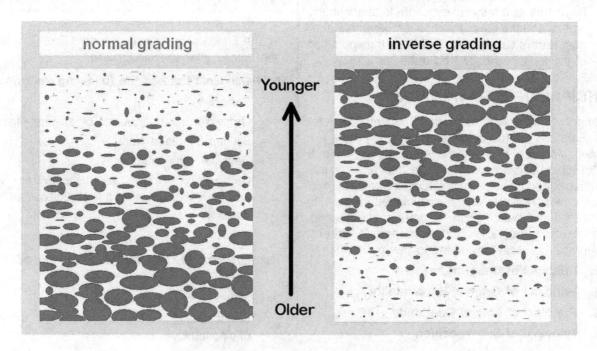

# Cross-bedding

Cross bedding forms when sediment come to rest at an angle and can form anywhere fluids, such as wind or water, carry sediment. The individual beds form as sediment moves up and over the windward or upstream side a ripple or dune and then become deposited on the downstream side. Small-scale cross bedding creates ripple marks. These structures are common on stream beds and on beach and lake shores.

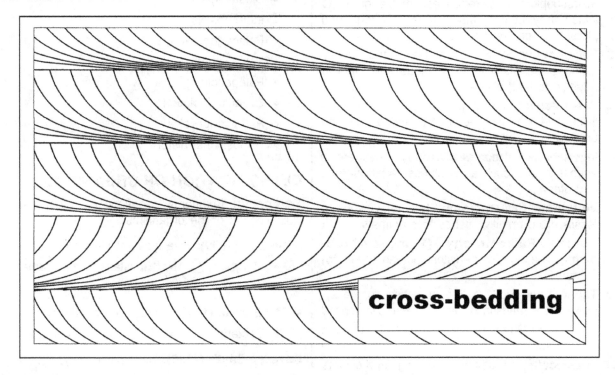

## Ripple marks

Ripple marks form in two forms—symmetric, or wave formed ripples and asymmetric, or current ripples. Wave-formed ripple form from the to-and-fro motion of waves and have a symmetrical profile. Current ripple marks form in response to water or wind currents flowing in one direction and have asymmetric profiles. The asymmetric profiles allow geologists to determine paleocurrent directions, in other words, which direction the wind or water was flowing from when the cross beds were deposited. This is possible due to the fact the longer side of the ripple always faces the upstream direction.

## Mud crack

This is another type of the sedimentary structures. These structures form when the clay-rich sediments found in muds dry and shrink. As the sediment shrinks crack begin to form in the sediment creating polygonal patterns called mud cracks. Over time these cracks become filled with other sediments which preserve the polygonal pattern formed by the cracking sediment. Mud cracks form in any environment that allows for the wetting and

subsequent drying of sediment such as playa lakes, marshes, seasonal rivers, or lake shores.

*Mud cracks*

**Biogenic Sedimentary Structures:** Some sedimentary structures formed by the action of the living organisms which is called biogenic sedimentary structures. Biogenic structures like tracks, burrows, trails etc.

## What is Palaeontology?

Palaeontology is the study of the history of life. A person who study palaeontology called palaeontologist. The main aim of palaeontologist to identify fossils and its origin as well as environments of that time when fossilization process done. Also reconstruct the past life with respect to the fossils evolution. Palaeontology is traditionally divided into various subdisciplines:

❏ **Micropaleontology:** Study of generally microscopic fossils, regardless of the group to which they belong, calcareous, siliceous and phosphatic composition.

❏ **Paleobotany:** Study of fossil plants; traditionally includes the study of fossil algae and fungi in addition to land plants.

❏ **Palynology:** Study of pollen and spores, both living and fossil, produced by land plants and protists.

❏ **Invertebrate Palaeontology:** Study of invertebrate animal fossils, such as molluscs, echinoderms, and others.

❏ **Vertebrate Paleontology:** Study of vertebrate fossils, from primitive fishes to mammals.

❏ **Human Paleontology (Palaeoanthropology):** The study of prehistoric human and proto-human fossils.

❏ **Taphonomy:** Study of the processes of decay, preservation, and the formation of fossils in general.

❏ **Ichnology:** Study of fossil tracks, trails, and footprints.

❏ **Paleoecology:** Study of the ecology and climate of the past, as revealed both by fossils and by other methods.

## What is Fossil?

Fossils defined as remains of plants and animals which is preserved in geological history. There are two main types of fossils, body fossils and trace fossils. Body fossils are the preserved remains of a plant or animal's body. Trace fossils are the remains of the activity of an animal, such as preserved trackways, footprints, fossilized egg shells, and nests.

### Conditions of fossils
- Hard parts
- Immediate burial

### Types of fossils
- Body fossils
- Trace fossils
- Derived fossils
- Living fossils
- Pseudo fossils
- Chemical fossils
- Remanie fossils
- Facies fossils

### Application of fossils

The application of fossils in different geological and geographical fields.

- Study of Chronostratigraphy
- Biostratigraphy
- Index fossils
- Palaeogeography
- Paleoclimate
- Paleoecology
- Organic evolution
- Paleogeophysics
- Depositional history

## CLASSIFICATION OF ORGANISMS

**Taxonomy:** Taxonomy is defined as the systematics classification of the organisms.

**Whittaker (1969):** Five types of kingdom.
- Monera
- Protista
- Plantae
- Fungi
- Animalia

**WOESE et al. (1990):** Three type of Kingdom
- Bacteria
- Archaea
- Eucarya

**Cavalier–Smith (1998):** Six type of kingdom.
- Bacteria
- Protozoa
- Chromista
- Plantae
- Fungi
- Animalia

## Species

The fundamental unit of the taxonomy is called species.

### Types of species
- Holotype
- Syntype
- Paratype
- Lectotype
- Neotype
- Topotype
- Metatype

## Classification of Homo sapiens

| Kingdom | Animalia |
|---|---|
| Phylum | Chordata |
| Subphylum | Vertebrata |
| Class | Mammalia |
| Order | Primate |
| Family | Hominidae |
| Genus | Homo |
| Species | Homo sapiens |

# PLATE TECTONICS AND ITS APPLICATION

The theory of plate tectonics was advanced in the 1960s and 1970s to generate new information about the Earth's history like ancient magnetism, the nature of the ocean floor, the flow of heat from the Earth's interior, and earthquake and volcanic distribution with the main aim of explaining how the earth's processes works. Plate tectonics deals the movement of the Earth's lithosphere plates that formed large and small plates. By definition the word "plate" in geologic terms means a large slab of solid rock. "Tectonics" is a part of the Greek root for "to build" and together the terms define how the Earth's surface is built up of moving plates. In other word, the theory of plate tectonics itself says that the Earth's lithosphere is made up of individual plates that are broken down into over a dozen large and small pieces of solid rock.

**According to Wikipedia**: "*Plate tectonics (from the Late Latin tectonicus, from the Greek:* TEKTOVIKOC *"pertaining to building") is a scientific theory describing the large-scale motion of Earth's lithosphere. The theoretical model builds on the concept of continental drift developed during the first few decades of the 20th century. The geoscientific community accepted plate-tectonic theory after seafloor spreading was validated in the late 1950s and early 1960s.*"

The Mechanism of plate tectonics :

- The Earth's surface is covered by a series of crustal plates.
- The ocean floors are continually moving, spreading from the center, sinking at the edges, and being regenerated.
- Convection currents beneath the plates move the crustal plates in different directions.
- The source of heat driving the convection currents is radioactivity deep in the Earth's mantle.

**Principles of Plate Tectonics**: There are various basic principles underlying the theory of plate tectonics. The fundamental principles include: main pillar of the plate motion.

- Plates
- Wilson cycle
- Convection
- Lithosphere and the asthenosphere
- Plate tectonic boundaries

**The Lithosphere and Asthenosphere**: The outer constitute the earth's outermost layer, the crust and the upper mantle. The lithosphere plate is predominantly solid consisting of dense rock made up of nickel and iron in the form of silicate rocks. The asthenosphere plate is mostly plastic like fluid due to its nature of high viscosity and mechanical weakness. The differences in these two sub-layers of the earth's crust are because of their mechanical properties, temperature, and the manner of heat transfer.

**Plates**: This is the principle stating that the Earth's outer shell is composed of several different hard and rigid plates including the North American, African, Eurasian, Antarctic, Pacific, South American, and Australian plates. There are also several minor plates such as Nazca, Arabian and the Philippines plates. These plates are conceived to be in constant motion.

**Wilson Cycle**: The Wilson cycle illustrates the lifecycles of oceans and continents. Particularly, it pertains to the rifting, drifting, and colliding of large continental plates to form a small ocean. Over time, the ocean broadens to form a bigger ocean and drifts the continental plates even further.

**Convection**: Convection is the principle defining the movement of the plates. This means, the movement of the plates are influenced by convection currents flowing in the heated, plastic asthenosphere layer below the plates. The convection currents arise because of the heat deep within the earth's core.

Due to the heating of the materials in the earth's core, they become less dense and rise up towards the mantle. As it rises higher it cools down and becomes denser then begins to sink. This cycle of heating and the rising and falling of the rock materials within the earth's interior brings about the convection currents.

## Plate Tectonic Boundaries

Boundaries defined as the regions where the plates meet. The tectonic boundaries result from the convection currents that bring about the movement of the plates which are mainly categorized into three including: divergent, convergent, and transform plate boundaries. The plate tectonic boundaries are usually associated with geological activities like volcanoes, earthquakes, and mountains as well as oceanic physical features. There are broadly three types of plate tectonic boundaries namely: Divergent Boundaries, Convergent Boundaries and Transform Boundaries.

**Divergent Boundaries (Ocean ridge)**: The divergent boundaries are formed as a result of the plate pulling apart of each other. Typically, it takes place when the plates move away in opposite directions. Along the boundaries, it is common to find geysers spurting superheated water or lava spews. The process widens the giant basins and renews the ocean floor. Occurrences such as earthquakes and volcanic activities are frequent along the divergent boundaries (rift). The

Great Rift Valley in Africa where plates pull apart is an example of a divergent boundary on land.

**Convergent Boundaries (Subduction zones)**: The convergent boundaries are formed as a result of the plates crashing together. The resultant impact at the time when the two plates collide ends up forming a rugged mountain range and at times the edge of one or both plates bends the other down into a deep seafloor trench. The Mariana Trench in the North Pacific Ocean is an example of a deep seafloor trench. A series of volcanoes frequently occurs parallel to the boundary and the trench. Also, strong earthquake waves covering a wide area are experienced on both sides of the boundary. Whenever oceanic crust tops one of the colliding plates, it sinks down the mantle where it starts to melt due to the high temperatures. This occurrence is known as subduction. Magma over onto the other plate and solidifies into new crust as granite. Hence, continental crust made of granite is created at convergent boundaries while the oceanic crust is destroyed.

**Transform Boundaries**: Divergent boundaries are formed due the effects of the plates sideswiping or sliding past each other. During the occurrence of divergent boundaries, artificial and natural structures within the edges of the plates are torn into pieces and carried in opposite directions.

The rocks within the boundary are completely destroyed as the plates sideswipe against each other, forming an undersea canyon or a linear fault valley. Also, as the plates slide past each other coupled with the jumping and jamming, strong earthquakes shake through an extensive boundary zone. No magma is ejected in divergent boundaries thus the crust is simply broken and cracked at the transformed margins but not destroyed or created. In this view, transform boundaries don't produce striking features like oceans or mountains but often triggers far-reaching earthquakes. An example of transform boundary is the San Andreas Fault in California.

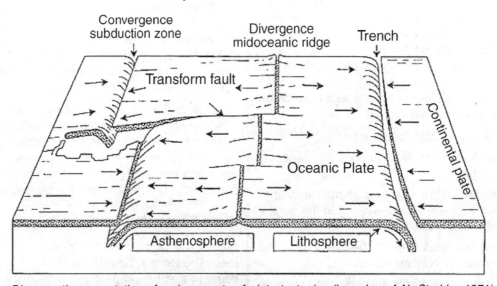

*Diagramatic presentation of main aspects of plate tectonics (based on A.N. Strahler 1971).*

## Rate of Plate Movement

The plate movement is the very interesting in the field of the earthquakes. Determine the plate movement by help of normal and reverse magnetic field with plate direction. The modern concept well accepted the movement of the plate in a particular direction. Some plates move less than 10 cm/year and some more than 10 cm/year by the convection cell mechanism. The Indian plate with Peninsular India and Australian continental portion subduction along the Himalayas forms the northern plate boundary in the form of continent – continent convergence.

**Example:** The Arctic Ridge has the slowest rate and the East Pacific is the fastest. The theory of the continental drift and sea floor spreading supports the dynamic motion of the plate.

### Application of Plate Tectonics

Study of the plate tectonics can help the following:

- Geological history of the area
- Plate direction
- Mineral resources
- Evolution of the ocean and continents
- Earthquakes, volcanoes
- Mountain building processes
- Minerals deposits

# What is Deformation?

Deformation of rock involves changes in the shape and/ or volume of these substances. Changes in shape and volume occur when stress and strain causes rock to buckle and fracture or crumple into folds. Stress is a force acting on a material that produces a strain. Stress is a force applied over an area and therefore has units of Force/area (like $lb/in^2$). Pressure is a stress where the forces act equally from all directions. If stress is not equal from all direction then stress is a differential stress. Three types of stress as follow:

- Tensional stress (extensional stress): Which stretches rocks when stress apply
- Compressional stress: Which squeezes rocks when compress stress develop
- Shear stress: Which result in slippage and translation due to the shear

When rocks deform they are said to *strain*. A strain is a change in size, shape, or volume of a material. We here modify that definition somewhat to say that a strain also includes any kind of movement of the material, including translation and tilting.

## Stage of Deformation

When stress apply a particular environment three stage deformation passes.

- ❏ **Elastic deformation:** In this type of deformation the strain is reversible.
- ❏ **Ductile deformation:** In this type of deformation the strain is irreversible.
- ❏ **Brittle deformation**: When strain apply the materials breaks.

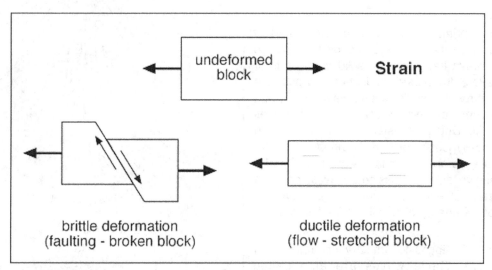

*Fig. Stage of deformation with example*

How a material behaves will depend on several factors :

- Temperature
- Confining rate
- Strain rate
- Composition

# What Is Seismology?

Seismology is the study of earthquakes and seismic waves that move through and around the earth. A seismologist is a scientist who studies earthquakes and seismic waves. Seismology is the study of the passage of *seismic* waves through the earth. Earthquake seismology is the best tool to study the interior of the earth. When an earthquake or explosion occurs, part of the energy released is as seismic waves that are transmitted in the earth. The waves are then detected and recorded by seismograms, which measure, amplify and record the motion of the ground. The information is then used to determine earthquake locations, the subsurface structures and etc.

# What are Seismic Waves?

**Seismic waves** are the waves of energy due to the sudden breaking of rock within the earth or an explosion. They are the energy that travels in different medium of the earth and is recorded on seismographs.

**Types of Seismic Waves :** There are several different kinds of seismic waves, and they all move in different ways. The two main types of waves are **body waves** and **surface waves**. Body waves can travel through the earth's inner layers, but surface waves can only move along the surface of the planet like ripples on water. Earthquakes radiate seismic energy as both body and surface waves.

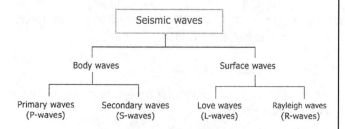

**Body waves:** Body wave is a type of seismic wave which travel through body of the earth by reflected, transmitted with Snell's law fallow. Body waves arrive first than the surface waves emitted by earthquakes. These waves are of a higher frequency than the surface waves. The two different types of body waves are:

## P–Waves

Also called the primary waves, which have fastest seismic waves and the first recorded by the seismic station. The P wave travel through solid rock, fluids or water, liquid layers of the earth. It pushes and pulls the rock it moves through just like sound waves push and pull the air. Sometimes animals can hear the P waves of an earthquake. Dogs, for instance, commonly begin barking hysterically just before an earthquake 'hits' (or more specifically, before the surface waves arrive). P – waves also known as compressional waves, particles move in the same direction that the wave is moving in the direction of the energy, also called "direction of wave propagation".

- ❏ P-Waves (P stands for primary or pressure or push-pull). These waves are also called **longitudinal waves** or compressional waves due to particle compression during their transport.

- ❏ These waves involve compression and rarefaction of the material as the wave passes through it but not rotation.

- ❏ P-wave is transmitted by particle movement back and forth along the direction of propagation of the wave.

- ❏ The most correct description of P-waves is it is a dilational or irrotational waves.

- ❏ P-waves has the greatest speed and appears first on seismograms.

## S–Waves

Secondary wave is a second type of the body wave, which is slower than the P-wave. The S-wave travel only solid medium, not a liquid medium. S - wave that led seismologists to conclude that the Earth's **outer core** is

a liquid. S waves move rock particles up and down, or side-to-side—perpendicular to the direction that the wave is traveling in (the direction of wave propagation).

- ❏ S-Waves (S stands for secondary or shear or shake). Also known as **transverse waves**.

- ❏ Because particle motions are transverse to the direction of movement of the wave front, or perpendicular to the ray.

- ❏ These waves involve shearing and rotation of the material as the wave passes through it, but not volume change.

- ❏ S-waves have speeds less than P-waves, and appear on seismograms after P-waves.

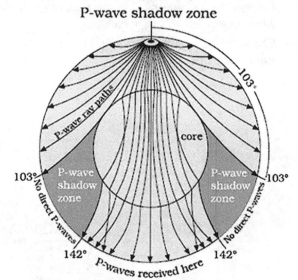

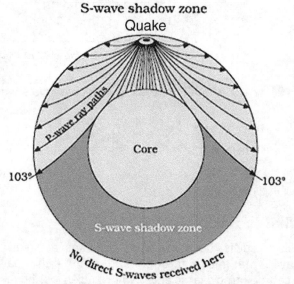

*P and S–waves shadow zone (Courtesy by Stephen Nelson)*

## Surface Waves

Surface waves are seismic waves that are guided along the surface of the Earth and the layers near the surface.

These waves do not penetrate the deep interior of the earth, and are normally generated by shallow earthquakes (nuclear explosions do not generate these surface waves). Surface waves are larger in amplitude and longer in duration than body waves. These waves arrive at seismograph after the arrival of P- and S-waves because of their slower velocities. The two different surface waves are:

## Love Waves

The Love wave is a type of surface wave, named after A.E.H. Love, a British mathematician who worked out the mathematical model for this kind of wave in 1911. This is the fastest surface waves and moves the ground from side to side, confined to the surface of the earth through horizontal motion.

❏ **Love waves** (named for A.E.H. Love, who discovered them) travel by a transverse motion of particles that is parallel to the ground surface. This wave is somewhat similar to S-waves.

❏ Love waves cannot exist in a uniform solid, and can only occur when there is a general increase of S-wave velocity with depth.

❏ Love waves existence is another proof of the Earth's vertical inhomogeneity. The particle motion is transverse and horizontal.

❏ Generally, Love wave velocities are greater than Rayleigh waves, so Love waves arrive before Rayleigh waves on seismograph.

## Rayleigh Waves

This type of surface waves named for the John William Strutt, Lord Rayleigh, mathematically defined waves in 1885. A Rayleigh wave rolls along the ground just like a wave rolls across a lake or an ocean. Because it rolls, it moves the ground up and down, and side-to-side in the same direction that the wave is moving. Most of the shaking felt from an earthquake is due to the Rayleigh wave, which can be much larger than the other waves.

❏ **Rayleigh waves** or descriptively called "ground roll" in exploration seismology.

❏ The particle motion of this wave is confined to a vertical plane containing the direction of propagation and retrogrades elliptically.

❏ The particle displacements are greatest at the surface and decrease exponentially downward.

❏ Rayleigh waves show dispersion, and its velocity is not constant but varies with wavelength. This wave is similar to how ocean waves propagate.

❏ $V_R < V_S$

## Seismic Wave Velocities

The velocities of P- and S-waves are given below in terms of the density ($\rho$) and elastic coefficients of a material:

$$V_p = \sqrt{(K + 4/3\ G)/\rho}$$

$$V_s = \sqrt{(G/\rho)}$$

If we note that the bulk modulus (K) and the rigidity modulus (G) are always positive, then evidently the velocity of P-waves must always be greater than S-waves. Shear waves (S-waves) cannot propagate through liquid. This is evident when we substitute G = 0 for liquids, then the velocity of S-waves goes to zero. This is how it was determined that the outer core consists of liquid.

Some times you will come across the bulk sound velocity: $V_\Phi = \sqrt{(K/\rho)}$.

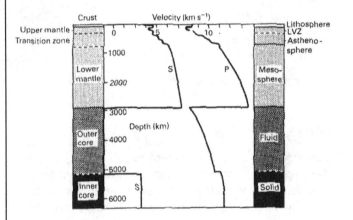

*Fig. Velocity of seismic waves in earth's interior*

## Types of Earthquakes

There are four different types of earthquakes

❏ Tectonic  ❏ Volcanic

❏ Collapse  ❏ Explosion

A **tectonic** earthquake is one that occurs when the earth's crust breaks due to geological forces on rocks and adjoining plates that cause physical and chemical changes.

A **volcanic** earthquake is any earthquake that results from tectonic forces which occur in conjunction with volcanic activity.

A **collapse** earthquake is small earthquakes in underground caverns and mines that are caused by seismic waves produced from the explosion of rock on the surface.

An **explosion** earthquake is an earthquake that is the result of the detonation of a nuclear and/or chemical device.

## Measuring of Earthquakes

An earthquake occurs and energy released in the form of the seismic waves travel in all directions. A point within the earth where the fault rupture starts is a **focus or hypocentre**.

Focus is the exact location within the earth where seismic waves generated. The epicentre is the point on the surface of the earth above the focus.

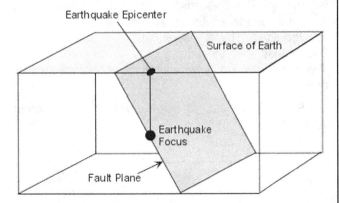

*Fig.: Focus and epicentre of the earthquake (Courtesy by Stephen Nelson)*

## SEISMOGRAPH

Seismograph is an Instrument which record seismic wave, during earthquake, waves through different velocity from focus to the surface of the earth. In an earthquake, vibrations caused by the breakage of rock along a fault zone radiate outward from the point of rupture. The instrument used to record and measure these vibrations is called a seismograph.

Traditional seismographs consisted of a sensing element, called a seismometer, an amplifier, and a hardcopy display unit often using photographic or heat-sensitive paper. The visual record produced by a seismograph is called a seismogram. In modern seismographs, the display is replaced or augmented with a digitizer and either local digitial storage (e.g., removable disks) or a telemetry system using radio, telephone or the Internet to send the digital data stream to a central recording and analysis site.

Modern seismograph can use following aspect:

- Time of the earthquake occurred
- Epicentre location
- Depth of the focus of earthquake
- Amount of the energy from the earthquake
- Destruction intensity

## Measurement of Earthquakes waves

Earthquakes measured in two ways.

- ❏ Intensity
- ❏ Magnitude.

**Intensity:** The intensity of the earthquake defined as in the terms of degree of damage to the surface and its effect losses not actual ground motion or wave amplitude which recorded by instrument. Intensity also helps to effect of earthquake to area destructed; it is not an accurate measure of the earthquake for many reasons. Two such reasons are: only the effect on an area showing the greatest intensity is reported, which can imply a greater or lesser intensity than what actually occurred, and the way in which seismic waves travel varies as they pass through different types of rocks, so some areas nearby may feel nothing because they are built on faulted rock, while other areas quite a distance from the foci will feel the effects because they are built on compact homogenous rocks.

**Magnitude:** Magnitude is a second type of earthquake measurement. Magnitude does not depend on population and effects to ground structures, but rather on wave amplitude and distance. Magnitude is determined using mathematical formulae and information from seismograms. One such magnitude scale is the Richter scale. This magnitude scale is logarithmic, meaning each step in magnitude is exponentially greater than the last.

To determine the Richter magnitude, information collected by seismometers is used. Using a seismogram, the time difference between the recording of the P wave and the S wave is determined and matched to a corresponding distance value. The single maximum amplitude recorded on the seismogram is calculated and a line is drawn between the amplitude scale and the distance scale. The line crosses another scale, which corresponds to the magnitude. While this type of measurement is the most well-known, the Richter scale is not as accurate a measurement as believed.

Effect of earthquakes in different mode as following:

- Damage to buildings
- Damage to infrastructure
- Landslides and rockslides
- Can result in floods
- Earthquakes can trigger tsunamis
- Leads to liquefaction

**Effect of earthquake intensity and magnitude:** The effect of earthquake in its effect to the human to the magnitude as well as intensity is given below.

| Richter Magnitude scale | Effects |
|---|---|
| 0 – 2 | Not felt by people |
| 2 – 3 | Felt by some people |
| 3 – 4 | Ceiling lights swing |
| 4 – 5 | Wall crack |
| 5 – 6 | Furniture moves |
| 6 – 7 | Some building collapse |
| 7 – 8 | Many buildings destroyed |
| More than 8 | Major destruction |

## What is Volcanoes?

A magma flow on the earth surface is called the lava, volcanoes is fissure type which content ash, gases, and rock fragments. When a hot molten material comes from the interior of earth formed different features developed in form of solid, liquid and gases.

**Why volcanoes form:** The magma comes on the surface due to its buoyancy, the hot, viscous and dense materials comes from the deeper earth due to difference in buoyancy. The lighter materials rise on the surface and its density. If the magma contains volatile elements (water and/or gases), when it reaches the surface, these volatiles will suddenly expand into steam and gas, causing a violent eruption. This tends to happen a lot of the magma is more acidic (has a higher silica content); with more basic magmas, there is usually a continuous, steady flow (like in Hawaii).

**Types of volcanoes:** The main three types.

❑ **Strato volcano** (or **composite volcano**): A type of volcano which conical with layers of solid lava flows mixed with layers of the other rock.

❑ **Cinder cone volcano:** In this type of volcano doesn't have any horizontal layers, and is instead a steep conical hill of tephra (volcanic debris) that accumulates around and downwind from the vent.

❑ **Shield volcano**: A type of volcano built entirely or mostly from fluid lava vents. They are named like this because when viewed from above, you can see just how massive and imposing they are – like a warrior's shield.

| Size limits of the grains | Unconsolidated products | Lithified products |
|---|---|---|
| 32 mm plus | Bomb Blocks | Agglomerates Volcanic breccia |
| 4 mm – 32 mm | Lapilli | Lapilli – tuff |
| Less than 4 mm | Ash and dust | Tuff |

## What is geomorphology?

### Definition

(Geo, G. the Earth; Morph, G. Form, ology G. the science of) Geomorphology is the science which study of landscapes. It define the systematic description of the landforms and its process that is responsible for development. Geomorphologist concern about the function of landforms which energy change to the landscape of lithology, structures, process. By the formation of features due to process is called landforms.

## GEOMORPHIC PROCESSES

A combined processes which change the earth surface is called the geomorphic processes, the main natural agencies like fluvial, Aeolian, glacial. Overall we can conclude in two types, exogenous and endogenous processes. The fluvial features like oxbow lake, meanders, delta, natural levee form due to rivers. In the desert area the aeolian process mainly involve in sand dunes and ripple features developed.

### Endogenic processes

Processes that operate from within the earth (Interior of the earth).

❑ **Tectonics processes**

❑ **Volcanism**: Intraplate hotspot activity (lava plateaus and volcanoes) arc volcanism, sea-floor spreading

❑ **Isostacy**

• **Epeirogenic processes**: Regional uplift and subsidence caused by mantle anomalies.

• **Isostastic processes**: Local subsidence and uplift caused by local loading and unloading

### Exogenic processes

These processes operate on the earth surface.

❑ Weathering and erosion

❑ Hydrologic cycle and related fluvial processes

❑ Glaciation

❑ Aeolian activity

❑ Biological activity and man

❑ Waves

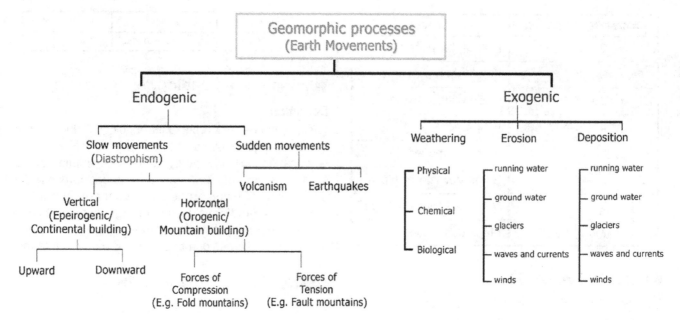

## What is Soil?

The study of soils as naturally occurring phenomena is called pedology, and a person who studies soils (soil scientist) is called a pedologist. Soils are complex mixtures of minerals, water, air, organic matter, and countless organisms that are the decaying remains of once-living things. It forms at the surface of land – it is the "skin of the earth." Soil is capable of supporting plant life and is vital to life on earth.

   **Important of Soils on earth:** There is some application regarding the soils.

   ❑ Soils play role  as media for growth of all kinds of plants on earth surface.

   ❑ Soils also effect the atmospheric conditions on the earth surfaces (absorption, radiation, emission).

   ❑ Soils also effect the habitat to our organisms.

   ❑ Soils serve the human life as dam, tunnel and others industries (engineering works).

## Soil Profile

Soil profile is the order of the soils which deposits in low level area, order of horizons. There are different types of soil, each with its own set of characteristics. Dig down deep into any soil, and you'll see that it is made of layers, or horizons (O, A, E, B, C, R). Put the horizons together, and they form a soil profile. Like a biography, each profile tells a story about the life of a soil. Most soils have three major horizons (A, B, C) and some have an organic horizon (O).

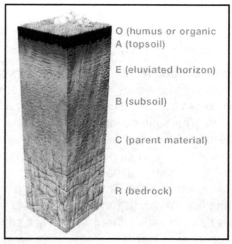

| Profiles | Location | Remarks |
|---|---|---|
| **O** | Humus/ organic materials | Organic materials of leaves, soils etc. |
| **A** | Top soil | Minerals matter from parent materials with organic, plant developed normally |
| **E** | Eluviated | Leached of clay, minerals, and organic matter, leaving a concentration of sand and silt particles of minerals like quart with resistant minerals. |
| **B** | Subsoil | Rich in minerals that leached (moved down) from the A or E horizons and accumulated here. |
| **C** | Parent material | The deposit at Earth's surface from which the soil developed. |
| **R** | Bed rock | A mass of rock such as granite, basalt, quartzite, limestone or sandstone that forms the parent material for some soils – if the bedrock is close enough to the surface to weather. This is not soil and is located under the C horizon. |

# WEATHERING

**Weathering** is the alteration and breakdown of rock minerals and rock masses when they are exposed to the atmosphere due to natural agencies. Weathering processes occur in situ, that is, in the same place, with no major movement of rock materials involved. Weathering is a fundamental Earth process which changes rocks from a hard state, to become much softer and weaker, making them more easily eroded. The type of weathering processes that occur at any particular location depend predominantly upon the climate:

## Type of Weathering Processes

❏ **Physical weathering**: The group of processes, such as frost wedging and volume changes of minerals that result in the mechanical disruption (mechanical disintegration and decompositions) of rocks (e.g. granular disintegration, exfoliation, joint block separation, shattering by changes in temperature or pressure). Physical weathering: mechanical processes dominate in cold and dry climates.

❏ **Chemical weathering**: The decay of rock forming minerals caused by water, temperature, oxygen, hydrogen and mild acids (e.g. solution, hydration, oxidation, carbonation). Disintegration and decompositions of rocks/minerals due to natural agencies in the chemical manner. Chemical weathering: processes of mineral decay dominate in warm and humid climates.

❏ **Biological weathering**: The group of processes that are caused by, or assisted by, the presence of vegetation, or to a lesser extent animals, including root wedging and the production of organic acids. Biological weathering: vegetation, and animals, tends to be more active in warm and humid climates.

**Weathering Controls:** The type, rate and extent of weathering depends upon several controlling factors as follows.

**Climate:** Climate is the main factor which direct effect the weathering processes, in types of physical, chemical and biological processes. The type of weathering processes that operates largely by determining the amount of water available and the temperature at which the processes occur. Chemical reactions are faster at higher temperatures, while frost wedging occurs in colder climates.

**Rock/mineral Type:** Determines the resistance of the rock to the weathering processes that operate in that particular environment. Each rock type is composed of a particular set of minerals, which are joined together by crystallisation, chemical bonding or cementing. When the forces of plate tectonics move these rocks from the environment in which they formed and expose them to the atmosphere they begin to weather.

- **Rock Structure**: Highly jointed or faulted rocks present many planes of weakness along which weathering agents (e.g. water) can penetrate into the rock mass.

- **Topography**: The slope angle determines the energy of the weathering system by controlling the rate at which water passes through the rock mass. Generally, higher, or tectonically active areas with steeper slopes have more dynamic weathering systems, whereas flat plains have slower weathering systems.

- **Erosion:** The dynamism and efficiency of erosion determines how rapidly any weathered material is removed, how frequently fresh rock is exposed to weathering, and if deeply weathered profiles are preserved.

**Time:** The duration of the period that the same type of weathering has been operating, uninterrupted by climatic change, earth movements, and other factors, determines the degree and depth to which the rocks have been weathered.

Drainage system: The main type of drainage pattern as follow.

❏ Dendritic

❏ Trellis

❏ Rectangular

❏ Radial

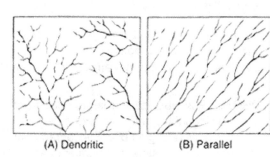

| (A) Dendritic | (B) Parallel |

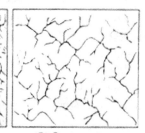

| (C) Trellis | (D) Rectangular |

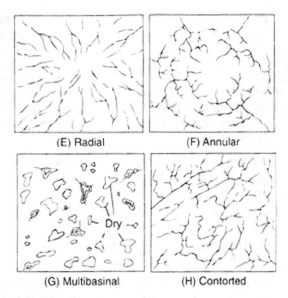

(E) Radial     (F) Annular

(G) Multibasinal     (H) Contorted

**Landforms made by Running Water:** The features developed due to the running water in the forms of the erosion, deposition and transportation processes.

**Erosion Types (Corrasion or Abration, Corrosion or Solution, Hydraulic Action):** Erosional Landforms due to Running Water as follow:

- Valleys
- Gorges
- Canyon
- Potholes
- Plunge pools
- Incised or Entrenched Meanders
- River Terraces

## Types of Transportation due to Running Water

After erosion, the eroded materials get transported with the running water and deposited in low level area. This transportation of eroded materials is carried in four ways:

- ❑ **Traction:** The heavier and larger rock fragments like gravels, pebbles etc. are forced by the flow of the river to roll along its bed. These fragments can be seen rolling, slipping, bumping and being dragged. This process is called as traction and the load transported in this way are called traction load.

- ❑ **Saltation:** Some of the fragments of the rocks move along the bed of a stream by jumping or bouncing continuously. This process is called as saltation.

- ❑ **Suspension:** The holding up of small particles of sand, silt and mud by the water as the stream flows is called suspension.

- ❑ **Solution:** Some parts of the rock fragments dissolved in the river water and transported. This type of transportation is called solution transportation.

- ❑ **Depositional Landforms due to Running Water:** The main features develop due to the running water in the form of depositions.

- ❑ **Alluvial Fans:** They are found in the middle course of a river at the foot of slope/ mountains. When the stream moves from the higher level break into foot slope plain of low gradient, it loses its energy needed to transport much of its load. Thus, they get dumped and spread as a broad low to the high cone-shaped deposits called an alluvial fan. The deposits are not roughly very well sorted.

- ❑ **Deltas:** Deltas are like an alluvial fan but develop at a different location. They are found in the mouth of the river, which is the final location of depositional activity of a river. Unlike alluvial fans, the deposits making up deltas are very well sorted with clear stratification. The coarser material settle out first and the finer materials like silt and clay are carried out into the sea.

- ❑ **Flood Plains:** Deposition develops a flood plain just as erosion makes valleys. A riverbed made of river deposits is the active flood plain and the flood plain above the bank of the river is the inactive flood plain.

- ❑ **Natural Levees:** Natural levees are found along the banks of large rivers. They are low, linear and parallel ridges of coarse deposits along the banks of a river. The levee deposits are coarser than the deposits spread by flood water away from the river.

## Meanders and oxbow lakes

Meanders are loop-like channel patterns develop over the flood and delta plains. It is not a type of landform it may be channel pattern due to depositions. They are formed basically because of three reasons: (i) propensity of water flowing over very gentle gradient to work laterally on the banks; (ii) unconsolidated nature of alluvial deposits making up the bank with many irregularities; (iii) Coriolis force acting on fluid water deflecting it like deflecting the wind.

- The concave bank of a meander is known as cut-off bank and the convex bank is known as a slip-off.

- As meanders grow into deep loops, the same may get cut-off due to erosion at the inflection point and are left as oxbow lakes.

- For large rivers, the sediments deposited in a linear fashion at the depositional side of a meander are called as Point Bars or Meander Bars.

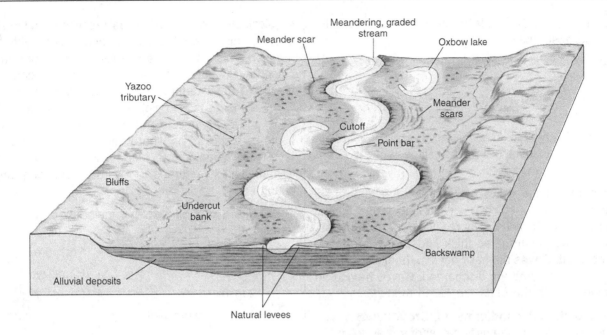

# Braided Channels

When selective deposition of coarser materials causes the formation of a central bar, it diverts the flow of river towards the banks, which increases lateral erosion. Similarly, when more and more such central bars are formed, braided channels are formed. Riverine Islands are the result of braided channels.

# Landforms made by Glacier

The natural agencies like glacier are also landforms due to erosions, transportation and depositions.

**Erosional land forms:** Erosional land forms developed due to glacier erosions as follow :

- Cirque
- Arte
- Hanging valley
- Fijords
- Horn
- Col
- Glacial trough
- Tarns

**Depositional land forms:** Depositional landforms formed due to the glacier depositions.

- Till
- Drumlin
- Morains

**Glacio–Fluvial deposits:** Glacial–fluvial mixed environments landforms as follows :

- Kames
- Erractics
- Varves
- Eskers
- Kettles
- Outwash plain

# Landforms made by Wind

The wind is the features developed in the arid regions in the forms of the erosion, transportation and depositions.

**Erosional landform (Deflation, Abrasion and Attrition):** The wind erosions landforms as follow.

- Mushroom rocks
- Demoiselles
- Desert pavement
- Zeugen
- Yardang
- Inselberges
- Blow-outs
- Millet – seed sand
- Ventifacts

## Depositional landforms (Ripple marks, sand dunes)

- Longitudinal sand dune
- Barchans
- Parabolic dune
- Transverse dune
- Foredune
- Seif

# Landforms made by Karst topography

Karst topography is the natural agencies which forms different land forms.

**Erosional Landforms due to Groundwater:** Sinkholes and caves are erosional landforms formed due to the action of ground water.

**Sinkholes:** It is erosional landform due to shallow rounded to sub rounded depressions, funnel shaped towards the bottom. When as sinkhole is formed solely through the process of solution, it is called as a **solution sink**. Some sinkhole starts its formation through the solution process but later collapse due to the presence of some caves or hollow beneath it and becomes a bigger sinkhole. These types are called as **collapse sinks**.

❏ The term **Doline** is sometimes used to refer collapse sinks.

❏ Solution sinks are more common than collapse sinks.

❏ When several sink holes join together to form valley of sinks.

❏ **Lapies** are the irregular grooves and ridges formed when most of the surfaces of limestone are eaten by solution process.

**Caves:** In the areas where there are alternative beds of rocks (non-soluble) with limestone or dolomite in between or in areas where limestone are dense, massive and occurring as thick beds, cave formation is prominent. Caves normally have an opening through which cave streams are discharged. Caves having an opening at both the ends are called tunnels.

**Depositional Landforms of Groundwater:** The mainly two types of depositional landform as follow:

**Stalactites and stalagmites:** They are formed when the calcium carbonates dissolved in groundwater get deposited once the water evaporates. These structures are commonly found in limestone caves. Stalactites are calcium carbonate deposits hanging as icicles while Stalagmites are calcium carbonate deposits which rise up from the floor. When a stalactite and stalagmite happened to join together, it gives rise to **pillars** or **columns** of different diameters.

## What is Climate?

**Weather** defined as the sudden change in our location due to the atmospheric conditions around us for a brief amount of time, and it can change rapidly. The weather can be foggy in the morning, sunny at noon, and rainy in the evening. This doesn't mean, however, that the climate changed from foggy to sunny and then to rainy over the course of a day.

**Climate** is the long variation average weather of an particular area. It doesn't describe the weather changes that happen over the course of days, weeks, or even months. It characterizes a region's general weather patterns that happen over the course of many years. Specifically, thirty years is the classic length of time used to determine an area's climate. So you could easily live in a place that is considered a dry climate, but still have a week of heavy rain.

## What Is Climate Change?

Climate change is a change in the usual weather found in a place. This is due to the variation of the temperature and pressure with respect of the months. It affects all physical, chemical and biological processes on the solar system, direct related to the ecosystem with time duration. This could be a change in how much rain a place usually gets in a year. Or it could be a change in a place's usual temperature for a month or season. Climate change is also a change in Earth's climate. This could be a change in Earth's usual temperature. Or it could be a change in where rain and snow usually fall on Earth. Weather can change in just a few hours. Climate takes hundreds or even millions of years to change.

**Element of Climate:** The main key of the climate as follows.

- Rainfall
- Temperature
- Sunshine
- Wind pressure belt
- Pressure
- Humidity
- Clouds

## Types of Climate Region

Global climates are often divided into five types:

- **Tropical**
- **Temperate**
- **Polar**
- **Dry**
- **Cold**

These climate divisions take a variety of factors into consideration, including altitude, pressure, wind patterns, latitude and geographical variation, such as high elevation (mountains) and low elevation (oceans). The five climate division is known as the Koppen Climate Classification System, named after founder Wladimir Koppen.

1. **Tropical climate region:** Tropical regions are characterized by high average temperatures and large amounts of rainfall. Biomes that have tropical climates include rainforest and savannas, according to Maps of World.com. The average monthly temperature in tropical climate regions is 64.4 degrees Fahrenheit and there tends to be little or no winter season.

2. **Dry region:** Dry regions experience very little rainfall and therefore have no permanent streams, according to Travel-University. They are also marked by large ranges in daily temperatures. In the desert, for example, temperatures can reach over 120 degrees Fahrenheit during the day, but may drop to 100 degrees or less at night. Dry regions are divided into semi-arid and arid zones.

3. **Temperate region:** Temperate regions are also known as meso-thermal or middle latitude climates. Summers tend to be quite warm with

little rainfall. Winters are moderate and wet. According to Travel-University.org, the coldest months in temperate regions tend to be between 26.6 and 64.4 degrees Fahrenheit. Temperate biomes include subtropical regions, Mediterranean areas, and marine regions.

4. **Cold climate:** Cold regions, also known as snow, micro-thermal or continental climates, have moderate rainfall and high seasonal variations in temperature. These regions tend to be found in central regions of land masses, such as the American Midwest. Average summer temperatures can be anywhere from 70 to 90 degrees. In the winter, the coldest month has an average temperature below 26 degrees Fahrenheit.

5. **Polar region:** Polar region are remarked by a lack of a true summer. The warmest temperatures are around 50 degrees Fahrenheit and these are short-lived. Large blocks of permanent ice and tundra are what make these regions distinctive. According to Blue Planet Biomes, polar climate regions usually only have four months of temperatures above freezing. They also tend to have months of little daylight.

## Causes of Climate Variation

Different causes for the type of climate.

- Latitude
- Elevation
- Ocean/wind currents
- Closeness to large bodies of water
- Terrain

**Koppen Climate Classification:** Koeppen's Classification of Climatic Regions of India is an empirical classification based on mean annual and mean monthly temperature and precipitation data.

❏ Koeppen identified a close relationship between the distribution of vegetation and climate.

❏ He selected certain values of temperature and precipitation and related them to the distribution of vegetation and used these values for classifying the climates.

❏ Koeppen recognized five major climatic groups, four of them are based on temperature and one on precipitation.

❏ The capital letters: A, C, D and E delineate humid climates and B dry climates.

### Climate Types According to Koeppen

| Group | Type | Letter Code | Characteristics |
|---|---|---|---|
| A-Tropical Humid Climate | Tropical wet | Af | No dry season |
| | Tropical monsoon | Am | Monsoonal, short dry season |
| | Tropical wet and dry | Aw | Winter dry season |
| B-Dry Climate | Subtropical steppe | BSh | Low-latitude semi arid or dry |
| | Subtropical desert | BWh | Low-latitude arid or dry |
| | Mid-latitude steppe | BSk | Mid-latitude semi arid or dry |
| | Mid-latitude desert | BWk | Mid-latitude arid or dry |
| C-Warm temperate (Mid-latitude) Climates | Humid subtropical | Cfa | No dry season, warm summer |
| | Mediterranean | Cs | Dry hot summer |
| | Marine west coast | Cfb | No dry season, warm and cool summer |
| D-Cold Snow-forest Climates | Humid continental | Df | No dry season, severe winter |
| | Subarctic | Dw | Winter dry and very severe |
| E-Cold Climates | Tundra | ET | No true summer |
| | Polar ice cap | EF | Perennial ice |
| H-Highland | Highland | H | Highland with snow cover |

## MULTIPLE CHOICE QUESTIONS

1. The drainage pattern that generally reflects a uniform lithological structure is
   (a) Centripetal     (b) Radial
   (c) Dendritic     (d) Trellis

2. Which station has more diurnal range than the annual range of temperature?
   (a) Singapore     (b) New York
   (c) London     (d) Moscow

3. Identify the oldest geological formations in India among the following:
   (a) Cuddapah series    (b) Vindhya series
   (c) Dharwar series    (d) Gondwana series

4. When a person moves from west to east in Himalayas the correct sequence of passes he crosses through will be
   (a) Punjab Himalayas – Kumaon Himalayas – Nepal Himalayas – Assam Himalayas
   (b) Kumaon Himalayas – Nepal Himalayas – Assam Himalayas – Punjab Himalayas
   (c) Punjab Himalayas – Nepal Himalayas – Assam Himalayas – Kumaon Himalayas
   (d) Assam Himalaya – Kumaon Himalayas – Nepal Himalayas – Punjab Himalayas

5. The temperate Grasslands in Africa are known as
   (a) Downs     (b) Veldt
   (c) Steppe     (d) Prairies

6. Grand Banks is located in
   (a) Northeast Atlantic
   (b) Northwest Atlantic
   (c) Northeast Pacific
   (d) Northwest Pacific

7. Which of the following regions has the highest population concentration in USA?
   (a) California
   (b) Northwest Pacific area
   (c) Texas
   (d) Northeast Atlantic area

8. Wind gap is a term associated with
   (a) Aeolian landforms
   (b) Coastal process
   (c) Underground water
   (d) River capture

9. Malaprabha is a major tributary for River
   (a) Krishna     (b) Godavari
   (c) Narmada     (d) Thunga Bhadra

10. The Indian National Centre for Ocean Information Services is located at
    (a) Mangalore     (b) Goa
    (c) Hyderabad     (d) Vishakapatnam

11. Which of the following countries leads in Bauxite production?
    (a) Australia     (b) Brazil
    (c) India     (d) China

12. Shivasamudram Hydro-electric Project is in
    (a) Karnataka     (b) Tamil Nadu
    (c) Maharashtra     (d) Andhra Pradesh

13. Which type of settlements is common in Deserts?
    (a) Dry point settlements
    (b) Piedmont settlements
    (c) Wet point settlements
    (d) Linear settlements

14. The R.F. for Survey of India quarter inch sheet is
    (a) 1 : 25000     (b) 1 : 50000
    (c) 1 : 63360     (d) 1 : 250000

15. Identify the wrongly matched pair of books and authors
    (a) Explanation in Geography – Harvey
    (b) Geography: A Modern Synthesis – Haggett
    (c) Theoretical Geography – Berry
    (d) Perspectives on the Nature of Geography – Hartshorne

16. Bundelkhand region is an example for
    (a) Macro region     (b) Meso region
    (c) Micro region     (d) Minor region

17. Manikiran in India is famous for harnessing
    (a) Wind energy     (b) Geothermal energy
    (c) Solar energy     (d) Tidal energy

18. During Second Five Year Plan a Steel plant was established with the collaboration of United Kingdom at
    (a) Rourkela     (b) Durgapur
    (c) Bhilai     (d) Bokaro

19. In the Recumbent type of fold the angle of the fold axis is
    (a) Horizontal     (b) Vertical
    (c) 60°     (d) 45°

20. Which among the following is significant for coal production in India?
    (a) Jaduguda     (b) Talcher
    (c) Ankaleshwar     (d) Khetri

21. The biggest oil discovery in last 20 years was made at Barmer in
    (a) Gujarat     (b) Assam
    (c) Rajasthan     (d) Andhra Pradesh

22. The Indian Institute of Tourism and Travel Management is located at
    (a) Goa            (b) Gwalior
    (c) Shimla         (d) Jaipur

23. Baku oilfields are located near the
    (a) Black Sea      (b) Barents Sea
    (c) Yellow Sea     (d) Caspian Sea

24. Dairying is a major economic activity in
    (a) Northwest Europe  (b) Northeast Europe
    (c) Northwest USA     (d) Northeast Africa

25. On maps Hachuring is a method to represent
    (a) Population density  (b) Relief
    (c) Settlements         (d) Age structure

26. Similar Triangle method is best suited for the enlargement and reduction of
    (a) Roads and Rivers  (b) Water bodies
    (c) Mountains         (d) Settlements

27. Zuider Zee refers to the largest area of
    (a) Flood             (b) Land reclamation
    (c) Land degradation  (d) Oil Pollution

28. In 2009 the growth rate of world population is estimated to be around
    (a) 1.2%     (b) 2.5%
    (c) 2.1%     (d) 2.3%

29. In soil profile zone of illuviation refers to
    (a) 'A' horizon   (b) 'B' horizon
    (c) 'C' horizon   (d) 'D' horizon

30. Which among the following is not associated with Karst land form?
    (a) Blind Valley  (b) Till
    (c) Uvalas        (d) Karren

31. When there is horizontal movement of rocks along a fault line in the ocean floor it is called
    (a) Graben         (b) Transform fault
    (c) Reverse fault  (d) Horst

32. Who among the following does not belong to the School of Subaerial Denudation?
    (a) Powell   (b) Davis
    (c) Penck    (d) Gilbert

33. Identify the correctly matched pair of ideas and authors
    (a) Unity in Diversity – Blache
    (b) Principle of Terrestrial Unity — Ritter
    (c) Pediplanation – W.M. Davis
    (d) Areal differentiation – Hartshorne

34. Identify the wrong statement from the following:
    (a) New towns and satellite belts are called Neutral regions

(b) Stamp attempted the first regional division of India based on physiography
(c) Sen Gupta and Galina divided India into Population Resource regions
(d) Metropolitan area is an example for Macro region

35. The concept of Dynamic Equilibrium was outlined by
    (a) Gilbert   (b) Chorley
    (c) Hack      (d) Wood

36. In 2008-2009 the State which has registered the highest growth rate in Indian exports is
    (a) Gujarat      (b) Maharashtra
    (c) Tamil Nadu   (d) Kerala

37. The Western Dedicated Freight Corridor Project in India links
    (a) Mumbai & Jaipur
    (b) Mumbai & Tughlakabad
    (c) Mumbai & Kochi
    (d) Jaipur & Kochi

38. Identify the correctly matched pair of region – major industry.
    (a) Pittsburgh – Textiles
    (b) Osaka – Steel
    (c) Ulsan – Chemicals
    (d) Toulouse – Aircraft

39. Tribal Area Development Planning is an example for
    (a) Formal region
    (b) Ad hoc region
    (c) Functional region
    (d) Axial region

40. In which area we will be able to witness Primary Ecological Succession?
    (a) New Volcanic islands
    (b) Mountain peaks
    (c) Dense forests
    (d) Estuaries

41. The Kyoto Protocol was initially adopted in
    (a) 1997   (b) 2003
    (c) 2005   (d) 2007

42. Who is considered as the Father of Human Geography
    (a) Brunhes   (b) Blache
    (c) Bowman    (d) Berry

43. The concept of Determinism was not supported by
    (a) Buckle   (b) Ratzel
    (c) Semple   (d) Febvre

44. Which of the following represents an Azonal process?
    (a) River
    (b) Glacier
    (c) Sea wave action
    (d) Underground water

45. Which of the following is NOT applicable to Central Business District?
    (a) Maximum residential population
    (b) High Land value
    (c) Intensive Land use
    (d) Maximum accessibility

46. Method of slope determination was not developed by
    (a) Wentworth
    (b) Robinson
    (c) Smith
    (d) Foster

47. Identify the map with the largest scale.
    (a) Map of India
    (b) Map of Kerala
    (c) Map of Kannur District
    (d) Map of Cochin city

48. Identify the correct statement from the following:
    (a) Zonal concept was first applied to Geomorphology
    (b) The term areal differentiation was coined by Carl Sauer
    (c) Stop and Go Determinism was outlined by Griffith Taylor
    (d) Diffusion idea and models were first developed by Chorley

49. Shevky and Bell applied Social Area Analysis first to
    (a) San Francisco region
    (b) Boston region
    (c) Chicago region
    (d) Greater London

50. Match the following:

    | Terms/Concept | Authors |
    | --- | --- |
    | 1. Haldenhang | A. Wegener |
    | 2. Tethys | B. Peltier |
    | 3. Pediplanation | C. Penck |
    | 4. Morphogenetic region | D. L. C. King |

    (a) 1-C, 2-A, 3-D, 4-B
    (b) 1-B, 2-C, 3-D, 4-A
    (c) 1-D, 2-A, 3-B, 4-C
    (d) 1-D, 2-B, 3-A, 4-C

51. Karst topography is characteristic of _____ terrain.
    (a) Granitic
    (b) Basaltic
    (c) Limestone
    (d) Granulitic

52. The topographic feature typical of formerly glaciated regions

    (a) Hanging valley
    (b) V-shaped valley
    (c) Yaardang
    (d) Cuesta

53. A river shows meandering course in its ___ stage.
    (a) Youthful
    (b) Old
    (c) Mountainous
    (d) Mature

54. Which is *not* true of lineation?
    (a) It is a directional property
    (b) When lineation is present foliation is also always present
    (c) It may be primary or secondary
    (d) Is useful in understanding the structural history of the rocks

55. An unconformity in which younger sedimentary rocks overlie igneous rocks
    (a) Angular unconformity
    (b) Disconformity
    (c) Non-sequence
    (d) Non-conformity

56. A chevron fold is one in which
    (a) The axis and crest do not coincide
    (b) The crest is rounded
    (c) The crest is pointed
    (d) The hinge line is always plunging

57. Sedimentary structures are not useful in
    (a) Interpreting palaeocurrent directions
    (b) Establishing stratigraphic sequence
    (c) Understanding the environment of deposition of rocks
    (d) Determining the age of formation

58. The outcrop of a bed will be a straight line on a map, irrespective of the topography, if the bed is
    (a) Vertical
    (b) Dipping
    (c) Horizontal
    (d) Affected by folding

59. The angle which a fault plane makes with the vertical plane
    (a) Dip
    (b) Rake
    (c) Hade
    (d) Pitch

60. There is a 4cm long line in a map of 1: 100000 scale. What will be the length of that line in a map of the same area of 1: 25000 scale?
    (a) 16 cm
    (b) 12 cm
    (c) 8 cm
    (d) 2 cm

61. Which is true of a craton?
    (a) Mainly covered by sedimentary rocks
    (b) Is a very small structural unit of the earth's crust
    (c) Largely unaffected by later orogenies
    (d) Consists mainly of Cambrian rocks

62. Which one of the following is true?
    (a) The Indian plate has both continental and oceanic components
    (b) The Antarctic plate has oceanic component only
    (c) The Arabian plate is a major plate
    (d) The Eurasian plate has continental component only

63. Mid-ocean ridges are associated with
    (a) Convergent boundary
    (b) Divergent boundary
    (c) Subduction zone
    (d) Conservative boundary

64. Among the following, which period has the shortest duration?
    (a) Tertiary
    (b) Quaternary
    (c) Cambrian
    (d) Triassic

65. Match the following and choose the correct answer :

| Unit | Part of classification/Scale |
|---|---|
| 1. System | A. Lithostratigraphic |
| 2. Zone | B. Chronostratigraphic |
| 3. Formation | C. Geologic Time Scale |
| 4. Era | D. Biostratigraphic |

    (a) 1-D, 2-C, 3-B, 4-A
    (b) 1-C, 2-B, 3-D, 4-A
    (c) 1-B, 2-D, 3-A, 4-C
    (d) 1-A, 2-C, 3-B, 4-D

66. The duration of time represented by an unconformity
    (a) Hiatus        (b) Diastem
    (c) Nonsequence   (d) Series

67. Which is true of an index fossil?
    (a) Limited geographical distribution
    (b) Narrow stratigraphic range
    (c) Large in size
    (d) Small in numbers

68. Which is the largest unit in the Geological Time Scale?
    (a) Eon       (b) Epoch
    (c) Period    (d) Era

69. Manganese deposits in Central India are associated with
    (a) Khondalite
    (b) Charnockite
    (c) Greywacke
    (d) Gondite

70. Match the following and choose the correct answer

| Formation | Age |
|---|---|
| 1. Cuddalore sandstone | A. Devonian |
| 2. Muth quartzite | B. Tertiary |
| 3. Chari formation | C. Cretaceous |
| 4. Uttatur formation | D. Jurassic |

    (a) 1-B, 2-A, 3-D, 4-C
    (b) 1-C, 2-D, 3-A, 4-B
    (c) 1-D, 2-C, 3-A, 4-B
    (d) 1-A, 2-C, 3-B, 4-D

71. A prominent anorthosite body in Kerala is located at
    (a) Perinthatta
    (b) Ambalavayal
    (c) Chengannur
    (d) Angadimogar

72. The rock in which graphite is mainly found in Kerala
    (a) Charnockite   (b) Granite
    (c) Khondalite    (d) Limestone

73. The rocks in which Glossopteris is found
    (a) Upper Gondwana
    (b) Lower Gondwana
    (c) Upper Siwalik
    (d) Karewas

74. The stratigraphic equivalent of Cuddapah Supergroup in North India
    (a) Rajmahal Traps
    (b) Vindhyan Supergroup
    (c) Delhi Supergroup
    (d) Aravalli Supergroup

75. The very old algal structure-bearing rocks of Rajasthan are called
    (a) Stromatolites   (b) Stalactites
    (c) Steatite        (d) Stalagmite

76. The diamond-bearing rocks of central India belongs to
    (a) Aravalli Supergroup
    (b) Bhima Supergroup
    (c) Vindhyan Supergroup
    (d) Sargur Supergroup

77. Match the following and choose the correct answer

| Formation | Environment of deposition |
|---|---|
| 1. Talchir tillite | A. Marine |
| 2. Barakar formation | B. Glacial |
| 3. Trichnopoly formation | C. Fluviatile |
| 4. Karewa formation | D. Arid |
| | E. Lacustrine |

(a) 1-A, 2-B, 3-E, 4-C
(b) 1-C, 2-A, 3-D, 4-E
(c) 1-D, 2-B, 3-E, 4-C
(d) 1-B, 2-C, 3-A, 4-E

78. Identify the gastropod
(a) Paradoxide     (b) Ostraea
(c) Productus     (d) Physa

79. Pygidium and glabella form part of
(a) Cephalapod     (b) Trilobite
(c) Graptolite     (d) Pelecypod

80. Star fishes, Sea urchins and blastoids belong to the phylum
(a) Brachiopoda     (b) Coelenterata
(c) Echinodermata     (d) Arthropoda

81. Foraminifers are found in
(a) Marine water only
(b) Brackish water only
(c) Fresh water only
(d) All the three waters

82. The stratigraphic range of Brachiopods
(a) Upper Devonian to Recent
(b) Upper Cambrian to Permian
(c) Lower Cambrian to Recent
(d) Middle Ordovician to Triassic

83. The half-life of Carbon-14 is
(a) 5570 years     (b) 55000 years
(c) 550000 years     (d) 550 years

84. When the strike of a bed is N-S, the true dip will be towards
(a) North East
(b) East or West
(c) North West
(d) None of the three

85. Agnatha was the earliest
(a) Trilobite     (b) Reptile
(c) Brachiopod     (d) Fish

86. Among the following which is the most primitive horse?
(a) Eohippus     (b) Hipparion
(c) Merychippus     (d) Equus

87. Which of the following did *not* happen in the evolution of man?
(a) Assumption of erect posture
(b) Lengthening of arms
(c) Reduction in the number and size of teeth
(d) Increase in cranial capacity

88. The crystal form with least number of faces
(a) Pinacoid     (b) Dome
(c) Pedion     (d) Pyramid

89. Which one is the type mineral of a hemimorphic class?
(a) Barite     (b) Tourmaline
(c) Beryl     (d) Gypsum

90. The crystal system characterized by three mutually perpendicular crystallographic axes of unequal length
(a) Tetragonal
(b) Triclinic
(c) Hexagonal
(d) Orthorhombic

91. Contact goniometer is used for measuring
(a) The number of crystal faces
(b) The interfacial angles of crystals
(c) The absolute hardness of crystals
(d) Refractive Index of crystals

92. A mineral commonly exhibiting penetration twin
(a) Fluorite
(b) Spinel
(c) Cassiterite
(d) Zircon

93. The crystal class exhibiting maximum number of elements of symmetry
(a) Hexoctahedral
(b) Ditetragonal dipyramidal
(c) Orthorhombic normal
(d) Dihexagonal dipyramidal

94. Which is an open crystal form?
(a) Scalenohedron
(b) Trapezohedron
(c) Dihexagonal dipyramid
(d) Brachydome

95. Mineral which generally shows zero birefringence?
(a) Hypersthene     (b) Beryl
(c) Garnet     (d) Staurolite

96. The minerals crystallizing under which system may exhibit dichroism?
(a) Isometric     (b) Tetragonal
(c) Monoclinic     (d) Orthorhombic

97. When the refractive index of the mineral is much higher than the mounting medium, the relief is
(a) High negative     (b) High positive
(c) Low negative     (d) Low positive

98. Identify the mineral which commonly causes pleochroic haloes in biotite
(a) Quartz     (b) Apatite
(c) Zircon     (d) Magnetite

99. Match the following and choose the correct answer :

| Mineral | Main cation |
|---------|-------------|
| 1. Almandine | A. Fe-Al |
| 2. Spessartite | B. Mg-Al |
| 3. Grossularite | C. Ca-Fe |
| 4. Pyrope | D. Mn-Al |
| | E. Ca-Al |

(a) 1-B, 2-A, 3-C, 4-E
(b) 1-C, 2-A, 3-D, 4-E
(c) 1-A, 2-D, 3-E, 4-B
(d) 1-E, 2-C, 3-A, 4-D

**100.** Which is an orthorhombic carbonate mineral?
(a) Dolomite    (b) Siderite
(c) Rhodocrocite    (d) Aragonite

**101.** Which one of the following statements is correct?
(a) Gypsum is softer than calcite but harder than apatite
(b) Quartz is harder than apatite but softer than topaz
(c) Corundum is softer than topaz but harder than orthoclase
(d) Fluorite is softer than calcite but harder than talc

**102.** Under which silicate family comes zoisite?
(a) Pyroxene    (b) Epidote
(c) Feldspathoid    (d) Olivine

**103.** Which one of the following has the highest specific gravity?
(a) Cinnabar    (b) Orthoclase
(c) Haematite    (d) Chalcopyrite

**104.** Which one is a phosphate mineral?
(a) Ilmenite    (b) Rutile
(c) Monazite    (d) None of the three

**105.** Which one is *not* a polymorph of $SiO_2$?
(a) Quartz    (b) Opal
(c) Tridymite    (d) Stishovite

**106.** Among the following which is the hardest sulphide mineral?
(a) Chalcopyrite    (b) Molybdenite
(c) Pyrite    (d) Stibnite

**107.** Identify the halide mineral
(a) Sphene    (b) Celestite
(c) Selenite    (d) Sylvite

**108.** The most abundant element in the crust of the earth
(a) Nitrogen    (b) Aluminium
(c) Oxygen    (d) Silicon

**109.** Which one shows the highest pH in nature?
(a) $CO_2$ – free water in contact with ultramafic rocks
(b) Weatherd ore solution containing pyrite
(c) Rain water
(d) Soil containing decayed organic matter

**110.** Na, K, Rb and Cs are principally _____ elements.
(a) Siderophile    (b) Chalcophile
(c) Atmophile    (d) Lithophile

**111.** Barium is a common trace element in
(a) Hypersthene and olivine
(b) Potash feldspar and biotite
(c) Hornblende and olivine
(d) Garnet and epidote

**112.** Siderolites are mainly made up of
(a) Siderite and calcite
(b) Nickel iron and silicates
(c) Silica-rich glass
(d) Olivine and pyroxene

**113.** For all exothermic reactions change in enthalpy is
(a) Positive    (b) Negative
(c) Zero    (d) Very high

**114.** The most widespread igneous rock in the crust of the earth
(a) Granite    (b) Rhyolite
(c) Basalt    (d) Andesite

**115.** Which is an undersaturated rock?
(a) Diorite    (b) Gabbro
(c) Rhyolite    (d) Dunite

**116.** In Poikilitic texture
(a) Smaller crystals are enclosed in larger crystals
(b) Larger crystals are enveloped in a ground-mass of smaller crystals
(c) All crystals are of the same size
(d) Glass exceeds crystals

**117.** Aplites are commonly found as
(a) Laccoliths    (b) Batholiths
(c) Dykes    (d) Lopoliths

**118.** Minette is a variety of
(a) Amphibole    (b) Carbonatite
(c) Lamprophyre    (d) Basalt

**119.** Which amphibole is common in igneous rocks?
(a) Hornblende    (b) Actinolite
(c) Anthophyllite    (d) Tremolite

**120.** **S.** Volcanic glasses older than carboniferous age are not known.
**R.** Glasses were not formed during pre-Carboniferous times.
(a) Both S and R are true
(b) S is true and R is false
(c) Both S and R are false
(d) R is true and S is false

**121.** The general sequence in the crystallization of minerals in igneous rocks is
(a) Ferromagnesian minerals, Quartz, Feldspar, Accessories
(b) Feldspar, Accessories, Ferromagnesian minerals, Quartz
(c) Accessories, Ferromagnesian minerals, Feldspar, Quartz,
(d) Ferromagnesian minerals, Accessories, Feldspar, Quartz

**122.** Fine grain size of igneous rocks indicate
(a) Slow cooling
(b) High mobility of ions
(c) Larger concentration of ions
(d) None of these

**123.** The term conglomerate indicates
(a) Grain size only
(b) Mineral composition only
(c) Mode of occurrence only
(d) Both grain size and composition

**124.** In Wentworth Udden Scale particles ranging in size between 1/16 mm and 1/256 mm are named
(a) Pebble
(b) Clay
(c) Sand
(d) Silt

**125.** In sandy shale
(a) Sand content is more than clay
(b) Sand and clay content are equal
(c) Clay content is more than sand
(d) Quartz pebbles are found with clay

**126.** Match the following and choose the correct answer

| *Rock* | *Class* |
|--------|---------|
| 1. Sandstone | A. Rudaceous |
| 2. Conglomerate | B. Argillaceous |
| 3. Shale | C. Calcareous |
| 4. Limestone | D. Arenaceous |

(a) 1-B, 2-C, 3-D, 4-A
(b) 1-C, 2-D, 3-A, 4-B
(c) 1-D, 2-A, 3-B, 4-C
(d) 1-A, 2-C, 3-D, 4-B

**127.** Which one is a typical evaporite?
(a) Clay
(b) Gypsum
(c) Bauxite
(d) Sulphur

**128.** The most conspicuous mineral in greensand is
(a) Apatite
(b) Microcline
(c) Glaucophane
(d) Glauconite

**129.** Laumontite, Lawsonite and glaucophane are typically found in
(a) Sedimentary rocks
(b) Metamorphic rocks
(c) Volcanic rocks
(d) Intrusive rocks

**130.** Serpentinites are formed by the metamorphism of
(a) Pelitic rocks
(b) Marls
(c) Ultramafic rocks
(d) Greywackes

**131.** The grass green clinopyroxene found in eclogite
(a) Augite
(b) Aegerine
(c) Diopside
(d) Omphacite

**132.** Which one is *not* true of contact metamorphism?
(a) Have regional extent
(b) Borders large igneous intrusions
(c) Effect of heat is predominant
(d) Contact aureoles are common

**133.** Which one has the maximum number of sets of cleavages?
(a) Sphalerite
(b) Halite
(c) Cummingtonite
(d) Diamond

**134.** Find the correct pair
(a) Stibnite – Antimony
(b) Magnesite – Manganese
(c) Galena – Zinc
(d) Cassiterite – Cobalt

**135.** Native sulphur is formed by
(a) Hydrothermal process
(b) Evaporation
(c) Supergene sulphide enrichment
(d) Sublimation

**136.** Find the correct pair
(a) Granite – Gypsum
(b) Anorthosite – Chromite
(c) Kimberlite – Chrysoberyl
(d) Gabbro – Cassiterite

**137.** The Si : O ratio in tectosilicates is
(a) 1 : 4
(b) 1 : 3
(c) 2 : 7
(d) 1 : 2

**138.** Match the following and choose the correct answer:

| *Deposit* | *Locality* |
|-----------|-----------|
| 1. Galena | A. Panna |
| 2. Chalcopyrite | B. Sukinda |
| 3. Chromite | C. Khetri |
| 4. Diamond | D. Zawar |
| | E. Kodarma |

(a) 1-B,2-D,3-A,4-E
(b) 1-D,2-C,3-B,4-A
(c) 1-C,2-E,3-A,4-B
(d) 1-E,2-A,3-D,4-C

**139.** Fissure veins, Saddle reefs and Stockworks are
(a) Contact metasomatic deposits
(b) Magmatic deposits

(c) Hydrothermal cavity filling deposits
(d) Hydrothermal replacement deposits

**140.** Which one of the following is *not* a product of residual process?
(a) Bauxite    (b) Clay
(c) Iron    (d) Gold

**141.** Emerald is a bright green gem variety of
(a) Chrysoberyl    (b) Beryl
(c) Chrysocolla    (d) Microcline

**142.** The common supergene sulphide of copper
(a) Bornite    (b) Chalcopyrite
(c) Bornonite    (d) Chalcocite

**143.** In Kerala glass sand deposits are located in
(a) Cherthala    (b) Chavara
(c) Payyangadi    (d) Neendakara

**144.** Which is a stratigraphic trap for petroleum?
(a) Monocline    (b) Unconformity
(c) Terrace    (d) Fissure

**145.** Which one of the following is true?
(a) Bituminous coal has high heating value
(b) Lignite is also called cambrian coal
(c) Peat is a variety of coal
(d) Anthracite has low heating value

**146.** Oxidation of sulphide minerals on the surface gives rise to
(a) Comb structure    (b) Gossan
(c) Pay streak    (d) Bonanza

**147.** Which is the most suitable method for the exploration of sulphide ore bodies?
(a) Self-potential    (b) Resistivity
(c) Seismic    (d) Magnetic

**148.** In which type of geophysical survey Geophones are used?
(a) Resistivity    (b) Magnetic
(c) Seismic    (d) Gravity

**149.** The East Coast Bauxite deposits of India had formed from
(a) Khondalite    (b) Kodurite
(c) Charnockite    (d) Basalt

**150.** Temporary or very short-lived streams are called
(a) Effluent    (b) Ephemeral
(c) Influent    (d) Obsequent

**151.** The mineral which gives the binding property for cement
(a) Calcite    (b) Bauxite
(c) Clay    (d) Gypsum

**152.** In selecting a building stone which one of the following is *not* considered?

(a) Availability    (b) Age
(c) Durability    (d) Strength

**153.** Vertical or inclined openings in underground mines which serve as a means of entry
(a) Shaft    (b) Cross-cut
(c) Stope    (d) Drift

**154.** The deepest underground mine in India is located at
(a) Kolar    (b) Zawar
(c) Malanjkhand    (d) Agnigundala

**155.** Bouguer anomaly is associated with ———— survey.
(a) Geological    (b) Magnetic
(c) Gravity    (d) Seismic

**156.** The main heavy metal pollutant which caused the Itaiitai disease in Japan
(a) Zinc    (b) Lead
(c) Mercury    (d) Cadmium

**157.** Natural levees are formed by ———— processes.
(a) Glacial    (b) Volcanic
(c) Aeolian    (d) Fluvial

**158.** In world fish production, the top rank is occupied by
(a) China    (b) Norway
(c) USA    (d) India

**159.** In Urban Geography, the Site and Situation approach was initiated by
(a) Griffith Taylor
(b) Raoul Blanchard
(c) Karl Hassert
(d) Lewis Mumford

**160.** In the Demographic Transition Model, the Late Expanding Stage is characterized by
(a) High Birth Rate and Low Death Rate
(b) Death rate declines further and birth rate begins to fall
(c) High Birth Rate and Declining Death Rate
(d) Declining Birth Rate and Low Death Rate

**161.** The example for boundary of divergent plates is
(a) Himalayas    (b) Alps
(c) Mid-Pacific Ridge    (d) Mid-Atlantic Ridge

**162.** Identify the FALSE statement with regard to Christaller's Central Place Theory?
(a) Christaller's theoretical area is called isotropic surface
(b) Christaller proposed three types of principles
(c) In Administrative Principle "k" value is 4
(d) In Marketing principle the range of a 'B' Place is 21 km.

163. The Mundra Ultra Mega Power Plant is located in
(a) Karnataka          (b) Andhra Pradesh
(c) Gujarat            (d) Jharkhand

164. Which of the following areas is NOT significant for iron ore mining?
(a) Krivoi Rog         (b) Kiruna
(c) Mesabi             (d) Karaganda

165. When both the limbs dip in the same direction the type of fold is called
(a) Over fold          (b) Recumbent fold
(c) Nappe              (d) Isoclinal fold

166. When the Sheet Number of a Survey of India topo sheet is given as 57 K/8/SE, the scale of the map is
(a) 1 : 1 million      (b) 1 : 100000
(c) 1 : 25000          (d) 1 : 10000

167. In terms of total production of steel in the world, India ranks
(a) Second             (b) Third
(c) Fourth             (d) Sixth

168. The driest part on the land surface of the earth is located in
(a) Sahara             (b) Atacama
(c) Sonara             (d) Arabia

169. The share of urban population to the total world population crossed 50% in
(a) 2005               (b) 2007
(c) 2009               (d) 2010

170. Who is regarded as the founder of Humanistic approach in Geography?
(a) Richard Peet       (b) Yi-Fu Tuan
(c) Brian J.L. Berry   (d) William Bunge

171. Identify the wrongly matched pair of landform and process
(a) Wind gap – River Capture
(b) Erratic – Underground Water
(c) Tombolo – Sea Waves
(d) Zeugen – Wind action

172. Pachmarhi is located in
(a) Chhota Nagpur      (b) Western Ghats
(c) Aravallies         (d) Satpura

173. Heartland theory was put forth by
(a) Ratzel             (b) Herbertson
(c) Mackinder          (d) Richthofen

174. In India Pawan Hans is associated with
(a) Helicopters        (b) Navy
(c) Air Force          (d) Railways

175. The Headquarters of the Intergovernmental Panel on Climate Change is located at
(a) Paris              (b) New York
(c) Geneva             (d) New Delhi

176. Hydel power generation is the highest in
(a) Australia          (b) Norway
(c) Switzerland        (d) Japan

177. The single largest type of land use in large metropolitan cities is
(a) Industrial         (b) Residential
(c) Transportational   (d) Commercial

178. The region which does not have Mediterranean type of climate is
(a) California
(b) Parts of South Africa
(c) Parts of Southwest Australia
(d) Southern Chile

179. Residual hill in a desert region
(a) Levees             (b) Playa
(c) Pediment           (d) Inselberg

180. The geographer who supported Neo-determinism is
(a) Semple             (b) Humboldt
(c) Blache             (d) Taylor

181. Identify the statement which is NOT correct
(a) Australia is the largest exporter of butter in the world
(b) India is the largest producer of milk in the world
(c) China is the largest producer of meat in the world
(d) Brazil is the largest exporter of beef in the world

182. Identify the wrongly matched pair of books and authors
(a) Radical Geography – Peet
(b) Explanation in Geography – Harvey
(c) Theoretical Geography – Berry
(d) Principles of Geomorphology – Thornbury

183. Sahel region is an area affected mostly by
(a) Earthquake         (b) Forest Fire
(c) Floods             (d) Drought

184. In the Survey of India 1 : 50000 scale maps, the sheet lying to the south of 57 B/8 will be
(a) 57 B/9             (b) 57 B/7
(c) 57 C/5             (d) 57 C/9

185. Which of the following is significant for renewable energy generation?
(a) Sasan              (b) Muppandal
(c) Ramagundam         (d) Kaiga

186. Sarva Siksha Abhiyan is a programme which is part of
(a) Sectoral planning
(b) Bottom-up planning
(c) Top-down planning
(d) Spatial planning

187. The average percentage of side lap in adjacent aerial photographs is
(a) 10 (b) 30
(c) 45 (d) 60

188. Malanjkhand is famous for
(a) Aluminium (b) Manganese
(c) Iron (d) Copper

189. A model describing the urban population density was formulated by
(a) Geddes (b) Berry
(c) Burgess (d) Newling

190. The Montreal Protocol aimed at ozone protection came into force in
(a) 1989 (b) 1993
(c) 1996 (d) 1997

191. India's first monorail was test driven in
(a) Kolkata (b) Mumbai
(c) Bengaluru (d) New Delhi

192. Mercalli Scale is used to measure
(a) Wind speed
(b) Earthquake intensity
(c) Humidity
(d) Hardness of minerals

193. Identify the correct statement: Hirakud Project developed on
(a) Mahanadi River
(b) Damodar Valley
(c) Ganga river
(d) Yamuna river

194. Simlipal National Park in India is located in
(a) Madhya Pradesh (b) Odisha
(c) Rajasthan (d) Meghalaya

195. The Zenithal projection with source of the light at the centre of the globe is called
(a) Gnomonic (b) Stereographic
(c) Orthographic (d) Equal area

196. Identify the statement which is FALSE
(a) The GPS system has a total of 24 satellites
(b) ERDAS is a GIS software package
(c) GRAM is designed in India
(d) Stereoimage is possible with CARTOSAT 2B satellite

197. Which one of the following is landlocked country?
(a) Vietnam (b) Myanmar
(c) Thailand (d) Laos

198. The idea of Positivism in Geography was introduced by
(a) Comte (b) Spate
(c) Brunhes (d) Chorley

199. NREGP is an example of
(a) Bottom-up Planning
(b) Top-down Planning
(c) Microlevel Planning
(d) Special Area Planning

200. Which of the following pair of Institutes/Facilities and Locations is wrong?
(a) Space Application Centre – Ahmedabad
(b) Master Control Facility for Satellite tracking – Shadnagar
(c) Indian Institute of Remote Sensing – Dehradun
(d) National Remote Sensing Centre – Hyderabad

201. In which type of data models a map is divided into a grid of squares or rectangular cells?
(a) Vector (b) Raster
(c) Scalar (d) Graphic

202. Hooke's law is applicable to:
(a) Elastic (b) Plastic
(c) Rupture (d) Flow

203. What is the condition for forming a normal fault?
(a) $\sigma 1$ horizontal (b) $\sigma 1$ vertical
(c) $\sigma 2$ vertical (d) $\sigma 2$ horizontal

204. Which one of the following is difficult to recognize in the field?
(a) Angular unconformity
(b) Nonconformity
(c) Disconformity
(d) Para unconformity

205. How the normal to a horizontal plane is represented on a stereogram?
(a) A vertical line
(b) An N-S line
(c) A point at the centre
(d) A point at the primitive circle

206. Which of the following is complementary to the dip?
(a) Strike (b) Hade
(c) Rake (d) Pitch

207. In which fold the orthogonal thickness of the bed is greater in the hinge than in limb?

(a) Similar      (b) Dissimilar
(c) Concentric      (d) Disharmonic

**208.** Which one of the following is not an indicator of a fault?
(a) Mylonite      (b) Gouge
(c) Breccia      (d) Conglomerate

**209.** With which of the following, transform fault is associated?
(a) Mid-ocean ridge      (b) Island arc
(c) Subduction zone      (d) None of the above

**210.** What is the average dip of Benioff zone?
(a) 45°      (b) 55°
(c) 65°      (d) 75°

**211.** The western continental margin of India represents?
(a) Active margin      (b) Passive margin
(c) Subduction zone      (d) Island arc

**212.** From which of the following lands the western India got rifted?
(a) Australia      (b) Antarctica
(c) Madgascar      (d) Arabia

**213.** Java-Sumatra is an example of which type of plate boundary?
(a) Divergent      (b) Convergent
(c) Transform fault      (d) Collision

**214.** Which of the following hot-spots caused Deccan volcanism?
(a) Marion      (b) Kergulian
(c) Reunion      (d) Karoo

**215.** Which of the following forms the dominant component of a greenstone belt?
(a) Charnockite      (b) Khondalite
(c) Metabasalt      (d) Eclogite

**216.** Which of the following is the youngest?
(a) Pennsylvanian      (b) Devonian
(c) Mississipian      (d) Permian

**217.** What is the age of the Deccan traps?
(a) 45 Ma      (b) 55 Ma
(c) 65 Ma      (d) 75 Ma

**218.** Which of the following is subdivided into Riphean and Vendian ?
(a) Neoproterozoic      (b) Mesoproterozoic
(c) Paleoproterozoic      (d) Phanerozoic

**219.** Which of the following Schist belts is the youngest?
(a) Shimoga
(b) Sargur
(c) Wynad
(d) Sathyamangalam

**220.** Which is the smallest lithostratigraphic unit?
(a) Group      (b) Member
(c) Bed      (d) Formation

**221.** Which is the chronostratigraphic equivalent of age?
(a) System      (b) Series
(c) Stage      (d) Sub-system

**222.** Which unit in the Cuddapah basin is the youngest?
(a) Kistna      (b) Papaghni
(c) Kurnool      (d) Cheyair

**223.** What is the age of Haimanta System?
(a) Silurian      (b) Devonian
(c) Ordovician      (d) Cambrian

**224.** Which is the oldest series of Jurassic of Cutch?
(a) Patcham      (b) Chari
(c) Katrol      (d) Umia

**225.** What is the age of Tipam sandstone?
(a) Miocene      (b) Eocene
(c) Oligocene      (d) Paleocene

**226.** Which one is correct geological age to the Warkallis formation?
(a) Miocene      (b) Eocene
(c) Cretaceous      (d) Cambrian

**227.** With which rocks the Neyveli lignite deposits are associated with?
(a) Gondwana      (b) Mesozoic
(c) Tertiary      (d) Quaternary

**228.** To which class trilobites belong to?
(a) Trilobita      (b) Curstacea
(c) Arthropoda      (d) Mollusca

**229.** To which phylum the class gastropoda belongs to?
(a) Arthropoda      (b) Echinoderma
(c) Porifera      (d) Mollusca

**230.** Which of the following is most important in the ammonoid characterization?
(a) Coiling      (b) Suture lines
(c) Siphuncle      (d) Septal necks

**231.** To which geologic age *belemenites* belong to?
(a) Cretaceous      (b) Triassic
(c) Cambrian      (d) Devonian

**232.** Which of the following is irregular echinoid?
(a) Holaster      (b) Salenia
(c) Pelstates      (d) Cidaris

**233.** Which of the following foraminifera is arenaceous?
(a) Orbitolites      (b) Textularia
(c) Lagena      (d) Globigerina

**234.** Which of the following is a Gondwana flora?
(a) Globigerina     (b) Goniopora
(c) Ptilophyllum    (d) Tetragraptus

**235.** Which of the following is not a trilobite?
(a) Olenus     (b) Phacops
(c) Olenellus  (d) Productus

**236.** What is the age of Archaeopteryx?
(a) Early Jurrasic   (b) Late Jurrasic
(c) Early Triassic   (d) Late Triassic

**237.** To which crystal system, the class with highest symmetry belongs to?
(a) Isometric   (b) Tetragonal
(c) Monoclinic  (d) Triclinic

**238.** How many horizontal reference axes are there in the hexagonal system?
(a) 1   (b) 2
(c) 3   (d) 4

**239.** Which have single face?
(a) Pedion   (b) Pinacoid
(c) Prism    (d) Pyramids

**240.** What is the axial ratio in isometric system?
(a) 1 : 1 : 1   (b) 1 : 2 : 3
(c) 1 : 3 : 2   (d) 2 : 3 : 1

**241.** In which crystal system epidote crystallizes?
(a) Tetragonal   (b) Orthorhombic
(c) Monoclinic   (d) Triclinic

**242.** What does a Quartz compensator measure?
(a) Optic sign    (b) Refractive index
(c) Optic angle   (d) Retardation

**243.** What is the optic nature of Calcite?
(a) Uniaxial positive   (b) Uniaxial negative
(c) Biaxial negative    (d) Biaxial positive

**244.** Which of the following does not affect the interference colour of a mineral?
(a) Relief         (b) Thickness
(c) Birefringence  (d) Orientation

**245.** Which of the following does Mg rich?
(a) Enstatite   (b) Ferrosilite
(c) Diopside    (d) None

**246.** Which of the following is not correct?
(a) Calcite : high relief
(b) Quartz : non pleochroic
(c) Cordierite : pleochroic haloes
(d) Staurolite : biaxial negative

**247.** Which of the following exhibits twinkling?
(a) Andalusite   (b) Cordierite
(c) Calcite      (d) Tremolite

**248.** Which of the following minerals has the lowest specific gravity?
(a) Magnesite   (b) Uraninite
(c) Chromite    (d) Native gold

**249.** What is the silicon : oxygen ratio in tectosilicates?
(a) 1 : 2   (b) 1 : 3
(c) 1 : 4   (d) 2 : 7

**250.** Name of the pyroxene with En, Fs and Wo components of 40, 30 and 30 respectively?
(a) Augite            (b) Ferroaugite
(c) Subcalcic augite  (d) Pigeonite

**251.** Which of the following is not a mica?
(a) Glauconite   (b) Zinnwaldite
(c) Vermiculite  (d) Lepidolite

**252.** Name of the plagioclase with An-75 and Ab-25?
(a) Andesine     (b) Bytownite
(c) Labradorite  (d) Oligoclase

**253.** Which of the following crystallizes in the isometric system?
(a) Haematite   (b) Ilmenite
(c) Rutile      (d) Chromite

**254.** Which of the following is caused by radiation damage?
(a) Migmatite   (b) Metamict
(c) Myrmekite   (d) Radiolaria

**255.** Which of the following minerals has the highest amount of Ti in it?
(a) Ilmenite   (b) Titanite
(c) Rutile     (d) Sphene

**256.** Which of the following is the stable phase at 300° C temperature and 4 kb pressure?
(a) Andalusite   (b) Sillimanite
(c) Kyanite      (d) Mullite

**257.** Which of the following is polymorphous with aragonite?
(a) Dolomite    (b) Calcite
(c) Magnesite   (d) Ankerite

**258.** Which shows the major elements in the order of decreasing abundance in the crust?
(a) Si-Al-O    (b) O-Si-Al
(c) Si-Al-Fe   (d) Si-Fe-Mg

**259.** Which of the following is an HREE?
(a) Ce   (b) Sm
(c) La   (d) Yb

**260.** Which of the following is a chalcophile element?
(a) Cr   (b) Mn
(c) Zn   (d) Cl

**261.** Which mineral precipitates at an environment of very low pH but very high Eh?

(a) Gypsum     (b) Anhydrite
(c) Pyrite     (d) Hematite

**262.** Where is the position of limestone fence in an Eh-pH diagram?
(a) Eh value of 0     (b) Eh value of +1
(c) Eh value of −1     (d) pH value of 8

**263.** Which is the radioactive isotope of carbon?
(a) Carbon-11     (b) Carbon-12
(c) Carbon-13     (d) Carbon-14

**264.** How much percentage of the Earth's crust is made up of sedimentary rocks?
(a) 5     (b) 10
(c) 20     (d) 30

**265.** Which lava flow has a submarine eruption?
(a) Pahoehoe     (b) aa
(c) Ropy     (d) Pillow

**266.** How to describe an igneous rock with mean grain diameter of 6 mm?
(a) Fine grained     (b) Very fine grained
(c) Medium grained     (d) Coarse grained

**267.** Which of the following textures indicate high-temperature skeletal crystallization?
(a) Spinifex     (b) Seriate
(c) Cumulate     (d) Rapikivi

**268.** Name a diagram which classifies plutonic rock with 30 % quartz, 45% orthoclase, 20% plagioclase and 5% mica?
(a) QAPF diagram     (b) AFM diagram
(c) ACF diagram     (d) AKF diagram

**269.** Name the volcanic equivalents to the granite
(a) Andesite     (b) Basalt
(c) Rhyolite     (d) Dacite

**270.** Which is the correct expression of Gibb's Phase Rule?
(a) $P + F = C + 2$     (b) $P + F = C- 2$
(c) $P - F = C + 2$     (d) $P + F = C + 1$

**271.** Which ternary system is regarded as petrogeny's residua system?
(a) Ab-Or-An     (b) Ab-Di-An
(c) Ab-Or-Qtz     (d) Fo-Fa-Di

**272.** Which diagram discriminates tholeiitic from calc-alkaline?
(a) ACF     (b) AKF
(c) AFM     (d) QAP

**273.** Which of the following is an ultramafic rock?
(a) Anorthosite     (b) Dunite
(c) Keratophyre     (d) Carbonatite

**274.** Which of the following is a sandstone rich in feldspar?

(a) Arenite     (b) Marl
(c) Arkose     (d) Quartzite

**275.** What is the term used to denote chemically precipitated carbonite mud?
(a) Sparite     (b) Microsparite
(c) Macrosparite     (d) Micrite

**276.** Which of the following heavy mineral indicates a metamorphic provenance?
(a) Zircon     (b) Ilmenite
(c) Kyanite     (d) Cassiterite

**277.** Which of the following metamorphic facies is of highest pressure?
(a) Granulite     (b) Hornblende-hornfels
(c) Pyroxene-hornfels     (d) Sanidinite

**278.** Which mineral is characteristic of blue-schist facies?
(a) Kyanite     (b) Corundum
(c) Cordierite     (d) Glaucophane

**279.** In which metamorphic textures, the grains show preferred orientation?
(a) Granoblastic     (b) Porphiroblastic
(c) Schistose     (d) Idioblastic

**280.** Which of the following is a mantle rock?
(a) Ophiolite     (b) Spilite
(c) Keratophyre     (d) Eclogite

**281.** Which of the following is not a high grade metamorphic rock?
(a) Charnockite     (b) Khondalite
(c) Eclogite     (d) Phyllite

**282.** Which of the following is not found as placer deposits?
(a) Gold     (b) Diamond
(c) Chromite     (d) Graphite

**283.** Which of the following is not a copper mineral?
(a) Pyrite     (b) Chalcopyrite
(c) Bornite     (d) Cuprite

**284.** What is the reservoir rock for Bombay High oil field?
(a) Sandstone     (b) Limestone
(c) Shale     (d) Clay

**285.** In which oil field is Ankaleswar?
(a) Bombay High     (b) Assam
(c) Cambay Basin     (d) Cauvery Basin

**286.** What is the age of Neyveli lignite deposits?
(a) Paleozoic     (b) Mesozoic
(c) Tertiary     (d) Quaternery

**287.** Deposits of which of the following is formed by supergene enrichment?
(a) Galena     (b) Magnetite
(c) Pyrolusite     (d) Bauxite

**288.** Which is the radioactive material in the beaches of Kerala?
    (a) Ilmenite
    (b) Monazite
    (c) Sillimanite
    (d) Garnet

**289.** Which of the following is a uranium mine?
    (a) Manavalakurichi
    (b) Jaduguda
    (c) Karnool
    (d) Agnigundala

**290.** By what process Ilmenite is separated from heavy mineral sands at Chavara?
    (a) Magnetic
    (b) Radioactive
    (c) Electrostatic
    (d) Vibration

**291.** Which metal is mined at Zawar mines?
    (a) Pb
    (b) Th
    (c) Co
    (d) Ta

**292.** With which rock types the chromite deposits of Karnataka are associated?
    (a) Felsic
    (b) Metamorphic
    (c) Ultramafic
    (d) Sedimentary

**293.** Ores of which metal is associated with koduritic rocks?
    (a) Fe
    (b) Cu
    (c) Mn
    (d) Mg

**294.** Which state has abundant gypsum deposits?
    (a) Bihar
    (b) Odisha
    (c) Rajasthan
    (d) Gujarat

**295.** Which gem is marketed in India as 'vaidoorya'?
    (a) Diamond
    (b) Topaz
    (c) Corundum
    (d) Chrysoberyl

**296.** With which of the following the term fusain is associated?
    (a) Mineral property
    (b) Coal petrography
    (c) Ore beneficiation
    (d) Gemstone grading

**297.** Which of the following is more applicable in groundwater exploration?
    (a) Gravity
    (b) Magnetic
    (c) Seismic
    (d) Resistivity

**298.** Which is the term used to refer to the economically mineable part of a measured ore reserve?
    (a) Proved
    (b) Probable
    (c) Indicated
    (d) Confirmed

**299.** Which logging device was first developed by petroleum industry as a measure of porosity?
    (a) Caliper
    (b) Sonic
    (c) SP
    (d) ISP

**300.** Which deposit can be explored by gravity survey?
    (a) Gold
    (b) Chromite
    (c) Bauxite
    (d) Graphite

**301.** Which exploration data has Milligals as unit?
    (a) Magnetic
    (b) Radioactive
    (c) Seismic
    (d) Gravity

**302.** Which is the cheapest and fastest drilling method?
    (a) Diamond
    (b) Percussion
    (c) Auger
    (d) Rotary

**303.** A leaky confining bed can be classed as:
    (a) Aquifer
    (b) Aquiclude
    (c) Aquitard
    (d) Aquaduct

**304.** The zone of saturation can be regarded as:
    (a) Vadose zone
    (b) Perched aquifer
    (c) Phreatic zone
    (d) Zone of aeration

**305.** Which of the following quantifies the ability of a porous medium to transport water?
    (a) Reynold's number
    (b) Hydraulic conductivity
    (c) Porosity
    (d) Permeability

**306.** What is the average TDS (mg/l) in stream water?
    (a) 100
    (b) 500
    (c) 1000
    (d) 1500

**307.** Which of the following commonly triggers landslides?
    (a) Tsunami
    (b) Earth quake
    (c) Tide
    (d) Nuclear explosion

**308.** Which type of mining is employed for exploiting coal?
    (a) Open cast alone
    (b) Underground alone
    (c) Both open cast and underground
    (d) Trenching

**309.** Which of the following parameters does not appear in Darcy's law?
    (a) Permeability
    (b) Hydraulic conductivity
    (c) Hydraulic gradient
    (d) Discharge

**310.** Which of the following term is synonymous with laterite?
    (a) Bauxite
    (b) Saprolite
    (c) Rhodonite
    (d) Teris

**311.** Which of the following contaminants in drinking water is more dangerous?
    (a) Chloride
    (b) Carbonate
    (c) Arsenic
    (d) Fluoride

**312.** What is the S-wave velocity in the earth's crust?
    (a) 4 km/s
    (b) 8 km/s
    (c) 20 km/s
    (d) 40 km/s

**313.** What is the highest magnitude of earthquake measured so far?
    (a) 9
    (b) 9.5
    (c) 10
    (d) 10.5

**314.** The super thermal power plant located near Singareni coal fields is

(a) Farakka     (b) Singarauli
(c) Korba     (d) Ramagundam

**315.** Mangrove forests cover more area in
(a) Gujarat     (b) West Bengal
(c) Tamil Nadu     (d) Odisha

**316.** The most important producer of nickel in the world is
(a) China     (b) Brazil
(c) Canada     (d) Venezuela

**317.** Match the following:

| List-I | List-II |
|---|---|
| A. Concentric Zone Theory | 1. Garrison |
| B. Fused Growth Theory | 2. Hoyt |
| C. Sector Theory | 3. Harris and Ullman |
| D. Multiple Nuclei Theory | 4. Burgess |

| | A | B | C | D |
|---|---|---|---|---|
| (a) | 4 | 1 | 2 | 3 |
| (b) | 4 | 3 | 1 | 2 |
| (c) | 4 | 1 | 3 | 2 |
| (d) | 1 | 2 | 3 | 4 |

**318.** Topographical maps are different from atlas maps as they are
(a) Representing only relief
(b) Large scale maps
(c) Small scale maps
(d) Drawn on different projections

**319.** The greatest number and wider variety of animals are found in
(a) Tropical grasslands
(b) Tropical forests
(c) Temperate forests
(d) Temperate grasslands

**320.** Which of the following nations of Europe has reached the last stage of the demographic transition?
(a) Portugal     (b) France
(c) Spain     (d) Italy

**321.** Which of the following statements is true?
(a) The westerlies are the dominant wind systems of middle latitude
(b) The westerlies are found on either side of the equator in the tropics
(c) The westerlies blow from east to west
(d) The westerlies are also known as cold and dry winds

**322.** Narrow bands of strong winds in the upper troposphere are called as
(a) Occlusion     (b) Cyclones
(c) Jet Streams     (d) Typhoons

**323.** The 'Heartland' concept was given by
(a) Hartshorn     (b) Haggett
(c) Taylor     (d) Mackinder

**324.** Icelandic type of volcanoes are characterized by
(a) Fissure eruptions     (b) Violent eruptions
(c) Silicic lava     (d) Explosive tephras

**325.** Most of the weather phenomena take part in the atmospheric layer
(a) Ionosphere     (b) Stratosphere
(c) Troposphere     (d) Exosphere

**326.** The reservoir located closer to Hospet
(a) Tungabhadra reservoir
(b) Stanley reservoir
(c) Krishnarajasagar
(d) Periyar reservoir

**327.** Karanpura is famous for
(a) Iron ore     (b) Manganese
(c) Copper     (d) Coal

**328.** The concept of 'Isolated State' was formulated by
(a) Christaller     (b) Von Thunen
(c) Malthus     (d) Weber

**329.** The projection most suitable for ocean navigation is
(a) Polar Zenithal Projection
(b) Sinusoidal Projection
(c) Mercator's Projection
(d) Molleweide Projection

**330.** The Earth Summit in 1992 was held at
(a) Stockholm     (b) Kyoto
(c) Rio de Janeiro     (d) London

**331.** South-west Asia is inhabited chiefly by
(a) Caucasians     (b) Mongoloids
(c) Negroides     (d) Austroloids

**332.** The scale of the one inch Indian toposheet converted into metric system is now available as
(a) 1: 5000     (b) 1: 25000
(c) 1: 50000     (d) 1: 100000

**333.** The point below the centre of the sensor on the ground is called as
(a) Geocentre
(b) Ground nadir centre
(c) Perspective centre
(d) Streocentre

**334.** The Survey of India (SOI) was established in the year
(a) 1767     (b) 1851
(c) 1867     (d) 1945

**335.** Which one of the following is to measure the height of an object more accurately?
(a) RADAR     (b) LiDAR
(c) DTM     (d) TIN

**336.** Mistral is found in
(a) North America
(b) South America
(c) Europe
(d) Australia

**337.** Which of the following National Highways does not pass through Kerala?
(a) N H 17
(b) N H 7
(c) N H 47
(d) N H 49

**338.** Find out the city that does not receive vertical sun rays:
(a) Chennai
(b) Hyderabad
(c) Nagpur
(d) Kanpur

**339.** Which are the states that are leading in the generation of wind power?
(a) Tamil Nadu and Kerala
(b) Tamil Nadu and Karnataka
(c) Tamil Nadu and Gujarat
(d) Tamil Nadu and Odisha

**340.** [A] : Japan is one of the leading industrial countries of the world.
[R] : Japan has a large mineral resources base
(a) Both [A] and [R] are true and [R] is the correct reason
(b) Both [A] and [R] are true but [R] is not the correct reason

(c) [A] is true but [R] is false
(d) [A] is false but [R] is true

**341.** When Survey of India toposheet has a number 58/K/7/SE, the R.F. will be
(a) 1 : 10000
(b) 1 : 20000
(c) 1 : 25000
(d) 1 : 50000

**342.** Which of the statements is **WRONG** with regard to Greek geographers?
(a) Anaximander prepared the first map of the world
(b) Miletus was developed by Greeks as a centre for geographical studies
(c) Hectataeus believed earth as a circular plane with Greece in the centre
(d) Herodotus measured the circumference of the earth almost correctly

**343.** Pittsburgh – Youngstown region is notable for the production of
(a) Aluminium
(b) Chemicals
(c) Iron & Steel
(d) Cotton Textiles

**344.** In 2018 the country which ranked second in coffee production next to Brazil is
(a) Colombia
(b) India
(c) Ivory coast
(d) Vietnam

## ANSWERS

| 1 | 2 | 3 | 4 | 5 | 6 | 7 | 8 | 9 | 10 |
|---|---|---|---|---|---|---|---|---|---|
| (c) | (a) | (c) | (a) | (d) | (b) | (a) | (d) | (a) | (c) |
| **11** | **12** | **13** | **14** | **15** | **16** | **17** | **18** | **19** | **20** |
| (a) | (a) | (a) | (d) | (c) | (b) | (b) | (a) | (a) | (b) |
| **21** | **22** | **23** | **24** | **25** | **26** | **27** | **28** | **29** | **30** |
| (c) | (b) | (d) | (d) | (b) | (a) | (a) | (a) | (b) | (b) |
| **31** | **32** | **33** | **34** | **35** | **36** | **37** | **38** | **39** | **40** |
| (b) | (a) | (c) | (c) | (c) | (a) | (b) | (b) | (c) | (d) |
| **41** | **42** | **43** | **44** | **45** | **46** | **47** | **48** | **49** | **50** |
| (a) | (c) | (b) | (b) | (b) | (a) | (d) | (a) | (a) | (a) |
| **51** | **52** | **53** | **54** | **55** | **56** | **57** | **58** | **59** | **60** |
| (c) | (a) | (d) | (a) | (a) | (c) | (d) | (c) | (c) | (a) |
| **61** | **62** | **63** | **64** | **65** | **66** | **67** | **68** | **69** | **70** |
| (c) | (d) | (b) | (b) | (c) | (a) | (b) | (a) | (a) | (a) |
| **71** | **72** | **73** | **74** | **75** | **76** | **77** | **78** | **79** | **80** |
| (a) | (c) | (a) | (c) | (a) | (c) | (d) | (d) | (b) | (c) |
| **81** | **82** | **83** | **84** | **85** | **86** | **87** | **88** | **89** | **90** |
| (d) | (c) | (a) | (b) | (a) | (a) | (b) | (c) | (b) | (d) |
| **91** | **92** | **93** | **94** | **95** | **96** | **97** | **98** | **99** | **100** |
| (b) | (c) | (a) | (c) | (c) | (b) | (b) | (c) | (c) | (d) |
| **101** | **102** | **103** | **104** | **105** | **106** | **107** | **108** | **109** | **110** |
| (b) | (b) | (a) | (d) | (b) | (c) | (d) | (c) | (a) | (d) |

| 111 | 112 | 113 | 114 | 115 | 116 | 117 | 118 | 119 | 120 |
|-----|-----|-----|-----|-----|-----|-----|-----|-----|-----|
| (a) | (b) | (a) | (a) | (d) | (a) | (c) | (c) | (a) | (d) |
| 121 | 122 | 123 | 124 | 125 | 126 | 127 | 128 | 129 | 130 |
| (c) | (d) | (a) | (d) | (c) | (c) | (b) | (d) | (b) | (c) |
| 131 | 132 | 133 | 134 | 135 | 136 | 137 | 138 | 139 | 140 |
| (d) | (a) | (a) | (a) | (d) | (b) | (d) | (b) | (c) | (d) |
| 141 | 142 | 143 | 144 | 145 | 146 | 147 | 148 | 149 | 150 |
| (b) | (d) | (a) | (b) | (c) | (b) | (a) | (c) | (d) | (b) |
| 151 | 152 | 153 | 154 | 155 | 156 | 157 | 158 | 159 | 160 |
| (d) | (b) | (a) | (a) | (c) | (d) | (d) | (a) | (a) | (b) |
| 161 | 162 | 163 | 164 | 165 | 166 | 167 | 168 | 169 | 170 |
| (d) | (c) | (c) | (d) | (d) | (c) | (b) | (b) | (c) | (b) |
| 171 | 172 | 173 | 174 | 175 | 176 | 177 | 178 | 179 | 180 |
| (b) | (d) | (c) | (a) | (c) | (b) | (d) | (b) | (c) | (d) |
| 181 | 182 | 183 | 184 | 185 | 186 | 187 | 188 | 189 | 190 |
| (b) | (c) | (d) | (c) | (b) | (b) | (b) | (d) | (b) | (a) |
| 191 | 192 | 193 | 194 | 195 | 196 | 197 | 198 | 199 | 200 |
| (b) | (b) | (a) | (b) | (d) | (c) | (d) | (a) | (a) | (b) |
| 201 | 202 | 203 | 204 | 205 | 206 | 207 | 208 | 209 | 210 |
| (b) | (a) | (b) | (c) | (b) | (b) | (b) | (d) | (a) | (a) |
| 211 | 212 | 213 | 214 | 215 | 216 | 217 | 218 | 219 | 220 |
| (b) | (c) | (b) | (c) | (c) | (d) | (c) | (a) | (d) | (c) |
| 221 | 222 | 223 | 224 | 225 | 226 | 227 | 228 | 229 | 230 |
| (c) | (c) | (d) | (a) | (a) | (b) | (c) | (b) | (d) | (b) |
| 231 | 232 | 233 | 234 | 235 | 236 | 237 | 238 | 239 | 240 |
| (a) | (a) | (b) | (c) | (d) | (c) | (a) | (c) | (a) | (a) |
| 241 | 242 | 243 | 244 | 245 | 246 | 247 | 248 | 249 | 250 |
| (c) | (d) | (c) | (a) | (a) | (a) | (c) | (c) | (a) | (a) |
| 251 | 252 | 253 | 254 | 255 | 256 | 257 | 258 | 259 | 260 |
| (a) | (b) | (d) | (b) | (a) | (b) | (b) | (b) | (d) | (c) |
| 261 | 262 | 263 | 264 | 265 | 266 | 267 | 268 | 269 | 270 |
| (c) | (d) | (d) | (a) | (d) | (d) | (a) | (a) | (c) | (b) |
| 271 | 272 | 273 | 274 | 275 | 276 | 277 | 278 | 279 | 280 |
| (c) | (c) | (b) | (c) | (d) | (c) | (a) | (d) | (c) | (c) |
| 281 | 282 | 283 | 284 | 285 | 286 | 287 | 288 | 289 | 290 |
| (d) | (d) | (a) | (b) | (c) | (c) | (a) | (b) | (b) | (b) |
| 291 | 292 | 293 | 294 | 295 | 296 | 297 | 298 | 299 | 300 |
| (a) | (c) | (c) | (b) | (d) | (b) | (d) | (a) | (a) | (b) |
| 301 | 302 | 303 | 304 | 305 | 306 | 307 | 308 | 309 | 310 |
| (d) | (d) | (a) | (c) | (d) | (b) | (b) | (c) | (a) | (a) |
| 311 | 312 | 313 | 314 | 315 | 316 | 317 | 318 | 319 | 320 |
| (c) | (b) | (c) | (d) | (b) | (c) | (a) | (a) | (c) | (a) |
| 321 | 322 | 323 | 324 | 325 | 326 | 327 | 328 | 329 | 330 |
| (a) | (c) | (d) | (a) | (c) | (a) | (d) | (b) | (c) | (c) |
| 331 | 332 | 333 | 334 | 335 | 336 | 337 | 338 | 339 | 340 |
| (d) | (d) | (b) | (a) | (b) | (b) | (b) | (a) | (c) | (c) |
| 341 | 342 | 343 | 344 |  |  |  |  |  |  |
| (c) | (c) | (c) | (d) |  |  |  |  |  |  |

# CHAPTER 2

# ASTRONOMY

## What is Solar System?

The Solar system consists as Sun, planets, stars, moons, comets, asteroids and meteoroids. It is a mixture of the all objects which exists in our universe. The Sun is the main source of the energy in the form of the electromagnetic spectrum in the solar system. The Sun's nearest known stellar neighbour is a red dwarf star called Proxima Centauri, at a distance of 4.3 light years away. The whole solar system, together with the local stars visible on a clear night, orbits the center of our home galaxy, a spiral disk of 200 billion stars we call the Milky Way.

The planets, most of the satellites of the planets and the asteroids revolve around the Sun in the same direction, in nearly circular orbits. When looking down from above the Sun's north pole, the planets orbit in a counter-clockwise direction. The planets orbit the Sun in or near the same plane, called the ecliptic. Pluto is a special case in that its orbit is the most highly inclined (18 degrees) and the most highly elliptical of all the planets. Because of this, for part of its orbit, Pluto is closer to the Sun than is Neptune. The axis of rotation for most of the planets is nearly perpendicular to the ecliptic. The exceptions are Uranus and Pluto, which are tipped on their sides.

## Composition of the Solar System

The Sun contains 99.85% of all the matter in the Solar System. The planets, which condensed out of the same disk of material that formed the Sun, contain only 0.135% of the mass of the solar system. Jupiter contains more than twice the matter of all the other planets combined. Satellites of the planets, comets, asteroids, meteoroids, and the interplanetary medium constitute the remaining

0.015%. The following table given below  list of the mass distribution within our Solar System :

- Sun : 99.85%
- Planets : 0.135%
- Comets : 0.01%
- Satellites : 0.00005%
- Minor Planets : 0.0000002%
- Meteoroids : 0.0000001%
- Interplanetary Medium : 0.0000001%

## Bode's Law

The Titius-Bode Law is rough empirical rule that predicts the spacing of the planets in the Solar System. The relationship was first pointed out by Johann Titius in 1766 and was formulated as a mathematical expression by J.E. Bode in 1778. It lead Bode to predict the existence of another planet between Mars and Jupiter in what we now recognize as the asteroid belt. The law relates the mean distances of the planets from the sun to a simple mathematic progression of numbers.

To find the mean distances of the planets, beginning with the following simple sequence of numbers:

| 0 | 3 | 6 | 12 | 24 | 48 | 96 | 192 | 384 |
|---|---|---|----|----|----|----|-----|-----|

With the exception of the first two, the others are simple twice the value of the preceding number.

Add 4 to each number:

| 4 | 7 | 10 | 16 | 28 | 52 | 100 | 196 | 388 |
|---|---|----|----|----|----|-----|-----|-----|

Then divide by 10:

| 0.4 | 0.7 | 1.0 | 1.6 | 2.8 | 5.2 | 10.0 | 19.6 | 38.8 |
|-----|-----|-----|-----|-----|-----|------|------|------|

The resulting sequence is very close to the distribution of mean distances of the planets from the Sun:

| Planets | Actual distance (A.U.) | Bode's law (Distance in A.U.) |
|---|---|---|
| Mercury | 0.39 | 0.4 |
| Venus | 0.72 | 0.7 |
| Earth | 1.00 | 1.0 |
| Mars | 1.52 | 1.6 |
| Asteroid belt | | 2.8 |
| Jupiter | 5.20 | 5.2 |
| Saturn | 9.54 | 10.0 |
| Uranus | 19.19 | 19.6 |

## Kepler's Law of Planetary Motion

Johannes Kepler, working with data painstakingly collected by Tycho Brahe without the aid of a telescope, developed three laws which described the motion of the planets across the sky.

1. **The Law of Orbits:** All planets move in elliptical orbits, with the sun at one focus.

### Kepler's First Law

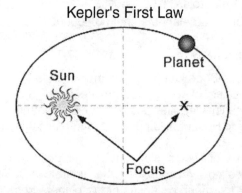

2. **The Law of Areas:** A line that connects a planet to the sun sweeps out equal areas in equal times.

### Kepler's Second Law

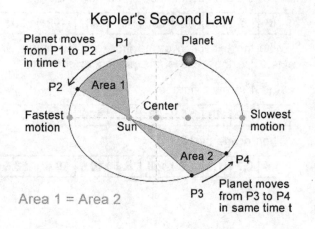

Area 1 = Area 2

3. **The Law of Periods:** The square of the period of any planet is proportional to the cube of the semi-major axis of its orbit. Kepler's laws were derived for orbits around the sun, but they apply to satellite orbits as well.

### Kepler's Third Law

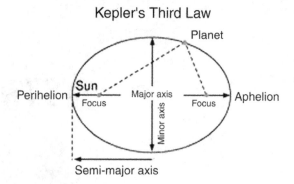

## What is Albedo?

Albedo is the fraction of solar energy/ shortwave radiation reflected from the earth back into space. It is a measure of the reflectivity of the earth's surface in percentage. Ice, especially with snow on top of it, has high albedo, most sunlight hitting the surface reflected back in the space. Water is much more absorbent and has less reflectivity. So, if there is a lot of water, more solar radiation is absorbed by the ocean than when ice dominates.

The proportion of solar radiation which is reflected by a non-luminous body is known as albedo. It is the measure of how reflective a body is. Dark coloured objects absorb most of the solar radiation which is incident on them and hence have a low albedo, whereas light-coloured ones have a high albedo, as they reflect most of the radiation incident upon them.

To find the albedo of any object, the amount of electromagnetic radiation incident upon it is measured first, then the amount of radiation diffusely reflected is measured. The ratio of the latter to the former gives the albedo of that object. It has no dimensions. Albedo is one for a perfectly white object and is zero for a perfectly black object; all objects have an albedo between this range.

There are different types of albedo, including Astronomical Albedo, Terrestrial Albedo and Single Scattering Albedo. Astronomical albedo the measure of the reflectivity of planets (except Earth), asteroids and other celestial bodies. Albedo of the Moon is .07 (some sources state that it is as high as 12%), that is, only 7% of the solar radiation which reaches the Moon is reflected back into space and an awesome 93% is absorbed by the Moon's surface! Thus the albedo is an indicator of the surface and atmospheric characteristics of a celestial body and therefore is important in the study of astronomy.

## Seasonal Effects on Albedo

**Summer:** To understand albedo better, we look at two scenarios. One, if you walk barefoot on the black soil during summer, you will feel a lot of heat and can even get burnt because the surface is absorbing and retaining more heat. Another person walking on white soil during the same season will not be burnt. This is basically because white surface tends to reflect more heat and absorb very little of it. Equally, if you touch a black car in summer it will feel much hotter than touching a white car. This is because black absorbs and retains heat while white car surface will reflect back the solar rays.

**Winter:** During this season, it is generally wet with either water or ice. Water reflects approximately 6% of the light and absorbs the rest. Ice, on the other hand, reflects 50% to 60% of the incoming solar heat, thereby remaining cooler. A snow-covered area reflects a lot of radiation, which is why skiers having a risk of getting sunburns while on the slopes. Albedo diminishes when the snow-covered places start to warm up.

## Spectral Classification

OBAFGKMC is the spectral type of the each word which have its own's surface temperature ranges. Each spectral type is divided into 10 subclasses, A0, A1, A2, ...A9 etc. The spectral types and sub-classes represent a temperature sequence, from hotter (O stars) to cooler (M stars), and from hotter (subclass 0) to cooler (subclass 9). The temperature defines the star's "colour" and surface brightness.

| Spectral Type | Surface Temperature | Distinguishing Features |
|---|---|---|
| O | > 25,000K | H; HeI; HeII |
| B | 10,000-25,000K | H; HeI; HeII absent |
| A | 7,500-10,000K | H; CaII; HeI and HeII absent |
| F | 6,000-7,500K | H; metals (CaII, Fe, etc) |
| G | 5,000-6,000K | H; metals; some molecular species |
| K | 3,500-5,000K | Metals; some molecular species |
| M | < 3,500K | Metals; molecular species (TiO!) |
| C | < 3,500K | Metals; molecular species (C2!) |

## SUN AND ITS LAYERS

Sun is its own atmosphere, which consists different layers. The atmosphere of the sun is composed of several layers, mainly the photosphere, the chromosphere and the corona. It's in these outer layers that the sun's energy, which has bubbled up from the sun's interior layers, is detected as sunlight.

**Photosphere:** The photosphere is the deepest layer of the Sun that we can observe directly. It reaches from the surface visible at the center of the solar disk to about 250 miles (400 km) above that. The temperature in the photosphere varies between about 6500 K at the bottom and 4000 K at the top (11,000 and 6700 degrees F, 6200 and 3700 degrees C). Most of the photosphere is covered by granulation. The lowest layer of the sun's atmosphere is the photosphere. It is about 300 miles (500 kilometers) thick. This layer is where the sun's energy is released as light. Because of the distance from the Sun to Earth, light reaches our planet in about eight minutes.

The photosphere is also the source of solar flares: tongues of fire that extend hundreds of thousands of miles above the sun's surface. Solar flares produce bursts of X-rays, ultraviolet radiation, electromagnetic radiation and radio waves. [Space Weather: Sunspots, Solar Flares & Coronal Mass Ejections].

**Chromosphere :** The next layer is the chromosphere. The chromosphere emits a reddish glow as super-heated hydrogen burns off. But the red rim can only be seen during a total solar eclipse. At other times, light from the chromosphere is usually too weak to be seen against the brighter photosphere. The chromosphere is a layer in the Sun between about 250 miles (400 km) and 1300 miles (2100 km) above the solar surface (the photosphere). The temperature in the chromosphere varies between about 4000 K at the bottom (the so-called temperature minimum) and 8000 K at the top (6700 and 14,000 degrees F, 3700 and 7700 degrees C), so in this layer (and higher layers) it actually gets hotter if you go further away from the Sun, unlike in the lower layers, where it gets hotter if you go closer to the center of the Sun.

The chromosphere may play a role in conducting heat from the interior of the sun to its outermost layer, the corona. "We see certain kinds of solar seismic waves channeling upwards into the lower atmosphere, called the chromosphere, and from there, into the corona," Junwei Zhao, a solar scientist at Stanford University in Stanford, California, and lead author on a recent study that tracked waves from sunspots, said in a statement. "This research gives us a new viewpoint to look at waves that can contribute to the energy of the atmosphere."

**Transition Region :** The transition region is a very narrow (60 miles/100 km) layer between the chromosphere and the corona where the temperature rises abruptly from about 8000 to about 500,000 K (14,000 to 900,000 degrees F, 7700 to 500,000 degrees C).

**Corona :** The third layer of the sun's atmosphere is the corona. It can only be seen during a total solar eclipse as well. It appears as white streamers or plumes of ionized gas that flow outward into space. Temperatures in the Sun's coronacan get as high as 3.5 million degrees Fahrenheit (2 million degrees Celsius). As the gases cool, they become the solar wind.

Why the corona is up to 300 times hotter than the photosphere, despite being farther from the solar core, has remained a long-term mystery.

The corona is the outermost layer of the Sun, starting at about 1300 miles (2100 km) above the solar surface (the photosphere). The temperature in the corona is 500,000 K (900,000 degrees F, 500,000 degrees C) or more, up to a few million K. The corona cannot be seen with the naked eye except during a total solar eclipse, or with the use of a coronagraph. The corona does not have an upper limit. (Credit: National Solar Observatory).

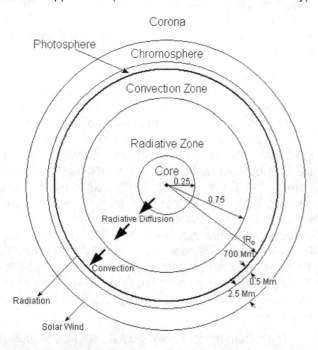

## Terrestrial Plants

### Mercury, Venus, Earth, Mars

Terrestrial (in Latin, terra means Earth) planets are Earth-like planets made up of rocks or metals with a hard surface - making them different from other planets that lack a solid surface. Terrestrial planets also have a molten heavy metal core, few moons, and topological features such as valleys, volcanoes and craters.

In our solar system, there are four terrestrial planets, which also happen to be the four closest to the sun: Mercury, Venus, Earth and Mars. During the creation of the solar system, there were likely more terrestrial planetoids, but they likely merged or were destroyed.

## Outer Planets

### Jupiter, Saturn, Uranus, Neptune

All planets are not terrestrial. In our solar system, Jupiter, Saturn, Uranus and Neptune are gas giants, also known as "Jovian planets" (meaning "Jupiter-like") because they are all huge compared to the terrestrial planets, and because they are gaseous in nature rather than having rocky surfaces (though some or all of them may have solid cores, astronomers say). It's unclear what the dividing line is between a rocky planet and a terrestrial planet; some super-Earths may have a liquid surface, for example. In our solar system, gas giants are much bigger than terrestrial planets, and they have thick atmospheres full of hydrogen and helium. On Jupiter and Saturn, hydrogen and helium make up most of the planet, while on Uranus and Neptune, the elements make up just the outer envelope. Landing on a gas giant is nearly impossible, since only the core is solid, and the atmosphere is storm-filled and very thick. It's also inhospitable to life as we know it.

According to NASA, "two of the outer planets beyond the orbit of Mars - Jupiter and Saturn - are known as gas giants; the more distant Uranus and Neptune are called ice giants." This is because, while the first two are dominated by gas, while the last two have more ice. All four contain mostly hydrogen and helium.

## Dwarf Planets

While similar to planets in many ways, dwarf planets shear their orbits around the sun with other objects such as asteroids or comets. The first five recognized dwarf planets are;

- Ceres
- Pluto
- Eris
- Haumea
- Makemake

## Comets

Comets are sometimes called dirty snowballs or "icy mudballs". They are a mixture of ices (both water and frozen gases) and dust that for some reason didn't get incorporated into planets when the solar system was formed. This makes them very interesting as samples of the early history of the solar system. When they are near the Sun and active, comets have several distinct parts.

### Parts of the Comets:

❏ **Nucleus:** In a comets part it consist as nucleus which relatively solid and stable, mostly ice and gas with a small amount of dust and other solids.

❏ **Coma:** Dense cloud of water, carbon dioxide and other neutral gases sublimed from the nucleus;

❏ **Hydrogen cloud:** Huge (millions of km in diameter) but very sparse envelope of neutral hydrogen;

- **Dust tail:** Up to 10 million km long composed of smoke-sized dust particles driven off the nucleus by escaping gases; this is the most prominent part of a comet to the unaided eye;
- **Ion tail:** As much as several hundred million km long composed of plasma and laced with rays and streamers caused by interactions with the solar wind.

Comets are invisible except when they are near the Sun. Most comets have highly eccentric orbits which take them far beyond the orbit of Pluto; these are seen once and then disappear for millennia. Only the short- and intermediate-period comets (like Comet Halley), stay within the orbit of Pluto for a significant fraction of their orbits.

## What Is An Asteroid?

Asteroids are small, rocky solar system's bodies that populate interplanetary space out to the orbit of Jupiter. There are millions of them, and they are often grouped by their composition.

The planetary science community refers to them as minor planets, a general term applied to solar system bodies smaller than moons. Asteroids are mainly made of materials left over from the formation of the inner solar system words. Most of them orbit the Sun between Mars and Jupiter, although there are groups of them that orbit closer. Asteroids come in three composition classes. C-types (chondrites) are made of clay and silicate rocks. S-types are the so-called "stony" asteroids and are made mostly of silicate rocks and nickel-iron mixtures. M-types are metallic nickel-iron. These categories indicate how far from the Sun they formed in the early solar system.

- Asteroids are clues to the formation of the rocky planets of our solar system. The objects we see today are leftover from a time when the solar system formed 4.5 billion years ago.
- Asteroids aren't the only things that hit Earth. Each day, more than 100 tons of material from asteroids and comets falls toward Earth. Most of it is destroyed by friction as it passes through our atmosphere.
- While asteroid impacts were more common in the past, they aren't as frequent today.
- An asteroid impact some 65 million years ago contributed to the extinction of the dinosaurs. (It was one of several factors that affected all life on Earth at that time).
- A car-sized meteoroid (a piece of asteroid) falls into Earth's atmosphere about once a year. The result is a beautiful fireball, but the meteoroid usually burns up before reaching the ground.
- Asteroids are rich in precious metals and other metals, as well as water.
- Some asteroids are actually blown-out comets. The ices are gone, and all that's left is the rocky material.
- Some asteroids have moons of their own.
- Most asteroids orbit the Sun in the Asteroid Belt, which lies between Mars and Jupiter.
- Asteroids are also referred to as minor planets or planetoids.

## Famous Asteroids

The best-known asteroids are 1 Ceres, which is 952 kilometres across, 2 Pallas (with a diameter of 544 kilometres), and 4 Vesta (roughly 580 km across). These are rocky minor planets, and astronomers have observed them since the 1800s. Ceres is a differentiated asteroid. That means it has a rocky core and a icy outer crust. It might have an internal ocean. Pallas has a very irregular shape, and may be what's left of an early protoplanet. Vesta is very bright and is likely the leftover of a rocky protoplanet.

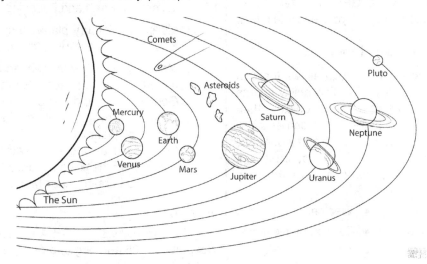

## Satellites

A circular objects in space, which may be small or big. It is mainly two types natural or artificial. In our space every planets have its own satellites. There are dozens upon dozens of natural satellites in the solar system, with almost every planet having at least one moon. Saturn, for example, has at least 53 natural satellites, and between 2004 and 2017, it also had an artificial one - the Cassini spacecraft, which explored the ringed planet and its moons.

❏ Artificial satellites, however, did not become a reality until the mid-20th century. The first artificial satellite was Sputnik, a Russian beach-ball-size space probe that lifted off on Oct. 4, 1957. That act shocked much of the western world, as it was believed the Soviets did not have the capability to send satellites into space.

❏ A satellite is a moon, planet or machine that orbits a planet or star. For example, Earth is a satellite because it orbits the sun. Likewise, the moon is a satellite because it orbits Earth. Usually, the word "satellite" refers to a machine that is launched into space and moves around Earth or another body in space.

❏ Earth and the moon are examples of natural satellites. Thousands of artificial, or man-made, satellites orbit Earth. Some take pictures of the planet that help meteorologists predict weather and track hurricanes. Some take pictures of other planets, the sun, black holes, dark matter or faraway galaxies. These pictures help scientists better understand the solar system and universe.

❏ Still other satellites are used mainly for communications, such as beaming TV signals and phone calls around the world. A group of more than 20 satellites make up the Global Positioning System, or GPS. If you have a GPS receiver, these satellites can help figure out your exact location.

## Why Are Satellites Important?

The bird's-eye view that satellites have allows them to see large areas of Earth at one time. This ability means satellites can collect more data, more quickly, than instruments on the ground. Satellites also can see into space better than telescopes at Earth's surface. That's because satellites fly above the clouds, dust and molecules in the atmosphere that can block the view from ground level.

- TV signal
- Climatic conditions
- Defence
- Weather
- Telecommunications
- GPS

## Space exploration in the solar system

There are different space exploration mission for a particular planets or satellites for research and its related information which show real story of our solar system. The following data covered by the NASA space centre.

❏ **Sun-studying spacecraft:** This observatory study about the knowledge of the Sun's history.

❏ **Wind:** This NASA probe launched in November 1994 to study the solar wind, the stream of charged particles flowing from the sun. The Wind spacecraft operates from a halo orbit around the Sun-Earth Lagrange point 1 (L1), a spot about 900,000 miles (1.5 million kilometers) from Earth (in the direction of the Sun). At Sun-Earth L1, the gravitational pulls of the two bodies interact in such a way that a probe can essentially park there. [Gallery: Solar System's Deep-Space Probes].

❏ **Solar and Heliospheric Observatory:** SOHO, a joint effort between the European Space Agency (ESA) and NASA, launched in December 1995 and also orbits around Sun-Earth L1. In addition to its sun-studying duties, SOHO has discovered more than 2,300 comets. The total mission cost is about 1 billion euros ($1.32 billion at current exchange rates).

❏ **Advanced Composition Explorer (ACE):** This mission was launched by NASA spacecraft in August 1997 to help researchers better understand and predict space weather. ACE also orbits Sun-Earth L1.

❏ **Solar Terrestrial Relations Observatory:** NASA's Sun-studying STEREO mission, which blasted off in October 2006, consists of two spacecraft, known as A and B. Both probes are in a heliocentric orbit, with A zipping around the sun faster than Earth and B lagging somewhat behind.

❏ **Mercury:** Mercury planets have its own mission to solve the mystery of the mercury planets.

❏ **Messenger:** NASA's Messenger mission (short for Mercury Surface, Space Environment, Geochemistry and Ranging) launched in August 2004 and arrived in orbit around the solar system's innermost planet in March 2011. Messenger has found solid evidence of water ice and carbon-containing organic compounds in the permanently shadowed craters near Mercury's poles.

## Venus

**Venus Express:** This ESA spacecraft blasted off in November 2005 and began orbiting Earth's hellishly hot "sister planet" in April 2006. Its main goal is to help scientists better understand the evolution of Venus' thick atmosphere.

**Akatsuki:** The Akatsuki mission, which launched in May 2010, was Japan's second attempt to send a probe to another planet, after 2003's ill-fated Nozomi mission to Mars. Akatsuki has had troubles as well, failing to insert into Venus orbit as planned in December 2010. The probe is now circling the sun, and mission managers plan to take another shot at Venus in November 2015.

**Earth's moon:** The earth's moon space mission have different purpose.

**Lunar Reconnaissance Orbiter:** LRO launched on June 18, 2009, and arrived in lunar orbit five days later. The $504 million, car-size NASA spacecraft is studying the lunar surface for scientific and exploration purposes; its observations should help researchers decide where to put a future human colony on the moon, NASA officials say.

**Artemis:** The two ARTEMIS spacecraft - short for Acceleration, Reconnection, Turbulence and Electrodynamics of the Moon's Interaction with the Sun - completed their unusual journey from Earth orbit to lunar orbit in July 2011. They had originally been part of a five-satellite, $200 million NASA mission called THEMIS (Time History of Events and Macroscale Interactions during Substorms), which launched in February 2007. [10 Coolest Moon Discoveries].

# Mars

**Mars Odyssey:** This venerable NASA orbiter launched in April 2001 and arrived at the Red Planet six months later to look for signs of past and present water activity. The $297 million spacecraft also serves as a communications relay between NASA's Mars rovers and their controllers on Earth.

**Mars Express:** This 150 million-euro ($198 million) ESA probe's main objective is to look for subsurface water from orbit. It launched in June 2003 and arrived at Mars in December of that year. Mars Express also aimed to put a lander, called Beagle 2, on the Martian surface, but this aspect of the mission failed.

**Mars Reconnaissance Orbiter:** NASA's MRO spacecraft launched in August 2005 and achieved Mars orbit in March 2006. Since then, it has been mapping the Red Planet's surface with unprecedented precision. In addition to their scientific value, MRO's observations have helped NASA decide where to land surface missions on the Red Planet. MRO is also the chief communications link between Mars surface craft and Earth.

**Opportunity Rover:** This golf-cart-size robot launched in July 2003 and landed in January 2004, three weeks after its twin, Spirit. Spirit and Opportunity were tasked with three-month missions to search for signs of past water activity on Mars; both found plenty of such evidence and kept on roving. Spirit stopped communicating with Earth in March 2010, but Opportunity is still going strong.

**Curiosity Rover:** The Curiosity rover dwarfs Spirit and Opportunity; it's the size of a small car and weighs a ton. Curiosity launched in November 2011 and pulled off a dramatic sky-crane landing on Aug. 5, 2012. Its main mission is to determine if its Gale Crater landing site has ever been capable of supporting microbial life.

**India's Mars Mission:** Indian Space Research Organisation (ISRO) first interdisciplinary Mars Orbiter Mission (MOM) in India. Morning at 09:08 GMT Indian Space Research Organisation (ISRO) successfully launched the Mars Orbiter Mission, also known as Mangalyaan, the country's first spacecraft destined for Mars. Over the next 300 days, it will slingshot around Earth and travel to mars to begin its science mission. If all goes well, Mangalyaan (Hindi for "Mars craft") should arrive around September 24, 2014 and ISRO will become the fourth space program to reach the red planet; only the United States, Europe, and the Soviet Union have achieved this so far.

- While orbiting Mars during its six month mission, Mangalyaan will analyze the Martian atmosphere for methane, a critical chemical for life. Methane does not last very long in the atmosphere, meaning a continual source must come from the planet itself. While a large amount of methane on Earth is produced by microbes, it can also originate from volcanic activity which might be more likely for Mars. The orbiter will also seek to determine weather patterns and will hopefully find clues about where the once-abundant water on the palnet's surface has gone.

- As with many space endeavours, some Indian citizens are questioning the importance of the $72 million mission. Nearly 68% of citizens in India live on less than US $2 per day, so many feel poverty eradication should take precedence over space exploration. This is a legitimate concern, but the mission actually stands to alleviate financial concerns.

- A successful space program will advance India's communication abilities though advanced satellites. Improved telemedicine will allow hospitals in remote areas to quickly connect with larger specialty hospitals, which can save lives. Advancing weather forecasting has the potential to save lives by better predicting storms coming in off the coast and can also be used to benefit agriculture. Improvements in technology could also create desperately-needed jobs, boosting per capita income.

- The space program is also remarkably efficient: the Polar Satellite Launch Vehicle (PSLV) developed in India that launched Mangalyaan into space has successfully completed 23 out of 25 launches, which equates to a 92% success rate. The current Mars mission was developed and launched in a mere 15 months, making today's launch all the more impressive.

- ISRO has 58 mission planned during the 2012-2017 time span, involving 33 satellites and 25 launch vehicles.

## Asteroid Belt's Space Observatory

**Dawn:** NASA's Dawn spacecraft launched in September 2007 and arrived at the protoplanet Vesta - the second-largest denizen of the main asteroid belt between Mars and Jupiter - in July 2011. Dawn departed Vesta in September 2012 to head to the belt's biggest body, Ceres. It should reach the dwarf planet in February 2015.

**Rosetta:** This ambitious ESA mission, which costs about 1 billion euros ($1.32 billion), aims to orbit and drop a lander on the comet 67P Churyumov-Gera-simenko. Rosetta launched in March 2004, executed flybys of two different asteroids in 2008 and 2010 and is set to meet up with the comet in mid-2014 near the orbit of Jupiter, about 420 million miles (675 million km) from Earth.

## Jupiter

**Juno:** This NASA spacecraft launched in August 2011 and is slated to arrive at Jupiter in August 2016. Over the course of one Earth year, Juno will study the gas giant's atmosphere, internal structure and magnetic field from orbit. Juno is the first solar-powered spacecraft ever to venture as far as Jupiter.

## Saturn

**Cassini:** The billion Cassini-Huygens mission, a joint effort involving NASA, ESA, and the Italian Space Agency, launched in October 1997 and achieved Saturn orbit in July 2004. The Cassini spacecraft has been studying Saturn, its rings and the planet's many moons ever since. In January 2005, the probe also delivered the Huygens lander to the surface of Titan, Saturn's largest moon.

## Pluto

**New Horizons:** This super-speedy NASA spacecraft launched in January 2006 and is set to fly by the Pluto system in July 2015, giving researchers their first-ever up-close look at the dwarf planet. After that, the $700 million probe may also fly by one or more objects in the Kuiper Belt, the ring of icy bodies beyond Neptune's orbit.

## Solar System's Edge

**Voyager 1 and 2:** NASA's twin Voyager probes launched in 1977 to study Saturn, Jupiter and their moons. The pair made many discoveries about these far-flung bodies, then checked out Uranus and Neptune and kept on flying.

Both spacecraft are now studying the unique conditions at the edge of the solar system, knocking on the door of interstellar space. Voyager 1-the most distant manmade object ever launched-is currently about 11 billion miles (18 billion km) from Earth, while Voyager 2 is 9 billion miles (15 billion km) from home. NASA has spent about $1 billion on the mission to date.

## The Sun is a Star

The core starts from the center and extends outward to encompass 25 percent of the Sun's radius. Its temperature is greater than 15 million degrees Kelvin [source: Montana]. At the core, gravity pulls all of the mass inward and creates an intense pressure. The pressure is high enough to force atoms of hydrogen to come together in nuclear fusion reactions -- something we try to emulate here on Earth. Two atoms of hydrogen are combined to create helium-4 and energy in several steps:

1. Two protons combine to form a deuterium atom (hydrogen atom with one neutron and one proton), a positron (similar to electron, but with a positive charge) and a neutrino.

2. A proton and a deuterium atom combine to form a helium-3 atom (two protons with one neutron) and a gamma ray.

3. Two helium-3 atoms combine to form a helium-4 atom (two protons and two neutrons) and two protons.

These reactions account for 85 per cent of the Sun's energy. The remaining 15 per cent comes from the reactions.

The Sun at the heart of our solar system is a yellow dwarf star, a hot ball of glowing gases. Its gravity holds the solar system together, keeping everything from the biggest planets to the smallest particles of debris in its orbit. Electric currents in the sun generate a magnetic field that is carried out through the solar system by the solar wind - a stream of electrically charged gas blowing outward from the sun in all directions.

The connection and interactions between the sun and Earth drive the seasons, ocean currents, weather, climate, radiation belts and aurorae. Though it is special to us, there are billions of stars like our sun scattered across the Milky Way galaxy.

# THE EARTH IN THE SOLAR SYSTEM

Earth is the third planet from the sun and the fifth largest in the solar system. Just slightly larger than nearby Venus, Earth is the biggest of the terrestrial planets. Our home planet is the only planet in our solar system known to harbor living things.

The name Earth is at least 1,000 years old. All of the planets, except for Earth, were named after Greek and Roman gods and goddesses. However, the name Earth is an English/German word, which simply means the ground.

- **Size and Distance:** With a radius of 3,959 miles (6,371 kilometers), Earth is the biggest of the terrestrial planets, and the fifth largest planet overall. From an average distance of 93 million miles (150 million kilometers), Earth is exactly one astronomical unit away from the sun because one astronomical unit (abbreviated as AU), is the distance from the sun to Earth. This unit provides an easy way to quickly compare planets' distances from the sun. It takes about eight minutes for light from the sun to reach our planet.

- **Orbit and Rotation:** As Earth orbits the Sun, it completes one rotation every 23.9 hours. It takes 365.25 days to complete one trip around the sun. That extra quarter of a day presents a challenge to our calendar system, which counts one year as 365 days. To keep our yearly calendars consistent with our orbit around the sun, every four years we add one day. That day is called a leap day, and the year it's added to is called a leap year.

Earth's axis of rotation is tilted 23.4 degrees with respect to the plane of Earth's orbit around the sun. This tilt causes our yearly cycle of seasons. During part of the year, the northern hemisphere is tilted toward the sun and the southern hemisphere is tilted away. With the sun higher in the sky, solar heating is greater in the north producing summer there. Less direct solar heating produces winter in the south. Six months later, the situation is reversed. When spring and fall begin, both hemispheres receive roughly equal amounts of heat from the sun.

- **Formation:** When the solar system settled into its current layout about 4.5 billion years ago, Earth formed when gravity pulled swirling gas and dust in to become the third planet from the sun. Like its fellow terrestrial planets, Earth has a central core, a rocky mantle and a solid crust.

- **Structure:** Earth is composed of four main layers, starting with an inner core at the planet's center, enveloped by the outer core, mantle and crust. The inner core is a solid sphere made of iron and nickel metals about 759 miles (1,221 kilometers) in radius. There the temperature is as high as 9,800 degrees Fahrenheit (5,400 degrees Celsius). Surrounding the inner core is the outer core. This layer is about 1,400 miles (2,300 kilometers) thick, made of iron and nickel fluids. In between the outer core and crust is the mantle, the thickest layer. This hot, viscous mixture of molten rock is about 1,800 miles (2,900 kilometers) thick and has the consistency of caramel. The outermost layer, Earth's crust, goes about 19 miles (30 kilometers) deep on average on land. At the bottom of the ocean, the crust is thinner and extends about 3 miles (5 kilometers) from the sea floor to the top of the mantle.

- **Surface:** Like Mars and Venus, Earth has volcanoes, mountains and valleys. Earth's lithosphere, which includes the crust (both continental and oceanic) and the upper mantle, is divided into huge plates that are constantly moving. For example, the North American plate moves west over the Pacific Ocean basin, roughly at a rate equal to the growth of our fingernails. Earthquakes result when plates grind past one another, ride up over one another, collide to make mountains, or split and separate.

- **Atmosphere:** Near the surface, Earth has an atmosphere that consists of 78 per cent nitrogen, 21 per cent oxygen, and 1 per cent other gases such as argon, carbon dioxide and neon. The atmosphere affects Earth's long-term climate and short-term local weather and shields us from much of the harmful radiation coming from the sun. It also protects us from meteoroids, most of which burn up in the atmosphere, seen as meteors in the night sky, before they can strike the surface as meteorites.

## Earth's Statistical information

| | |
|---|---|
| **Mass (kg)** | 5.976e + 24 |
| **Planet type^** | Terrestrial |
| **Moon** | 1 |
| **Mass (Earth = 1)** | 1.0000e + 00 |
| **Equatorial radius (km)** | 6,378.14 |
| **Equatorial radius (Earth = 1)** | 1.0000e+00 |
| **Mean density (gm/cm³)** | 5.515 |
| **Mean distance from the Sun (km)** | 149,600,000 |
| **Mean distance from the Sun (Earth = 1)** | 1.0000 |
| **Rotational period (days)** | 0.99727 |
| **Rotational period (hours)** | 23.9345 |
| **Orbital period (days)** | 365.256 |
| **Mean orbital velocity (km/sec)** | 29.79 |
| **Orbital eccentricity** | 0.0167 |
| **Tilt of axis (degrees)** | 23.45 |
| **Orbital inclination (degrees)** | 0.000 |
| **Equatorial escape velocity (km/sec)** | 11.18 |
| **Equatorial surface gravity (m/sec²)** | 9.78 |
| **Visual geometric albedo** | 0.37 |
| **Mean surface temperature** | 15°C |
| **Atmospheric pressure (bars)** | 1.013 |
| **Atmospheric Composition** | |
| Nitrogen | 77% |
| Oxygen | 21% |
| Other | 2% |

## SPACE SCIENCE

The space science is the branch of science which deals the our solar system which consists Sun, planets, moons, galaxies, stars and objects which exists in our universe. Our sky is a layer of the different compositions which is thermosphere, ionosphere etc.

## Layers of the Atmosphere

The atmosphere consists of the different layers like thermosphere, stratosphere, mesosphere and exosphere which all about the different behaviour of the temperature, pressure and others chemical, physical properties.

**Thermosphere:** The thermosphere is a layer of Earth's atmosphere. The thermosphere is directly above the mesosphere and below the exosphere. It extends from about 90 km (56 miles) to between 500 and 1,000 km (311 to 621 miles) above our planet.

The boundary between the thermosphere and the exosphere above it is called the thermopause. At the bottom of the thermosphere is the mesopause, the boundary between the thermosphere and the mesosphere below.

To understand where the thermosphere is, we need to understand the other layers of the atmosphere starting from the Earth's surface. Near the surface to about 7 miles above is the troposphere. This is where clouds we see in the sky are. Near the edge of the troposphere and into the next layer, the stratosphere, which put simply, is where airplanes fly. The stratosphere extends from 7 miles above the surface to about 20 miles above the surface. After the stratosphere is the mesosphere, which extends upward to 50 miles above the surface.

After the mesosphere, we have the layer called the thermosphere. The thermosphere extends from about 50 miles above the surface of Earth to about 600 miles above our planet. Beyond that is the exosphere, which is the layer that turns into outer space at the edge.

**Magnetosphere:** A magnetosphere is the volume of space around an astronomical object that is controlled by that object's magnetic field. The Earth's magnetosphere is the cavity formed by the Earth's magnetic field in the flow of plasma from the Sun known as the solar wind. The interaction with the solar wind deforms the Earth's basically dipolar magnetic field, compressing the field lines on the day side and stretching them out to form a long comet-like tail on the night side.

A magnetosphere is the region around a planet dominated by the planet's magnetic field. Other planets in our solar system have magnetospheres, but Earth has the strongest one of all the rocky planets: Earth's magnetosphere is a vast, comet-shaped bubble, which has played a crucial role in our planet's habitability. Life on Earth initially developed and continues to be sustained under the protection of this magnetic environment. The magnetosphere shields our home planet from solar and cosmic particle radiation, as well as erosion of the atmosphere by the solar wind - the constant flow of charged particles streaming off the sun.

Earth's magnetosphere is part of a dynamic, interconnected system that responds to solar, planetary, and interstellar conditions. It is generated by the convective motion of charged, molten iron, far below the surface in Earth's outer core. Constant bombardment by the solar wind compresses the sun-facing side of our magnetic field. The sun-facing side, or dayside, extends a distance of about six to 10 times the radius of the Earth. The side of the magnetosphere facing away from the sun - the nightside - stretches out into an immense magnetotail, which fluctuates in length and can measure hundreds of Earth radii, far past the moon's orbit at 60 Earth radii.

**Solar wind:** The solar wind is a stream of energized, charged particles, primarily electrons and protons, flowing outward from the Sun, through the solar system at speeds as high as 900 km/s and at a temperature of 1 million degrees (Celsius). It is made of plasma."The solar wind is caused by the hot solar corona, which is the outermost layer of the solar atmosphere, expanding into space. The corona is the "rim" of the Sun that is visible to the naked eye during a solar eclipse. The solar wind is what blows the tails of comets back away from the bodies of comets as they go through the solar system.

The Sun's outer atmosphere, the super-hot corona, is the source of the solar wind, a steady outflow of charged particles from the Sun. These particles have gained enough energy to fill the heliosphere, a region of space that extends well past the orbit of Pluto. As these particles flow past Earth's orbit, they're traveling at an average of 400 kilometers per second. Though the Sun can lose more than a million tons of material each second, the amount is still negligible compared to the Sun's total mass.

The solar wind is primarily composed of roughly equal numbers of protons and electrons, as well as a few heavier ions. The particles' velocities are highest over coronal holes, areas near the Sun's poles associated with "open" magnetic field lines that allow material to flow more easily into space. Particles flow out more slowly near the Sun's equator, where magnetic field lines loop back on themselves and trap coronal material.

## The Influence of solar surface activities to the Earth

The main source of the energy on the earth surface is Sun, heating the surface of the atmosphere, ocean and warm the planet. The solar radiation is the main phenomenon of the climate and weather conditions in the form of the albedo and clouds. The amount of radiation given off by the Sun changes with solar activity like solar flares or sunspots. Solar activity is known to vary in cycles, like the 11-yr sunspot cycle (and longer cycles). Some scientists have wondered if changes in our weather and climate might be linked with short or long term solar cycles. Weather is the current atmospheric conditions, including temperature, rainfall, wind, and humidity for a given area, while climate is the general weather conditions over a longer amount of time. This has been an active area of research for decades.

Some scientists tried to find a link between changes in Earth's weather and solar variability. Although some scientists reported such correlations, later studies have not been able to find the same result, casting in doubt or disproving the original studies. Examples include studies of the relationship between the number of sunspots and changes in wind patterns, or between cosmic rays and clouds.

## MULTIPLE CHOICE QUESTIONS

1. Which among the following does not get sun's vertical rays?
   (a) Delhi          (b) Bangalore
   (c) Hyderabad      (d) Mumbai

2. Which of the following satellites has the best radiometric resolution?
   (a) LANDSAT        (b) CARTOSAT
   (c) IKONOS         (d) QUICKBIRD

3. The number of satellites in the GPS system is
   (a) 16             (b) 19
   (c) 22             (d) 24

4. The amount of generation of power from solar energy by the National Solar Mission by 2020 is
   (a) 5000 MW        (b) 20000 MW
   (c) 30000 MW       (d) 50000 MW

5. An International Transshipment Container Terminal is being built at
   (a) Vallarpadam
   (b) Vishakapatnam
   (c) Mundra
   (d) Ratlam

6. Identify the correct order in terms of increasing wavelength
   (a) Visible, Ultraviolet, Infrared, Microwaves
   (b) Visible, Microwaves, Ultraviolet, Infrared
   (c) Ultraviolet, Infrared, Visible, Microwaves
   (d) Ultraviolet, Visible, Infrared, Microwaves

7. Which of the following sensor is used in IRS satellites?
   (a) TM             (b) HRV
   (c) LISS           (d) MSS

8. In which place IRS data collection and storage is in operation?
   (a) Dehra Dun      (b) Bangalore
   (c) Shadnagar      (d) Ahmedabad

9. Who among the following outlined Rank size rule?
   (a) Berry          (b) Clark
   (c) Dickinson      (d) Zip

10. Sanson- Flamstead projection is also called
    (a) Polyconic projection
    (b) Mercator equal area projection
    (c) Sinusoidal projection
    (d) Conical projection

11. In which of the projections distortion is more in the case of polar regions?
    (a) Cylindrical equal area
    (b) Zenithal
    (c) Conical
    (d) Molleweide

12. Which of the following cities has a Regional Remote Sensing Service Centre?
    (a) Jodhpur          (b) Jaipur
    (c) Hyderabad        (d) Kolkata

13. SPOT is a remote sensing satellite launched by
    (a) France           (b) USA
    (c) Japan            (d) Russia

14. The Primate pattern of cities was explained by
    (a) Mumford          (b) Jefferson
    (c) Taylor           (d) Nelson

15. Which of the following statements is correct?
    (a) Aurousseau outlined the urban land use model first
    (b) Tanner indicated Density crater in his model of urban population density
    (c) In Christaller's central place theory K = 4 under marketing principle
    (d) Dickinson outlined City and City region concept in detail

16. Which among the following projections is most suitable for navigation?
    (a) Polyconic        (b) Lambert
    (c) Bonne's          (d) Mercator

17. Spate outlined the principles of the concept of
    (a) Probabilism
    (b) Positivism
    (c) Pragmatism
    (d) Behavioralism

18. Which of the following statements is not correct?
    (a) The temporal resolution of IRS IC is 24 days
    (b) INSAT 4B is a Sun Synchronous satellite
    (c) Oceansat-2 was launched on 2009
    (d) RISAT is the first Radar Imaging Satellite launched by India

19. **Assertion [A] :** In a seismograph S waves are recorded first.
    **Reasoning [R] :** S waves travel only through solid matter.

    (a) Both [A] and [R] are true and [R] is the correct reason
    (b) Both [A] and [R] are true but [R] is Not the correct reason
    (c) [A] is true but [R] is false.
    (d) [A] is false but [R] is true.

20. The hypothesis proposed by Kant and LaPlace on the origin of solar system
    (a) Tidal hypothesis
    (b) Nebular hypothesis
    (c) Planetesimal hypothesis
    (d) Cloud hypothesis

21. The range of wave length of the visible region of the electromagnetic spectrum.
    (a) $0.7 - 3.0$ μm        (b) $0.7 - 1.0$ μm
    (c) $0.4 - 0.7$ μm        (d) $3 - 5$ μm

22. The basic spatial entities in GIS are
    (a) Scale, Projection and Generalization
    (b) Points, Lines and Areas
    (c) Projections, Legends and Georeference
    (d) Latitude, Longitude and Coordinates

23. "Rubber sheeting" in GIS is related to
    (a) Data editing
    (b) Data transfer
    (c) Data input
    (d) Map projection

24. Which is *not* true of GPS?
    (a) Useful in photogrammetry
    (b) Developed by United States
    (c) The orbital height of satellites is > 20000 Kms
    (d) It has 42 satellites

25. The Temporal resolution of Cartosat 2B is
    (a) 4 days           (b) 7 days
    (c) 12 days          (d) 22 days

26. Which of the following is a Geostationary satellite altitude?
    (a) 36000 km         (b) 30000 km
    (c) 700 km           (d) 900 km

27. What is the age of the Earth?
    (a) 3.5 b.y.         (b) 4.5 b.y.
    (c) 5.5 b.y.         (d) 6.5 b.y.

28. Which of the following is formerly known as ERTS?
    (a) IRS-1            (b) IRS-2
    (c) Aryabhatta       (d) LANDSAT

29. Which GIS technique makes a continuous map by composting a large number of map sheets?
    (a) Rubber sheeting  (b) Edge matching
    (c) Attribute editing (d) Mosaic

30. The term geo-referencing in map interpretation means:
    (a) To relate with respect to toposheet
    (b) Location of points from base station
    (c) The position with respect to base station
    (d) Location of points with respect to co-ordinates

31. Which one of the following is a sensor fitted with the Indian satellite?
    (a) TM
    (b) LISS IV
    (c) HRV
    (d) MSS

32. Which of the following satellites has the best spatial resolution?
    (a) SPOT
    (b) CARTOSAT 2
    (c) IRS 1D
    (d) IKONOS

33. The present day discontinuous expansion of cities into rural areas is characterised as
    (a) Urban fringe
    (b) Urban growth
    (c) Urban sprawl
    (d) Urban dynamics

34. An imaginary line from where elevations/heights are measured is known as
    (a) International Date Line
    (b) Datum line
    (c) Agonic line
    (d) Level line

35. To detect an aircraft, RADAR makes use of
    (a) Sound waves
    (b) Electric waves
    (c) Microwaves
    (d) Ultrasonic waves

36. The international protocol to protect the ozone layer is the
    (a) Montreal Protocol
    (b) Kyoto Protocol
    (c) Vienna Protocol
    (d) Cartegene Protocol

37. *Geography: A Modern Synthesis* is authored by
    (a) Berry
    (b) Peet
    (c) Isard
    (d) Hagett

38. Rainfall that occurs due to the intense heating of the atmosphere from below is
    (a) Orographic rainfall
    (b) Convectional rainfall
    (c) Cyclonic rainfall
    (d) Frontal rainfall

39. The periodic winds is
    (a) Monsoon wind
    (b) Winter wind
    (c) Summer wind
    (d) Tropical wind

40. The headquarters of World Meteorological Organisation is located at
    (a) London
    (b) New York
    (c) Paris
    (d) Geneva

41. Which of the following is a pioneer of white revolution in India?
    (a) Aavin
    (b) Amul
    (c) Milma
    (d) Cavin

42. The concept of least cost to location theory was introduced by
    (a) Weber
    (b) Losch
    (c) Haggett
    (d) Dicey

43. Growth Pole concept was put forth by
    (a) Misra
    (b) Perroux
    (c) Haggerstrand
    (d) Losch

44. Christaller's concept of centrality is based upon
    (a) Hierarchy
    (b) Principle of least effort
    (c) Range of goods
    (d) Law of gravitation

45. Points exactly on the opposite sides of the earth which form two points for diameter of the earth are called
    (a) Aphelion
    (b) Antipodes
    (c) Antipoles
    (d) Apogee

46. The GPS system developed by European Agency is called
    (a) GAGAN
    (b) GALILEO
    (c) GLONASS
    (d) NNRSS

47. TM is associated with
    (a) IRS ID
    (b) SPOT
    (c) LANDSAT
    (d) CARTOSAT

48. Which of the following statements is **WRONG**?
    (a) Line joining points in each meridian having the highest average temperature is called Thermal equator
    (b) Annual thermal equator lies to the southern hemisphere because of less land area
    (c) Equator and thermal equator are two different lines
    (d) Thermal equator moves north and south due to apparent movement of sun's rays

49. The National Highway connecting Salem with Thiruvananthapuram is
    (a) NH 44
    (b) NH 45
    (c) NH 47
    (d) NH 49

50. In 2011, the share of population in urban agglomerations to total urban population in Kerala is
    (a) 65%
    (b) 70%
    (c) 80%
    (d) More than 90%

51. Which of the following satellites helps in Communication?
   (a) CARTOSAT (b) IRS ID
   (c) RESOURCESAT (d) INSAT

52. Which of the following describes Radio metric resolution?
   (a) 1.6 metres (b) 22 days
   (c) 8 bit data (d) Band 7

53. A zone of specific distance around coverage features useful for proximity analysis in GIS is called
   (a) Polygon (b) Buffer
   (c) Layer (d) Island

54. Appearance of jagged lines on a raster display is called
   (a) Cascade (b) Clump
   (c) Rubber Sheeting (d) Aliasing

55. In Digital Image Processing data from sources other than Remote Sensing used to assist in analysis and classification is called
   (a) Ancillary data (b) Raster data
   (c) Vector data (d) Metadata

56. Which of the following is associated with Active Remote Sensing?
   (a) AVHRR (b) LISS
   (c) RBV (d) SLAR

57. If an area is to be mapped on large scale the most useful satellite will be
   (a) LANDSAT (b) SPOT
   (c) IKONOS (d) IRS ID

58. Identify the **WRONG** statement
   (a) Climatic Geomorphology is also sometimes known as Process Geomorphology
   (b) German and French geographers contributed more to Climatic Geomorphology
   (c) Sea wave action is considered as a Zonal process
   (d) Peltier's scheme of Morphogenetic region is widely used

59. All the planets revolve round the Sun in
   (a) Elliptical orbit (b) Spherical orbit
   (c) Circular orbit (d) Not defined

60. The surface temperature of the Sun is about
   (a) 10800 °F (b) 1080 °F
   (c) 100800 °F (d) 10080 °F

61. The shape of the earth is
   (a) Spherical (b) Elliptical
   (c) Circular (d) All the above

62. Zones that are characterized by shallow, intermediate and deep seismicity, negative gravity anomaly, very low heat flow and sites for sediment accumulations are :
   (a) Subduction Zones
   (b) Transform Fault Zones
   (c) Constructive Plate Margins
   (d) Triple Junctions

63. The field strengths of the Earth's magnetic field are usually expressed in :
   (a) Kilogauss (KG)
   (b) Nano Tesla (nT)
   (c) Ampere/meter (A/m)
   (d) Volts/meter (V/m)

64. When a set of seismic waves meet a gap they tend to spread out on other side, the phenomenon can be described as :
   (a) Refraction
   (b) Reflection
   (c) Diffusion
   (d) Diffraction

65. In the tropics the net radiation throughout the year is :
   (a) Positive
   (b) Negative
   (c) Zero
   (d) Positive in summer and negative in winter

66. Solar flux density reaching earth (solar constant) is :
   (a) ~1200 W/m$^2$ (b) ~1000 W/m$^2$
   (c) ~1400 W/m$^2$ (d) ~800 W/m$^2$

67. The Earth's average albedo is :
   (a) ~31% (b) ~25%
   (c) ~40% (d) ~20%

68. The average composition of planet Earth corresponds to :
   (a) Peridotite (b) Harzburgite
   (c) Siderite (d) Chondrite

69. The most abundant element in the solar system is:
   (a) Helium (b) Oxygen
   (c) Hydrogen (d) Nitrogen

70. The reflectance and emittance of a feature over a variety of wavelengths is referred to _____
   (a) Spatial resolution
   (b) Spectral resolution
   (c) Temporal resolution
   (d) Radiometric resolution

71. Salinity of groundwater can be estimated using _____
    (a) Seismic Survey
    (b) Magnetic Survey
    (c) Gravity Survey
    (d) Electrical Resistivity Survey

72. If 'a' is equatorial radius and 'c' is the polar radius, then the geometrical flattening of the earth is
    (a) (a – c)/a          (b) (c – a)/a
    (c) (a + c)/a          (d) (a – c)/c

73. In Satellite meteorology, water vapour imagery is derived for the radiance at the atmospheric window region _____ $\mu$m
    (a) 5 – 6              (b) 1 – 2
    (c) 8 – 10            (d) All the above

74. Which is nearest star to the earth?
    (a) Alfa Centaury      (b) Sun
    (c) Proxima Centaury  (d) Dog Star

75. The planet with maximum satellites is:
    (a) Earth             (b) Saturn
    (c) Jupiter           (d) Pluto

76. Which planet is called 'red planet'?
    (a) Mars             (b) Jupiter
    (c) Mercury          (d) Earth

77. Which planet is called 'Double Planet'?
    (a) Venus            (b) Uranus
    (c) Pluto            (d) Earth

78. Which is largest satellite in Solar System?
    (a) Moon             (b) Ganymede
    (c) Europa           (d) Cheron

79. Total time taken by Sun-rays reaches earth in (approximately)
    (a) 8 seconds        (b) 8 minutes
    (c) 4.3 seconds      (d) 1 light year

80. Which is smallest planet of our Solar System?
    (a) Pluto            (b) Earth
    (c) Venus            (d) Mercury

81. Which is brightest planet of our Solar System?
    (a) Venus            (b) Mercury
    (c) Uranus           (d) Saturn

82. Hale Bopp' is a newly discovered _____ of solar system.
    (a) Planet           (b) Meteore
    (c) Satellite        (d) Comet

83. Charon' is the satellite of _____.
    (a) Earth            (b) Saturn
    (c) Pluto            (d) Neptune

84. A family or system of millions and millions of stars are called _____.
    (a) Galaxy           (b) Asteroids
    (c) Universe         (d) Solar System

85. That is the name of our galaxy?
    (a) Alfa Centauri    (b) Proxima Centauri
    (c) Milky Way        (d) Neptune

86. What is the shape of our galaxy 'Milky Way'?
    (a) Circular         (b) Spherical
    (c) Spiral           (d) Elliptical

87. The terms Orion and Great Bear for
    (a) Solar System     (b) Constellation
    (c) Star             (d) Planet

88. Our Solar System is an orderly system of
    (a) One star         (b) Two stars
    (c) Three stars      (d) Four stars

89. Number of planets exist in Solar system
    (a) 9 (Nine)         (b) 6 (Six)
    (c) 7 (Seven)        (d) 10 (Ten)

90. The word 'planet' define as
    (a) Wanderer         (b) Pollution
    (c) Celestial body   (d) Heavenly body

91. A celestial body which having its own heat and light is called
    (a) Star             (b) Moon
    (c) Planet           (d) Satellite

92. A swarm of small bodies in between the two Planets of Solar System is called 'asteroids' which are those two Planets?
    (a) Neptune and Pluto
    (b) Jupiter and Saturn
    (c) Mars and Jupiter
    (d) Earth and Venus

93. Which planet takes the longest time in completing one revolution around the Sun?
    (a) Pluto            (b) Neptune
    (c) Uranus           (d) Saturn

94. Big Bang Theory' discuss
    (a) The formation of universe
    (b) Formation of Solar System
    (c) Formation of constellation
    (d) The origin and evolution of earth's crust

95. A system which have millions and millions of galaxies called?
    (a) Space            (b) Constellation
    (c) Solar System     (d) Universe

**96.** A celestial object which revolves around a planet just as a planet revolves around the Sun is called
(a) Moon
(b) Satellite
(c) Great Bear
(d) Asteroid

**97.** The Sun revolves around galaxy once in every 250 million years, this revolution time is called
(a) Cosmic or Galactic Year
(b) Sidereal Year
(c) Leap Year
(d) Mean Solar Year

**98.** Which planet nearly have equal rotation and revolution time to the earth
(a) Venus
(b) Uranus
(c) Mars
(d) Mercury

**99.** The Earth have rank in the Solar System away from the Sun
(a) 5th
(b) 6th
(c) 3rd
(d) 4th

**100.** The direction of rotation of the earth on its axis is?
(a) Eastward
(b) North to South
(c) Westward
(d) South to North

**101.** A celestial body which revolves round the Sun and receives heat and light from it is called
(a) Planet
(b) Satellite
(c) Star
(d) Orion

**102.** Which planet does take the least time in completing one revolution around the Sun?
(a) Earth
(b) Mercury
(c) Mars
(d) Venus

**103.** What is the most accurate description of the shape of the earth?
(a) A geoid
(b) An oblate spheroid
(c) A flat disc
(d) A spherical

**104.** Presently the farthest planet from the Sun is
(a) Uranus
(b) Venus
(c) Pluto
(d) Neptune

**105.** The scientists have discovered that Milky Way is having two components, the disc and spherical. What may be the central object of Milky Way?
(a) A black hole
(b) Vaccum
(c) A large Magellanic Cloud
(d) A neutron star

**106.** The Magellanic Cloud are visible from
(a) Southern hemisphere
(b) Northern hemisphere
(c) Earth and Mars
(d) Mercury and Venus

**107.** The Planetoids are in between
(a) Saturn and Jupiter
(b) Mars and Jupiter
(c) Earth and Mars
(d) Mercury and Venus

**108.** Which planets show phases
(a) Venus
(b) Saturn
(c) Earth
(d) Jupiter

**109.** Which is the Brightest star?
(a) Sirius
(b) Proxima Centauri
(c) Alpha Centauri
(d) Polaris

**110.** Which two main gases support the formation of the stars?
(a) Hydrogen and oxygen
(b) Nitrogen and helium
(c) Hydrogen and nitrogen
(d) Hydrogen and helium

**111.** Aurorae are produced by the collision of charged particles from Earth's magnetosphere which is due to
(a) Ozone layer
(b) Solar wind
(c) Radio waves
(d) Ionosphere

**112.** Milky Way diameter is approx.
(a) 1000 light years
(b) 10000 light years
(c) 100000 light years
(d) 1000000 light years

**113.** Which star is at center of our Solar system?
(a) Moon
(b) Sun
(c) Earth
(d) Pluto

**114.** The diameter of the Sun is
(a) 1,392,684 km
(b) 1,493,785 km
(c) 1,000,000 km
(d) 1,250,556 km

**115.** The mass percentage of Sun in solar system
(a) 1%
(b) 51%
(c) 99%
(d) 3%

**116.** Number of stars in the Milky Way?
(a) 100 million
(b) 100 billion
(c) 10 million
(d) 10 billion

**117.** The age of the Sun is about
(a) 4.6 billion years
(b) 4.6 million years
(c) 4.5 billion years
(d) 4.5 million years

**118.** The distance between Sun and Earth is
(a) 149,600,000 km
(b) 251,600,000 km
(c) 300,600,000 km
(d) 100,500,000 km

**119.** The elemental composition of the Sun is
(a) Hydrogen and oxygen
(b) Hydrogen and helium
(c) Oxygen and helium
(d) Nitrogen and oxygen

**120.** Which planet is also called Morning Star or Evening Star?
(a) Venus     (b) Earth
(c) Pluto     (d) Mars

**121.** The diameter of the earth
(a) 12,000 km     (b) 12,742 km
(c) 12,542 km     (d) 12,642 km

**122.** Largest planet in our Solar System
(a) Jupiter     (b) Mars
(c) Earth     (d) Saturn

**123.** Which planet is closest to the Sun?
(a) Mercury     (b) Venus
(c) Mars     (d) Jupiter

**124.** The hottest planets in our solar system
(a) Venus     (b) Mars
(c) Pluto     (d) Earth

**125.** Which star is called Earth's satellite?
(a) Moon     (b) Pluto
(c) Ceras     (d) Meena

**126.** The average distance of moon from earth is
(a) 384,400 km     (b) 284,500 km
(c) 484,300 km     (d) 184,200 km

**127.** The age of the Moon is
(a) 4.5 billion years     (b) 4.5 million years
(c) 4.0 billion years     (d) 4.0 million years

**128.** The orbital period of the Moon is
(a) 27 days     (b) 30 days
(c) 365 days     (d) 1 days

**129.** The circumference of the Moon is
(a) 11,000 km     (b) 10,917 km
(c) 9,917 km     (d) 7,817 km

**130.** Which planet has the most volcanoes?
(a) Venus     (b) Mars
(c) Jupiter     (d) Earth

**131.** Which planets have no moons
(a) Venus and Mercury
(b) Earth and Venus
(c) Mercury and Earth
(d) Mars and Venus

**132.** A person who weighs 200 pounds on earth, what would he weigh on the surface of Mars?
(a) 76 pounds     (b) 152 pounds
(c) 38 pounds     (d) 200 pounds

**133.** The planets which have spins opposite to the others
(a) Mars     (b) Venus
(c) Pluto     (d) Earth

**134.** When was the first man made object sent into space?
(a) 1957     (b) 1961
(c) 1952     (d) 1971

**135.** Who was the first person to set foot on the Moon?
(a) Neil Armstrong
(b) Sunita William
(c) Valentine Tereshkova
(d) APJ Abdul Kalam

**136.** The average surface temperature of the Moon day and night respectively
(a) 107 and −153 °C
(b) −153 and 107 °C
(c) 100 and −100 °C
(d) 150 and −150 °C

**137.** The equatorial circumference of the Earth?
(a) 40,030 km     (b) 30,030 km
(c) 4030 km     (d) 3030 km

**138.** Number of natural satellite of the Earth
(a) One     (b) Two
(c) Six     (d) Eight

**139.** The position of planet by the angle make with the Sun as seen from the earth. The angle is called the
(a) Elongation     (b) Ecliptic
(c) Epicycle     (d) Retardation

**140.** Which planet has greatest eccentricity?
(a) Pluto     (b) Jupiter
(c) Mars     (d) Mercury

**141.** Phobos is a moon of the which planet?
(a) Jupiter     (b) Mars
(c) Venus     (d) Saturn

**142.** On which of the following planets would the Sun rise in the west?
(a) Venus     (b) Mars
(c) Mercury     (d) Pluto

**143.** A planets which turned on its side with an axis tilt of 98 degrees
(a) Neptune     (b) Earth
(c) Mars     (d) Uranus

**144.** The angle that the full moon takes up in the night sky is equal to
(a) 1/2 degree     (b) 1/3 degree
(c) 1/8 degree     (d) 1/16 degree

145. The period from one full moon to the next is
(a) 30.5 days          (b) 28.5 days
(c) 29.5 days          (d) 27.5 days

146. When a superior planet is at opposition it is making an angle with Sun
(a) 90 degrees          (b) 0 degrees
(c) 45 degrees          (d) 180 degrees

147. Albedo refers to
(a) Wobbling motion of a planet
(b) Phase change of the planet
(c) Amount of light reflected by the planet
(d) Brightness of the star

148. The law that says that all planets orbit the sun in elliptical orbits is which of Kepler's law?
(a) First law          (b) Second law
(c) Third law          (d) Bode's law

149. The astronomer who discovered that Mars orbits the Sun in an elliptical orbit
(a) Bode          (b) Laplace
(c) Kepler          (d) Kant

150. The orbital plane of the moon inclined from the ecliptic?
(a) 5 degrees          (b) 10 degrees
(c) 15 degrees          (d) 45 degrees

151. In the lowest level of the photosphere of the Sun, the temperature is:
(a) 100 degrees Kelvin
(b) 6,000 degrees Kelvin
(c) 10,000 degrees Kelvin
(d) 13,000 degrees Kelvin

152. A Galactic year is the length of time that it takes our sun to orbit the galaxy. In Earth years, how long is a Galactic year?
(a) 100 million years    (b) 230 million years
(c) 620 million years    (d) 940 million years

153. A first magnitude star is how many times brighter than a second magnitude star?
(a) 1.5          (b) 2.5
(c) 5.5          (d) 7.5

154. Name of the star which is brightest in the sky?
(a) Sirius          (b) Moon
(c) Ceras          (d) Pluto

155. A pulsar is defined as
(a) Neutron star          (b) Proton star
(c) Electron star          (d) Helium star

156. The best shape of the our galaxy
(a) Spiral          (b) Elliptical
(c) Spherical          (d) Convex

157. A black hole with the mass of the earth would be the size of:
(a) The Sun          (b) The Moon
(c) A bowling ball          (d) A marble

158. Which planets are never visible at midnight?
(a) Venus and Earth
(b) Mars and Mercury
(c) Mars and Jupiter
(d) Mercury and Venus

159. Most stars are cooler than the sun. These stars, the planets, interstellar clouds and star-forming regions emit most of their radiant energy in the:
(a) Infrared          (b) Visible
(c) Radiowave          (d) X-ray

160. Astronomers use Cepheids principally for _____ measure.
(a) Size
(b) Distance
(c) Chemical compound
(d) Velocity

161. In between most asteroids located?
(a) Mars and Jupiter
(b) Mars and Venus
(c) Earth and Mars
(d) Mercury and Venus

162. Which of the following can be used to see through Venus's clouds?
(a) RADAR          (b) X–ray
(c) Telescope          (d) Ultraviolet

163. What is the process by which the source of the energy in a supernova explosion?
(a) Fusion
(b) Radiation
(c) Centripetal force
(d) Centrifugal force

164. The Sun rotates about equator its own axis approximately
(a) 27 days
(b) Once 24 hours
(c) Once 364 days
(d) Varies with solar latitude

165. What is the farthest planet from the sun?
(a) Pluto          (b) Neptune
(c) Venus          (d) Mars

166. The Magellanic cloud is a:
(a) Nebula
(b) Galaxy
(c) Super nova remnant
(d) Star cluster

**167.** Which planet has the shortest year?
(a) Mercury (b) Venus
(c) Pluto (d) Earth

**168.** The gravity on the moon is what fraction of the gravity on the earth?
(a) 1/3 (b) 1/6
(c) 1/4 (d) 1/2

**169.** What is the motion called when a planet seems to be moving westward in the sky?
(a) Retrograde
(b) Parallax
(c) Opcentric
(d) Reverse parallax

**170.** A device which would not work on the Moon is:
(a) Thermometer (b) Siphon
(c) Spectrometer (d) Spring balance

**171.** What is great red Spot?
(a) Jupiter (b) Mars
(c) Earth (d) Venus

**172.** The rapidly moving stream of charged particles that is being driven away from the sun
(a) Solar wind (b) Solar reflection
(c) Solar water (d) Solar heat

**173.** The name of the biggest asteroid known as
(a) Ceres (b) Vesta
(c) Manas (d) Eoras

**174.** One Jupiter day is equal to
(a) 30 hrs 30 min (b) 10 hrd 10 min
(c) 5 hrs 50 min (d) 9 hrs 50 min

**175.** The Andromeda Galaxy is types of
(a) Elliptical (b) Spiral
(c) Irregular (d) Spherical

**176.** A planet in solar system has a day which lasts longer than its year
(a) Venus (b) Earth
(c) Mars (d) Jupiter

**177.** Heliocentric means around
(a) Jupiter (b) Moon
(c) Sun (d) Earth

**178.** A planet greatest distance from the sun is called
(a) Aphelion (b) Perihelion
(c) Helix (d) Eccentricity

**179.** Refracting telescopes always contain
(a) Lenses (b) Mirrors
(c) Films (d) Spectrum

**180.** A comet's tail points in direction
(a) Towards Sun
(b) Towards the Earth
(c) Behind the comet orbit
(d) Away from the Sun

**181.** Spectral line splitting due to the influence of magnetic field
(a) Zeeman effect (b) Planck effect
(c) Boltzmann effect (d) Light effect

**182.** The study of the origin and evolution of the universe is called
(a) Tomography (b) Cosmology
(c) Selenology (d) Universology

**183.** According to Kepler's Law, all orbits of the planets are
(a) Ellipse (b) Parabola
(c) Hyperbola (d) Square

**184.** What type of visible star is the coolest?
(a) O (b) A
(c) G (d) M

**185.** The outer boundary of the Sun's magnetic field is
(a) Heliopause (b) Magneopose
(c) Electropause (d) Geomagnetic

**186.** The _____ rises in the west.
(a) Saturn (b) Venus
(c) Pluto (d) Mars

**187.** The angle when full moon takes in night sky is
(a) 1/8 degrees (b) 1/2 degrees
(c) 1/4 degrees (d) 1/16 degrees

**188.** Schmidt, Cassegrainian, and Galilean examples of?
(a) Telescopes (b) Microscopes
(c) Cameras (d) RADAR

**189.** Shortest year of the planet
(a) Mercury (b) Venus
(c) Earth (d) Mars

**190.** Geocentric means
(a) Mars (b) Sun
(c) Earth (d) Moon

**191.** Mostly contents of Venus atmosphere is
(a) Oxygen (b) Carbon dioxide
(c) Nitrogen (d) Water

**192.** The magnetic field of the planet is
(a) Dynamo effect
(b) Doppler effect
(c) Photo effect
(d) Rotation effect

# ANSWERS

| 1 | 2 | 3 | 4 | 5 | 6 | 7 | 8 | 9 | 10 |
|---|---|---|---|---|---|---|---|---|---|
| (b) | (a) | (d) | (b) | (a) | (d) | (c) | (a) | (d) | (b) |

| 11 | 12 | 13 | 14 | 15 | 16 | 17 | 18 | 19 | 20 |
|---|---|---|---|---|---|---|---|---|---|
| (c) | (c) | (a) | (b) | (b) | (d) | (d) | (d) | (d) | (b) |

| 21 | 22 | 23 | 24 | 25 | 26 | 27 | 28 | 29 | 30 |
|---|---|---|---|---|---|---|---|---|---|
| (c) | (d) | (a) | (d) | (d) | (a) | (b) | (c) | (d) | (b) |

| 31 | 32 | 33 | 34 | 35 | 36 | 37 | 38 | 39 | 40 |
|---|---|---|---|---|---|---|---|---|---|
| (b) | (b) | (a) | (b) | (c) | (a) | (d) | (c) | (a) | (d) |

| 41 | 42 | 43 | 44 | 45 | 46 | 47 | 48 | 49 | 50 |
|---|---|---|---|---|---|---|---|---|---|
| (b) | (a) | (b) | (a) | (b) | (c) | (c) | (b) | (a) | (a) |

| 51 | 52 | 53 | 54 | 55 | 56 | 57 | 58 | 59 | 60 |
|---|---|---|---|---|---|---|---|---|---|
| (d) | (c) | (a) | (d) | (d) | (b) | (a) | (c) | (a) | (d) |

| 61 | 62 | 63 | 64 | 65 | 66 | 67 | 68 | 69 | 70 |
|---|---|---|---|---|---|---|---|---|---|
| (a) | (a) | (b) | (d) | (a) | (c) | (a) | (d) | (c) | (b) |

| 71 | 72 | 73 | 74 | 75 | 76 | 77 | 78 | 79 | 80 |
|---|---|---|---|---|---|---|---|---|---|
| (d) | (a) | (c) | (a) | (c) | (a) | (c) | (b) | (b) | (d) |

| 81 | 82 | 83 | 84 | 85 | 86 | 87 | 88 | 89 | 90 |
|---|---|---|---|---|---|---|---|---|---|
| (a) | (d) | (c) | (a) | (c) | (d) | (b) | (a) | (a) | (c) |

| 91 | 92 | 93 | 94 | 95 | 96 | 97 | 98 | 99 | 100 |
|---|---|---|---|---|---|---|---|---|---|
| (c) | (c) | (b) | (b) | (d) | (a) | (a) | (d) | (c) | (a) |

| 101 | 102 | 103 | 104 | 105 | 106 | 107 | 108 | 109 | 110 |
|---|---|---|---|---|---|---|---|---|---|
| (a) | (b) | (b) | (c) | (a) | (a) | (b) | (a) | (a) | (d) |

| 111 | 112 | 113 | 114 | 115 | 116 | 117 | 118 | 119 | 120 |
|---|---|---|---|---|---|---|---|---|---|
| (b) | (c) | (b) | (a) | (c) | (b) | (c) | (a) | (b) | (a) |

| 121 | 122 | 123 | 124 | 125 | 126 | 127 | 128 | 129 | 130 |
|---|---|---|---|---|---|---|---|---|---|
| (b) | (b) | (a) | (a) | (a) | (a) | (a) | (a) | (b) | (a) |

| 131 | 132 | 133 | 134 | 135 | 136 | 137 | 138 | 139 | 140 |
|---|---|---|---|---|---|---|---|---|---|
| (a) | (a) | (b) | (a) | (a) | (a) | (a) | (a) | (a) | (a) |

| 141 | 142 | 143 | 144 | 145 | 146 | 147 | 148 | 149 | 150 |
|---|---|---|---|---|---|---|---|---|---|
| (b) | (a) | (d) | (a) | (c) | (d) | (c) | (a) | (c) | (a) |

| 151 | 152 | 153 | 154 | 155 | 156 | 157 | 158 | 159 | 160 |
|---|---|---|---|---|---|---|---|---|---|
| (b) | (b) | (b) | (a) | (a) | (a) | (a) | (d) | (b) | (b) |

| 161 | 162 | 163 | 164 | 165 | 166 | 167 | 168 | 169 | 170 |
|---|---|---|---|---|---|---|---|---|---|
| (a) | (a) | (a) | (a) | (a) | (b) | (a) | (b) | (a) | (a) |

| 171 | 172 | 173 | 174 | 175 | 176 | 177 | 178 | 179 | 180 |
|---|---|---|---|---|---|---|---|---|---|
| (b) | (a) | (a) | (b) | (b) | (a) | (c) | (a) | (b) | (a) |

| 181 | 182 | 183 | 184 | 185 | 186 | 187 | 188 | 189 | 190 |
|---|---|---|---|---|---|---|---|---|---|
| (a) | (b) | (a) | (d) | (b) | (b) | (b) | (a) | (a) | (b) |

| 191 | 192 |
|---|---|
| (b) | (a) |

# CHAPTER 3

# ATMOSPHERE

As we know earth is the only planets where life exists due to presence of the water, air and other necessary things, all those, mixture of our surrounding environments which is atmosphere. Our atmosphere consists of the air and its components which is different manner like solid, liquid and gases. The important points as follow:

- Atmosphere is the air surrounding the earth.

- The atmosphere is a mixture of different gases. It contains life-giving gases like Oxygen for humans and animals and carbon dioxide for plants.

- It envelops the earth all round and is held in place by the gravity of the earth.

- It helps in stopping the ultraviolet rays harmful to the life and maintains the suitable temperature necessary for life.

- Generally, atmosphere extends up to about 1600 km from the earth's surface. However, 99% of the total mass of the atmosphere is confined to the height of 32 km from the earth's surface.

## Constituents of the Atmosphere

The atmosphere composed of about 78 per cent nitrogen, 21 per cent oxygen and 0.93 per cent argon, remaining trace elements like water vapour, carbon dioxide and ozone. The constituents of the atmosphere effects the weather condition, climate change on the earth to change our daily life. The atmosphere can be divided into vertical layers determined by the way **temperature** changes with height. The layer closest to the surface is the troposphere, which contains over 80% of the atmos-pheric **mass** and nearly all the water vapour. The next layer, the stratosphere, contains most of the atmosphere's ozone, which absorbs high **energy radiation** from the **sun** and makes life on the surface possible. Above the stratosphere are the mesosphere and thermosphere. These two layers include regions of charged **atoms** and molecules, or ions. Called the ionosphere, this region is important to **radio** communications, since **radio waves** can bounce off the layer and travel great distances. It is thought that the present atmosphere developed from gases ejected by volcanoes. Oxygen, upon which all **animal** life depends, probably built up as excess emissions from plants that produce it as a waste product during **photosynthesis**. Human activities may be affecting the levels of some important atmospheric components, particularly **carbon** dioxide and ozone.

### Permanent Gases of the Atmosphere

| Constituent | Formula | Percentage by volume |
|---|---|---|
| Nitrogen | $N_2$ | 78.08 |
| Oxygen | $O_2$ | 20.95 |
| Argon | Ar | 0.93 |
| Carbon dioxide | $CO_2$ | 0.036 |
| Neon | Ne | 0.002 |
| Helium | He | 0.0005 |
| Krypton | Kr | 0.001 |
| Xenon | Xe | 0.00009 |
| Hydrogen | $H_2$ | 0.00005 |

- Carbon dioxide ($CO_2$) affects the earth's climate and plays a large support role in the **biosphere**, the collection of living things that populate the earth's surface. Only about 0.0325% of the atmosphere is $CO_2$. Carbon dioxide is required by **plant** life for photosynthesis, the process of using sunlight to store energy as simple sugars, upon which all life on Earth depends.

- Carbon dioxide is also one of a class of compounds called greenhouse gases. These gases are made up of molecules that absorb and emit infrared radiation, which we feel as **heat**. The solar energy radiated from the sun is mostly in the visible range, within a narrow band of wavelengths. This radiation is absorbed by the earth's surface, then reradiated back out to **space** not as visible **light**, but as longer wavelength infrared radiation.

- Greenhouse gas molecules absorb some of this radiation before it escapes to space, and re-emit some of it back toward the surface. In this way, these gases trap some of the escaping heat and increase the overall temperature of the atmosphere. If the atmosphere had no green-house gases, it is estimated that the earth's surface would be 90°F (32°C) cooler.

- Water vapour ($H_2O$) is found in the atmosphere in small and highly variable amounts. While it is nearly absent in most of the atmosphere, its **concentration** can range up to 4% in very warm, humid areas close to the surface. Despite its relative scarcity, atmospheric water probably has more of an impact on the earth than any of the major gases, aside from oxygen.

- Water vapour participates in the **hydrologic cycle**, the process that moves water between the oceans, the land surface waters, the atmosphere, and the **polar ice caps**. This water cycling drives **erosion** and rock **weathering**, determines the earth's **weather**, and sets up climate conditions that make land areas dry or wet, habitable or inhospitable. When cooled sufficiently, water vapour forms **clouds** by condensing to liquid water droplets, or at lower temperatures, solid **ice** crystals. Besides creating rain or snow, clouds affect Earth's climate by reflecting some of the energy coming from the sun, making the **planet** somewhat cooler. Water vapour is also an important greenhouse gas. It is concentrated near the surface and is much more prevalent near the tropics than in the polar regions.

- Ozone ($O_3$) is almost all found in a layer about 9–36 mi (15–60 km) in altitude. Ozone gas is irritating to peoples' eyes and skin, and chemically attacks rubber and plant **tissue**. Nevertheless, it is vital to life on Earth because it absorbs most of the high energy radiation from the sun that is harmful to plants and animals. A portion of the energy radiated by the sun lies in the ultraviolet (UV) region. This shorter wavelength radiation is responsible for suntans, and is sufficiently powerful to harm cells, cause skin **cancer**, and burn tissue, as anyone who has had a painful sunburn knows.

- The ozone molecules, along with molecules of $O_2$, absorb nearly all the high energy UV rays, protecting the earth's surface from the most damaging radiation. The first step in this process occurs high in the atmosphere, where $O_2$ molecules absorb very high energy UV radiation. Upon doing so, each absorbing **molecule** breaks up into two oxygen atoms. The oxygen atoms eventually collide with another $O_2$ molecule, forming a molecule of ozone, $O_3$ (a third molecule is required in the collision to carry away excess energy). Ozone in turn may absorb UV of slightly longer wavelength, which knocks off one of its oxygen atoms and leaves $O_2$.

- The free oxygen atom, being very reactive, will almost immediately recombine with another $O_2$, forming more ozone. The last two steps of this cycle keep repeating but do not create any new chemical compounds; they only act to absorb ultraviolet radiation. The amount of ozone in the stratosphere is minute. If it were all transported to the surface, the ozone gas would form a layer about 0.1–0.16 in (2.5–4.0 mm) thick. This layer, as thin as it is, is sufficient to shield the earth's occupants from harmful solar radiation.

## Aerosols

In addition to gases, the atmosphere has a wide variety of tiny particles suspended in the air, known collectively as **aerosols**. These particles may be liquid or solid, and are so small that they may require very long times to settle out of the atmosphere by gravity. Examples of aerosols include bits of suspended **soil** or **desert sand**, tiny smoke particles from a forest fire, **salt** particles left over after a droplet of **ocean** water has evaporated, plant pollen, volcanic dust plumes, and particles formed from the **pollution** created by a **coal** burning power plant. Aerosols significantly affect the atmospheric heat balance, cloud growth, and optical properties.

- Aerosols cover a very wide size range. Raindrops suspended in a cloud are about 0.04–0.24 in (1–6 mm) in diameter. Fine desert sand and cloud droplets range in diameter down to about 0.0004 in (0.01 mm). Sea salt particles and smoke particles are 1/100th of this, about 0.0001 mm, or 0.1 micrometer, in diameter (1 micrometer = one thousandth of a millimeter). Smallest of all are the particles that form when certain gases condense; that is, when several gas molecules come together to form a stable cluster. These are the Aitkin nuclei, whose diameters can be measured down to a few nanometers (1 nanometer = one millionth of a millimeter).

- Some aerosols are just the right size to efficiently scatter sunlight, making the atmosphere look hazy. Under the right conditions, aerosols act as collecting points for water vapor molecules, encouraging the growth of cloud droplets and speeding the formation of clouds. They may also play a role in Earth's climate; the aerosols are known to reflect a portion of incoming solar radiation back to space, which lowers the temperature of the earth's surface. Current research is focused on estimating how much cooling is provided by aerosols, as well as how and when aerosols form in the atmosphere.

## THE ATMOSPHERE'S LAYERS

The different layers in the atmosphere which have own character due to its variable gases and heights due to solar radiations.

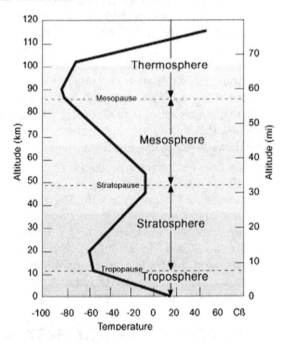

## The Troposphere

The troposphere contains over 80% of the mass of the atmosphere, along with nearly all of the water vapour. This layer contains the air we breathe, the winds we observe and the clouds that bring our rain. In fact, all of what we know as "weather" occurs in the troposphere,

whose name means "changing sphere." All of the cold fronts, warm fronts, high and low pressure systems, **storm** systems, and other features seen on a weather **map** occur in this lowest layer. Severe thunderstorms may penetrate the tropopause.

- Within the troposphere the temperature drops with increasing height at an average **rate** of about 11.7°F per every 3,281 ft (6.5°C per every 1,000 meters). This quantity is known as the lapse rate. When air begins to rise, it will expand and cool at a faster rate determined by the laws of **thermodynamics**.

- This means that if a parcel of air begins to rise, it will soon find itself cooler and denser than its surroundings, and will sink back downward. This is an example of a stable atmosphere—vertical air **motion** is prevented. Due to the fact that air masses move around in the troposphere, a cold air mass may move into an area and have a higher lapse rate. That is, its temperature drops off more quickly with height.

- Under these weather conditions, air that begins rising and cooling will become warmer than its surroundings. It then is like a hot-air **balloon**, it is less dense than the surrounding air and is buoyant, so it will continue to rise and cool in a process called **convection**. If this is sustained, the atmosphere is said to be unstable and the rising parcel of air will cool to the point where its water vapor condenses to form cloud droplets.

- The air parcel is now a convective cloud. If the buoyancy is vigorous enough, a storm cloud will develop as the cloud droplets grow to the size of raindrops and begin to fall out of the cloud as rain. Thus under certain conditions, the temperature profile of the troposphere makes possible storm clouds and **precipitation**.

- During a strong **thunderstorm**, cumulonimbus clouds (the type that produce heavy rain, high winds, and hail) may grow tall enough to reach or extend into the tropopause. Here they run into strong stratospheric winds, which may shear off the top of the clouds and stop their growth. One can see this effect in the "anvil" clouds associated with strong summer thunderstorms.

## The Stratosphere

The beginning of the stratosphere is defined as that point where the temperature reaches a minimum and the lapse rate abruptly drops to **zero**. This temperature structure has one important consequence: it inhibits rising air. Any air that begins to rise will become cooler and denser than the surrounding air. The stratosphere, then, is very stable.

Although the stratosphere has very little water, clouds of ice crystals may form at times in the lower stratosphere over the polar regions. Early Arctic explorers named these clouds nacreous or mother-of-pearl clouds because of their iridescent appearance. More recently, very thin, widespread clouds have been found to form in the polar stratosphere under extremely cold conditions. These clouds, called polar stratospheric clouds, or PSCs, appear to be small crystals of ice or frozen mixtures of ice and **nitric acid**. PSCs play a key role in the development of the ozone hole, which is described below.

- The stratosphere contains most of the ozone found in the earth's atmosphere. In fact, the presence of ozone is the reason for the temperature profile found in the stratosphere. As described previously, ozone and oxygen gas both absorb short wave solar radiation. In the series of reactions that follow, heat is released. This heat warms the atmosphere in the layer at about 12–27 mi (20–45 km) and gives the stratosphere its characteristic temperature increase with height.

- The ozone layer has been the subject of some concern. In 1985, scientists from the British Antarctic Survey noticed that the amount of stratospheric ozone over the South Pole was dropping sharply during the spring months, recovering somewhat as spring turned to summer. An examination of the historical records revealed that the springtime ozone losses had begun around the late 1960s and had grown much more severe by the late 1970s. By the mid-1980s virtually all the ozone was disappearing from parts of the polar stratosphere during the late winter and early spring. These ozone losses, dubbed the ozone hole, were the subject of intense research both in the field and in the laboratory.

## The Mesosphere and Thermosphere

The upper mesosphere and the lower thermosphere contain charged atoms and molecules (ions in a region known as the ionosphere. The atmospheric constituents at this level include nitrogen gas, atomic oxygen and nitrogen (O and N), and nitric oxide (NO). All of these are exposed to strong solar **emission** of ultraviolet and X-ray radiation, which can result in ionization, knocking off an **electron** to form an atom or molecule with a positive charge. The ionosphere is a region enriched in free electrons and positive ions. This charged particle region affects the propagation of radio waves, reflecting them as a mirror reflects light.

- The ionosphere makes it possible to tune in radio stations very far from the transmitter; even if the radio waves coming directly from the transmitter are blocked by **mountains** or the curvature of the earth, one can still receive the waves bounced off the ionosphere. After the sun sets, the numbers of electrons and ions in the lower layers drop drastically, since the sun's radiation is no longer available to keep them ionized. Even at night, however, the higher layers retain some ions. The result is that the ionosphere is higher at night, which allows radio waves to bounce for longer distances. This is the reason that one can frequently tune in more distant radio stations at night than during the day.

- The upper thermosphere is also where the bright nighttime displays of colors and flashes known as the aurora occur. The aurora are caused by energetic particles emitted by the sun. These particles become trapped by **Earth's magnetic field** and collide with the relatively few gas atoms present above about 60 mi (100 km), mostly atomic oxygen (O) and nitrogen gas ($N_2$). These collisions cause the atoms and molecules to emit light, resulting in spectacular displays.

- The Earth environment as we know it exists because of the energy it receives from the Sun. Radiant energy from the Sun powers the atmospheric and oceanic circulations that profoundly influence the state of the biosphere. Without solar radiation, photosynthesis would cease. Solar radiation and high energy particles impinge continually on the envelope of gases and plasma that surrounds and protects the narrow habitable layer of the Earth's surface.

- Geometric relationships modulate solar inputs to the Earth. The seasonal progression of weather is controlled by the tilt of the Earth's axis of rotation relative to the direction normal to the Earth's orbital plane and by orbital eccentricity and precession. In addition, small periodic variations in the Earth's orbital parameters over time scales of tens of thousands of years (Milankovitch cycles).

## THE ATMOSPHERIC ENERGY SYSTEM

The atmospheric energy system is totally depends on the solar radiation.

### Short-wave Radiation

- The ultra-violet component of the sun's radiation is absorbed in the stratosphere in a complex process involving ozone and resulting in heating.

- As the short-wave radiation passes through the troposphere it is reflected, scattered and absorbed.
- Scattering of light produces our blue skies. Some scattered light reaches the ground as diffuse radiation. It allows us to see objects not in direct sunlight.
- Reflection can take place from clouds or the ground. The term 'albedo' is used to indicate the proportion of light reflected from a surface. Snow has a high albedo, pine forest has a low albedo.
- Water can have a high or a low albedo, depending upon the solar angle.

**Long-wave Radiation**

- The atmosphere and Earth's surface are the main sources of long-wave radiation.
- Some atmospheric gases absorb particular wavelengths of long-wave radiation very effectively.
- Few gases absorb wavelengths between 8 μm and 12 μm, so radiation of this wavelength can escape to space through the 'radiation window'.
- Clouds are very effective absorbers of long-wave radiation, so help to keep temperatures warmer than would otherwise be the case at night.

## The Greenhouse Effect

The level of carbon dioxide in the atmosphere has increased since the Industrial Revolution. With other gases that have the same effect of absorbing long-wave radiation also increasing, the natural greenhouse effect of the atmosphere should increase. It must be stressed that the gases of the atmosphere, particularly water vapour and carbon dioxide, provide a natural greenhouse effect. The increases in gaseous pollution lead to an 'enhanced greenhouse effect'.

## The Global Radiation Balance

Adding together the short and long-wave radiation received at the surface from the sun and the atmosphere, it would appear that the surface is gaining more energy than it loses through reflection of short-wave radiation and emission of long-wave radiation. It does not get hotter because other processes help it to lose heat.

**Spatial variability of radiation exchanges**

- The angle of the sun's rays is very important. If the rays are at 90° to a surface, it will receive the maximum intensity of radiation. As the angle decreases, so the intensity of the solar beam declines.

- Longer path-lengths of sunlight through the atmosphere will decrease the intensity of sunlight by giving rise to more scattering and absorption.
- Long-wave radiation emission is less variable than short-wave radiation receipt, because it is based on absolute temperature.
- Taking the atmosphere and surface together, we find a radiation surplus between approximately 38°N and 38°S, and a deficit of radiation polewards of these latitudes.

## The Energy Balance

The energy surplus at the surface is transferred to the atmosphere as sensible and latent heat. Sensible heat is the convectional exchange of warm air down the temperature gradient. It is most important over heated land surfaces such as deserts.

- Latent heat transfer takes place through the convection of moist air containing evaporated water vapour. Eventually, after cooling, the latent heat is added to the atmosphere during condensation. This helps to compensate for the radiation deficit. It is most important over the tropical oceans.
- In the atmospheric circulation we can also include kinetic energy and potential energy as well as sensible and latent heat.
- Although we have stressed the role of the atmosphere in transferring energy vertically and horizontally, we must not forget that ocean currents also transfer heat.

**Temperature Effects**: Temperatures respond to inputs of energy. Where some of the radiant energy is used in evaporation, less energy is available for heating. In the tropics, seasonal differences in temperature are small, and the diurnal variation is more important. The sun never strays far from an overhead position at noon.

## Moisture, Clouds and Precipitation

The troposphere is also known as the weather sphere. This is due to the water vapour in the air. After the tropopause, water vapor doesn't exist in the atmosphere.

## Measurement of Water in the Air

The amount of water in the air can be measured in different ways. The **specific humidity** of air is a measure of how much water is in the air. Warmer air can hold more water than colder air. When the air reaches its capacity, it is **saturated**. This capacity doubles for about every 11°C rise in temperature. The term more often used is **relative humidity**. This is the measure of how much water is in the air divided by how much it can hold. The relative humidity reading is given as a per cent. The relative humidity for saturated air is 100 per cent.

## Finding Relative Humidity

The relative humidity can be found by two different methods. One involves the use of a **hygrometer**. This is a pointer attached to a piece of hair. As the humidity increases, the hair stretches out. This is your typical "bad hair day." When the humidity drops, the hair shrinks, causing the needle to point in a different direction. The other method requires the use of two thermometers and a chart.

## DEFINITIONS:

There are several different methods for defining the amount of water vapour in the atmosphere. The definition used depends on the application.

*Specific humidity*: Measures mass of water vapour in a fixed total mass of air. In general it is greater in the tropics (16 g/kg) than in the polar regions (4 g/kg). This definition is used when we are interested in the actual amount of water that is in the atmosphere as a gas. The specific humidity remains constant as long as you do not add or take out water vapour molecules from the volume of air.

*Mixing ratio*: Mass of water vapour in a fixed mass of remaining dry air. Since there are so few molecules of water vapour in a volume of air, as compared to $N_2$ and $O_2$, the value of the mixing ratio is similar to the specific humidity. Changing the temperature of the air parcel does not affect the parcels mixing ratio.

*Absolute humidity*: Mass of water vapour in a fixed volume of air, or the water vapour density. We don't ever use this definition so don't bother memorizing it.

*Actual vapour pressure*: The amount of water vapour in terms of the amount of pressure that the water vapor molecules exert. It is expressed in units of mb. We use the actual vapour pressure when discussing evaporation and condensation. It is therefore of use when we discuss clouds.

*Saturation vapour pressure:* Pressure that water vapour molecules would exert if the air were saturated at a given temperature, its units are mb. Saturation vapour pressure increases with rising temperature. Saturation vapour pressure just above liquid water is greater than that over ice. At temperatures below freezing it takes more vapour molecules to saturate air directly above water than it does to saturate air directly above ice. This is important for precipitation.

*Relative humidity:* Ratio of the amount of water vapour actually in the air compared to the amount of water vapour required for saturation at that particular temperature and pressure. This is one method that nightly weather persons report. It is expressed as a percentage. Increasing or decreasing the amount of water vapour in the air changes the relative humidity. A change in temperature will also bring about a change in relative humidity.

*Dew point temperature*: The temperature to which air would have to be cooled (with no change in air pressure or water content) for saturation to occur. When the dew point is below 32F (0C) it is called the Frost point.

- *The Heat Index*: Combines air temperature with relative humidity to determine an 'apparent' temperature - what the temperature 'feels like'.

- Boiling point decreases with altitude. Boiling occurs when saturation vapour pressure of escaping bubbles is greater than the total atmospheric pressure.

## Humidity and Clouds

To form clouds we need to change the phase of the atmospheric water vapour to either a liquid or a solid. To do this we have to increase the relative humidity to near 100%. We can accomplish this by either cooling the air or by evaporating water vapour into the air. Most clouds form by cooling the air through lifting.

From the hydrological cycle we know atmospheric water vapour content is the surface. Water must evaporate (or sublime) from the surface. The rate of evaporation is a function of temperature of the water, the temperature of the air, the relative humidity of the air, the wind speed and the surface area of the water. Think of the bathroom hand-dryers:

- They blow out warm air (saturation vapour pressure increases with increasing temperature).

- The air is fast moving (increased wind speed increases evaporation).

- You rub your hands underneath them (You are spreading-out the water on you hands - increasing its surface area).

## Air Pressure and Motion

Wind speed and direction respond to pressure gradient forces that exist between high and low pressure areas. In the Northern Hemisphere and because of the rotation of the earth, winds circulate in a clockwise fashion around areas of high pressure and in a counter-clockwise manner around regions of lower pressure. Air pressure decreases relatively slowly with height in regions dominated by warm air and relatively rapidly with height in areas where cold air prevails. As a result, wind patterns in the upper atmosphere tend to flow in an oscillating manner around major pockets of warm and cold air.

## Force acting on the wind:

Wind results from physical forces that act on the air.

- A force is an influence on a body which causes the body to accelerate (change speed or direction). Newton's First Law of Motion states that a body at rest will remain at rest, and a body in motion will remain in motion unless acted upon by an unbalanced force. If forces balance (no net force), then we have either no motion or uniform motion in a straight line.

  Differences in air pressure (called a pressure gradient) lead to air motion.

- Air "parcels" will try to move from areas of high pressure to areas of low pressure. In addition, colder temperatures near the poles generally are associated with higher pressures than warmer temperatures near the equator. Thus, unequal solar heating of the earth directly causes large-scale winds, called the jet stream.

  The larger the difference in air pressure, the stronger the winds.

- Newton's 2nd Law of Motion states that the acceleration (rate of change of velocity) of a body is directly proportional to the net force upon the body, or $F = ma$, where $F$ = force, $m$ = mass, and $a$ = acceleration.

  The primary forces that cause large-scale motion in the atmosphere are as follows:

- Gravitational force—It keeps the molecules in the atmosphere from moving into space. Gravity's influence is stronger near the earth's surface and weaker aloft.

- Vertical pressure gradient force—It closely balances gravity so that all the molecules in the atmosphere are not forced into the lowest meter above the ground. The vertical pressure gradient force results from molecules in the high pressure near the earth's surface trying to move upward where the pressure is lower.

- Horizontal pressure gradient force—It results from the high and low pressure systems (highs, lows, troughs and ridges) in the atmosphere. Air will tend to move from high pressure to low pressure.

- Coriolis force—It is the force that results from Earth's rotation.

- Friction—It is the drag exerted on the air by the earth's surface (e.g., plants, trees, buildings, mountains, etc.).

- Centrifugal force—It is the tendency for a body to resist a change in direction.

## Pressure Gradient Force

- Horizontal pressure gradient force—It results from the high and low pressure systems (highs, lows, troughs and ridges) in the atmosphere. Air tends to move air from regions of high pressure to regions of low pressure.

- "Gradient" refers to how rapidly a quantity (such as pressure or temperature) changes in a given distance. It can be thought of as measure of "steepness", like the topography on a contour plot.

- The larger the gradient, the stronger the wind.

- Strong winds are found in areas of tightly packed isobar. In general, the closer the isobars are to one another on a weather map, the greater is the pressure gradient force (be careful to look at the intervals).

**Friction:** The drag on the air by the earth's surface (e.g., plants, trees, buildings, mountains, etc.).

Friction always acts opposite to air motion and, hence, reduces wind speed. Its greatest effect is near the earth's surface and rapidly decreases with height (within lowest 1 km).

**Coriolis force:** It is the force that results from Earth's rotation. The Coriolis force solely results from living on a rotating object — Earth. It acts only on objects moving with respect to the earth's surface (e.g., the air, planes, birds, missiles, etc.). It is only significant over long distances (e.g., hundreds or thousands of miles) and long-time spans (e.g., 12 hours or longer). Hence, tornadoes are not influenced by the Coriolis force. Neither is the water draining in your sink.

Example of the Coriolis force: Suppose Mark and Jane are on a merry-go-round rotating counterclockwise (when viewed from above). Mark throws a ball directly to Jane. Mark misses. Why? But Jane rotated away from the straight-line path of the ball while the ball was in the air. However, to Mark, it looks like the ball curved to the right.

- Think of the earth as the merry-go-round when looked at from above the North Pole, or below the South Pole. From those vantage points, Earth is rotating counterclockwise in the Northern Hemisphere and clockwise in the Southern Hemisphere.

- To someone on the earth, air blowing in a straight line seems to blow to the right in the Northern Hemisphere and to the left in the Southern Hemisphere.

- The Coriolis force always will deflect objects to the right in the Northern Hemisphere and to the left in the Southern Hemisphere.

- The Coriolis force will never change the speed of an object, only its direction.

- Air currents, which exist as a response to pressure forces, are "deflected" by the rotation of the earth.

- If Earth did not rotate, air currents would flow directly from areas of high pressure to areas of low pressure. However, because Earth does rotate, air currents ultimately become involved in a tug-of-war between pressure gradient forces and the Coriolis force. The result is that air circulates counterclockwise around areas of low pressure in the Northern Hemisphere and clockwise around areas of high pressure.

**Centrifugal force:** It is the tendency for a body to resist a change in direction. If we have a ball tied to a string and throw it around in a circle at a constant speed, we feel a "force" pulling the ball outward. This is the centrifugal force. It is the same force that makes you lean to the right when a car makes a left turn, or the force that you feel riding a roller coaster.

- The centrifugal force will try to pull air parcels outward if they are moving in a curved path around a ridge or a trough.

- The magnitude of the centrifugal force is related to both the speed of the air parcel and the radius of curvature (how tightly it goes around the curve).

# WEATHER SYSTEM AND PATTERN

**Weather** is the condition of the atmosphere at a particular time and place. It refers to such conditions of the local atmosphere as temperature, atmospheric pressure, humidity (the amount of water contained in the atmosphere), precipitation (rain, snow, sleet, & hail), and wind velocity. Because the amount of heat in the atmosphere varies with location above the Earth's surface, and because differing amounts of heat in different parts of the atmosphere control atmospheric circulation, the atmosphere is in constant motion. Thus, weather is continually changing in a complex and dynamic manner.

The Earth's weather and climate system represent complex interactions between the oceans, the land, the sun, and the atmosphere. That these interactions are complex is evidence by the difficulty meteorologists have in predicting weather on a daily basis. Understanding climate change is even more difficult because humans have not been around long enough to record data on the long term effects of these processes. Still, we do know that the main energy source for changing weather patterns and climate is solar energy from the Sun.

## Wind Systems

There are different wind system in different location to the oceans and continents. Two main type of the wind system; high pressure and low pressure.

- **High Pressure Centers :** In zones where air descends back to the surface, the air is more dense than its surroundings and this creates a center of high atmospheric pressure. Since winds blow from areas of high pressure to areas of low pressure, winds spiral outward away from the high pressure. But, because of the Coriolis Effect, such winds, again will be deflected toward the right in the northern hemisphere and create a general clockwise rotation around the high pressure center. In the southern hemisphere the effect is just the opposite, and winds circulate in a counterclockwise rotation about the high pressure center. Such winds circulating around a high pressure center are called **anticyclonic wins.**

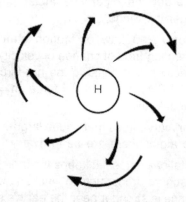

- **Low Pressure Centers :** In zones where air ascends, the air is less dense than its surroundings and this creates a center of low atmospheric pressure, or low pressure center. Winds blow from areas of high pressure to areas of low pressure, and so the surface winds would tend to blow toward a low pressure center, But, because of the Coriolis Effect, these winds are deflected. In the northern hemisphere they are deflected towards the right, and fail to arrive at the low pressure center, but instead circulate around it in a counter clockwise fashion as shown here. In the southern hemisphere the circulation around a low pressure center would be clockwise. Such winds are called **cyclonic winds.**

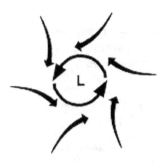

## Global Winds

Earth's orbit around the sun and its rotation on a tilted axis causes some parts of Earth to receive more solar radiation than others. This uneven heating produces global circulation patterns, offsite link. For example, the abundance of energy reaching the equator produces hot humid air that rises high into the atmosphere. A low pressure area forms at the surface and a region of clouds forms at altitude. The air eventually stops rising and spreads north and south towards the Earth's poles. About 2000 miles from the equator, the air falls back to Earth's surface blowing towards the pole and back to the equator. Six of these large convection currents cover the Earth from pole to pole.

## Air Masses

These global wind patterns drive large bodies of air called air masses. Air masses are thousands of feet thick and extend across large areas of the Earth. The location over which an air mass forms will determine its characteristics. For example, air over the tropical ocean becomes exceptionally hot and humid. Air over a high latitude continent may become cold and dry. You have probably noticed the temperature rapidly dropping on a nice warm day as a cold air mass pushed a warm one out the way.

## Fronts

The location where two air masses meet is called a front. They can be indirectly observed using current weather maps, which can be used to track them as the move across the Earth. Cold fronts, generally shown in blue, occur where a cold air mass is replacing a warm air mass. Warm fronts, shown in red, occur where warm air replaces cold air.

## Jet Streams

The local weather conditions that we experience at the Earth's surface are related to these air masses and fronts. However the environment far above us impacts their movement. High in the atmosphere, narrow bands of strong wind, such as the jet streams, steer weather systems and transfer heat and moisture around the globe.

## Coriolis Effect

As they travel across the Earth, air masses and global winds do not move in straight lines. Similar to a person trying to walk straight across a spinning Merry-Go-Round, winds get deflected from a straight-line path as they blow across the rotating Earth. In the Northern Hemisphere air veers to the right and in the Southern Hemisphere to the left. This motion can result in large circulating weather systems, as air blows away from or into a high or low pressure offsite link area. Hurricanes and nor'easters are examples of these cyclonic systems.

# CLIMATE AND CLIMATE CHANGE

*Climate* refers to the average weather characteristics of a given region. Climate, although it does change over longer periods of geologic time, is more stable over short periods of time like years and centuries. The fact that the Earth has undergone fluctuation between ice ages and warmer periods in the recent past (the last ice age ended about 10,000 years ago) is testament to the fact that climate throughout the world as has been changing through time.

## Climate Change

Because human history is so short compared to the time scales on which global climate change occurs, we do not completely understand the causes. However, we can suggest a few reasons why climates fluctuate.

- Long term variations in climate (tens of millions of years) on a single continent are likely caused by drifting continents. If a continent drifts toward the equator, the climate will become warmer. If the continent drifts toward the poles, glaciations can occur on that continent.

- Short-term variations in climate are likely controlled by the amount of solar radiation reaching the Earth. Among these are astronomical factors and atmospheric factors.

- Astronomical Variation in the eccentricity of the Earth's orbit around the sun has periods of about 400,0000 years and 100,000 years.

- Variation in the tilt of the Earth's axis has a period of about 41,000 years.

- Variation in the way the Earth wobbles on its axis, called precession, has a period of about 23,000 years.

- The combined effects of these astronomical variations results in periodicities similar to those observed for glacial - interglacial cycles.

**Atmospheric Factors :** The composition of the Earth's atmosphere can be gleaned from air bubbles trapped in ice in the polar ice sheets. Studying drill core samples of such glacial ice and their contained air bubbles reveals the following:

- During past glaciations, the amount of $CO_2$ and methane, both greenhouse gasses that tend to cause global warming, were lower than during interglacial episodes.

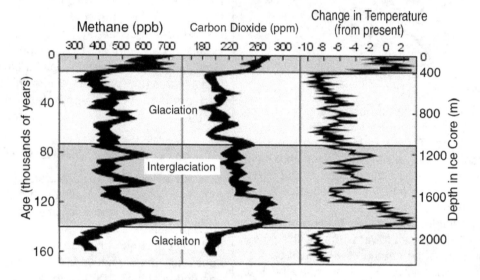

- During past glaciations, the amount of dust in the atmosphere was higher than during interglacial periods, thus more heat was likely reflected from the Earth's atmosphere back into space.

- The problem in unraveling what this means comes from not being able to understand if lowgreenhouse gas concentration and high dust content in the atmosphere caused the ice ages or if these conditions were caused by the ice ages.

- Changes in Oceanic Circulation: Small changes in ocean circulation can amplify small changes in temperature variation produced by astronomical factors.

- Other factors: The energy output from the sun may fluctuate.

- Large explosive volcanic eruptions can add significant quantities of dust to the atmosphere reflecting solar radiation and resulting in global cooling.

## Climate of India

India experiences variety of climates ranging from tropical in the south to temperate and alpine in the Himalayan north. The elevated areas receive sustained snowfall during winters. The Himalayas and the Thar Desert strongly influence the climate of the country. The Himalayas work as a barrier to the frigid katabatic winds, which blow down from Central Asia. The Tropic of Cancer passes through the middle of the country

and this makes its climate more tropical. India is a big tropical country and is famous for its diverse climatic features.

## Different Types of Climatic Regions

The climates of India are mainly divided into four different groups. The classification of these groups is based on the Koppen's climate classification system.

❑ **Tropical Wet (Humid):** The tropical wet (humid) climate group in India is divided into two sub parts—tropical monsoon climate or the tropical wet climate, and tropical wet and dry climate or savannah climate. The Western Ghats, the Malabar Coast, southern Assam, Lakshadweep and Andaman and Nicobar Islands have the tropical monsoon climate. It experiences moderate to high temperature with seasonal but heavy rainfall. The months from May to November experience the most rainfall and the rain received during this period is sufficient for vegetation throughout the year. Tropical wet and dry climate or the savannah climate is most common in the country and prevails mainly in the inland peninsular region of the country except for some portion of the Western Ghats. The summers are extremely hot and the rainy season extends from the month of June to September.

❑ **Tropical Dry:** The tropical dry climate group is divided into three subdivisions-(a) tropical semi-arid (steppe) climate, (b) sub-tropical arid (desert) climate and (c) sub-tropical semi-arid (steppe) climate. Karnataka, central Maharashtra, some parts of Tamil Nadu and Andhra Pradesh experience the tropical semi-arid (steppe) climate. Rainfall is very unreliable in this type of climate and the hot and dry summers are experienced from March to May. With scanty and erratic rainfall and extreme summers, western Rajasthan witnesses the sub-tropical arid (desert) climate. The areas of the tropical desert that runs from the regions of Punjab and Haryana to Kathiawar witness the sub-tropical semi-arid (steppe) climate. The maximum temperature in summers goes up to 40°C and the rains are unreliable and generally take place during summer monsoon season in this climate.

❏ **Sub-tropical Humid Climate:** This climate is witnessed by most of the North and Northeast India. Summers are very hot, while in winters, temperature can plunge to as low as 0°C. Rainfall mainly occurs in summers but snowfall or occasional rainfall in winters is also witnessed in some areas. The hottest months are May and June and frost also occurs for few months in winters.

❏ **Mountain Climate:** The temperature falls by 0.6°C for every 100 m rise in altitude in the Himalayas and results in a number of climates from tropical to tundra. The trans-Himalayan belt, which is the northern side of the western Himalayas, is cold, arid and windswept. There is less rain in the leeward side of the mountains whereas heavy rainfall is received by the well exposed slopes. Heaviest snowfall occurs between the months of December to February.

## Seasons of India

India generally witnesses four types of seasons. During these seasons, strong variations in temperature takes place in the country. The different types of seasons experienced in India are as follows:

❏ **Winter:** Generally the months of January and February are considered as the start of winter season in the country. However, in some parts of north-western India, the season begins from December. Generally, the average temperature during this season is about 10-15°C in northwest regions. In southeast region of mainland India, the average temperature is about 20-25°C. The western Himalayas, the extreme north-eastern parts and Kerala and Tamil Nadu, experience rains during this season.

❏ **Summer/Pre-monsoon/Thunderstorm/Hot Weather:** The country experiences this season from March till June. In the interior peninsular regions, the mean daily temperature is recorded at 30-35°C. The maximum temperature in daytime in Central India crosses 40°C in many areas. In some regions, temperature is high during daytime while in the nights, low temperature is recorded. The coastal areas of the country have mild temperature during this season due to the influence of land and sea breezes. Thunderstorms with rains and hail influence the weather in the land areas of the country. These thunderstorms are seen in the north-eastern and eastern parts of Bihar, Assam and West Bengal. In the plains of north-west India, hot and dry winds, along with dust winds, are frequently experienced.

❏ **Rainy/South-west Monsoon (WS Monsoon):** The months from July to September are the most significant. About 75% of the total rainfall of the country is supplied by the monsoon torrents during this season. The exact period of the SW monsoon in a region depends upon the onset and withdrawal time of the season. For instance, it remains in west Rajasthan for about 75 days while for 120 days in the south-western regions of the country. The SW monsoon reaches in two branches: the Arabian Sea and the Bay of Bengal branch. The Arabian Sea branch extends towards the low-pressure area over Thar Desert and is about three times stronger than the Bay of Bengal branch. The northern hemispheric temperatures, El Nino, snow cover, sea surface temperature and many other are some of the local and global phenomenon which influences the monsoons in the country. The SW starts to weaken by 1 September in Rajasthan and from 15 September in some north-western parts of the country. The monsoons in India are very important for the economy of the country as it affects the agriculture which is the mainstay of a huge workforce of the nation.

❏ **Autumn/Post Monsoon/Northeast Monsoon/ Retreating SW Monsoon:** This season prevails in the country from the months of October to December. It is a transition season which is related to the establishment of the north-easterly wind regime over the subcontinent of the country. A large part of the country experiences cool, dry, and dense Central Asian air masses. Some parts of Tamil Nadu, Kerala, Karnataka and Andhra Pradesh receive about 35% of their total rainfall during this season. A decline in the mean temperature from 38°C in October to 28°C in November takes place during this season. The characteristic features of this season include decrease in humidity level and clear skies in most parts of the central and northern India.

## Factors Affecting India's Climate

There are certain factors which affect the climate of India:

❏ **Latitude:** The Tropic of Cancer passes through the middle of India and extends from Mizoram in the east and Rann of Kutch in the west; and considerably affects the climate of the country. To the south of the Tropic of Cancer lies the southern part of the country which belongs to the tropical area and to its north lies the northern half of India which belongs to the sub-tropical area. Therefore, India experiences both sub-tropical and tropical climates.

❏ **Altitude:** In the north, India is bounded by mountains with an average height of 6,000 metres and in the south, has a vast coastline with maximum elevation of about 30 metres. The Himalayas act as a barrier against the cold winds from Central Asia. Therefore due to the altitude of these mountains, the Indian subcontinent experiences milder winters than Central Asia.

❏ **Monsoon Winds:** The 'monsoon winds' is the most dominating factor influencing the climate of India. It is often called the monsoon climate. A reversal in the monsoon winds can bring a change in the season of the country, for instance the extreme summer season suddenly changing to the rainy or monsoon season. The entire country receives rainfall due to the south-west summer monsoons from the Bay of Bengal and Arabian Sea.

❏ **Western Disturbances and Tropical Cyclones:** Large parts of peninsular India get influenced by the tropical cyclones which originate in the Arabian Sea and the Bay of Bengal. Most of the cyclones originate in the Bay of Bengal and influence the climatic conditions at the time of the south-west monsoon season. The western disturbances originate over the Mediterranean Sea and influence the weather conditions in the Western Himalayan region.

## Climate Related Calamities

Climate related calamities are a great cause of loss to the life and property. Some of the natural disasters that have been experienced in the country are as follows:

• **Landslides and Floods:** Floods are the most common natural disaster in India and are caused due to the inadequate capacity within the river banks to carry high flows which are brought down from the upper catchment because of the heavy rains. Almost the entire country is flood prone and the precipitation events like torrential rains and flash floods have become common in central India in the last few decades. But, the regions located in the Indo-Gangetic plains and northeast India are more prone to floods. Erratic, excess or untimely monsoon rains can kill thousands of people and also harm the agriculture of the country.

• **Droughts:** Drought is a situation which arises due to the scarcity of water. In India, agriculture depends on the rains or the monsoon season as a source of water. But, the shortage or failure of water results in the below-average crop yields. Climatic factors such as high wind, high temperature and low humidity also add to the severity of drought in India. Andhra Pradesh, Rajasthan, Gujarat, Odisha, some parts of Maharashtra and Karnataka are some of the drought-prone areas in the country. India has witnessed many famines such as Bengal famine of 1770, 1876-77, 1899 and 1943 which took lives of millions of people.

• **Tropical Cyclones:** These are the most devastating natural disasters which result in massive loss of life and property. In India, the lives of the coastal habitants are highly affected due to cyclones. The areas near the Bay of Bengal and Indian Ocean are the most cyclone-prone regions of the country. Coastal regions of Odisha, West Bengal, Tamil Nadu and Andhra Pradesh are more exposed to cyclones. During the time of cyclone, heavy rains, winds with high speed and storm surge are also experienced which also affect the lives of the people as it becomes difficult for them to get relief and supplies during this phenomenon. A super cyclone, Cyclone 05B that struck Odisha on 29 October 1999 is considered to be the deadliest cyclone in the country in the past few decades. It was considered equivalent to Category 5 hurricane.

## Climatic Regions in India

The various climatic regions of India are given below:

| Name of Climatic Region | States or Territories |
|---|---|
| Tropical Rainforest | Assam and parts of the Sahyadri Mountain Range |
| Tropical Savannah | Sahyadri Mountain Range and parts of Maharashtra |
| Tropical and subtropical steppe | Parts of Punjab and Gujarat |
| Tropical Desert | Most parts of Rajasthan |
| Moist subtropical with winter | Parts of Punjab, Assam, and Rajasthan |
| Mountain climate | Parts of Jammu & Kashmir, Himachal Pradesh and Uttarakhand |
| Drought | Rajasthan, Gujarat, and Haryana |
| Tropical semi-arid steppe | Tamil Nadu, Maharashtra, and other parts of South India |

## Characteristics of Rainfall in India: The rainfall measurement in parts of India.

| Type of Rainfall | Areas |
|---|---|
| **Areas of very little rainfall (lower than 50 cm):** | Western Rajasthan, northern part of Kashmir, the Deccan Plateau and Punjab. |
| **Areas of low precipitation (50-100 cm):** | Eastern Rajasthan, Upper Ganga basin, Southern plains of Karnataka, Punjab, Tamil Nadu, and Andhra Pradesh. |
| **Areas of comparatively heavy rainfall (100-200 cm):** | Southern areas of Gujarat, north-eastern Peninsular region, east Tamil Nadu, eastern Maharashtra, Western Ghats, Odisha, Madhya Pradesh, and the central Gangetic basin. |
| **Areas of heavy rainfall (more than 200 cm):** | The western seashores, the Western Ghats, Hills of Meghalaya, and the Sub-Himalayan range territories in North East. West Bengal, Assam, Western Coast, and southern part of east Himalayas. |

# MULTIPLE CHOICE QUESTIONS

1. Which among the following is categorized as high altitude clouds?
   (a) Cirrus
   (b) Nimbus
   (c) Stratus
   (d) Cumulus

2. The boundary separating troposphere from stratosphere is called
   (a) Tropopause
   (b) Mesopause
   (c) Plimsoll line
   (d) Stratopause

3. As per Wegener the separation of South America from Africa took place during
   (a) Carboniferous
   (b) Triassic
   (c) Jurassic
   (d) Permian

4. Identify the correct statement with regard to atmospheric pressure.
   (a) Atmospheric pressure is directly proportional to temperature
   (b) The Aleutian low pressure is of thermal origin
   (c) The average atmospheric pressure is around 1013 millibar
   (d) Subtropical regions have a continuous belt of high pressure

5. Beaufort scale of wind speed ranges from
   (a) 0 to 8
   (b) 0 to 10
   (c) 0 to 12
   (d) 1 to 12

6. Which of the following local wind is nicknamed as "The Doctor"?
   (a) Khamsin
   (b) Scirocco
   (c) Harmattan
   (d) Loo

7. Which among the following is not a greenhouse gas?
   (a) Methane
   (b) Hydrogen
   (c) Nitrous oxide
   (d) Ozone

8. The term Horse Latitudes usually indicates the latitudes between
   (a) 28° and 32° N
   (b) 15° and 18° N
   (c) 45° and 49° S
   (d) 45° and 49° N

9. As on 2009 the number of Biosphere reserves in India is
   (a) 18
   (b) 10
   (c) 12
   (d) 15

10. Mistral cold wind passes through the valley of
    (a) Rhine
    (b) Danube
    (c) Rhone
    (d) Seine

11. The normal date of onset of monsoon at Mumbai is
    (a) 10th June
    (b) 15th June
    (c) 20th June
    (d) 1st July

12. Identify the wrong statement with regard to Troposphere.
    (a) Most of the weather phenomena occur in Troposphere
    (b) There is Normal lapse rate of temperature in this layer
    (c) Ozone layer in Troposphere helps blocking of ultraviolet rays from sun
    (d) Extension of Troposphere is more at the equator than at the poles

13. The first person to attempt a division of world into natural regions on climate is
    (a) Miller
    (b) Trewertha
    (c) Herbertson
    (d) Critchfield

14. Growth Pole theory was outlined by Perroux in
    (a) 1949
    (b) 1959
    (c) 1969
    (d) 1979

15. The critical temperature at which an unsaturated air becomes saturated is called
    (a) Wet Bulb temperature
    (b) Wet Adiabatic Lapse rate
    (c) Dew point
    (d) Condensation

16. A low uniform layer of cloud resembling fog
    (a) Stratus
    (b) Nimbus
    (c) Cumulus
    (d) Cirrus

17. Which of the following is the youngest in Geological Time Scale?
    (a) Cretaceous
    (b) Permian
    (c) Palaeocene
    (d) Silurian

18. The GPS System being developed by European Space Agency is called
    (a) GLONASS
    (b) Galileo
    (c) COMPASS
    (d) QZSS

19. In the genetic classification of streams, those which develop in weaker strata are called
    (a) Subsequent
    (b) Resequent
    (c) Consequent
    (d) Insequent

20. The Panna Biosphere reserve in India is in:
    (a) Madhya Pradesh
    (b) Himachal Pradesh
    (c) Uttar Pradesh
    (d) West Bengal

21. The layer of atmosphere which helps communication is
    (a) Ozone layer
    (b) Stratosphere
    (c) Ionosphere
    (d) Mesosphere

22. Minamata disease was the result of
    (a) Water pollution
    (b) Air pollution
    (c) Noise pollution
    (d) Nuclear Accident

23. The growth pole theory was put forth by Perroux in
    (a) 1955
    (b) 1965
    (c) 1975
    (d) 1985

24. Which of the following type of aerial photographs can be used as a map?
    (a) Vertical photograph
    (b) Oblique photograph
    (c) Orthophoto
    (d) High Oblique photograph

25. Schaeffer's ideas on the methodology of study of Geography is called
    (a) Exceptionalism
    (b) Behaviouralism
    (c) Pragmatism
    (d) Positivism

26. The RF of a Survey of India sheet 58K is
    (a) 1 : 25000
    (b) 1 : 50000
    (c) 1 : 63360
    (d) 1 : 250000

27. In which of the following areas, producer component of ecosystem is almost absent?
    (a) Dense forests
    (b) Deserts
    (c) Deep sea
    (d) Mangroves

28. In the interior parts of continents, rainfall is mostly due to
    (a) Cyclone
    (b) Relief
    (c) Convection
    (d) Front

29. Which of the following cities has the highest annual range of temperature?
    (a) Mumbai
    (b) London
    (c) Bangkok
    (d) Moscow

30. After China and India the third most populous country in the world is

(a) Pakistan      (b) Indonesia
(c) Bangladesh    (d) USA

**31.** Occlusion is a process associated with
(a) Condensation
(b) Precipitation
(c) Temperate Cyclone
(d) Cloud formation

**32.** Which of the following is a functional region?
(a) Siberia       (b) Middle East
(c) Metropolitan area   (d) Veldt

**33.** The band used for identification of rocks and minerals is
(a) Band 4      (b) Band 5
(c) Band 3      (d) Band 7

**34.** For the world as a whole the Infant Mortality rate per 1000 live births is
(a) Less than 50    (b) 51 to 75
(c) 76 to 100      (d) More than 100

**35.** P-E Index is used in the climatic classification by
(a) Koeppen      (b) Trewartha
(c) Miller        (d) Thornthwaite

**36.** Among the Project Tiger Reserves in India, the largest in area is
(a) Sariska      (b) Nagarjunasagar
(c) Kaziranga    (d) Manas

**37.** Krivoi Rog is known for its
(a) Iron ore      (b) Copper
(c) Bauxite      (d) Coal

**38.** The range between Kargil in the north west and Shipki la in the south east is
(a) Lesser Himalayas   (b) Zaskar range
(c) Pir Panjal range    (d) Karakoram range

**39.** Ban Sagar Project is on the river
(a) Mahanadi      (b) Indravadi
(c) Sone        (d) Tapti

**40.** Clear nights are cooler than cloudy nights because of
(a) Condensation    (b) Radiation
(c) Insolation      (d) Conduction

**41.** The temperature at which the water vapour condenses is called as
(a) Freezing point   (b) Evaporation
(c) Dew point      (d) Dew level

**42.** The presence of incised meanders indicates that the area has experienced
(a) Eustatic changes
(b) Glaciation in the past
(c) Rejuvenation
(d) Faulting

**43.** Match the following:

| List-I | List-II |
| --- | --- |
| A. Areal differentiation | 1. Haggett |
| B. Behavioural approach | 2. Haggerstrand |
| C. Locational analysis | 3. Hartshorne |
| D. Diffusion of Innovation | 4. Gould |

| | A | B | C | D |
| --- | --- | --- | --- | --- |
| (a) | 4 | 3 | 1 | 2 |
| (b) | 3 | 4 | 1 | 2 |
| (c) | 2 | 1 | 3 | 4 |
| (d) | 1 | 2 | 3 | 4 |

**44.** A telegram was sent from Greenwich at 12 noon. The time for transmission was 12 minutes. The telegram reached its destination at 6 p.m. The longitude of the destination is
(a) 97° E      (b) 87° E
(c) 87° W      (d) 97° W

**45.** Orogeny and epirogeny during the Quarternary and Tertiary are referred as
(a) Cenozoic-tectonism
(b) Paleo-tectonism
(c) Neo-tectonism
(d) Piliocene-tectonism

**46.** The hot dusty winds from the Sahara towards the Mediterranean Sea is called
(a) Chinook      (b) Fohn
(c) Mistral      (d) Sirocco

**47.** The statement 'Man is the product of the Earth' is by
(a) Huntington    (b) Montesque
(c) Ptolemy      (d) Semple

**48.** The atmospheric temperature is maximum during
(a) 10 a.m. to 11 a.m.
(b) 11 a.m. to 12 noon
(c) 12 noon to 1 p.m.
(d) 2 p.m. to 3 p.m.

**49.** The ship breaking industry is located at
(a) Morvi      (b) Alang
(c) Hazira      (d) Dwarka

**50.** 'Resources are not; they become' stated by
(a) Marx      (b) Dumont
(c) Zimmerman    (d) Ricardo

**51.** Umland is an example of a
(a) Homogeneous region
(b) Formal region
(c) Nodal region
(d) Uniform region

**52.** Rank-size rule was postulated by
(a) Johnson      (b) Zipf
(c) Taylor      (d) Hagett

53. Which one of the following surfaces is useful to draw the Zenithal projections?
    (a) Cylindrical surface
    (b) Conical surface
    (c) Spherical surface
    (d) Plane surface

54. The tendency of pollutants to become concentrated in successive trophic levels is known as
    (a) Bio-remediation
    (b) Bio-magnification
    (c) Bio-piracy
    (d) Bio-rhythm

55. Which one of the following has the longest wave length?
    (a) IR
    (b) UV
    (c) Blue
    (d) Gamma

56. A model of population growth that characterises a society moving through and completing the industrial revolution and associated health care is
    (a) Demographic transition
    (b) Malthus theory
    (c) Ricardo model
    (d) Carl Saunder Model

57. An erosional landform produced by glaciers
    (a) Morraine
    (b) Arete
    (c) Till plain
    (d) Esker

58. Deposits of opaque with rough textured crystals of ice is
    (a) Sleet
    (b) Hail
    (c) Graupel
    (d) Rime

59. A device that aids 3-D vision
    (a) Pantograph
    (b) Psudoscope
    (c) Telescope
    (d) Stereoscope

60. In image processing, contrast stretching is employed for
    (a) Image classification
    (b) Image enhancement
    (c) Image rectification
    (d) Image detection

61. To understand the influence of a point, line and area over the surrounding, we employ
    (a) Filtering
    (b) Fussy logic
    (c) Buffering
    (d) DEM

62. The primary cause of acid rain around the world is
    (a) Carbon di-oxide
    (b) Sulphur di-oxide
    (c) Carbon monoxide
    (d) Ozone

63. The weather conditions associated with an anticyclone are
    (a) Hot and wet
    (b) Cold and severe
    (c) Wet and cold
    (d) Fine and dry

64. To find out the location of an object using GPS, minimum number of satellites required is
    (a) 2
    (b) 3
    (c) 4
    (d) 5

65. Weinganga is a tributary of the river
    (a) Krishna
    (b) Godavari
    (c) Mahanadi
    (d) Narmada

66. Which one of the following is a foot loose industry?
    (a) Iron and steel
    (b) Sugar
    (c) Hosiery
    (d) Cement

67. Losch introduced the concept of
    (a) Isolated State
    (b) Central Place
    (c) Economic Landscape
    (d) Sector Relationship

68. Which one of the following is a tool of PRA?
    (a) Transect
    (b) Questionnaire
    (c) Schedule
    (d) Telephonic Interview

69. The depopulated town due to its economic collapse is called as a
    (a) Market town
    (b) Nodal town
    (c) Decentralized town
    (d) Ghost town

70. Roche Moutonne is a landform associated with the action of
    (a) Glacier
    (b) River
    (c) Wind
    (d) Sea waves

71. Palaeozoic glacial evidence supporting continental drift was found in
    (a) North America
    (b) Europe
    (c) Siberia
    (d) South America

72. Which of the following layers of atmosphere helps communication?
    (a) Stratosphere
    (b) Mesosphere
    (c) Ionosphere
    (d) Exosphere

73. When an unsaturated air mass goes up the initial rate of cooling is called
    (a) Dry Adiabatic Lapse rate
    (b) Wet Adiabatic Lapse rate
    (c) Normal Lapse rate
    (d) Environmental Lapse rate

74. The part of Himalayas between Rivers Kali and Sutlej is known as
    (a) Kumaon
    (b) Pir Panjal
    (c) Siwaliks
    (d) Zaskar range

75. Which of the following pairs is CORRECT?
    (a) Mistral – Hot wind
    (b) Sleet – Precipitation
    (c) Hail – Condensation
    (d) Trough – High pressure

76. National Waterway 1 links
    (a) Kollam and Kottapuram
    (b) Allahabad and Haldia
    (c) Sadiya and Dhurbri
    (d) Kakinada and Puducherry

77. Among the given States the share of Forests to the total area is the highest in
    (a) Goa          (b) Kerala
    (c) Andhra Pradesh  (d) Odisha

78. Identify the landform which is different from the other three
    (a) Monadnock    (b) Hum
    (c) Inselberg    (d) Mesa

79. Which of the following is NOT a form of condensation?
    (a) Fog          (b) Frost
    (c) Hail         (d) Cloud

80. Identify the FALSE statement among the following
    (a) Clouds are classified as per form
    (b) Cirrus is a high altitude cloud
    (c) Cumulus clouds generally indicate fair weather
    (d) Altocumulus clouds are also called "Mackerel sky"

81. The steel industry which was established during the Third Five Year Plan is
    (a) Bokaro       (b) Bhilai
    (c) Rourkela     (d) Durgapur

82. Coalescence of alluvial fans at the foothill region of semiarid regions is called
    (a) Bajada       (b) Playa
    (c) Pediment     (d) Arroyo

83. Which of the following climatic types of Koppen has rare occurrence?
    (a) Cs           (b) Cf
    (c) Ds           (d) Df

84. Which of the following deserts is considered as the driest?
    (a) Sahara       (b) Kalahari
    (c) Gobi         (d) Atacama

85. Which is NOT represented on the map of Indian Daily Weather Report?
    (a) Absolute temperature
    (b) Wind velocity
    (c) Cloud cover
    (d) Mist

86. Raw, Keen. Muggy and Scorching are the terms associated with
    (a) Climatograph (b) Climograph
    (c) Climatic graph (d) Ergograph

87. The term Saprotroph in the Ecosystem refers to
    (a) Green Plants (b) Herbivores
    (c) Carnivores   (d) Decomposers

88. A transition zone where plant communities naturally merge into one another is called
    (a) Biotope      (b) Biotite
    (c) Ecotone      (d) Ecotope

89. Homeostasis in ecosystem refers to
    (a) Food web     (b) Food pyramid
    (c) Energy flow  (d) Natural balance

90. In Planning, the terms Spread effect and Backwash effect are explained by
    (a) Perroux      (b) Minshull
    (c) Myrdal       (d) Duncan

91. RISAT 1 was launched in
    (a) 2009         (b) 2010
    (c) 2012         (d) 2013

92. Which of the following rivers in Kerala flow eastward?
    (a) Chaliyar     (b) Neyyar
    (c) Kabani       (d) Achankoil

93. The longest river in Peninsular India is
    (a) Narmada      (b) Mahanadi
    (c) Krishna      (d) Godavari

94. The Kiriburu iron ore mine supplies iron ore mainly to the steel plant at
    (a) Bokaro       (b) Bhilai
    (c) Jamshedpur   (d) Bhadravathi

95. The normal atmospheric pressure on the surface of the earth is
    (a) 990 mb       (b) 1003 mb
    (c) 1013 mb      (d) 1023 mb

96. Potential Evapotranspiration is used in climatic classification of
    (a) Miller       (b) Koppen
    (c) Thornthwaite (d) Trewartha

97. The eye in a tropical cyclone is a region of
    (a) Strong winds
    (b) Heavy rain
    (c) Calm weather
    (d) High barometric pressure

98. Haldenhang is a term in slope used to refer
    (a) Free Face    (b) Buried Face
    (c) Debris Slope (d) Wash Slope

99. Which of the following has air bubbles trapped inside at the time of its formation?
    (a) Pumice       (b) Sandstone
    (c) Shale        (d) Gneiss

100. Which of the following statements regarding National Highways is FALSE?

(a) The new numbering of National Highways was implemented in April 2010

(b) All north-south oriented Highways will have even numbers

(c) All east-west oriented Highways will have odd numbers

(d) Under the new scheme the longest National Highway is NH 27

**101.** Most of the mineral wealth in India is concentrated in
(a) Malwa plateau
(b) Chhotanagpur plateau
(c) Baghelkhand plateau
(d) Mysore plateau

**102.** Which of the following is NOT a landform due to rejuvenation of a river?
(a) Knickpoint
(b) Incised meander
(c) River terrace
(d) Shoal

**103.** Identify the WRONG statement
(a) In an earthquake hypocenter refers to the focus
(b) In the shadow zone no seismic waves are recorded
(c) In Richter scale each increase in number indicates ten times increase in magnitude
(d) S waves travel through both solid and liquid

**104.** The GPS system developed by the Soviet Union is called
(a) GAGAN       (b) GALILEO
(c) GLANOSS     (d) IRNSS

**105.** The side lap in an aerial photograph varies from
(a) 10 to 20%   (b) 10 to 40%
(c) 20 to 40%   (d) 40 to 60%

**106.** Who is considered as the "Father of GIS?"
(a) Tomlinson   (b) Fisher
(c) Chang       (d) Burrough

**107.** Which of the following is NOT a greenhouse gas?
(a) Water vapour (b) Ozone
(c) Methane      (d) Hydrogen

**108.** The cloud that occur in a thunderstorm is
(a) Altostratus  (b) Nimbus
(c) Cirrus       (d) Cumulonimbus

**109.** The term 'Mackerel sky' refers to the cloud type
(a) Cumulus      (b) Stratus
(c) Cirrocumulus (d) Cirrostratus

**110.** The number of agro-climatic regions identified for Development planning in India is:

(a) 10           (b) 15
(c) 21           (d) 25

**111.** The largest producer of Manganese in the world is
(a) China        (b) Australia
(c) USA          (d) India

**112.** As per Indian Puranas Saka dwipa refers to the present day
(a) Africa       (b) Southeast Asia
(c) Europe       (d) Central Asia

**113.** Which of the following pairs is TRUE?
(a) Vidal de la Blache – Population geography
(b) Haggett – Locational Analysis
(c) Berry – Urban Population Density model
(d) Humboldt – Erdkunde

**114.** Which of the following statements with regard to Lapse rate is WRONG?
(a) Normal Lapse rate is around 6.6°C per 1000 m of elevation
(b) Air which has 100% Relative Humidity cools at Dry Adiabatic Lapse Rate
(c) When Environmental Lapse rate is less than that of an air parcel, stability occurs
(d) Wet Adiabatic Lapse rate is less due to release of latent heat by condensation

**115.** Which of the following statements with regard to humidity is TRUE?
(a) Moisture holding capacity of an air parcel is directly proportional to its temperature
(b) Moisture holding capacity of an air parcel is inversely proportional to its temperature
(c) The temperature at which an air parcel becomes saturated is called condensation
(d) Absolute humidity is measured in g/kg of air

**116.** Which of the following statements is WRONG?
(a) Fog is a form of precipitation
(b) In areas of cool ocean currents, advection fog is common
(c) Dew is a form of condensation
(d) Smog occurs in industrial temperate regions during winter

**117.** Which of the following statements regarding urban population in Kerala is TRUE?
(a) Malappuram experienced the highest 2001-11 decadal growth rate
(b) Ernakulam had a higher 2001-11 decadal growth rate than Thiruvananthapuram
(c) Kozhikode and Alappuzha had almost similar level of urbanization in 2011
(d) Number of census towns increased from 99 in 2001 to 261 in 2011

**118.** Which of the following is a low level cloud?
(a) Cirrus (b) Cirrocumulus
(c) Stratus (d) Altocumulus

**119.** The Indian National Cartographic Association was established in
(a) 1979 (b) 1981
(c) 1986 (d) 1991

**120.** Identify the WRONG statement
(a) Early world map was prepared by Anaximander
(b) Ptolemy's first volume of *Geography* dealt with mathematical cartography
(c) *Orbis Terranum* was prepared by Greeks
(d) As per Indian ancient cartography Plasca Dwipa covered most of Africa

**121.** World Biodiversity Day is observed on
(a) April 22 (b) May 5
(c) May 22 (d) June 5

**122.** Which of the following statements is TRUE?
(a) Stability is minimum in the Climax ecosystem
(b) Primary ecological succession may be observed in areas destroyed by forest fires
(c) The term ecosystem homeostasis refers to energy cycle
(d) Ecotone refers to boundary between two biomes

**123.** Trickling down effect and Polarization effect are the ideas explained by
(a) Myrdal (b) Perroux
(c) Boudville (d) Hirschman

**124.** Intensive Agricultural District Programme is an example of
(a) Integrated planning (b) Sectoral planning
(c) Nodal planning (d) Macro planning

**125.** In the ecosystem Autotrophs refer to
(a) Primary producers (b) Herbivores
(c) Carnivores (d) Decomposers

**126.** Montreal Protocol refers to the
(a) Emission of $CO_2$
(b) Depletion of ozone
(c) Control of methane
(d) Emission of CO

**127.** The radiometric resolution of IKONOS satellite is
(a) 6 bit (b) 8 bit
(c) 9 bit (d) 11 bit

**128.** Which among the following statements relating to LANDSAT 8 is wrong?
(a) LANDSAT 8 was launched in 2013
(b) It has Operational Land Imager and Thermal Infrared Sensors

(c) The temporal resolution of LANDSAT 8 is 10 days
(d) The panchromatic spatial resolution of this satellite is 15 meters

**129.** Mark the *correct* order of ion mobility in a generalized chemical weathering zone :
(a) Al > Na > K > $SO_4$
(b) Na > $SO_4$ > K > Ca
(c) Na > K > Si > Al
(d) Ca > Mg > Fe > $SO_4$

**130.** In lapse rate, adiabatic means that there is :
(a) No exchange of heat
(b) Exchange of heat
(c) Latent heat release
(d) Heat gain

**131.** Temperature inversion occurs when :
(a) Cold air covers warm air
(b) Warm air covers cold air
(c) There is moisture adiabatic lapse rate
(d) There is dry adiabatic lapse Rate

**132.** A line which seperates outer space and earth's atmosphere
(a) Durand line (b) Karman line
(c) Space line (d) Venus line

**133.** Height of mesosphere which lies after troposphere is
(a) 80 – 85 km (b) 70 – 80 km
(c) 110 – 130 km (d) 95 – 105 km

**134.** Second highest layer of Earth's atmosphere is
(a) Stratosphere (b) Mesosphere
(c) Troposphere (d) Thermosphere

**135.** Troposphere layer of atmosphere extends from Earth to
(a) 38 km (b) 32 km
(c) 20 km (d) 12 km

**136.** Thermosphere consists of
(a) Troposphere (b) Ionosphere
(c) Lithosphere (d) Hydrosphere

**137.** A large scale movement of Air through troposphere of atmosphere
(a) Sound circulation
(b) Atmospheric circulation
(c) Infrared circulation
(d) Radioactive circulation

**138.** The atmospheric density decreases with
(a) Increases in longitude
(b) Increase in altitude
(c) Increases in latitude
(d) Decrease in latitude

**139.** Troposphere bounded by boundary is known as
(a) Mesopause    (b) Thermopause
(c) Tropopause    (d) Stratopouse

**140.** A line which separate stratosphere and troposphere is called
(a) Mesopause    (b) Tropopause
(c) Thermopause    (d) Stratopause

**141.** The relation between altitude and atmospheric density is
(a) Inversely proportional
(b) Directly proportional
(c) Common relation
(d) No relation

**142.** CFCs are primarily used as
(a) Refrigerants
(b) Fuels of crafts
(c) Repairers of troposphere
(d) Repairers of troposphere

**143.** Ozone layer is part of
(a) Stratosphere    (b) Mesosphere
(c) Thermosphere    (d) Troposphere

**144.** Layer of atmosphere which accessed by jet-powered aircraft is
(a) Thermopause    (b) Stratopause
(c) Tropopause    (d) Mesopause

**145.** Which is not a part of greenhouses gases
(a) Methane    (b) Carbon dioxide
(c) Oxygen    (d) Nitrous oxide

**146.** Refractive index of Air is
(a) Less than 1    (b) Less than 0
(c) Greater than 2    (d) Greater than 1

**147.** Study of Earth's atmosphere and processes in atmosphere
(a) Morphology
(b) Biology
(c) Aerology
(d) Environmental biology

**148.** The name of the outermost layer of atmosphere
(a) Troposphere    (b) Thermosphere
(c) Exosphere    (d) Mesosphere

**149.** The second layer of the Earth's atmosphere is
(a) Stratosphere    (b) Mesosphere
(c) Troposphere    (d) Ionosphere

**150.** Clouds seen in atmosphere with naked eye
(a) Oxygenous clouds
(b) Helium clouds
(c) Nitrogenous clouds
(d) Hydrogenous clouds

**151.** Mesosphere layer is used by
(a) Aircrafts    (b) Sounding rockets
(c) Space stations    (d) All the above

**152.** Height of exosphere is
(a) 3000 to 10,000 km
(b) 5000 to 10,000 km
(c) 1000 to 10,000 km
(d) 700 to 10,000 km

**153.** Percentage of oxygen in atmosphere of Earth
(a) 20.94%    (b) 45.94%
(c) 35.95%    (d) 25.94%

**154.** Region of atmosphere which occupies area below the thermosphere and above stratosphere is classified as
(a) Exosphere    (b) Troposphere
(c) Thermosphere    (d) Mesosphere

**155.** Second most abundant constituent of dry air in terms of volume after nitrogen is
(a) Nitrogen    (b) Helium
(c) Carbon dioxide    (d) Oxygen

**156.** Ionosphere layer of atmosphere is part of the
(a) Mesosphere    (b) Troposphere
(c) Exosphere    (d) Thermosphere

**157.** Third largest layer of Earth's atmosphere is
(a) Troposphere    (b) Stratosphere
(c) Ionosphere    (d) Mesosphere

**158.** Layer of earth's atmosphere which is used by International Space Station is known as
(a) Stratosphere    (b) Thermosphere
(c) Hydrosphere    (d) Troposphere

**159.** Lowest layer of Earth's atmosphere is
(a) Troposphere    (b) Stratosphere
(c) Ionosphere    (d) Mesosphere

**160.** Atmosphere of Earth becomes thinner and thinner with the
(a) Increases in latitude
(b) Increases in altitude
(c) Increase in longitude
(d) Decrease in altitude

**161.** Height of the thermosphere is
(a) 150 to 800 km    (b) 80 to 700 km
(c) 100 to 700 km    (d) 300 to 800 km

**162.** Energy received by the earth from the Sun is known as
(a) Ozone radiation    (b) Lunar radiation
(c) Ionize radiation    (d) Solar radiation

**163.** Percentage of nitrogen in atmosphere of Earth is
(a) 91.08%    (b) 85.08%
(c) 78.08%    (d) 65.05%

**164.** Earth's atmosphere extend hundreds of kilometres above the
(a) Surface
(b) Planets
(c) Atmosphere
(d) Sky

**165.** A blanket of gases surrounding planet is known as
(a) Temperature
(b) Season
(c) Ozone
(d) Atmosphere

**166.** Study of earth's atmosphere including climate and weather is known as
(a) Geology
(b) Astrology
(c) Climatology
(d) Meteorology

**167.** Match the following:

| List-I | List-II |
|---|---|
| A. Thiruvananthapuram | 1. Nodal town |
| B. Nagpur | 2. Mining town |
| C. Neyveli | 3. Industrial town |
| D. Jamshedpur | 4. Administrative town |

|  | A | B | C | D |
|---|---|---|---|---|
| (a) | 4, | 1, | 2, | 3 |
| (b) | 4, | 2, | 1, | 3 |
| (c) | 4, | 1, | 3, | 2 |
| (d) | 4, | 3, | 1, | 2 |

# ANSWERS

| 1 | 2 | 3 | 4 | 5 | 6 | 7 | 8 | 9 | 10 |
|---|---|---|---|---|---|---|---|---|---|
| (a) | (a) | (a) | (d) | (a) | (c) | (b) | (d) | (a) | (c) |
| **11** | **12** | **13** | **14** | **15** | **16** | **17** | **18** | **19** | **20** |
| (a) | (c) | (c) | (a) | (c) | (a) | (c) | (b) | (d) | (a) |
| **21** | **22** | **23** | **24** | **25** | **26** | **27** | **28** | **29** | **30** |
| (c) | (a) | (a) | (c) | (a) | (b) | (c) | (a) | (d) | (d) |
| **31** | **32** | **33** | **34** | **35** | **36** | **37** | **38** | **39** | **40** |
| (b) | (c) | (b) | (d) | (d) | (b) | (a) | (b) | (c) | (c) |
| **41** | **42** | **43** | **44** | **45** | **46** | **47** | **48** | **49** | **50** |
| (c) | (a) | (b) | (a) | (c) | (d) | (c) | (d) | (b) | (c) |
| **51** | **52** | **53** | **54** | **55** | **56** | **57** | **58** | **59** | **60** |
| (d) | (b) | (a) | (b) | (a) | (b) | (b) | (d) | (d) | (b) |
| **61** | **62** | **63** | **64** | **65** | **66** | **67** | **68** | **69** | **70** |
| (d) | (b) | (d) | (c) | (b) | (c) | (b) | (a) | (d) | (a) |
| **71** | **72** | **73** | **74** | **75** | **76** | **77** | **78** | **79** | **80** |
| (a) | (c) | (a) | (a) | (a) | (b) | (a) | (b) | (a) | (a) |
| **81** | **82** | **83** | **84** | **85** | **86** | **87** | **88** | **89** | **90** |
| (a) | (a) | (b) | (a) | (a) | (b) | (d) | (c) | (d) | (c) |
| **91** | **92** | **93** | **94** | **95** | **96** | **97** | **98** | **99** | **100** |
| (c) | (c) | (a) | (a) | (c) | (c) | (a) | (c) | (a) | (d) |
| **101** | **102** | **103** | **104** | **105** | **106** | **107** | **108** | **109** | **110** |
| (b) | (d) | (d) | (c) | (c) | (a) | (d) | (d) | (c) | (b) |
| **111** | **112** | **113** | **114** | **115** | **116** | **117** | **118** | **119** | **120** |
| (a) | (a) | (a) | (b) | (d) | (a) | (a) | (c) | (a) | (b) |
| **121** | **122** | **123** | **124** | **125** | **126** | **127** | **128** | **129** | **130** |
| (c) | (d) | (d) | (a) | (d) | (a) | (d) | (c) | (c) | (a) |
| **131** | **132** | **133** | **134** | **135** | **136** | **137** | **138** | **139** | **140** |
| (a) | (b) | (a) | (b) | (d) | (b) | (b) | (b) | (c) | (b) |
| **141** | **142** | **143** | **144** | **145** | **146** | **147** | **148** | **149** | **150** |
| (a) | (a) | (a) | (b) | (c) | (d) | (c) | (c) | (a) | (d) |
| **151** | **152** | **153** | **154** | **155** | **156** | **157** | **158** | **159** | **160** |
| (d) | (d) | (a) | (d) | (d) | (d) | (d) | (b) | (a) | (d) |
| **161** | **162** | **163** | **164** | **165** | **166** | **167** | | | |
| (b) | (d) | (c) | (a) | (d) | (d) | (a) | | | |

# CHAPTER 4

# HYDROSPHERE

**Hydrography** is the branch of applied sciences which deals with the measurement and description of the physical features of oceans, seas, coastal areas, lakes and rivers, as well as with the prediction of their change over time, for the primary purpose of safety of navigation and in support of all other marine activities, including economic development, security and defence, scientific research, and environmental protection.

❏ Hydrography is the science that measures and describes the physical features of the navigable portion of the Earth's surface and adjoining coastal areas. Hydrographic surveyors study these bodies of water to see what the "floor" looks like.

❏ NOAA's Office of Coast Survey conducts hydrographic surveys to measure the depth and bottom configuration of water bodies. That data is used to update nautical charts and develop hydrographic models. This information is vital to navigating the ocean and our nation's waterways.

❏ Hydrographical surveys are also used in NOAA's Integrated Ocean and Coast Mapping program, providing information for a number of purposes, including seafloor structural construction, laying pipelines and cables, dredging, anchoring and understanding fish habitats.

❏ **Surveying** with multibeam echo sounders is the primary method of obtaining hydrographic data. By mapping out water depth, the shape of the seafloor and coastline, the location of possible obstructions and physical features of water bodies, hydrography helps to keep our maritime transportation system moving safely and efficiently. Multibeam echo sounder beams sweep the seafloor as the ship passes over the survey area. Multibeam echo sounder beams bounce off the seafloor and return to the ship where the depth is recorded.

## HYDROGRAPHERS

Measure water depth, and search for shoals, rocks, & wrecks that could be hazards to navigation. They also collect information on:

- Water level & tides
- Currents
- Temperature
- Salinity
- Wind
- Waves

## Significance of Hydrography

In addition to supporting safe and efficient navigation of ships, hydrography underpins almost every other activity associated with the sea, including:

- Resource exploitation – fishing, minerals
- Environmental protection and management
- Maritime boundary delimitation
- National marine spatial data infrastructures
- Recreational boating
- Maritime defence and security
- Tsunami flood and inundation modelling
- Coastal zone management
- Tourism
- Marine science

# RELIEF OF THE OCEAN

Relief of the ocean due to diferent tectonics processes like plate motions, volcanic avtivity, erosional and depositional. The relief of the Ocean as different as following:

Four major divisions in the ocean relief are:

1. The continental shelf,
2. The continental slope,
3. The continental rise,
4. The Deep Sea Plain or the abyssal plain.

## Minor Ocean Relief Features

- Ridges,
- Seamounts,
- Trenches,
- Sleeps,
- Island arcs,
- Coral reefs,
- Sea-scarps.
- Hills,
- Guyots,
- Canyons,
- Fracture zones,
- Atolls,
- Submerged volcanoes and

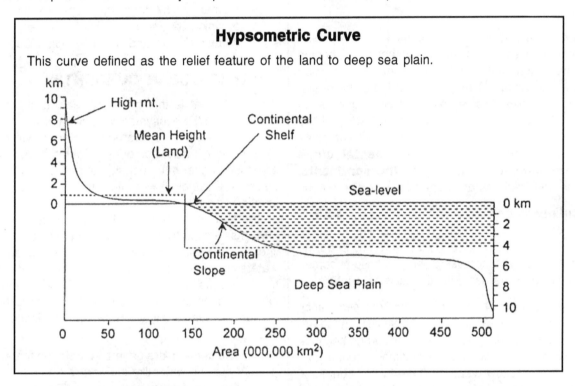

## Hypsometric Curve

This curve defined as the relief feature of the land to deep sea plain.

## Continental Shelf

The continental shelf is the upper zone of the continents which gently sloping seaward. This is cover area shallow sea and gulfs. The total area cover about 7.5% of the total ocean cover, and the slope is 1 or less than 1 degree. Shelf break is a very steep slope area. This is very economic important zone for the deposits of the petroleum. The shelf is formed mainly due to:

### Submergence of a part of a continent

- Relative rise in sea level
- Sedimentary deposits brought down by rivers

There are various types of shelves based on different sediments of terrestrial origin:

- Glaciated shelf (Surrounding Greenland),
- Coral reef shelf (Queensland, Australia),
- Shelf of a large river (Around Nile Delta),
- Shelf with dendritic valleys (At the Mouth of Hudson River)
- Shelf along young mountain ranges (Shelves between Hawaiian Islands).

❑ **Width:** The average width of continental shelves is between **70 – 80 km.** The shelves are almost absent or very narrow along some of the margins like the coasts of Chile, the west coast of Sumatra, etc. [Ocean– Continent Convergence and Ocean–Ocean Convergence]. It is up to 120 km wide along the eastern coast of USA. On the contrary, the **Siberian shelf** in the Arctic Ocean, the largest in the world, stretches to 1,500 km in width.

❑ **Depth:** The depth of the shelves also varies. It may be as shallow as 30 m in some areas while in some areas it is as deep as 600 m.

### Significance of Continental Shelf

- Marine food comes almost entirely from continental shelves;

- They provide the richest fishing grounds;

- They are potential sites for economic minerals [20% of the world production of petroleum and gas comes from shelves. Poly-metallic nodules (manganese nodules; concentric layers of iron and manganese hydroxides) etc. are good sources of various mineral ores like manganese, iron, copper, gold etc.]

**Continental slope:** The continental slope connects the continental shelf and the ocean basins. It begins where the bottom of the continental shelf sharply drops off into a steep slope. The gradient of the slope region varies between **2-5°**. The depth of the slope region varies between 200 and 3,000 m. The seaward edge of the continental slope loses gradient at this depth and gives rise to **continental rise. The continental slope boundary indicates the end of the continents**. Canyons and trenches are observed in this region.

**Continental rise:** The continental slope **gradually** loses its steepness with depth. When the slope reaches a level of between **0.5° and 1°**, it is referred to as the continental rise. With increasing depth the rise becomes virtually flat and merges with the **abyssal plain.**

**Deep sea plain or abyssal plain:** Deep sea planes are gently sloping areas of the ocean basins. These are the **flattest** and smoothest regions of the world because of **terrigenous** [denoting marine sediment eroded from the land] **and shallow water sediments** that buries the irregular topography. It covers nearly **40%** of the ocean floor. The depths vary between 3,000 and 6,000 m. These plains are covered with fine-grained sediments like clay and silt.

## Ocean Deeps or Trench

The trenches are relatively steep sided, narrow basins (Depressions). These areas are the deepest parts of the oceans. They are of tectonic origin and are formed during ocean – ocean convergence and ocean continent convergence.

- They are some 3-5 km deeper than the surrounding ocean floor.

- The trenches lie along the fringes of the deep-sea plain at the bases of continental slopes and along island arcs.

- The trenches run parallel to the bordering fold mountains or the island chains.

- The trenches are very common in the Pacific Ocean and form an almost continuous ring along the western and eastern margins of the Pacific.

- The Mariana Trench off the Guam Islands in the Pacific Ocean is the deepest trench with, a depth of more than 11 kilometres.

- They are associated with active volcanoes and strong earthquakes (Deep Focus Earthquakes like in Japan). This makes them very significant in the study of plate movements.

- As many as 57 deeps have been explored so far; of which 32 are in the Pacific Ocean; 19 in the Atlantic Ocean and 6 in the Indian Ocean.

## WHAT IS OCEAN CURRENT?

Ocean Current is the important feature in the ocean which effects the ecosystem with climate, weather, wind and also abiotic component of the environments. Currents may be surface or depth of the ocean, globally or locally. Winds, water density, and tides all drive ocean currents. Coastal and sea floor features influence their location, direction, and speed. Earth's rotation results in the Coriolis Effect which also influences ocean currents. Similar to a person trying to walk in a straight line across a spinning merry-go-round, winds and ocean waters get deflected from a straight line path as they travel across the rotating Earth. This phenomenon causes ocean currents in the Northern Hemisphere to veer to the right and in the Southern Hemisphere to the left.

- The currents are generated from the forces acting upon the water like the earth's rotation, the wind, the temperature and salinity differences and the gravitation of the moon.

- The depth contours, the shoreline and other currents influence the current's direction and strength.

- Ocean currents can flow for thousands of kilometers.

- They are very important in determining the climates of the continents, especially those regions bordering on the ocean.

- Perhaps the most striking example is the Gulf Stream, which makes northwest Europe much more temperate than any other region at the same latitude.

- Deep ocean currents are driven by density and temperature gradients.

- Thermohaline circulation, also known as the ocean's conveyor belt, refers to the deep ocean density-driven ocean basin currents.

- These currents, which flow under the surface of the ocean and are thus hidden from immediate detection, are called submarine rivers.

## Surface Currents

Large-scale surface ocean currents are driven by global wind systems that are fueled by energy from the sun. These currents transfer heat from the tropics to the polar regions, influencing local and global climate. The warm Gulf Stream originating in the tropical Caribbean, for instance, carries about 150 times more water than the Amazon River. The current moves along the U.S. East Coast across the Atlantic Ocean towards Europe. The heat from the Gulf Stream keeps much of Northern Europe significantly warmer than other places equally as far north. Currents found in the upper 1,300 feet of the ocean are called **surface currents**.

**Key to affect the Surface Currents:** We examine some of the forces that determine the direction of these currents.

**Gravity**: The surface of the ocean is not even. Due to this, **gravity** has an impact on the flow of water in the ocean. The earth's gravity pulls at water, causing it to flow downward from higher surface levels. You will notice the impact of gravity as it is mentioned alongside various other forces throughout this lesson.

**Wind:** Wind is the driving force behind our oceans' surface currents. In other words, most surface currents are caused by wind, which has the greatest impact on these currents. As the wind blows over the water's surface, it produces friction. This friction pushes the water along and forms a current moving in the same direction the wind is blowing. The current will continue in the direction of the wind until other factors - such as nearing a land mass or colliding with another ocean current - cause the water to build up and move in different ways.

**Coriolis Effect:** The spinning of the earth deflects movement. This is called the **Coriolis Effect** . We usually see no impact from the spinning of the earth, but we do notice its effect on surface currents because they are large and move over long distances. The Coriolis Effect comes into play when water being pushed by the wind piles up into mounds. As gravity pulls the water down the slope of the mound, the Coriolis Effect forms a current that creates spiral patterns called **gyres** that help push the current forward. These gyres move clockwise in the Northern Hemisphere and counterclockwise in the Southern Hemisphere.

**Continental deflection:** We briefly mentioned earlier that nearing a land mass is one factor that causes water to build up and change direction. When water building up or changing direction occurs near a very large land mass, or continent, it is called **continental deflection**. Since the earth is not completely covered in water, continental deflection plays a large role in the overall direction of surface currents. The water can't travel over or through the continent, so it is forced to move around it.

## Deep Ocean Currents

Differences in water density, resulting from the variability of water temperature (*thermo*) and salinity (*haline*), also cause ocean currents. This process is known as thermohaline circulation. In cold regions, such as the North Atlantic Ocean, ocean water loses heat to the atmosphere and becomes cold and dense. When ocean water freezes, forming sea ice, salt is left behind causing surrounding seawater to become saltier and denser. Dense-cold-salty water sinks to the ocean bottom.

- Surface water flows in to replace the sinking water, which in turn becomes cold and salty enough to sink. This "starts" the global conveyer belt, a connected system of deep and surface currents that circulate around the globe on a 1000 year time span. This global set of ocean currents is a critical part of Earth's climate system as well as the ocean nutrient and carbon dioxide cycles.

- Deep currents in oceans are caused by a large amount of sinking surface water. Surface water is the upper layer of water closest to the top surface. The sun can easily reach this top layer, heat up the surface water and evaporate some of the water.

- When the surface water becomes extremely cold, the lower temperature and the additional salt causes the surface water to become more dense than the water beneath it, and thus the surface water sinks down to the deep water layers of the ocean in a circulation process known as thermohaline circulation. Thermohaline circulation, or the sinking of highly dense surface water, is the source of deep currents in oceans.

## Deep Ocean Origin

Thermohaline circulation can only develop in extremely cold regions where the temperature of the air is low enough to make the surface water very cold, highly salty and more dense than the water beneath it. Thus, deep currents generally occur in the higher latitude regions of the Earth, such as North Atlantic Deep Water and Antarctic Bottom Water, and from these frigid poleward regions the deep currents flow at a relatively slow pace towards the equator.

*Characteristics*

After the thermohaline circulation process, the surface water that sinks down to the deep ocean does not mix well with the water beneath it, and thus it is easy to identify the sinking water masses using scientific data. Deep currents can be distinguished by the extremely cold water temperatures, the relatively high concentration of oxygen and the high salt levels that all result from sinking surface water. Because of these conditions, the water in deep ocean currents is also very dense.

## Circulation Pattern

Many deep currents follow a specific circulation pattern as they travel around the planet, and the pattern usually forms a cycle. Most sinking deep water currents form in the North Atlantic, near Iceland, and from there the deep current begins its circulation pattern.

- The highly dense water in the deep current flows southward passed the southern edge of Africa, travels across the southern Indian Ocean, flows passed the east side of Australia, and merges into the North Pacific. Once the deep current enters the North Pacific, increasing temperatures cause a lower density in the deep water, and in turn the water becomes more buoyant and rises up to the surface again.

- The surface water in the North Pacific then flows south, sliding between Asia and Australia, wraps around the southern edge of Africa again—but this time moving west—and then flows across the South Atlantic. From the South Atlantic, the water connects with the Gulf Stream and flows up north again.

- Once it returns to the colder, higher latitudes of the North Atlantic, the dense surface water sinks back down to the lower deep water, forms a deep current and repeats the entire cycle again.

## CURRENTS OF THE INDIAN OCEAN

- The pattern of circulation of ocean currents in the Indian Ocean differs from the general pattern of circulation in the Atlantic and the Pacific Oceans.

- This is because the Indian Ocean is blocked by the continental masses in the north.

- The general pattern of circulation in the southern hemisphere of the Indian Ocean is anti-clockwise as that of the other oceans.

- In the northern hemisphere, there is a clear reversal of currents in the winter and summer seasons, which are completely under the influence of the seasonal changes of monsoon winds.

*Indian Ocean:*
*Northern Hemisphere during winter*

During winter, Sri Lanka divides the currents of the Arabian Sea from those of the Bay of Bengal. The **North East Monsoon Drift** flows westward just south of Sri Lanka with a countercurrent flow between it and the South Equatorial Current. During the winter season, in the northern section, the Bay of Bengal and the Arabian Sea are under the influence of North East Monsoon Winds. These North East Monsoon winds drive the waters of the Bay of Bengal and the Arabian Sea westward to circulate in an anti-clockwise direction.

*Indian Ocean:*
*Northern Hemisphere during summer*

In summer, the northern part comes under the influence of the South West Monsoon. It results in an easterly movement of water in the Bay of Bengal and the Arabian Sea in a clockwise direction. This current is called as the **South West Monsoon Drift**. In the Indian Ocean, the summer currents are more regular than those of the winter.

*Indian Ocean:*
*Southern Hemisphere*

In the southern part, the South Equatorial Current which flows from east to west is strengthened by its corresponding current of the Pacific Ocean. It then turns southward along the coast of Mozambique in Africa. A part of this current moving in between the African mainland and the Mozambique is called as the warm **Mozambique Current**. After the confluence of these two parts, the current is called as **Agulhas Current**. Agulhas Current merges with the West Wind Drift when it crosses the Indian Ocean. A branch of this merged current flows along the western coast of the Australia as cold **West Australian Current**. It later joins with the South Equatorial Current to complete the circuit.

*Conclusion*

As mentioned above, the quick-way to remember ocean currents is to remember the gyres. Currents in the **western part** of every continent is **cold**. Currents coming from the **polar region** are generally **cold**. Currents **near to equator** are generally **warm**.

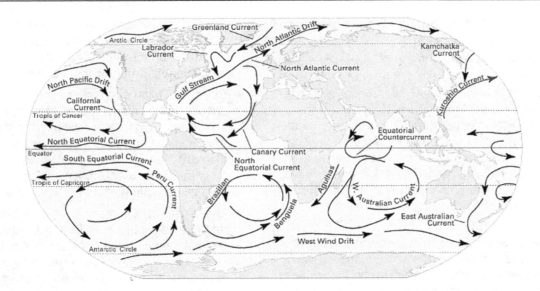

## CURRENTS IN THE INDIAN OCEAN

The oceanic current systems in the Indian Ocean are affected by the contour of the landmass and monsoon winds. The consistent system of ocean currents cannot be developed in Indian Ocean as it is surrounded by the Indian subcontinent, Africa and Australia on three sides. The characteristic feature of the currents in the northern Indian Ocean is that there occurs change in flow direction twice a year due to north-east and south-west monsoon winds.

| *Name* | *Nature* | *Significance* |
|---|---|---|
| North-East Monsoon Current | Warm Current | Important for sea-trade, cultural interaction |
| South-West Monsoon Current | Warm Current | |

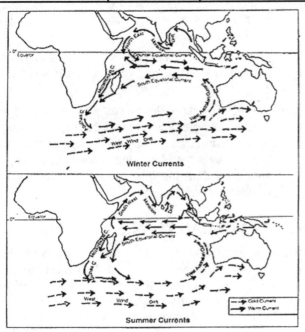

## Effect of Ocean Currents

Ocean currents are large masses of surface water that circulate in regular patterns around the oceans. Those that flow from equatorial regions polewards have a higher surface temperature and are warm currents. Those that flow from polar regions equator wards have a lower surface temperature and are cold currents.

- Ocean current are generated by wind, Coriolis force, temperature and salinity gradients, and tides.

- Ocean currents greatly affect earth's climate by transferring heat from the tropics to polar regions, and transferring precipitation to coastal regions.

- The most famous example of ocean currents is the Gulf Stream, which makes northwest Europe much more temperate than any other region at that latitude.

- Surface ocean currents are generally driven by wind, and circulate in clockwise direction in the northern hemisphere and anticlockwise in the southern hemisphere (due to prevailing winds). Surface currents make up about 10% of all ocean currents.

- Deep ocean currents, called thermohaline circulation, are driven by water density and temperature gradients. Also known as the world's conveyor belts, these deep ocean currents supply heat to polar regions and thereby regulate sea ice formation.

- Deep ocean currents make up about 90% of all ocean currents.

- Ocean currents are measured in Sverdrup (Sv), with 1 Sv being equivalent to a flow rate of 1 million cu. m per second.

The underlying **factors determining the direction of currents** are explained below :

A. **The Planetary Winds:** Trade Winds which move equatorial waters polewards and westwards and warm the eastern coasts of continents. While westerlies result in a north-easterly flow of water in the northern hemisphere. The planetary winds are probably the dominant influence on the flow of ocean currents. The strongest evidence is in the North Indian Ocean. Here the direction of the currents changes completely with the direction of the monsoon winds which come from the north-east in winter and south-west in summer.

B. **Temperatures:** As warm water is lighter and rises, and cold water is denser and sinks, warm equatorial waters move slowly along the surface polewards, while the heavier cold waters of the Polar Regions creep slowly along the bottom of the sea Equator-wards.

C. **Salinity:** Water of high salinity are denser than waters of low salinity. Hence waters of low salinity flow on the surface of waters of high salinity while waters of high salinity flow at the bottom towards waters of low salinity.

D. **The earth's rotation:** The earth's rotation deflects freely moving objects, including ocean currents, to the right. In the northern hemisphere this is a clockwise direction (e.g. the circulation of the Gulf Stream Drift and the Canaries Current). In the southern hemisphere it is an anti-clockwise direction (e.g. the Brazilian Current and the West Wind Drift).

E. **Land:** A land mass always obstructs and diverts a current. For instance, the tip of southern Chile diverts part of the West Wind Drift northwards as the Peruvian Current. Similarly the 'shoulder' of Brazil at Cape Sao Roque, divides the west-flowing equatorial currents into the Cayenne Current which flows north-westwards and the Brazilian Current which flows south-westwards.

## WHAT IS TIDES?

Tides refer to the rise and fall of our oceans' surfaces. It is caused by the attractive forces of the Moon and Sun's gravitational fields as well as the centrifugal force due to the Earth's spin. As the positions of these celestial bodies change, so do the surfaces' heights. For example, when the Sun and Moon are aligned with the Earth, water levels in ocean surfaces fronting them are pulled and subsequently rise.

- The Moon, although much smaller than the Sun, is much closer. Now, gravitational forces decrease rapidly as the distance between two masses widen. Thus, the Moon's gravity has a larger effect on tides than the Sun. In fact, the Sun's effect is only about half that of the Moon's.

- Since the total mass of the oceans does not change when this happens, part of it that was added to the high water regions must have come from somewhere. These mass-depleted regions then experience low water levels. Hence, if water on a beach near you is advancing, you can be sure that in other parts of the world, it is receding.

- Most illustrations containing the Sun, Moon, Earth and tides depict tides to be most pronounced in regions near or at the equator. On the contrary, it is actually in these regions where the difference in high tide and low tide are not as great as those in other places in the world.

- Tides cause changes in the depth of the sea, and also produce oscillating currents known as tidal streams, making prediction of tides important for coastal navigation.

- The strip of seashore that is submerged at high tide and exposed at low tide, the intertidal zone, is an important ecological product of ocean tides.

- The changing tide produced at a given location on the Earth is the result of the changing positions of the Moon and Sun relative to the Earth coupled with the effects of the rotation of the Earth and the local bathymetry (the underwater equivalent to topography or terrain).

- Though the gravitational force exerted by the Sun on the Earth is almost 200 times stronger than that exerted by the Moon, the tidal force produced by the Moon is about twice as strong as that produced by the Sun.

- The reason for this is that the tidal force is related not to the strength of a gravitational field, but to its gradient.

- The field gradient decreases with distance from the source more rapidly than does the field strength; as the Sun is about 400 times further from the Earth than is the Moon, the gradient of the Sun's field, and thus the tidal force produced by the Sun, is weaker.

## WHAT IS OCEAN WAVE?

This is the type of energy, which travel through medium in water. It is mechanical waves, due to wind direction and velocity. Waves are the forward movement of the ocean's water due to the oscillation of water particles by the frictional drag of wind over the water's surface.

## Size of the Wave

Waves have crests (the peak of the wave) and troughs (the lowest point on the wave). The wavelength, or horizontal size of the wave, is determined by the horizontal distance between two crests or two troughs. The vertical size of the wave is determined by the vertical distance between the two. Waves travel in groups called wave trains.

## Different Kinds of Waves

Waves can vary in size and strength based on wind speed and friction on the water's surface or outside factors such as boats. The small wave trains created by a boat's movement on the water are called wake. By contrast, high winds and storms can generate large groups of wave trains with enormous energy. In addition, undersea earthquakes or other sharp motions in the seafloor can sometimes generate enormous waves, called tsunamis (inappropriately known as tidal waves) that can devastate entire coastlines. Finally, regular patterns of smooth, rounded waves in the open ocean are called swells. Swells are defined as mature undulations of water in the open ocean after wave energy has left the wave generating region. Like other waves, swells can range in size from small ripples to large, flat-crested waves.

## Wave Energy and Movement

When studying waves, it is important to note that while it appears the water is moving forward, only a small amount of water is actually moving.

- Instead, it is the wave's energy that is moving and since water is a flexible medium for energy transfer, it looks like the water itself is moving.

- In the open ocean, the friction moving the waves generates energy within the water. This energy is then passed between water molecules in ripples called waves of transition.

- When the water molecules receive the energy, they move forward slightly and form a circular pattern.

- As the water's energy moves forward toward the shore and the depth decreases, the diameter of these circular patterns also decreases. When the diameter decreases, the patterns become elliptical and the entire wave's speed slows. Because waves move in groups, they continue arriving behind the first and all of the waves are forced closer together since they are now moving slower. They then grow in height and steepness. When the waves become too high relative to the water's depth, the wave's stability is undermined and the

entire wave topples onto the beach forming a breaker.

- Breakers come in different types-all of which are determined by the slope of the shoreline. Plunging breakers are caused by a steep bottom; and spilling breakers signify that the shoreline has a gentle, gradual slope.

- The exchange of energy between water molecules also makes the ocean crisscrossed with waves traveling in all directions. At times, these waves meet and their interaction is called interference, of which there are two types. The first occurs when the crests and troughs between two waves align and they combine.

- This causes a dramatic increase in wave height. Waves can also cancel each other out though when a crest meets a trough or vice-versa. Eventually, these waves do reach the beach and the differing size of breakers hitting the beach is caused by interference farther out in the ocean.

## Ocean Waves and The Coast

Since ocean waves are one of the most powerful natural phenomena on Earth, they have a significant impact on the shape of the Earth's coastlines. Generally, they straighten coastlines. Sometimes though, headlands composed of rocks resistant to erosion just into the ocean and force waves to bend around them. When this happens, the wave's energy is spread out over multiple areas and different sections of the coastline receive different amounts of energy and are thus shaped differently by waves.

- Coastal landforms caused by deposition include barrier spits, bay barriers, lagoons, tombolos and even beaches themselves. A barrier spit is a landform made up of material deposited in a long ridge extending away from the coast. These partially block the mouth of a bay, but if they continue to grow and cut off the bay from the ocean, it becomes a bay barrier.

- A lagoon is the water body that is cut off from the ocean by the barrier. A tombolo is the landform created when deposition connects the shoreline with islands or other features.

- In addition to deposition, erosion also creates many of the coastal features found today. Some of these include cliffs, wave-cut platforms, sea caves and arches. Erosion can also act in removing sand and sediment from beaches, especially on those that have heavy wave action.

# TSUNAMIS

A tsunami (pronounced sue-**nahm**-ee) is a series of huge waves that can cause great devastation and loss of life when they strike a coast.Tsunamis are caused by an underwater earthquake, a volcanic eruption, an submarine rockslide, or, more rarely, by an asteroid or meteoroid crashing into in the water from space. Most tsunamis are caused by underwater earthquakes, but not all underwater earthquakes cause tsunamis - an earthquake has to be over about magnitude 6.75 on the Richter scale for it to cause a tsunami. About 90 per cent of all tsunamis occur in the Pacific Ocean.

Many tsunamis could be detected before they hit land, and the loss of life could be minimized, with the use of modern technology, including seismographs (which detect earthquakes), computerized offshore buoys that can measure changes in wave height, and a system of sirens on the beach to alert people of potential tsunami danger.

**The Word Tsunami:** The word tsunami comes from the Japanese word meaning "harbor wave." Tsunamis are sometimes incorrectly called "tidal waves" — tsunamis are not caused by the tides (tides are caused by the gravitational force of the moon on the sea). Regular waves are caused by the wind.

**The Development of a Tsunami:** A tsunami starts when a huge volume of water is quickly shifted. This rapid movement can happen as the result of an underwater earthquake (when the sea floor quickly moves up or down), a rock slide, a volcanic eruption, or another high-energy event. After the huge volume of water has moved, the resulting wave is very long (the distance from crest to crest can be hundred of miles long) but not very tall (roughly 3 feet tall). The wave propagates (spreads) across the sea in all directions; it can travel great distances from the source at tremendous speeds.

**The Size of a Tsunami:** Tsunamis have an extremely long wavelength (wavelength is the distance between the crest (top) of one wave and the crest of the next wave) — up to several hundred miles long. The period (the time between two successive waves) is also very long — about an hour in deep water. In the deep sea, a tsunami's height can be only about 1 m (3 feet) tall. Tsunamis are often barely visible when they are in the deep sea. This makes tsunami detection in the deep sea very difficult.

**The Speed of a Tsunami:** A tsunami can travel at well over 970 kph (600 mph) in the open ocean - as fast as a jet flies. It can take only a few hours for a tsunami to travel across an entire ocean. A regular wave (generated by the wind) travels at up to about 90 km/hr.

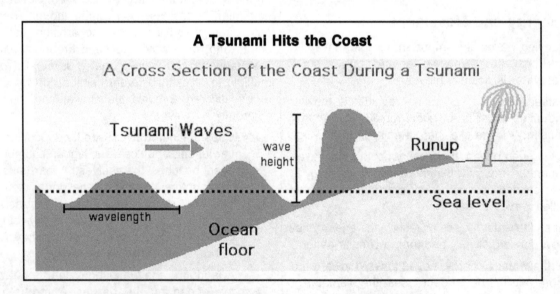

- As a tsunami wave approaches the coast (where the sea becomes shallow), the trough (bottom) of a wave hits the beach floor, causing the wave to slow down, to increase in height (the amplitude is magnified many times) and to decrease in wavelength (the distance from crest to crest).
- At landfall, a tsunami wave can be hundreds of meters tall. Steeper shorelines produce higher tsunami waves.

- In addition to large tsunami waves that crash onto shore, the waves push a large amount of water onto the shore above the regular sea level (this is called runup).
- The runup can cause tremendous damage inland and is much more common than huge, thundering tsunami waves.

**Tsunami Warning Systems:** Tsunami warning systems exist in many places around the world. As scientists continuously monitor seismic activity (earthquakes), a series of buoys float off the coast and monitor changes in sea level. Unfortunately, since tsunamis are not very tall in height when they are out at sea, detection is not easy and there are many false alarms. Sirens at affected beaches may be activated — do not ignore them!

**Wind-Generated Waves vs. Tsunami Waves:** Regular waves (caused by the wind) are very different from tsunami waves. Tsunami waves are much faster than wind-generated waves and they have a much longer wavelength (the distance from crest to crest). In the deep sea, tsunami waves are very small, but by the coast, they dwarf regular waves.

## How often do Tsunamis Occur?

Tsunamis are very rare. There are roughly six major tsunamis each century.

**Tiny Model of a Tsunami:** You can make a tiny model of a tsunami by dropping a rock into a bowl of water, causing ripples to propagate (travel) outwards from the site of impact. Another way is to slightly jolt the bowl of water and watch it slosh over the rim on one side.

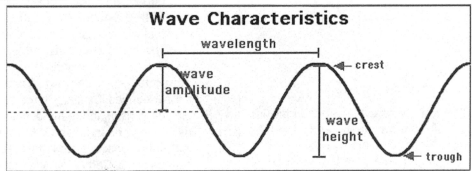

## What is Ocean Chemistry?

The chemical properties of the ocean are important to understand because the marine environment supports the greatest abundance of life on earth. This life is largely made up of the same chemicals that comprise the ocean—water and salts.

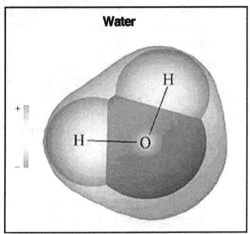

- A water molecule is made up of two hydrogen atoms joined to one oxygen atom by weak hydrogen bonds, $H_2O$. The hydrogen atoms are slightly positively charged and the oxygen atom is slightly negatively charged which is what attracts the atoms to each other and forms the weak hydrogen bond.

- Water is present in the marine environment as a liquid, a solid, and a gas regulated by temperature. Heat causes the water molecules to move. The greater the heat, the faster they move until the movement causes the hydrogen bonds to break converting liquid water to gas. Water turns to vapor at 100 degree C.

- Cold slows down the movement of water molecules and their density increases. As water gets colder the hydrogen bonds override the motion of the molecules and water begins to crystallize forming water's solid state—ice. Ice is formed at 0 degree C.

- Ice is, however, less dense than liquid water because it expands as it freezes causing the molecules to grow farther apart. The decrease in density causes ice to float.

- Density differences between different masses of seawater are one of the major driving forces of deep-sea circulation.

- Similarly, temperature regulates the surface tension and viscosity of water. In spite of its weak hydrogen bonds, water has a strong surface tension that will support small animals or objects.

## Salts

Salts are the most common chemical dissolved by ocean water. Salts are made up of electrically charged particles known as ions. The ions are either positively or negatively charged, and most salts are comprised of ions with opposite charges.

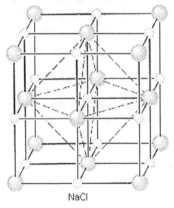

NaCl

## Gases

Gases are also dissolved by seawater. Carbon dioxide ($CO_2$) is dissolved in ocean water and used by phytoplankton to produce plant matter. Oxygen and nitrogen dissolved at the surface from the atmosphere are also present in seawater. Conversely, the ocean also releases these gases into the atmosphere. Like solids, temperature also regulates the dissolution of gases; however, the rate of dissolution is reversed for gases: cold water holds gases better than warm water. This is an important distinction because marine life depends on oxygen and carbon dioxide for metabolic processes such as respiration.

- Although it is often where the warmest ocean water is found, the ocean's surface, primarily the top 20m where photosynthesis takes place and where most marine life lives, contains the highest concentration of oxygen. The ocean's oxygen minimum layer, or the depth at which oxygen becomes depleted, is usually around 500 m. As the ocean gets deeper, however, seawater becomes oxygenated again from cold oxygen rich water that has sunk (remember cold water increases in density and therefore sinks) from the surface.

- The oxygen does not get used in the deep as readily as it does closer to the surface, and oxygen levels are therefore maintained to sustain life in the deep sea.

- In our industrial society, fossil fuels are being burned at record levels. The oceans are a vital component of the atmosphere and the air we breathe, given their role in carbon dioxide removal.

- Carbon dioxide is needed by phytoplankton to produce plant material during photosynthesis which absorbs carbon dioxide and produces oxygen. But it won't be long before the amount of carbon dioxide in the atmosphere exceeds the ability of the ocean to absorb and process it. $CO_2$ absorption on land is also reaching critical mass because of deforested rain and other forests that play an important role in $CO_2$ uptake and oxygen production.

- Carbon dioxide is a greenhouse gas in the atmosphere contributing to global warming, which is beginning to show an impact on the planet. Sea levels and surface temperatures are rising, ice is melting, and weather patterns are changing.

- The degree to which global warming will impact the Earth is under heavy debate, and the study of global warming is difficult because observations must be made over time. What is known is that the amount of carbon dioxide in the atmosphere continues to rise and no one knows the consequences. Similarly, if the amount of carbon dioxide is rising in the atmosphere, then it is also rising in the oceans, and little is known about the long-term consequences of high $CO_2$ levels in the oceans either. Carbon dioxide resulting from human pollution is absorbed in the upper 10% of the ocean, which is the ocean zone with the greatest biological activity.

- Recent research on the impact of $CO_2$ levels indicated that the acidity of $CO_2$ could decrease the ocean's surface pH levels dramatically— potentially to levels that have not been as low in 5 million years. In addition, rising surface temperatures cause corals to expel the symbiotic algae needed for their survival resulting in coral bleaching.

- These are problems that could easily imbalance the ocean's chemistry and disrupt important biological processes such as food webs and wide-scale marine life productivity. More research is critically needed to determine the impact of $CO_2$ in the atmosphere and in the ocean.

## Major Elements in Seawater

Elements present in amounts greater than 1 mg/litre are called major elements (Table 1). These elements determine the salinity of seawater. Their ratios with salinity or with each other are nearly constant. They are also known as conservative elements. Common salt (sodium chloride) is the principal ingredient of seawater that makes it salty. It exists in solution as separate hydrated sodium ions ($Na^+$) and hydrated chloride ions ($Cl^-$).

**Major Elements present in Seawater of 34.5 ppt Salinity, their Ionic Forms, and their Levels**

| Elements | Concentration (mg/lit) | % weight |
|---|---|---|
| **Cations** | | |
| $Na^+$ | 10500 | 30.42 |
| $Mg^{2+}$ | 1350 | 3.91 |
| $Ca^{2+}$ | 400 | 1.16 |
| $K^+$ | 380 | 1.10 |
| $Sr^{2+}$ | 8 | 0.02 |
| **Anions** | | |
| $Cl^+$ | 19000 | 55.04 |
| $SO_4^{2-}$ | 2665 | 7.69 |
| $CO_3^{2-}$ | 140 | 0.41 |
| $Br^-$ | 65 | 0.19 |
| $BO_3^{3-}$ | 20 | 0.06 |
| $SiO_3^{2-}$ | 8 | 0.02 |
| $F^-$ | 1 | 0.003 |

## Salinity and the Main Salt Ions

The salinity of sea water (usually 3.5%) is made up by all the dissolved salts shown in the above table. Interestingly, their proportions are always the same, which can be understood if salinity differences are caused by either evaporating fresh water or adding fresh water from rivers. Freezing and thawing also matter.

- Salinity affects marine organisms because the process of osmosis transports water towards a higher concentration through cell walls. A fish with a cellular salinity of 1.8% will swell in fresh water and dehydrate in salt water. So, saltwater fish drink water copiously while excreting excess salts through their gills. Freshwater fish do the opposite by not drinking but excreting copious amounts of urine while losing little of their body salts.

- Marine plants (seaweeds) and many lower organisms have no mechanism to control osmosis, which makes them very sensitive to the salinity of the water in which they live.

- The main nutrients for plant growth are nitrogen (N as in nitrate $NO_3^-$, nitrite $NO_2^-$, ammonia $NH_4^+$), phosporus (P as phosphate $PO4^{3-}$) and potassium (K) followed by Sulfur (S), Magnesium (Mg) and Calcium (Ca). Iron (Fe) is an essential component of enzymes and is copiously available in soil, but not in sea water (0.0034 ppm). This makes iron an essential nutrient for plankton growth.

- Plankton organisms (like diatoms) that make shells of silicon compounds furthermore need dissolved silicon salts ($SiO_2$) which at 3 ppm can be rather limiting.

**The main salt ions that make up 99.9% are the following:**

| Chemical ion | Valence | concentration ppm, mg/kg | part of salinity % | molecular weight | mmol/ kg |
|---|---|---|---|---|---|
| Chloride Cl | -1 | 19345 | 55.03 | 35.453 | 546 |
| Sodium Na | +1 | 10752 | 30.59 | 22.990 | 468 |
| Sulfate $SO_4$ | -2 | 2701 | 7.68 | 96.062 | 28.1 |
| Magnesium Mg | +2 | 1295 | 3.68 | 24.305 | 53.3 |

| | | | | | |
|---|---|---|---|---|---|
| Calcium Ca | +2 | 416 | 1.18 | 40.078 | 10.4 |
| Potassium K | +1 | 390 | 1.11 | 39.098 | 9.97 |
| Bicarbonate $HCO_3$ | −1 | 145 | 0.41 | 61.016 | 2.34 |
| Bromide Br | −1 | 66 | 0.19 | 79.904 | 0.83 |
| Borate $BO_3$ | −3 | 27 | 0.08 | 58.808 | 0.46 |
| Strontium Sr | +2 | 13 | 0.04 | 87.620 | 0.091 |
| Fluoride F | −1 | 1 | 0.003 | 18.998 | 0.068 |

## Dissolved gases in Seawater

The gases dissolved in sea water are in constant equilibrium with the atmosphere but their relative concentrations depend on each gas' solubility, which depends also on salinity and temperature. As salinity increases, the amount of gas dissolved decreases because more water molecules are immobilised by the salt ion. As water temperature increases, the increased mobility of gas molecules makes them escape from the water, thereby reducing the amount of gas dissolved.

Inert gases like nitrogen and argon do not take part in the processes of life and are thus not affected by plant and animal life. But non-conservative gases like oxygen and carbondioxide are influenced by sea life. Plants reduce the concentration of carbondioxide in the presence of sunlight, whereas animals do the opposite in either light or darkness.

| Gas molecule | % in atmosphere | % in surface seawater | ml/litre sea water | mg/kg (ppm) in sea water | molecular weight | mmol/kg |
|---|---|---|---|---|---|---|
| Nitrogen $N_2$ | 78% | 47.5% | 10 | 12.5 | 28.014 | 0.446 |
| Oxygen $O_2$ | 21% | 36.0% | 5 | 7 | 31.998 | 0.219 |
| Carbondioxide $CO_2$ | 0.03% | 15.1% | 40 | 90 * | 42.009 | 2.142 |
| Argon | 1% | 1.4% | . | 0.4 | 39.948 | 0.01 |

One kg of fresh water contains 55.6 mol $H_2O$ *also reported as 80 mg/kg

## MULTIPLE CHOICE QUESTIONS

1.  The most important states in the production of groundnut are
    (a) Gujarat & Andhra Pradesh
    (b) Gujarat & Tamil Nadu
    (c) Tamil Nadu & Karnataka
    (d) Andhra Pradesh & Tamil Nadu

2.  Intergovernmental panel on Climate Change was constituted in the year
    (a) 1986          (b) 1988
    (c) 1991          (d) 1984

3.  In an ecosystem the term Homeostasis refers to
    (a) Natural Balance
    (b) Succession
    (c) Energy transfer
    (d) Trophic level

4.  The decomposers in an ecosystem are also called
    (a) Saprotrophs       (b) Autotrophs
    (c) Sere              (d) Biotope

5.  Erdkunde was a term used by
    (a) Ritter            (b) Kant
    (c) Richthofen        (d) Humboldt

6.  Which among the following region for Selva?
    (a) Tropical forest region
    (b) Humid forest region
    (c) Subtropical forest region
    (d) Cold forest region

7.  Lines joining places of equal travel time from a given centre is called
    (a) Isochrone         (b) Isohyet
    (c) Isopleth          (d) Isohaline

8. The seasonal migration between mountains and plains by man and animals in the Central Asian region is called
   (a) Nomadism      (b) Pastoralism
   (c) Transhumance   (d) Immigration

9. Which of the following measures the amount of water vapour in g/kg of air?
   (a) Moisture index    (b) Specific Humidity
   (c) Relative humidity (d) Absolute humidity

10. Which of the following is an example for forms of condensation?
    (a) Mist    (b) Rainfall
    (c) Sleet   (d) Hail

11. In Survey of India toposheets 59 D / 10 of scale, will be
    (a) 1 : 50000   (b) 1 : 5000
    (c) 1 : 2500    (d) 1 : 20000

12. In normal Atlas maps physiography is usually shown by
    (a) Spot heights
    (b) Contours
    (c) Hill shading
    (d) Isochromatic method

13. Three Mile Island disaster is associated with
    (a) Water Pollution   (b) Nuclear Reactor
    (c) Air Pollution     (d) Natural Hazard

14. Which of the following is not a part of Temperate Cyclone?
    (a) Warm Sector   (b) Eye
    (c) Cold Front    (d) Warm Front

15. The Nagapatnam port which is in the east coast, is at
    (a) Tamil Nadu       (b) Karnataka
    (c) Andhra Pradesh   (d) Meghalaya

16. In 2008-2009, the most important item of export from India was
    (a) Gems & Jewellery
    (b) Textiles and Readymade garments
    (c) Handicrafts
    (d) Leather products

17. According to the Theory of Parallel Retreat of Slopes the steepest part of the slope is known as
    (a) Wash slope    (b) Scarp
    (c) Debris slope  (d) Basal slope

18. Isotropic surface was the base for the model developed by
    (a) Myrdal    (b) Christaller
    (c) Weber     (d) Perroux

19. "Cf" in Koppen's system of climatic classification represents
    (a) St. Lawrence type
    (b) Subtropical humid type
    (c) Continental climatic type
    (d) Mediterranean type

20. In terms of total volume of trade the most important sea route is
    (a) Suez Canal route
    (b) North Atlantic Sea route
    (c) Panama Canal route
    (d) Cape Sea route

21. The Trans Siberian Railway links St. Petersberg with
    (a) Novosibirsk   (b) Irkutsk
    (c) Vladivostok   (d) Verkhoyansk

22. The standard database query system in a relational database system is called
    (a) SQL    (b) TIGER
    (c) SCSI   (d) GRS 80

23. Which of the following is not a GIS software package?
    (a) MapInfo   (b) GRAM
    (c) ArcInfo   (d) ERDAS

24. Match the following:

| Terms | Phenomenon |
|---|---|
| A. Vernal Equinox | 1. Precipitation |
| B. Foehn | 2. September 22 |
| C. Hygroscopic nuclei | 3. Warm local wind |
| D. Warm sector | 4. Temperate cyclone |

|   | A | B | C | D |
|---|---|---|---|---|
| (a) | 3 | 1 | 4 | 2 |
| (b) | 2 | 3 | 1 | 4 |
| (c) | 4 | 1 | 2 | 3 |
| (d) | 4 | 2 | 1 | 3 |

25. **Assertion [A]:** Thermal inversion is more common in intermontane basins during winter nights.
    **Reasoning [R]:** Cold air descends from the top along the slope and collects in the basin.
    (a) Both [A] and [R] are true and [R] is the correct reason
    (b) Both [A] and [R] are true, but [R] is Not the correct reason
    (c) [A] is true, but [R] is false.
    (d) [A] is false, but [R] is true.

26. **Assertion [A]:** Temperate cyclone has warm and cold fronts at its maturity.
    **Reasoning [R]:** Occlusion refers to the dissipation of temperate cyclone.

(a) Both [A] and [R] are true and [R] is the correct reason

(b) Both [A] and [R] are true, but [R] is Not the correct reason

(c) [A] is true, but [R] is false.

(d) [A] is false, but [R] is true.

**27.** Which one of the following was *not* suggested by Alfred Wegener as evidence of Continental Drift Hypothesis?
(a) Fit of continents
(b) Distribution of glacial sediments in different continents
(c) Similarity in geological structures
(d) Sea-floor spreading

**28.** The period in which the Alpine-Himalayan orogeny took place
(a) Tertiary        (b) Cambrian
(c) Ordovician      (d) Cretaceous

**29.** Richter Scale measures _____ of earthquakes.
(a) Intensity
(b) Depth to focus
(c) Magnitude
(d) Intensity and Magnitude

**30.** For almost all groundwater motion, the Reynold's Number is
(a) Between 1 and 5
(b) >10
(c) Between 5 and 10
(d) <1

**31.** Which of these is a major cation in ground water?
(a) Silicon         (b) Potassium
(c) Aluminium       (d) Iron

**32.** The Ghyben – Herzberg equation is related to
(a) Safe yield
(b) Quality of ground water
(c) Recharge of wells
(d) Fresh and saline water interface

**33.** Among the following which is not considered as an atmospheric pollutant?
(a) $SO_2$          (b) $NO_2$
(c) Dust            (d) $O_3$

**34.** Which one is correct with regard to confined aquifers?
(a) Permeable layer is sandwiched between impermeable layers
(b) Impermeable layer is found between permeable layers
(c) Porous layer overlies impermeable layer only
(d) Porous layer underlies impermeable layer only

**35.** Who devised the method of stream ordering?
(a) Gilbert         (b) Strahler
(c) Chorley         (d) Taylor

**36.** The annual average temperature of which of the following cities will be the lowest?
(a) London          (b) Rome
(c) Lahore          (d) Singapore

**37.** Large scale uranium deposits have been recently discovered in
(a) Jharkhand
(b) Andhra Pradesh
(c) Rajasthan
(d) Bihar

**38.** Protolan charts helped
(a) Navigation
(b) Astronomy
(c) Modern cartography
(d) Map reproduction

**39.** Who outlined that a real differentiation is the central theme of Geography?
(a) Harvey          (b) Hartshorne
(c) Herbertson      (d) Humboldt

**40.** Aspect of Slope plays a crucial role in controlling temperature in
(a) Equator
(b) Coastal regions
(c) Mid-latitude Mountains
(d) Deserts

**41.** Spalling is a term associated with
(a) Fault
(b) Weathering
(c) Glacial action
(d) Sea Floor Spreading

**42.** Identify the statement which is WRONG
(a) The Decomposers in an Ecosystem are also called Saprotrophs
(b) Each stage in the Ecological succession is called Sere
(c) Omnivores complicate the food web of an ecosystem
(d) Ecotone refers to the ecosystem in the interior part of deserts

**43.** Hadley cell is a term associated with
(a) Tropical Cyclone
(b) General Circulation of the atmosphere
(c) Polar air mass
(d) Temperate Cyclone

**44.** Foehn is a local hot wind that blows over
(a) Himalayas       (b) Andes
(c) Rockies         (d) Alps

45. In the top 10 largest cities in the world, Delhi ranks
    (a) Third            (b) Fifth
    (c) Seventh          (d) Ninth

46. Which Indian satellite provides radar imaging?
    (a) RESOURCESAT      (b) CARTOSAT 2B
    (c) RISAT            (d) OCEANSAT

47. In Geomorphology, Systems approach was explained by
    (a) Chorley          (b) Cotton
    (c) Hack             (d) Wooldridge

48. The standard measurements of the earth's shape and size adopted by the International Union of Geodesy and Geophysics is called
    (a) GRS 80           (b) SCSI
    (c) TIGER            (d) DIGEST

49. The Indian Meteorological Department has its headquarters at
    (a) Kolkata          (b) Bengaluru
    (c) Pune             (d) Hyderabad

50. The idea of Sea floor spreading was proposed by
    (a) W.M. Davis       (b) Wegener
    (c) Hess             (d) Penck

51. Which of the following statements is correct?
    (a) Period between 500 BC to 500 AD is called Early Dynastic period in urban growth
    (b) Patrick Geddes first used the term Megalopolis
    (c) Necropolis is the term used by Mumford for ghost towns
    (d) Shevky and Williams developed Social Area Analysis approach to cities

52. The earlier model which was used for the prediction of Monsoon was developed by
    (a) Gowarikar        (b) IPCC
    (c) Koteeswaran      (d) Miller

53. Which of the following Satellites has a Radiometric resolution of 11 bit data
    (a) SPOT 5
    (b) IRS ID
    (c) CARTOSAT 2B
    (d) IKONOS

54. Identify the statement which is wrong
    (a) Anaximander prepared the first map of the world
    (b) Eratosthenes measured the circumference of the world
    (c) Orbis Terrarum was the contribution of Greeks
    (d) Maps of the Early Medieval Period are called T-O maps

55. An isopleth map of rainfall distribution of an area consists of
    (a) Isochrones       (b) Isohyets
    (c) Isohalines       (d) Isobars

56. Karanpura area in the Damodar River Basin is significant for
    (a) Iron ore         (b) Bauxite
    (c) Coal             (d) Manganese

57. When one travels from New Delhi to Patna he will not cross the River
    (a) Yamuna           (b) Ganges
    (c) Kosi             (d) Ghaghra

58. Which of the following statements is wrong?
    (a) The first major steel producing unit was started at Kulti
    (b) During Second Five Year Plan three Public Sector steel plants were established
    (c) The Rourkela steel plant was established with the collaboration of UK
    (d) Vizag steel plant was conferred Navaratna status in 2010

59. In the Koeppen's Classification of climates which subtype is considered rare?
    (a) 'As' type        (b) 'Cf' type
    (c) 'Cs' type        (d) 'Df' type

60. Which of the following statements is correct?
    (a) The Icelandic Low Pressure is due to thermal origin
    (b) The Subtropical High Pressure belts are permanent over land areas
    (c) At an altitude of about 6000 metres atmospheric pressure is reduced to 50%
    (d) Sub polar Low pressure is a continuous belt in the northern hemisphere

61. Which of the following is not a process associated with rock weathering?
    (a) Carbonation      (b) Solifluction
    (c) Exfoliation      (d) Chelation

62. In India, cement production is more concentrated in
    (a) Tamil Nadu & Gujarat
    (b) Gujarat & Bihar
    (c) Gujarat & Andhra Pradesh
    (d) Tamil Nadu & Andhra Pradesh

63. Which of the following regions is different from the other three?
    (a) Mediterranean    (b) Himalayas
    (c) Rockies          (d) Andes

64. Indravati is part of the drainage basin of River
    (a) Mahanadhi        (b) Godavari
    (c) Krishna          (d) Cauvery

65. Identify the correct sequence of glacial periods from the oldest to the youngest
    (a) Gunz, Mindel, Riss, Wurm
    (b) Mindel, Riss, Gunz, Wurm
    (c) Wurm, Riss, Gunz, Mindel
    (d) Riss, Wurm, Mindel, Gunz

66. The Headquarters of Survey of India is at
    (a) Hyderabad    (b) Bengaluru
    (c) Kolkata    (d) Dehradun

67. Population density of a district at the block level is best represented by
    (a) Choropleth    (b) Isopleth
    (c) Compound bar    (d) Dot map

68. Country like Chile can be best represented by
    (a) Conical Projection with one standard parallel
    (b) Mercator Projection
    (c) Zenithal Gnomonic Projection
    (d) Sinusoidal Projection

69. Which of the following seas is not the source region for tropical cyclones?
    (a) Caribbean Sea
    (b) Mediterranean Sea
    (c) Bay of Bengal
    (d) Philippines Sea

70. National Food Security Mission was launched in
    (a) 2001-02    (b) 2003-04
    (c) 2007-08    (d) 2010-11

71. In the USA, the concentration of population is comparatively higher in the
    (a) Northeastern part
    (b) Southeastern part
    (c) Northwestern part
    (d) Southwestern part

72. The dry porous area of pebbles and boulders at the foothills of Himalayas is called
    (a) Bhabar    (b) Bhangar
    (c) Terai    (d) Khadar

73. Which of the following is considered the largest oilfield in the world?
    (a) Burgan    (b) Kirkuk
    (c) Abqaiq    (d) Ghawar

74. When the temperature of an air mass increases or decreases without addition or removal of heat the process is called
    (a) Adiabatic process
    (b) Normal Lapse Rate
    (c) Occlusion
    (d) Thermal inversion

75. Identify the wrongly matched pair among the following
    (a) Beaufort scale – Wind speed
    (b) Cloud – Form of Precipitation
    (c) Dew point – Saturation of air parcel
    (d) Mistral – Cold local wind

76. The contribution of Greeks was more in the field of
    (a) Economic Geography
    (b) Social Geography
    (c) Cultural Geography
    (d) Mathematical Geography

77. Identify the WRONG statement from the following
    (a) An unsaturated air cools at Dry Adiabatic Lapse Rate
    (b) After Dew point, an air parcel cools at Wet Adiabatic Lapse Rate
    (c) Thermal inversion is common in winter nights at the intermontane basins
    (d) An air mass becomes unstable when the environment is warmer than it

78. Among the following the Geographer who has not contributed to the Locational Analysis approach is
    (a) Haggett    (b) Bunge
    (c) Peet    (d) Morrill

79. Whose model explains peneplanation and cycle of erosion?
    (a) Davis    (b) Pheniq
    (c) King    (d) Gilbert

80. Which of the following is a coastal feature?
    (a) Kettle    (b) Esker
    (c) Cirque    (d) Fjord

81. Which rock type is commonly seen along coral reef?
    (a) Sandstone    (b) Limestone
    (c) Marble    (d) Clay

82. San Andreas Fault is example of a
    (a) Strike-slip fault    (b) Horst
    (c) Graben    (d) Thrust fault

83. Normal lapse rate of the atmosphere is
    (a) 50 C per 1000 metres
    (b) 6.50 C per 1000 metres
    (c) 10 C per 1000 metres
    (d) 2.50 C per 1000 metres

84. The waterway that runs through much of coastal Andhra Pradesh and ends in northern Tamil Nadu
    (a) Cauveri Canal
    (b) Ganga Canal
    (c) Buckingham Canal
    (d) Bakra Canal

85. Which of the following districts is not rich in iron ore deposits?
(a) Durg
(b) Sundargarh
(c) Mayurbhanj
(d) Singhbum

86. The newer alluvium in the Ganga Plain is known as
(a) Bhabar
(b) Terai
(c) Bhangar
(d) Khadar

87. The river that originates from Amarkantak plateau is
(a) Kosi
(b) Cauvery
(c) Narmada
(d) Krishna

88. The first treatise on cartography was by
(a) Mercator
(b) Aristotle
(c) Copernicus
(d) Ptolemy

89. Weathering of concentric shells of rocks is called as
(a) Exfoliation
(b) Monodnocks
(c) Solution
(d) Attrition

90. Rain, hail and squall winds are associated with
(a) Cirrus clouds
(b) Stratus clouds
(c) Cumulus clouds
(d) Cumulonimbus clouds

91. Creep is associated with
(a) Weathering
(b) Mass wasting
(c) Erosion
(d) Deposition

92. The person who declared Geography as 'Erdkunde' is
(a) Ritter
(b) Kant
(c) Humboldt
(d) Powell

93. Atomic power plant in Gujarat State is located at
(a) Kota
(b) Kakrapara
(c) Kalpakkam
(d) Tarapur

94. G.H. Smith introduced the concept of
(a) Average slope
(b) Partial slope
(c) Total slope
(d) Relative relief

95. Which of the following is NOT the work of rivers?
(a) Pot holes
(b) Waterfalls
(c) Tombolo
(d) Meanders

96. A transition zone between two different air masses
(a) Occlusion
(b) Front
(c) Cyclone
(d) Wedge

97. The concept of graded stream was phrased by
(a) Mackin
(b) Leopold
(c) Maddock
(d) Holmes

98. Most places in Western Europe is habitable than places in the same latitude in Eastern Europe.

This is due to the influence of:
(a) Low pressure over North Sea
(b) Gulf Stream
(c) Cold current in the Atlantic Ocean
(d) Ozone hole over Western Europe

99. Sirhind canal receives water from the river
(a) Beas
(b) Ravi
(c) Chenab
(d) Sutlej

100. Chikmagalur is important for the cultivation of
(a) Cardamom
(b) Coffee
(c) Tea
(d) Cocoa

101. 'Endrumpf' is phrased by
(a) Davis
(b) Johnson
(c) Penck
(d) Holmes

102. The rate of change of temperature within the rising air before condensation is called
(a) Lapse rate
(b) Dry adiabatic rate
(c) Wet adiabatic rate
(d) Environmental lapse rate

103. Pot holes are found in the _____ stage of a river.
(a) Young
(b) Mature
(c) Old
(d) Penultimate

104. Equatorial regions are cooler than the subtropical regions. This is because of
(a) Cool currents
(b) Higher altitude
(c) Cloudiness
(d) Warm currents

105. Which of the following terms was first phrased by Patrick Geddes?
(a) Urbanism
(b) Conurbation
(c) Metropolis
(d) Eopolis

106. The seasonal migration between mountains and plains by man and animals in the Central Asian region is called
(a) Nomadism
(b) Pastoralism
(c) Transhumance
(d) Immigration

107. The contour interval of a one inch map is
(a) 10 feet
(b) 50 feet
(c) 100 feet
(d) 150 feet

108. The sensors in the satellites record the _____ radiation from the surface of the earth.
(a) Reflected
(b) Scattered
(c) Absorbed
(d) Transmitted

109. A trophic level refers to an
(a) Area in the tropics
(b) Organism's position in a food chain

(c) Organism's position in an ecosystem

(d) Organism's position in a biome

110. The pyramid is useful to represent
    (a) Population growth rate
    (b) Age and sex ratio
    (c) Birth ratio
    (d) Death ratio

111. Mississippi delta is an example of a/an
    (a) Estuarine delta       (b) Cuspate delta
    (c) Arcuate delta         (d) Bird-foot delta

112. Which one of the following is the correct sequence of cloud forms in ascending order of height from the bottom?
    (a) Stratus, altocumulus and cirrus
    (b) Cirrus, cumulus and stratus
    (c) Cumulus, cirrus and stratus
    (d) Stratus, cirrus and cumulus

113. One remembers Dudley Stamp for his contributions to the
    (a) Land use survey
    (b) Quantitative analysis
    (c) Qualitative analysis
    (d) Deductive reasoning

114. Climatograph represents
    (a) Rainfall              (b) Temperature
    (c) Relative humidity     (d) Visibility

115. The headquarters of South Central Railway is located at
    (a) Bangalore             (b) Vijayawada
    (c) Secunderabad          (d) Mangalore

116. The largest and most extensive beach placer deposits in the world are in
    (a) Alaska
    (b) Kerala
    (c) Brazil
    (d) Republic of Nauru

117. Role of private sector is negligible in the case of
    (a) Indicative planning
    (b) Long-term planning
    (c) Economic planning
    (d) Imperative planning

118. Who discovered the instrument 'astrolabe'?
    (a) Hectaeus              (b) Heredotus
    (c) Hipparchus           (d) Anaximander

119. Imaginary lines joining places having equal degree of cloudiness are known as
    (a) Isotherms             (b) Isohyets
    (c) Isochrones            (d) Isopnephs

120. The term dry summer subtropics refers to
    (a) 'Ds' climate          (b) 'Cs' climate
    (c) 'Dw' climate          (d) 'Cw' climate

121. Systematic regionalization of world agriculture was attempted by
    (a) Whittlessey           (b) Stamp
    (c) Taylor                (d) Ritter

122. The way in which an introduction of an activity acts as stimulus effecting a series of positive changes is known as
    (a) Multinational effect
    (b) Multiplier effect
    (c) Multipurpose effect
    (d) Multispectral effect

123. **Assertion [A]:** Thermal Equator mostly lies to the north of the True Equator.
    **Reasoning [R]:** Large land masses are found in the Northern Hemisphere.
    (a) Both [A] and [R] are true and [R] is the correct reason
    (b) Both [A] and [R] are true, but [R] is not the correct reason
    (c) [A] is true, but [R] is false
    (d) [A] is false, but [R] is true

124. Louis Agassiz has propounded the concept of
    (a) Isostasy
    (b) Ice Age
    (c) Sea Floor Spreading
    (d) Convection Currents

125. Identify the WRONG statement
    (a) Studies on Mid-Atlantic Ridge led to the concept of Sea Floor Spreading
    (b) East coast of Asia is an example for Convergent Plate boundary
    (c) Pangaea started breaking during Permian period
    (d) Wegener assumed an equator-ward and a westward force for continental drift

126. Cfa in Koppen's Climatic classification indicates
    (a) Mediterranean region
    (b) Humid Subtropics
    (c) Steppe region
    (d) Marine West coasts

127. Which part of India comes under Koppen's "As" type of climate?
    (a) Aravalli              (b) Coastal Tamil Nadu
    (c) Konkan                (d) Vidarbha

128. Which of the following statements is WRONG?
    (a) Shallow continental shelf helps fishing in North Sea region

(b) Mixing ocean currents make Grand Banks as a major fishing ground

(c) Tropical areas provide conducive atmosphere for fishing

(d) Peru is the country with the largest fish production in the world

129. Country where Nuclear power has the largest share to the total power generation is
(a) Canada
(b) France
(c) Germany
(d) Japan

130. Which of the following regions has a higher diurnal range than annual range of temperature?
(a) Equatorial region
(b) Tropical Desert
(c) Tropical Monsoon
(d) Steppe region

131. In both the hemispheres the term Horse Latitudes refer to latitudes between
(a) 20° and 25°       (b) 45° and 50°
(c) 30° and 35°       (d) 40° and 45°

132. The port developed under Public Private Partnership Programme is
(a) Krishnapatnam     (b) Machilipatnam
(c) Nagapatnam        (d) Vishakapatnam

133. Among the districts of Kerala maximum increase in census towns occurred between 2001 and 2011 in
(a) Ernakulam         (b) Kannur
(c) Thrissur          (d) Thiruvananthapuram

134. Barmer basin in Rajasthan is notable for the mining of
(a) Copper            (b) Lignite
(c) Iron ore          (d) Oil

135. Which of the following is notable for generation of renewable energy?
(a) Korba             (b) Kayathar
(c) Obra              (d) Ramagundam

136. Pawan Hans provides services related to
(a) Transport
(b) Telecommunication
(c) Tourism
(d) Information Technology

137. When isobars are very closely spaced the pressure gradient is
(a) Low               (b) Stable
(c) High              (d) Moderate

138. Which of the following is a source region for Tropical cyclones?

(a) Black Sea
(b) Caribbean Sea
(c) Red Sea
(d) Mediterranean Sea

139. Most of rainfall in Western Europe is due to
(a) Convection        (b) Fronts
(c) Monsoon           (d) Orography

140. As per Census 2011 the highest literacy rate among the given States is in
(a) Himachal Pradesh
(b) Tamil Nadu
(c) Maharashtra
(d) Gujarat

141. Which of the following States are significant for production of tobacco?
(a) Andhra Pradesh & Gujarat
(b) Andhra Pradesh & Bihar
(c) Gujarat & Karnataka
(d) Karnataka & Bihar

142. As per ancient Indian Cartography Krauca Dwipa refers to
(a) South Asia
(b) West Africa
(c) Northwest Europe
(d) North Asia

143. The map projection which was developed by Hassler is known as
(a) Polyconic         (b) Bonne's
(c) Gnomonic          (d) Stereographic

144. Beaufort Scale ranges from
(a) 0 to10            (b) 1 to 10
(c) 0 to 12           (d) 1 to 12

145. Wave theory of Frontogenesis was propounded by
(a) Kendrew           (b) Thornthwaite
(c) Miller            (d) Bjerkenes

146. A region which approaches totality of the combined physical, biotic and social content of area is called
(a) Growth centre     (b) Growth pole
(c) Hinterland        (d) Compage

147. In Zenithal projection when the source of light is from infinity the projection is called
(a) Orthographic      (b) Orthomorphic
(c) Gnomonic          (d) Stereographic

148. Climatograph is a diagram developed by
(a) Foster            (b) Geddes
(c) Munns             (d) Taylor

149. On a Map, Hachuring is used as a method to represent
    (a) Drainage
    (b) Settlements
    (c) Transport
    (d) Relief

150. International Projection is a modified form of
    (a) Aitoff's projection
    (b) Lambert's projection
    (c) Polyconic projection
    (d) Sinusoidal projection

151. Nearest neighbour technique is used to study the distribution of
    (a) Industries
    (b) Settlements
    (c) Waterbodies
    (d) Forests

152. **Assertion (A):** Snow line occurs at lower altitude in Western Himalayas than Eastern Himalayas.
    **Reasoning (R):** Western Himalayas have a more northerly location than Eastern Himalayas.
    (a) Both "A" and "R" are true and "R" is the correct explanation for "A"
    (b) Both "A" and "R" are true, but "R" is NOT the correct explanation for "A".
    (c) "A" is True, but "R" is False
    (d) "A" is False, but "R" is True

153. **Assertion (A):** Vegetation in Mediterranean regions exhibit xerophytic characteristics.
    **Reasoning (R):** Mediterranean region receives more rain in summer.
    (a) Both "A" and "R" are true and "R" is the correct explanation for "A"
    (b) Both "A" and "R" are true, but "R" is NOT the correct explanation for "A".
    (c) "A" is True, but "R" is False
    (d) "A" is False, but "R" is True

154. Identify the CORRECT statement
    (a) Wegener assumed that North America broke away from Pangaea first
    (b) Appalachian mountains are part of the Fold Mountains formed due to continental drift
    (c) The concept of Sea Floor spreading was explained by Hess
    (d) Palaeozoic glacial evidence in North America gave support to Continental drift theory

155. Uvala is a landform associated with the action of
    (a) Weathering
    (b) River
    (c) Wind
    (d) Underground water

156. A Satellite which helps weather forecasting is
    (a) SPOT
    (b) LANDSAT
    (c) IRS ID
    (d) INSAT 4B

157. The annual range of temperature is the highest in
    (a) Subpolar regions
    (b) Mediterranean regions
    (c) Equatorial regions
    (d) Tropical Monsoon regions

158. Warm sector and Occlusion are terms associated with
    (a) Tropical Cyclone
    (b) Thunderstorms
    (c) Temperate Cyclone
    (d) Tornadoes

159. Which of the following is NOT significant for coal mining in the world?
    (a) Mesabi
    (b) Karaganda
    (c) Donetz
    (d) Silesia

160. The Product-Moment Correlation technique was outlined by
    (a) Zipf
    (b) Monkhouse
    (c) Pearson
    (d) Spearman

161. The maximum number of emigrants from Kerala is found in
    (a) Saudi Arabia
    (b) United Arab Emirates
    (c) Kuwait
    (d) Oman

162. The term *Primate City* was explained by
    (a) Jefferson
    (b) Carter
    (c) Burgess
    (d) Karl Hassert

163. Who among the following has not attempted functional classification of towns?
    (a) Harris
    (b) Smith
    (c) Nelson
    (d) Hoyt

164. Ghost Town is also called as
    (a) Polis
    (b) Necropolis
    (c) Eopolis
    (d) Tyrannopolis

165. Among the following pair of countries which are most significant for bauxite production?
    (a) Australia & China
    (b) Jamaica & Australia
    (c) Jamaica & India
    (d) India & Brazil

166. Which of the following statements is WRONG?
    (a) China is the largest exporter of textiles in the world
    (b) Osaka region in Japan is one of the major areas for textile production
    (c) India ranks fourth in textile export in the world
    (d) USA ranks third in the total cotton production in the world

**167.** The world's largest sea port in terms of its handling capacity is
(a) Rotterdam    (b) Singapore
(c) Shanghai    (d) Hong Kong

**168.** Christaller measured the volume of trade in his Central Place Theory by the number of
(a) Telephones    (b) Shops
(c) Banks    (d) Market Centres

**169.** Koppen's Cs type of climate is prevalent in
(a) Mediterranean
(b) California
(c) North Australia
(d) Peru

**170.** Which of the following statements with regard to El Nino is CORRECT?
(a) It refers to the warming of sea surface in western Pacific Ocean
(b) It refers to the cooling of sea surface in western Pacific Ocean
(c) It refers to the warming of sea surface in eastern Pacific Ocean
(d) It refers to the cooling of sea surface in eastern Pacific Ocean

**171.** Which of the following is different from the other three?
(a) Cfa    (b) Cs
(c) Cfa    (d) Dw

**172.** GSAT 16 was launched in December
(a) 2009    (b) 2014
(c) 2012    (d) 2011

**173.** Identify the CORRECT statement
(a) According to Davis, tropical humid climate is normal for Cycle of erosion
(b) Relief decreases in the youthful stage of Normal Cycle of erosion
(c) Maximum relief is observed at the beginning of mature stage in the Cycle of erosion
(d) Davisian Cycle of erosion is also referred to as the concept of Pediplanation

**174.** Which of the following cities experiences the vertical rays of the sun?
(a) New Delhi    (b) Moscow
(c) London    (d) Singapore

**175.** As per 2011 Census the highest decadal growth rate occurred in the district of
(a) Kozhikode    (b) Malappuram
(c) Kasaragod    (d) Palakkad

**176.** "Continental drift theory" was given by
(a) Alfred Wegener    (b) Laplace
(c) Kant    (d) Morgon

**177.** Which was mega ocean?
(a) Pangaea    (b) Panthalassa
(c) Laurasia    (d) All the above

**178.** Which is largest ocean?
(a) Indian ocean    (b) Pacific ocean
(c) Atlantic ocean    (d) Arctic ocean

**179.** Mauna Kea located in
(a) Pacific ocean    (b) Indian ocean
(c) Southern ocean    (d) Northern ocean

**180.** Origin of Seamunt is
(a) Volcanic
(b) Plutonic
(c) Sedimentary organic deposits
(d) Sedimentary inorganic deposits

**181.** Labrador current is
(a) Cold current    (b) Warm current
(c) Gulf current    (d) Not defined

**182.** Which parameter influence the ocean current
(a) Solar energy    (b) Wind
(c) Gravity    (d) All the above

**183.** Canyons and trenches are found in region of
(a) Continental slope
(b) Continental shelf
(c) Deep sea plain
(d) Mid-oceanic ridge

**184.** Mt. Fujiyama in Japan is example of
(a) Volcanic mountain
(b) Fold mountain
(c) Block mountain
(d) None of these

**185.** If an engineering structure has to be built in an area covered with water, the area is surrounded by a wall made of combination of various materials, such structure is referred to as :
(a) Cofferdam
(b) Pilaster
(c) Cut and Cover
(d) Caissons or Piers

**186.** A tributary stream which flows for some distance parallel to the main channel as the levees prevent it from entering main stream is called :
(a) Yazoo river    (b) Crevasse splay
(c) Sabkha stream    (d) Yardang

**187.** The transition between Laminar flow and turbulent flow occurs when the ratio of the inertia fluid force is significantly larger than :
(a) Viscous fluid forces
(b) Turbulent flow
(c) Laminar flow
(d) Bed load

**188.** Which of the following statements is *true* for Ekman transport in ocean ?
(a) It causes upwelling in coastal regions
(b) It leads to decrease in biological productivity
(c) It causes downwelling of surface waters
(d) Due to Ekman transport the upper layer of the ocean exhibit a net motion parallel to the wind direction

**189.** The pelagic sediment in deep-sea floor, known as ooze, consists dominantly of :
(a) Wind-blown clay particles
(b) Turbidities
(c) Tiny shells of marine organisms
(d) Phosphates

**190.** As per the BIS for drinking water, the desirable limit of TDS is :
(a) 300 mg/l           (b) 750 mg/l
(c) 75 mg/l            (d) 0.01 mg/l

**191.** Below the carbonate compensation depth (CCD), much of the carbonate is dissolve(d). The CCD around meter for calcite is:
(a) 1000 m             (b) 2000 m
(c) 5000 m             (d) 10 m

**192.** The Leeuwin current is about _____ meters deep.
(a) 500                (b) 100
(c) 250                (d) 300

**193.** Deep water is often rich in _____ .
(a) Dissolved gases    (b) Plant life
(c) Nutrients          (d) Both (a) and (c)

**194.** The density of sea water increases with _____
(a) Increase of salinity
(b) Increase of temperature
(c) Decrease in Temperature
(d) Both (a) and (b)

**195.** The most common carrier in meteorology
(a) Weather forecasting
(b) Climate change
(c) Broadcasting
(d) Climate post casting

**196.** Which is effect on atmospheric pressure?
(a) Altitude           (b) Temperature
(c) Earth rotation     (d) All the above

**197.** Consider the following statements and identify the right ones:
1. Air pressure decreases when air descends.
2. Air pressure at sea level is lower than at the mountain top.
(a) 1 only             (b) 2 only
(c) Both               (d) None of these

**198.** Weight of water vapour per unit weight of air is
(a) Relative humidity
(b) Absolute humidity
(c) Specific humidity
(d) None of the above

**199.** The ratio of air's actual water vapour content to its water vapour capacity at a given temperature is called
(a) Relative humidity
(b) Specific humidity
(c) Absolute humidity
(d) None of the above

**200.** Match the following:
1. Cirrus          A. Feather
2. Cumulus         B. Heap
3. Stratus         C. Layer type
4. Nimbus          D. Rain cloud
(a) 1-A, 2-B, 3-C, 4-D
(b) 1-A, 2-C, 3-B, 4-D
(c) 1-D, 2-C, 3-B, 4-A
(d) 1-D, 2-C, 3-A, 4-B

**201.** The seaward extension of the continent from shoreline to the continental edge is called
(a) Continental slope
(b) Continental rise
(c) Continental shelf
(d) All the above

**202.** The abrupt change of gradient at the edge of the continental shift to formation of
(a) Continental shelf
(b) Continental slope
(c) Continental rise
(d) None of the above

**203.** The undulating plain lying beyond the continental rise is called
(a) Abyssal plain      (b) Structural plain
(c) Saturated plain    (d) None of the above

**204.** The greatest known ocean deep is
(a) Challenger deep    (b) Richards deep
(c) Java trench        (d) Yap trench

**205.** Consider the following statements and identify the right ones.
1. Hypolimnium layer represents vertical zone of ocean water.
2. Thermocline layer witnesses rapid rate of increase in temperature with increasing depth.
(a) 1 only             (b) 2 only
(c) Both               (d) None of these

**206.** Consider the following statements and identify the right ones.

1. The top most layer of ocean water is called the thermocline layer.
2. The highest salinity in water is found in the Lake Van.
(a) 1 only       (b) 2 only
(c) Both 1 and 2  (d) None of these

207. Consider the following statements and identify the right ones.
1. The temperature increases according to the increasing depth of the ocean.
2. The temperature gradually increases from equator towards the poles.
(a) 1 only       (b) 2 only
(c) Both 1 and 2  (d) None of these

208. Consider the following statements and identify the right ones.
1. The surface temperature of the seas increases from equator towards the poles.
2. The temperature at the ocean bottom varies from equator towards the pole.
(a) 1 only       (b) 2 only
(c) Both 1 and 2  (d) None of these

209. Consider the following statements and identify the right ones.
1. Euphotic zone do not receive solar rays.
2. Aphotic zone receives solar radiation.
(a) 1 only       (b) 2 only
(c) Both 1 and 2  (d) None of these

210. Identify the factors that are affected by ocean currents.
(a) Temperature   (b) Precipitation
(c) Humidity      (d) All the above

211. The periodic phenomenon of alternate rise and fall in sea level is known as
(a) Tides         (b) Waves
(c) Tsunami       (d) Currents

212. The position if the sun, the earth and the moon are in straight line is called
(a) Cliff         (b) Seiche
(c) Conjunction   (d) Syzygy

213. The situation of the solar eclipse when sun, moon are in one side of the earth is called as
(a) Cliff         (b) Conjunction
(c) Seiche        (d) Syzygy

214. The oscillatory movements in the water produced by winds
(a) Tides         (b) Waves
(c) Tsunamis      (d) None of these

215. Which is the causes of the waves
(a) Underwater volcanic explosion
(b) Underwater landslides
(c) Slippage of seafloor along earthquake fault
(d) All the above

216. The cold layer extending up to the ocean floor is called
(a) Hypolimnion layer
(b) Thermocline layer
(c) Epilimnion layer
(d) None of the above

217. The origin of Himalayas can best be explained by
(a) Continental Drift Theory
(b) Ocean Floor Mapping
(c) Sea Floor Spreading
(d) Plate Tectonics theory

218. The wind system in the equatorial region is called
(a) Trades        (b) Monsoon
(c) Doldrums      (d) Westerlies

219. Doldrums is an area of
(a) Low pressure  (b) Low rainfall
(c) Low humidity  (d) Low temperature

220. Which process is most destructive?
(a) Tornado       (b) Typhoon
(c) Willy willy   (d) Cyclone

221. The atmospheric pressure in earth's atmosphere
(a) Decreases with height
(b) Increases with height
(c) Remains constant with height
(d) First increases then decreases with height

222. Hurricanes cyclonic storms is example of
(a) South China Sea
(b) Indian Ocean
(c) West Indies and the Gulf of Mexico
(d) West Pacific Ocean

223. Increase in carbon dioxide in atmosphere due to
(a) Fall in the earth temperature
(b) Rise in the earth temperature
(c) Increases in ultraviolet rays
(d) Uniforms earth temperature

## ANSWERS

| 1 | 2 | 3 | 4 | 5 | 6 | 7 | 8 | 9 | 10 |
|---|---|---|---|---|---|---|---|---|---|
| (a) | (b) | (a) | (d) | (a) | (a) | (c) | (c) | (a) | (d) |

| 11 | 12 | 13 | 14 | 15 | 16 | 17 | 18 | 19 | 20 |
|---|---|---|---|---|---|---|---|---|---|
| (a) | (d) | (c) | (a) | (a) | (c) | (b) | (b) | (b) | (c) |
| 21 | 22 | 23 | 24 | 25 | 26 | 27 | 28 | 29 | 30 |
| (c) | (a) | (d) | (b) | (a) | (a) | (d) | (a) | (c) | (c) |
| 31 | 32 | 33 | 34 | 35 | 36 | 37 | 38 | 39 | 40 |
| (b) | (d) | (b) | (d) | (b) | (a) | (b) | (a) | (b) | (c) |
| 41 | 42 | 43 | 44 | 45 | 46 | 47 | 48 | 49 | 50 |
| (b) | (d) | (b) | (d) | (a) | (c) | (c) | (a) | (c) | (c) |
| 51 | 52 | 53 | 54 | 55 | 56 | 57 | 58 | 59 | 60 |
| (b) | (d) | (d) | (a) | (b) | (c) | (d) | (c) | (a) | (c) |
| 61 | 62 | 63 | 64 | 65 | 66 | 67 | 68 | 69 | 70 |
| (d) | (c) | (a) | (b) | (b) | (d) | (d) | (b) | (a) | (c) |
| 71 | 72 | 73 | 74 | 75 | 76 | 77 | 78 | 79 | 80 |
| (a) | (b) | (d) | (a) | (c) | (d) | (d) | (d) | (a) | (b) |
| 81 | 82 | 83 | 84 | 85 | 86 | 87 | 88 | 89 | 90 |
| (b) | (a) | (b) | (a) | (a) | (a) | (c) | (d) | (b) | (d) |
| 91 | 92 | 93 | 94 | 95 | 96 | 97 | 98 | 99 | 100 |
| (b) | (a) | (b) | (a) | (c) | (a) | (a) | (b) | (d) | (b) |
| 101 | 102 | 103 | 104 | 105 | 106 | 107 | 108 | 109 | 110 |
| (c) | (b) | (a) | (c) | (b) | (b) | (a) | (a) | (b) | (b) |
| 111 | 112 | 113 | 114 | 115 | 116 | 117 | 118 | 119 | 120 |
| (d) | (a) | (a) | (b) | (c) | (a) | (d) | (c) | (d) | (b) |
| 121 | 122 | 123 | 124 | 125 | 126 | 127 | 128 | 129 | 130 |
| (d) | (b) | (a) | (b) | (c) | (b) | (c) | (b) | (b) | (c) |
| 131 | 132 | 133 | 134 | 135 | 136 | 137 | 138 | 139 | 140 |
| (c) | (d) | (a) | (d) | (b) | (a) | (c) | (d) | (a) | (b) |
| 141 | 142 | 143 | 144 | 145 | 146 | 147 | 148 | 149 | 150 |
| (b) | (a) | (a) | (c) | (c) | (a) | (a) | (d) | (d) | (c) |
| 151 | 152 | 153 | 154 | 155 | 156 | 157 | 158 | 159 | 160 |
| (d) | (a) | (c) | (c) | (d) | (d) | (b) | (c) | (b) | (c) |
| 161 | 162 | 163 | 164 | 165 | 166 | 167 | 168 | 169 | 170 |
| (b) | (a) | (d) | (c) | (a) | (c) | (c) | (d) | (a) | (c) |
| 171 | 172 | 173 | 174 | 175 | 176 | 177 | 178 | 179 | 180 |
| (d) | (b) | (d) | (c) | (b) | (a) | (b) | (b) | (a) | (a) |
| 181 | 182 | 183 | 184 | 185 | 186 | 187 | 188 | 189 | 190 |
| (a) | (d) | (a) | (a) | (a) | (a) | (a) | (a) | (c) | (a) |
| 191 | 192 | 193 | 194 | 195 | 196 | 197 | 198 | 199 | 200 |
| (c) | (d) | (d) | (c) | (a) | (d) | (c) | (c) | (a) | (a) |
| 201 | 202 | 203 | 204 | 205 | 206 | 207 | 208 | 209 | 210 |
| (c) | (b) | (a) | (a) | (a) | (b) | (d) | (d) | (d) | (a) |
| 211 | 212 | 213 | 214 | 215 | 216 | 217 | 218 | 219 | 220 |
| (a) | (d) | (a) | (b) | (d) | (a) | (d) | (a) | (a) | (a) |
| 221 | 222 | 223 |
| (a) | (c) | (b) |

CPSIA information can be obtained
at www.ICGtesting.com
Printed in the USA
BVHW010741080521
606853BV00013B/370